*Fundamentals
of mathematical
physics*

fundamentals
of mathematical
physics

EDGAR A. KRAUT

ASSISTANT PROFESSOR OF PHYSICS AND GEOPHYSICS,

UNIVERSITY OF CALIFORNIA, LOS ANGELES

McGraw-Hill Book Company

NEW YORK   ST. LOUIS   SAN FRANCISCO   TORONTO   LONDON   SYDNEY

Fundamentals of Mathematical Physics

To Renée and Ted

preface

The primary aim of this book is to provide the student of physics with most of the mathematical tools required for the study of electromagnetic theory and quantum mechanics.

The only preparation expected of the reader is the completion of the first two years of college calculus and physics.

At UCLA, the material on matrix algebra, vector analysis, Fourier series, and ordinary differential equations is given in the physics department in a one-semester course entitled Mathematical Methods of Physics. This course is normally taken by physics majors during their junior year. The course is also taken by many undergraduate and graduate students enrolled in other science departments. All the material in the book can be covered in two semesters or three quarters.

As given at UCLA, the mathematical methods course provides the tools which may then be applied to the context of other physics courses. If the material in this book is not to be used this way, the instructor should provide the physical motivation himself. Some physics is involved in the examples and in the problems at the end of each chapter. This is particularly true of the second half of the book. The problems range from trivial to difficult. Even the best student will find some of them challenging. The student who does the less trivial exercises will usually find that he has learned something worth remembering.

Chapter 1 is essentially a review of material which the reader has probably seen many times before. The book really "starts" with Chapter 2. The aim here is to permit the reader to rapidly acquire sufficient skill in manipulating real and complex matrices so that they will not constitute a stumbling block when he first encounters them in courses in classical and quantum mechanics. Most physics students are curious about what tensors are and what one does with them. I have tried to satisfy this curiosity in Chapter 2 without getting too deeply involved in details. Vector calculus, discussed in Chapter 3, is one of the most important new mathematical tools that an aspiring physics student must learn. In writing this chapter I have tried particularly to emphasize the idea that integral formulas relate the values taken on by the *derivative* of a function throughout a domain to the values which the *function itself* assumes on the boundary of the domain. This approach permits a unified and systematic development of integral formulas in more than one dimension. Topological restrictions on integral formulas have been treated in somewhat more detail than is customary in elementary texts. In physical applications, volume, surface, and line integrals are often taken over regions which move and deform with time. It is necessary to know how to differentiate such integrals with respect to time and how the appropriate formulas are derived. Finally, integral theorems involving regions of discontinuity must be suitably modified in order for the theorems to remain valid. It is in this connection that boundary conditions arise naturally. Though seldom discussed in elementary works, the modifications are carefully outlined here.

A short treatment of complex variables appears in Chapter 4. The central idea in this chapter is that a function of a complex variable can be represented by a power series, or as a contour integral, and that such a function provides a conformal mapping of one surface onto another. The fact that these three characteristics, though equivalent, were really the basis of three separate developments of the subject is not often emphasized in contemporary treatments, which tend to present the subject as a single unified entity. However, I think some historical remarks help the beginner to understand complex analysis more easily.

I have chosen to emphasize Riemann surfaces because they seem to cause beginners a lot of trouble. It is pointed out that a Riemann surface need not necessarily be a stack of flat sheets and that a closed curved surface such as a torus can also be a Riemann surface. Contour integration is also discussed in some detail, and a point is made of the fact that it may be easier to evaluate some integrals by using those residues outside a closed contour instead of those inside.

Chapter 5 is a discussion of finite- and infinite-range integral transforms. The concept of a finite integral transform may not be the shortest way to present Fourier series; however it has many advantages where applications are involved. By use of integration by parts with appropriate kernels, the solution of many problems in ordinary and partial differential equations is reduced to a standard procedure involving evaluating a certain transform and then inverting it.

Chapter 6 treats ordinary differential equations, particularly those which give rise to the special functions of mathematical physics. The properties of most of these special functions are examined, and their graphs are given. It is pointed out that most of the special functions of mathematical physics are solutions of a Sturm-Liouville differential equation and that they consequently enjoy certain important orthogonality properties. The last chapter, Chapter 7, provides an opportunity to apply all previous work to the solution of partial differential equations. I have tried to unify this chapter around the idea that there is a general method for handling problems involving linear partial differential equations. This method involves two steps. In the first step, one formally represents the solution of a partial differential equation in terms of a Green's function with the aid of one or another of the integral theorems developed in Chapter 3. Next, one calculates this Green's function for the particular coordinate system of interest by taking integral transforms or by using expansions in terms of appropriate special functions. This procedure is illustrated in some detail for the classical partial differential equations of mathematical physics, and many useful identities are derived in the process.

In closing I would like to point out that a course in the spirit of this book is not a substitute for any course in pure mathematics. The student has much to gain in maturity and perspective from a rigorous mathematical study of any of the topics dealt with here. Certainly, he should study at least one of them in a formal junior or senior mathematics course.

I would like to thank my students and colleagues for numerous useful suggestions, comments, and criticisms. Additional comments will be most gratefully received.

EDGAR A. KRAUT

contents

vector algebra

INTRODUCTION

In elementary physics one learns that a vector is a quantity which has a magnitude and a direction. The rule for adding vectors is then chosen so as to be useful in describing the motion of a material object. For example, consider three points, say O, P_1, and P_2, which are not necessarily in a straight line. If a body is displaced in a straight line from O to P_1 and then along another straight line from P_1 to P_2, the final position of the body is at P_2. However, the body may also be placed at P_2 by displacing it along the straight line directly joining O to P_2. The single displacement $\mathbf{OP}_2$ represents the combined effect of the two displacements $\mathbf{OP}_1$ and $\mathbf{P}_1\mathbf{P}_2$. It is convenient to represent a displacement such as $\mathbf{OP}_1$ by an arrow of proper length and direction (Fig. 1-1).

If $\mathbf{P}_1\mathbf{P}_2$ is applied after $\mathbf{OP}_1$ we represent it by placing the origin of arrow $\mathbf{P}_1\mathbf{P}_2$ at the end point of $\mathbf{OP}_1$, then the combined displacement $\mathbf{OP}_2 = \mathbf{OP}_1 + \mathbf{P}_1\mathbf{P}_2$ is the arrow leading from the origin of $\mathbf{OP}_1$ to the end point of $\mathbf{P}_1\mathbf{P}_2$. This is the diagonal of the parallelogram with sides $\mathbf{OP}_1$ and $\mathbf{P}_1\mathbf{P}_2$. This rule for finding $\mathbf{OP}_1 + \mathbf{P}_1\mathbf{P}_2$ is the familiar parallelogram law of vector addition.

A displacement $\mathbf{OP}_1 = \mathbf{x}$ may be doubled to give a new displacement $2\mathbf{x}$ or halved to give a displacement $\frac{1}{2}\mathbf{x}$. A negative multiple such as $-2\mathbf{x}$ represents a displacement twice as large as $\mathbf{x}$ but in the direction opposite to $\mathbf{x}$. In general, if $\mathbf{x}$ is multiplied by any real number c, the result $c\mathbf{x}$ represents a displacement c times as large as $\mathbf{x}$. The direction of $c\mathbf{x}$ is along $\mathbf{x}$ for $c > 0$ and opposite to $\mathbf{x}$ for $c < 0$.

In the plane, a vector $\mathbf{A}$ may be represented by an arrow with origin at $(0,0)$ and end point at some suitable point (a_1,a_2). Then the vector sums and scalar multiples may be computed in terms of the coordinates, using the rules

$$(a_1,a_2) + (b_1,b_2) = (a_1 + b_1, a_2 + b_2) \tag{1-1}$$

$$c(a_1,a_2) = (ca_1,ca_2) \tag{1-2}$$

It follows from Eqs. (1-1) and (1-2) that the vectors $\mathbf{x}$, $\mathbf{y}$, and $\mathbf{z}$ obey the algebraic rules

$$\mathbf{x} + \mathbf{y} = \mathbf{y} + \mathbf{x} \qquad \mathbf{x} + (\mathbf{y} + \mathbf{z}) = (\mathbf{x} + \mathbf{y}) + \mathbf{z} \tag{1-3}$$

$$c(\mathbf{x} + \mathbf{y}) = c\mathbf{x} + c\mathbf{y} \qquad 1\mathbf{x} = \mathbf{x} \tag{1-4}$$

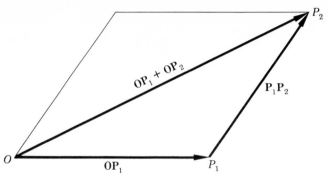

Figure 1-1 Parallelogram law of vector addition.

These rules are used to *define* vectors in an abstract way as follows. A *vector space* is defined as a *set* S whose *elements* are called *vectors*. The vectors are characterized by the following axioms:

1. To every pair, $\mathbf{x}$ and $\mathbf{y}$, of vectors in S there corresponds a vector $\mathbf{x} + \mathbf{y}$, called the sum of $\mathbf{x}$ and $\mathbf{y}$, and such that
(*a*) Addition is commutative, $\mathbf{x} + \mathbf{y} = \mathbf{y} + \mathbf{x}$
(*b*) Addition is associative, $\mathbf{x} + (\mathbf{y} + \mathbf{z}) = (\mathbf{x} + \mathbf{y}) + \mathbf{z}$
(*c*) There exists in S a unique vector $\mathbf{0}$, called a null vector, such that $\mathbf{x} + \mathbf{0} = \mathbf{x}$ for every vector $\mathbf{x}$, and
(*d*) To every vector $\mathbf{x}$ in S there corresponds a unique vector $-\mathbf{x}$ such that $\mathbf{x} + (-\mathbf{x}) = \mathbf{0}$.
2. To every pair, c and $\mathbf{x}$, where c is a real (or complex) number and $\mathbf{x}$ is a vector in S, there corresponds a vector $c\mathbf{x}$ in S, called the product of c and $\mathbf{x}$, in such a way that
(*a*) Multiplication by real or complex numbers is associative, $b(c\mathbf{x}) = (bc)\mathbf{x}$, and
(*b*) $1\mathbf{x} = \mathbf{x}$ for every vector $\mathbf{x}$
(*c*) Multiplication is distributive with respect to vector addition, $c(\mathbf{x} + \mathbf{y}) = c\mathbf{x} + c\mathbf{y}$, and
(*d*) Multiplication by vectors is distributive with respect to arithmetical addition, $(b + c)\mathbf{x} = b\mathbf{x} + c\mathbf{x}$.

If the numbers c entering into axiom 2 are all real, then the set S is a real vector space; if the numbers c are complex then S is called a "complex vector space." Suppose that the numbers c are all real. Let R^n, $n = 1,2,3, \ldots$, be the set of all ordered n-tuples of real numbers. If $\mathbf{x} = (x_1,x_2, \ldots ,x_n)$ and $\mathbf{y} = (y_1,y_2, \ldots ,y_n)$ are elements of R^n, then we define

$$\mathbf{x} + \mathbf{y} = (x_1 + y_1, x_2 + y_2, \ldots , x_n + y_n) \tag{1-5}$$

$$c\mathbf{x} = (cx_1,cx_2, \ldots ,cx_n) \tag{1-6}$$

$$\mathbf{0} = (0,0, \ldots ,0) \tag{1-7}$$

$$-\mathbf{x} = (-x_1,-x_2, \ldots ,-x_n) \tag{1-8}$$

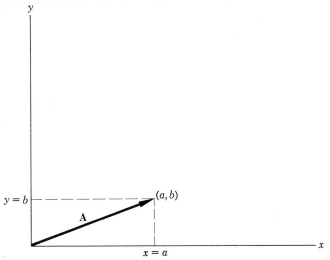

Figure 1-2 Geometric representation of the two-dimensional vector $\mathbf{A} = (a,b)$.

It is easy to verify that all the axioms of 1 and 2 are satisfied. Therefore R^n is a real vector space. One usually refers to R^n as an n-dimensional real coordinate space.

In summary, we have two completely equivalent ways of looking at vectors. We can regard vectors as abstract entities which combine with one another according to the axioms of 1 and 2, or we can regard vectors as ordered n-tuples of real numbers which obey the laws (1-5) to (1-8). The latter viewpoint is closer to the original geometric idea of a vector, and for this reason we shall adopt it here.

1-1 DEFINITIONS

Scalars

A scalar is a single real number, and a complex scalar is a single complex number.

Vectors

A two-dimensional vector (Fig. 1-2) is an ordered pair of real numbers such as (1,2) or (a,b). Geometrically, the vector (a,b) can be thought of as the position vector of the point $x = a$, $y = b$ in a two-dimensional rectangular Cartesian coordinate system in which x is measured along the abscissa and y is measured along the ordinate. The vector (a,b) is represented by the symbol

$$\mathbf{A} = (a,b) \tag{1-9}$$

The letters a and b, respectively, are called the first and second or x and y components of the vector $\mathbf{A}$.

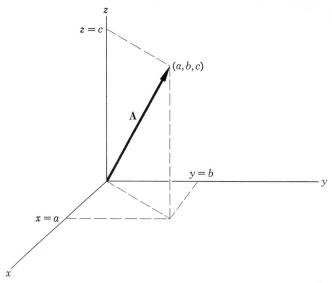

Figure 1-3 Geometric representation of the three-dimensional vector **A** $= (a,b,c)$.

A three-dimensional vector (Fig. 1-3) is an ordered triple of real numbers such as (1,2,3) or (a,b,c). Geometrically, the vector (a,b,c) is thought of as the position vector of the point $x = a$, $y = b$, $z = c$ in a three-dimensional rectangular Cartesian coordinate system whose axes are labeled x, y, and z. The vector (a,b,c) is represented by the symbol

$$\mathbf{A} = (a,b,c) \tag{1-10}$$

The letters a, b, and c are called the x, y, and z components of the vector **A**.

An n-dimensional vector is an ordered set of n real numbers such as (1,2,3, . . . ,n) or $(a_1, a_2, . . . , a_n)$. Geometrically, the vector $(a_1, a_2, . . . , a_n)$ is thought of as the position vector of the point $x_1 = a_1$, $x_2 = a_2$, . . . , $x_n = a_n$, in an n-dimensional rectangular Cartesian coordinate system with axes labeled x_1, x_2, . . . , x_n. The vector $(a_1, a_2, . . . , a_n)$ is represented by the symbol

$$\mathbf{A} = (a_1, a_2, . . . , a_n) \tag{1-11}$$

The letter a_1 is called the x_1 component of **A**, a_2 is called the x_2 component of **A**, and so on.

1-2 EQUALITY OF VECTORS AND NULL VECTORS

If $\mathbf{A} = (a_1, a_2, . . . , a_n)$ and $\mathbf{B} = (b_1, b_2, . . . , b_n)$, then

$$\mathbf{A} = \mathbf{B}$$

if and only if

$$a_1 = b_1, \ a_2 = b_2, \ . . . \ , \ a_n = b_n \tag{1-12}$$

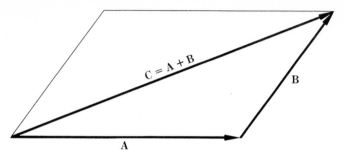

Figure 1-4 Parallelogram law of vector addition.

If all the components of a vector are zero, then it is called a "zero vector" or "null vector," thus:

$$\mathbf{0} = (0,0) \tag{1-13}$$

or

$$\mathbf{0} = (0,0,0) \tag{1-14}$$

or

$$\mathbf{0} = (0,0, \ldots ,0) \tag{1-15}$$

1-3 VECTOR OPERATIONS

Vectors can be added to, subtracted from, and multiplied by other vectors. Vectors can also be multiplied by scalars. If $\mathbf{A} = (a,b)$ and $\mathbf{B} = (c,d)$, then the addition of vectors $\mathbf{A}$ and $\mathbf{B}$ is defined in terms of the addition of the components of their respective representations (a,b) and (c,d), thus:

$$\mathbf{C} = \mathbf{A} + \mathbf{B} = (a,b) + (c,d) = (a + c, \, b + d) \tag{1-16}$$

In general, if $\mathbf{A} = (a_1,a_2, \ldots ,a_n)$ and $\mathbf{B} = (b_1,b_2, \ldots ,b_n)$, then

$$\begin{aligned}\mathbf{C} = \mathbf{A} + \mathbf{B} &= (a_1,a_2, \ldots ,a_n) + (b_1,b_2, \ldots ,b_n) \\ &= (a_1 + b_1, \, a_2 + b_2, \ldots , \, a_n + b_n) \end{aligned} \tag{1-17}$$

The student should verify for himself that the definition of vector addition given in Eq. (1-1) is consistent with the parallelogram law of vector addition (Fig. 1-4) taught in elementary physics courses.

If $\mathbf{A} = (a_1,a_2, \ldots ,a_n)$, then the norm, magnitude, or length of $\mathbf{A}$ is defined by

$$|\mathbf{A}| = + \sqrt{a_1^2 + a_2^2 + \cdots + a_n^2} \tag{1-18}$$

If λ is a scalar, then multiplication of the vector $\mathbf{A}$ by the scalar λ is defined by

$$\mathbf{C} = \lambda \mathbf{A} = (\lambda a_1, \lambda a_2, \ldots ,\lambda a_n) \tag{1-19}$$

Scalar product

The scalar or "dot" product of $\mathbf{A} = (a_1,a_2, \ldots ,a_n)$ and $\mathbf{B} = (b_1,b_2, \ldots ,b_n)$

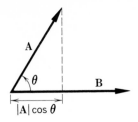

$$\mathbf{A} \cdot \mathbf{B} = |\mathbf{A}||\mathbf{B}| \cos \theta$$

Figure 1-5 The scalar product $\mathbf{A} \cdot \mathbf{B}$.

is defined by (Fig. 1-5)

$$\mathbf{A} \cdot \mathbf{B} = \sum_{k=1}^{n} a_k b_k = a_1 b_1 + a_2 b_2 + \cdots + a_n b_n \tag{1-20}$$

Notice that

$$\mathbf{A} \cdot \mathbf{A} = |\mathbf{A}|^2 = \sum_{k=1}^{n} a_k^2 = a_1^2 + a_2^2 + \cdots + a_n^2 \tag{1-21}$$

DEFINITION: The cosine of the angle between $\mathbf{A}$ and $\mathbf{B}$ is *defined* by

$$\cos (\mathbf{A},\mathbf{B}) = \frac{\mathbf{A} \cdot \mathbf{B}}{|\mathbf{A}||\mathbf{B}|} \tag{1-22}$$

Thus

$$\cos (\mathbf{A},\mathbf{B}) = \frac{\displaystyle\sum_{k=1}^{n} a_k b_k}{\left(\displaystyle\sum_{k=1}^{n} a_k^2\right)^{1/2} \left(\displaystyle\sum_{k=1}^{n} b_k^2\right)^{1/2}} \tag{1-23}$$

Vector product

The vector or "cross" product of a pair of three-dimensional vectors such as $\mathbf{A} = (a_1, a_2, a_3)$ and $\mathbf{B} = (b_1, b_2, b_3)$ is the vector defined by (Fig. 1-7)

$$\mathbf{A} \times \mathbf{B} = (a_2 b_3 - a_3 b_2, \ a_3 b_1 - a_1 b_3, \ a_1 b_2 - a_2 b_1) \tag{1-24}$$

The vector product will only be defined for three-dimensional vectors.

The student should now verify the following properties of the cross product:

$$\mathbf{A} \times \mathbf{B} = -(\mathbf{B} \times \mathbf{A}) \tag{1-25}$$

$$\mathbf{A} \times \mathbf{A} = 0 \tag{1-26}$$

$$\mathbf{A} \cdot (\mathbf{A} \times \mathbf{B}) = 0 \tag{1-27}$$

$$\mathbf{B} \cdot (\mathbf{A} \times \mathbf{B}) = 0 \tag{1-28}$$

The vectors $\mathbf{A}$ and $\mathbf{B}$ are called "parallel" (antiparallel) if there is a positive (negative) scalar such that

$$\mathbf{A} = \lambda \mathbf{B} \tag{1-29}$$

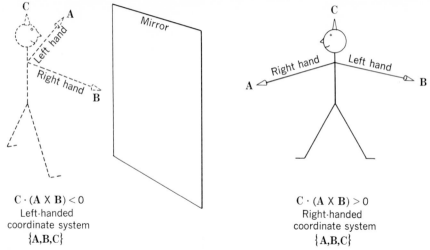

C · (A X B) < 0
Left-handed
coordinate system
{A,B,C}

C · (A X B) > 0
Right-handed
coordinate system
{A,B,C}

Figure 1-6 The mirror image of a right-handed coordinate system is a left-handed coordinate system.

If **A** and **B** are neither parallel nor antiparallel and are not zero vectors, then Eqs. (1-22), (1-27), and (1-28) show that $\mathbf{A} \times \mathbf{B}$ is perpendicular to both **A** and **B**. Therefore, $\mathbf{A} \times \mathbf{B}$ is perpendicular to the plane determined by **A** and **B**. The ordered triple of vectors {A,B,C} is called a "right-handed" triple if and only if

$$\mathbf{C} \cdot (\mathbf{A} \times \mathbf{B}) > 0 \tag{1-30}$$

The ordered triple of vectors {A,B,C} is called a "left-handed" triple if and only if

$$\mathbf{C} \cdot (\mathbf{A} \times \mathbf{B}) < 0 \tag{1-31}$$

If $\mathbf{C} = (\mathbf{A} \times \mathbf{B})$ and **C** is not a zero vector, then the triple {A,B,C} is right-handed. The vector **C** defines the direction in which a "right-handed screw" will advance if its head is turned from **A** to **B**. This is the basis of the "right-hand rule" of elementary physics.

Suppose now that the vectors **A** and **B** determine a plane. Choose a set of rectangular Cartesian coordinate axes labeled x, y, and z in such a manner that the vectors **A** and **B** lie in the x, y plane. Let the x axis be chosen so that it coincides with the direction of **A**. Then

$$\mathbf{A} = (|\mathbf{A}|,0,0) \tag{1-32}$$

$$\mathbf{B} = (|\mathbf{B}| \cos \theta, |\mathbf{B}| \sin \theta, 0) \tag{1-33}$$

The vector **A** has only a single component directed along the x axis. This component has a magnitude equal to the length of vector **A**. Vector **B** has no z component since by definition it lies in the x, y plane. It does have x and y components which are equal to $|\mathbf{B}| \cos \theta$ and $|\mathbf{B}| \sin \theta$, respectively. The angle θ is measured from the x axis to the vector **B** in the x, y plane. Since **A** lies along the x axis, the angle θ is also the angle between the vectors **A** and **B**. In this special

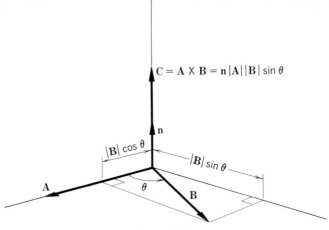

Figure 1-7   The vector product **A** × **B**.

(x,y,z) coordinate system Eqs. (1-24), (1-32), and (1-33) give

$$\mathbf{A} \times \mathbf{B} = [0,0,|\mathbf{A}||\mathbf{B}|\sin (\mathbf{A},\mathbf{B})] \tag{1-34}$$

Writing

$$\mathbf{n} = (0,0,1) \tag{1-35}$$

and noting Eq. (1-19), we obtain

$$\mathbf{A} \times \mathbf{B} = \mathbf{n}|\mathbf{A}||\mathbf{B}|\sin (\mathbf{A},\mathbf{B}) \tag{1-36}$$

Notice that the vector **n** is perpendicular to both **A** and **B** and thus to the x, y plane. In selecting the angle from **A** to **B** to be used in computing sin (**A**,**B**) the indeterminacy arising from the possibility of choosing either the interior or exterior angles between **A** and **B** is eliminated by requiring that the triple {**A**,**B**,**n**} be right-handed. Then if $|\mathbf{A}| > 0$, $|\mathbf{B}| > 0$, and **A** and **B** are neither parallel nor antiparallel, (1-30) gives

$$\sin (\mathbf{A},\mathbf{B}) > 0 \tag{1-37}$$

Thus we always choose the interior angle between vectors **A** and **B** in computing Eq. (1-36). If **A** and **B** are parallel or antiparallel, the vector product vanishes as a result of Eqs. (1-25) and (1-26).

The scalar product of Eqs. (1-32) and (1-33) gives

$$\mathbf{A} \cdot \mathbf{B} = |\mathbf{A}||\mathbf{B}|\cos (\mathbf{A},\mathbf{B}) \tag{1-38}$$

in agreement with Eq. (1-22). In obtaining Eqs. (1-36) and (1-38) we have used a special system of coordinates in which **A** has only one nonzero component and **B** only two. The scalar and vector products, however, depend only upon the lengths of the two vectors and the angle between them and thus not upon the coordinate system used to give their representations.

1-4 EXPANSION OF VECTORS

To expand a vector means to represent it as the sum of some other vectors. As it stands, this definition is not sufficiently precise. Clearly, a displacement vector in the x, y plane can be regarded as the resultant of many *different pairs* of displacement vectors, which also lie in the x, y plane. On the other hand, a vector perpendicular to the x, y plane can *never* be represented as the sum of vectors lying entirely in the x, y plane. It seems that in the first case the vectors in the x, y plane provide too many expansions, while in the second case they provide no expansions at all.

We can eliminate the problem of too many expansions by selecting certain vectors and insisting that all expansions be made with these. The problem of no expansions can be avoided by making sure that the vector we are trying to expand lies in the "right" space. In order to say this in a precise way several new terms must be introduced.

Linear independence

DEFINITION: The vectors $\{i_1, i_2, \ldots, i_n\}$ are called "linearly independent" if and only if the only solution of

$$c_1 i_1 + c_2 i_2 + \cdots + c_n i_n = 0 \tag{1-39}$$

is

$$c_1 = 0, c_2 = 0, \ldots, c_n = 0 \tag{1-40}$$

Otherwise they are linearly dependent.

Two immediate consequences of this definition are that if $\{i_1, i_2, \ldots, i_n\}$ is a linearly independent set of vectors, then no i_k can be a zero vector, and no i_k can be a linear combination of the preceding ones. (The student should prove these assertions.) The next concept we shall introduce has to do with generalizing the idea of the "right" space.

Linear manifold

If a subset M of the vector space S is such that, for all scalars a and b, M contains the vector $ax + by$ whenever it contains the vectors $\mathbf{x}$ and $\mathbf{y}$, then M is a linear manifold.

REMARK: Clearly the x, y plane in (x,y,z) space is a linear manifold. In fact, any plane passing through the origin in R^3 space is a linear manifold. (A linear manifold in R^n for $n \geq 4$ is called a "hyperplane.") It follows from the definition that a linear manifold must always contain the null vector, for it contains $\mathbf{x} - \mathbf{x}$ whenever it contains $\mathbf{x}$, where $\mathbf{x}$ is any vector in M.

A set of vectors $\{x_1, x_2, \ldots, x_n\}$ in M is said to *span* M if *every* vector $\mathbf{A}$ in M can be represented as a linear combination of

$\{\mathbf{x}_1, \mathbf{x}_2, \ldots, \mathbf{x}_n\}$; i.e., there are scalars $\{c_1, c_2, \ldots, c_n\}$ depending on $\mathbf{A}$ such that

$$\mathbf{A} = c_1\mathbf{x}_1 + c_2\mathbf{x}_2 + \cdots + c_n\mathbf{x}_n \tag{1-41}$$

We see that when $\mathbf{A}$ lies in a linear manifold, then $\mathbf{A}$ can be expanded in terms of the vectors which span the manifold. However, the expansion of $\mathbf{A}$ is not yet unique. To make it unique we must assume not only that $\mathbf{A}$ lies in the manifold spanned by the vectors $\{\mathbf{x}_1, \mathbf{x}_2, \ldots, \mathbf{x}_n\}$, but also that the vectors $\{\mathbf{x}_1, \mathbf{x}_2, \ldots, \mathbf{x}_n\}$ are *linearly independent*.

When the vectors $\{\mathbf{x}_1, \mathbf{x}_2, \ldots, \mathbf{x}_n\}$ span M and are also linearly independent, then we say that they form a *basis* for M. In this case the representation (1-41) is unique. To see this one notes that if the representation is not unique, there can be a second such representation,

$$\mathbf{A} = a_1\mathbf{x}_1 + a_2\mathbf{x}_2 + \cdots + a_n\mathbf{x}_n \tag{1-42}$$

As a result, subtracting Eq. (1-41) from Eq. (1-42) gives

$$\mathbf{0} = (a_1 - c_1)\mathbf{x}_1 + (a_2 - c_2)\mathbf{x}_2 + \cdots + (a_n - c_n)\mathbf{x}_n \tag{1-43}$$

Since the basis vectors are assumed linearly independent,

$$a_1 = c_1, \, a_2 = c_2, \, \ldots, \, a_n = c_n \tag{1-44}$$

Therefore Eq. (1-41) must be unique. We have now solved the expansion problem we posed in the beginning. We have shown that any arbitrary vector lying in a linear manifold can be *uniquely* expanded in any basis of the manifold. Thus in our initial example, we should choose for a basis two particular vectors which span the x, y plane and which are linearly independent. The right space for an arbitrary vector to lie in, in order to have a unique expansion, is then the x, y plane itself. This example is geometrically obvious in R^3 but not quite as obvious in R^n.

Dimension

The linear manifold formed by the x, y plane has a basis consisting of two vectors, so we say that it is two-dimensional. In general, a linear manifold having a basis which contains n vectors is called "n-dimensional." As a consequence of the definition of dimension, any n-dimensional manifold must contain n linearly independent vectors which form the basis of the manifold. One can show that any set of $n + 1$ vectors in an n-dimensional linear manifold must be linearly dependent.

EXAMPLE 1-1: R^n. The n-dimensional real coordinate space R^n is obviously a linear manifold since if $\mathbf{x} = (x_1, x_2, \ldots, x_n)$ and $\mathbf{y} = (y_1, y_2, \ldots, y_n)$ are ordered n-tuples of numbers belonging to R^n, then $a\mathbf{x} + b\mathbf{y}$ must also be an ordered n-tuple of numbers. Therefore it must also belong to R^n.

The ordered n-tuples

$$\mathbf{e}_1 = \{1,0, \ldots ,0\}, \mathbf{e}_2 = \{0,1,0, \ldots ,0\}, \ldots , \mathbf{e}_n = \{0,0, \ldots ,1\} \qquad (1\text{-}45)$$

are a set of vectors which span R^n because any vector

$$\mathbf{A} = \{a_1,a_2, \ldots ,a_n\}$$

in R^n is an ordered n-tuple, and any n-tuple can always be written as

$$\mathbf{A} = \{a_1,a_2, \ldots ,a_n\} = a_1\{1,0, \ldots ,0\} + a_2\{0,1,0, \ldots ,0\} + \cdots + a_n\{0,0, \ldots ,1\} \qquad (1\text{-}46)$$

i.e., as

$$\mathbf{A} = a_1\mathbf{e}_1 + a_2\mathbf{e}_2 + \cdots + a_n\mathbf{e}_n \qquad (1\text{-}47)$$

Furthermore, the vectors $\{\mathbf{e}_1,\mathbf{e}_2, \ldots ,\mathbf{e}_n\}$ are linearly independent since Eq. (1-45) requires that the only solution of

$$c_1\mathbf{e}_1 + c_2\mathbf{e}_2 + \cdots + c_n\mathbf{e}_n = 0 \qquad (1\text{-}48)$$

be

$$c_1 = 0, c_2 = 0, \ldots , c_n = 0$$

Hence the set of vectors $\{\mathbf{e}_1,\mathbf{e}_2, \ldots ,\mathbf{e}_n\}$ spans R^n and is linearly independent. Thus they form a basis for R^n. Since the basis for R^n contains n vectors, R^n is an n-dimensional linear manifold by definition.

The scalar product rule (1-20) applied to $\{\mathbf{e}_1,\mathbf{e}_2, \ldots ,\mathbf{e}_n\}$ shows that

$$\mathbf{e}_i \cdot \mathbf{e}_j = \begin{cases} 1 & i = j \\ 0 & i \neq j \end{cases} \qquad (1\text{-}49)$$

Thus each vector in the basis has unit length and is orthogonal to every vector of the basis, except itself. A basis satisfying Eq. (1-49) is called an *orthonormal* basis. Choosing an orthonormal basis in a linear manifold corresponds to introducing a set of rectangular Cartesian coordinates in the manifold and then expressing any vector in the manifold in terms of its components along the coordinates axes.

In R^n any arbitrary vector $\mathbf{A}$ has a unique expansion

$$\mathbf{A} = \sum_{k=1}^{n} a_k\mathbf{e}_k \qquad (1\text{-}50)$$

in terms of the orthonormal basis (1-45). The expansion coefficients a_k are obtained by projecting $\mathbf{A}$ along each coordinate axis,

$$a_k = \mathbf{A} \cdot \mathbf{e}_k \qquad (1\text{-}51)$$

EXAMPLE 1-2: R^3. Any vector $\mathbf{A}$ in R^3 is an ordered triple $\mathbf{A} = (a_1,a_2,a_3)$ and can be written as

$$\mathbf{A} = a_1(1,0,0) + a_2(0,1,0) + a_3(0,0,1) \qquad (1\text{-}52)$$

or as

$$\mathbf{A} = a_1\mathbf{e}_1 + a_2\mathbf{e}_2 + a_3\mathbf{e}_3 \qquad (1\text{-}53)$$

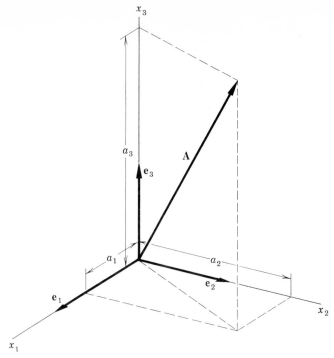

$$A = a_1\mathbf{e}_1 + a_2\mathbf{e}_2 + a_3\mathbf{e}_3$$

Figure 1-8   Expansion of vector **A** in terms of an orthonormal basis $\{\mathbf{e}_1,\mathbf{e}_2,\mathbf{e}_3\}$.

The vectors $\mathbf{e}_1 = (1,0,0)$, $\mathbf{e}_2 = (0,1,0)$, $\mathbf{e}_3 = (0,0,1)$ span R^3, are linearly independent, and form an orthonormal basis for R^3, since

$$\mathbf{e}_1 \cdot \mathbf{e}_2 = 0 \quad \mathbf{e}_1 \cdot \mathbf{e}_3 = 0 \quad \mathbf{e}_2 \cdot \mathbf{e}_3 = 0 \tag{1-54}$$

$$\mathbf{e}_1 \cdot \mathbf{e}_1 = 1 \quad \mathbf{e}_2 \cdot \mathbf{e}_2 = 1 \quad \mathbf{e}_3 \cdot \mathbf{e}_3 = 1 \tag{1-55}$$

A rectangular Cartesian coordinate system can be introduced so that the x_1, x_2, and x_3 axes point in the directions of $\mathbf{e}_1$, $\mathbf{e}_2$, and $\mathbf{e}_3$ respectively. The components a_1, a_2, and a_3 of the vector **A** are measured along the x_1, x_2, and x_3 axes, respectively. Notice that

$$a_1 = \mathbf{A} \cdot \mathbf{e}_1 \quad a_2 = \mathbf{A} \cdot \mathbf{e}_2 \quad \text{and} \quad a_3 = \mathbf{A} \cdot \mathbf{e}_3 \tag{1-56}$$

since

$$a_1 = \mathbf{A} \cdot \mathbf{e}_1 = |\mathbf{A}| \cos (\mathbf{A},\mathbf{e}_1) \tag{1-57}$$

The component a_1 of the vector **A** is geometrically the projection of the vector **A** along the x_1 axis. A similar remark applies to the other components of **A**.

The space R^3 is special in that the vector cross product is defined only for R^3. The student should verify that an orthonormal basis in R^3 satisfies

$$\mathbf{e}_1 \times \mathbf{e}_2 = \mathbf{e}_3 \quad \mathbf{e}_2 \times \mathbf{e}_3 = \mathbf{e}_1 \quad \mathbf{e}_3 \times \mathbf{e}_1 = \mathbf{e}_2 \tag{1-58}$$

$$\mathbf{e}_2 \times \mathbf{e}_1 = -\mathbf{e}_3 \quad \mathbf{e}_3 \times \mathbf{e}_2 = -\mathbf{e}_1 \quad \mathbf{e}_1 \times \mathbf{e}_3 = -\mathbf{e}_2 \tag{1-59}$$

$$\mathbf{e}_1 \times \mathbf{e}_1 = 0 \quad \mathbf{e}_2 \times \mathbf{e}_2 = 0 \quad \mathbf{e}_3 \times \mathbf{e}_3 = 0 \tag{1-60}$$

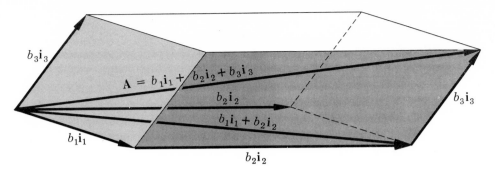

$$\mathbf{A} = b_1\mathbf{i}_1 + b_2\mathbf{i}_2 + b_3\mathbf{i}_3$$

Figure 1-9 Expansion of vector **A** in terms of a linearly independent but nonorthogonal basis $\{\mathbf{i}_1, \mathbf{i}_2, \mathbf{i}_3\}$.

Oblique bases

Any basis of R^n which is not an orthogonal basis is called an "oblique" basis. For example, any pair $\{\mathbf{i}_1, \mathbf{i}_2\}$ of nonorthogonal, linearly independent vectors in the plane R^2 constitutes an oblique basis for R^2. Such a basis corresponds to introducing an oblique coordinate system in R^2 because any vector in R^2 can be written as

$$\mathbf{A} = b_1\mathbf{i}_1 + b_2\mathbf{i}_2 \tag{1-61}$$

where b_1 and b_2 are the components of **A** *measured along the oblique axes*. The magnitude of **A** becomes

$$\mathbf{A} \cdot \mathbf{A} = |\mathbf{A}|^2 = b_1{}^2 + b_2{}^2 + 2b_1b_2 \cos (\mathbf{i}_1, \mathbf{i}_2) \tag{1-62}$$

in oblique coordinates, provided $|\mathbf{i}_1| = 1$ and $|\mathbf{i}_2| = 1$.

EXERCISE: Show that Eq. (1-62) is the law of cosines for an oblique triangle.

Schmidt orthogonalization process

Given the set of n linearly independent vectors $\{\mathbf{i}_1, \mathbf{i}_2, \ldots, \mathbf{i}_n\}$, the Schmidt process enables one to construct another set of n linearly independent unit vectors, $\{\mathbf{e}_1, \mathbf{e}_2, \ldots, \mathbf{e}_n\}$, such that $\mathbf{e}_i \cdot \mathbf{e}_j = 0$ whenever $i \neq j$.

The Schmidt process begins with the statement that the vectors of the set $\{\mathbf{i}_1, \mathbf{i}_2, \ldots, \mathbf{i}_n\}$ are linearly independent. Then

$$c_1\mathbf{i}_1 + c_2\mathbf{i}_2 + \cdots + c_n\mathbf{i}_n = 0 \tag{1-63}$$

can be satisfied only by choosing $c_1 = 0$, $c_2 = 0$, $\ldots$, $c_n = 0$. It follows that $\mathbf{i}_1 \neq \mathbf{0}$; for if it were zero, the numbers $c_1 = 1$, $c_2 = 0$, $c_3 = 0$, $\ldots$, $c_n = 0$ would satisfy Eq. (1-63), and hence the vectors would be linearly dependent, contradicting our hypothesis. Let

$$\mathbf{e}_1 = \frac{\mathbf{i}_1}{|\mathbf{i}_1|}$$

Then

$$|\mathbf{e}_1| = \frac{|\mathbf{i}_1|}{|\mathbf{i}_1|} = 1$$

and the set $\{\mathbf{e}_1, \mathbf{i}_2, \ldots, \mathbf{i}_n\}$ is still a linearly independent set. Next choose

$$\mathbf{e}_2' = \mathbf{i}_2 - (\mathbf{i}_2 \cdot \mathbf{e}_1)\mathbf{e}_1$$

and notice that

$$\mathbf{e}_2' \cdot \mathbf{e}_1 = (\mathbf{i}_2 \cdot \mathbf{e}_1) - (\mathbf{i}_2 \cdot \mathbf{e}_1) = 0$$

so that $\mathbf{e}_2'$ is orthogonal to $\mathbf{e}_1$. Let

$$\mathbf{e}_2 = \frac{\mathbf{e}_2'}{|\mathbf{e}_2'|}$$

then $\mathbf{e}_2$ and $\mathbf{e}_1$ are orthogonal unit vectors. The set of vectors $\{\mathbf{e}_1, \mathbf{e}_2, \mathbf{i}_3, \ldots, \mathbf{i}_n\}$ is still linearly independent. Define $\mathbf{e}_3'$ by

$$\mathbf{e}_3' = \mathbf{i}_3 - (\mathbf{i}_3 \cdot \mathbf{e}_1)\mathbf{e}_1 - (\mathbf{i}_3 \cdot \mathbf{e}_2)\mathbf{e}_2$$

Dotting $\mathbf{e}_3'$ with $\mathbf{e}_1$ and $\mathbf{e}_2$ shows that $\mathbf{e}_3'$ is orthogonal to both $\mathbf{e}_1$ and $\mathbf{e}_2$. The vector

$$\mathbf{e}_3 = \frac{\mathbf{e}_3'}{|\mathbf{e}_3'|}$$

gives the unit vector orthogonal to both $\mathbf{e}_1$ and $\mathbf{e}_2$. We now have the linearly independent set $\{\mathbf{e}_1, \mathbf{e}_2, \mathbf{e}_3, \mathbf{i}_4, \ldots, \mathbf{i}_n\}$. A repetition of this constructive procedure yields the linearly independent orthonormal set $\{\mathbf{e}_1, \mathbf{e}_2, \mathbf{e}_3, \ldots, \mathbf{e}_n\}$ where

$$\mathbf{e}_1 = \frac{\mathbf{i}_1}{|\mathbf{i}_1|} \tag{1-64}$$

and

$$\mathbf{e}_m = \frac{\mathbf{i}_m - \sum\limits_{k=1}^{m-1} (\mathbf{e}_k \cdot \mathbf{i}_m)\mathbf{e}_k}{\left| \mathbf{i}_m - \sum\limits_{k=1}^{m-1} (\mathbf{e}_k \cdot \mathbf{i}_m)\mathbf{e}_k \right|} \tag{1-65}$$

for $2 \leq m \leq n$.

1-5 VECTOR IDENTITIES

There are certain vector identities which every student of physics must know. Some of these are given in this section. They should be verified and then committed to memory. The verification of an identity consists simply of showing that it holds when the operations involved are actually carried out using arbitrary but definite vectors. For example, to verify that

$$\mathbf{A} \times \mathbf{B} = -(\mathbf{B} \times \mathbf{A})$$

let $\mathbf{A} = (a_1, a_2, a_3)$ and $\mathbf{B} = (b_1, b_2, b_3)$. Then from Eq. (1-24),

$$\mathbf{A} \times \mathbf{B} = (a_2 b_3 - a_3 b_2, \ a_3 b_1 - a_1 b_3, \ a_1 b_2 - a_2 b_1)$$

and

$$\mathbf{B} \times \mathbf{A} = (b_2a_3 - b_3a_2,\ b_3a_1 - b_1a_3,\ b_1a_2 - b_2a_1)$$

Hence $\mathbf{A} \times \mathbf{B} = -(\mathbf{B} \times \mathbf{A})$. Now let $\mathbf{A} = (a_1,a_2,a_3)$, $\mathbf{B} = (b_1,b_2,b_3)$, $\mathbf{C} = (c_1,c_2,c_3)$, and $\mathbf{D} = (d_1,d_2,d_3)$, and verify the following identities:

$$\mathbf{A} \times \mathbf{B} = \begin{vmatrix} \mathbf{e}_1 & \mathbf{e}_2 & \mathbf{e}_3 \\ a_1 & a_2 & a_3 \\ b_1 & b_2 & b_3 \end{vmatrix} \tag{1-66}$$

where $\mathbf{e}_1$, $\mathbf{e}_2$, and $\mathbf{e}_3$ are as defined in Sec. 1-4.

$$\mathbf{A} \cdot (\mathbf{B} \times \mathbf{C}) = \begin{vmatrix} a_1 & a_2 & a_3 \\ b_1 & b_2 & b_3 \\ c_1 & c_2 & c_3 \end{vmatrix} \tag{1-67}$$

$$\mathbf{A} \times (\mathbf{B} \times \mathbf{C}) = (\mathbf{A} \cdot \mathbf{C})\mathbf{B} - (\mathbf{A} \cdot \mathbf{B})\mathbf{C} \tag{1-68}$$

$$(\mathbf{A} \times \mathbf{B}) \cdot (\mathbf{C} \times \mathbf{D}) = (\mathbf{A} \cdot \mathbf{C})(\mathbf{B} \cdot \mathbf{D}) - (\mathbf{A} \cdot \mathbf{D})(\mathbf{B} \cdot \mathbf{C}) \tag{1-69}$$

$$(\mathbf{A} \times \mathbf{B}) \times (\mathbf{C} \times \mathbf{D}) = [\mathbf{A} \cdot (\mathbf{B} \times \mathbf{D})]\mathbf{C} - [\mathbf{A} \cdot (\mathbf{B} \times \mathbf{C})]\mathbf{D}$$
$$= [\mathbf{A} \cdot (\mathbf{C} \times \mathbf{D})]\mathbf{B} - [\mathbf{B} \cdot (\mathbf{C} \times \mathbf{D})]\mathbf{A} \tag{1-70}$$

$$\mathbf{A} \cdot (\mathbf{B} \times \mathbf{C}) = (\mathbf{A} \times \mathbf{B}) \cdot \mathbf{C} = (\mathbf{C} \times \mathbf{A}) \cdot \mathbf{B} = \mathbf{C} \cdot (\mathbf{A} \times \mathbf{B})$$
$$= \mathbf{B} \cdot (\mathbf{C} \times \mathbf{A})$$
$$= (\mathbf{B} \times \mathbf{C}) \cdot \mathbf{A} \tag{1-71}$$

1-6 PROBLEMS AND APPLICATIONS

1. Show that the area of a parallelogram with sides $\mathbf{A}$ and $\mathbf{B}$ is given by $|\mathbf{A} \times \mathbf{B}|$.
2. Prove that the volume of a parallelepiped with base vectors $\mathbf{B}$ and $\mathbf{C}$ and edge vector $\mathbf{A}$ is given by $\mathbf{A} \cdot (\mathbf{B} \times \mathbf{C})$.
3. Show that the condition for linear independence of the vectors $\mathbf{A}$, $\mathbf{B}$, and $\mathbf{C}$ is that $\mathbf{A} \cdot (\mathbf{B} \times \mathbf{C}) \neq 0$.
4. Prove that the condition for the set of vectors $\{\mathbf{i}_1,\mathbf{i}_2,\ \ldots\ ,\mathbf{i}_n\}$ to be linearly dependent is that

$$\begin{vmatrix} \mathbf{i}_1 \cdot \mathbf{i}_1 & \mathbf{i}_1 \cdot \mathbf{i}_2 & \cdots & \mathbf{i}_1 \cdot \mathbf{i}_n \\ \mathbf{i}_2 \cdot \mathbf{i}_1 & \mathbf{i}_2 \cdot \mathbf{i}_2 & \cdots & \mathbf{i}_2 \cdot \mathbf{i}_n \\ \cdot & \cdot & & \cdot \\ \cdot & \cdot & & \cdot \\ \cdot & \cdot & & \cdot \\ \mathbf{i}_n \cdot \mathbf{i}_1 & \mathbf{i}_n \cdot \mathbf{i}_2 & \cdots & \mathbf{i}_n \cdot \mathbf{i}_n \end{vmatrix} = 0$$

5. Show that Cauchy's inequality

$$\sum_{k=1}^{n} a_k b_k \leq \left(\sum_{k=1}^{n} a_k^2 \right)^{1/2} \left(\sum_{k=1}^{n} b_k^2 \right)^{1/2}$$

follows from the definition of the scalar product.
6. Let a pair of planes intersect in space, and suppose that their line of intersection is in the direction $\mathbf{A}$. Let $\mathbf{A}$ and $\mathbf{B}$ determine one plane and $\mathbf{A}$ and $\mathbf{D}$ determine the other plane. What is the geometrical

significance of the expressions $(\mathbf{A} \times \mathbf{B}) \cdot (\mathbf{A} \times \mathbf{D})$ and $(\mathbf{A} \times \mathbf{B}) \times (\mathbf{A} \times \mathbf{D})$?

7. Four vectors have directions which are outward perpendiculars to the four faces of a tetrahedron. The lengths of these four vectors are equal to the areas of the faces they represent. Show that the sum of these four vectors is a zero vector.

8. Prove that $(\mathbf{x} - \mathbf{a}) \cdot \mathbf{b} = 0$ represents the equation of a plane passing through the point $\mathbf{a}$ and perpendicular to the vector $\mathbf{b}$.

9. Find the vector equation of a line through a given point and parallel to a given vector.

10. Find the vector equation of a line passing through two given points.

11. Find the vector equation of a line through a given point and perpendicular to two given vectors.

matrix and tensor algebra

2-1 DEFINITIONS

A matrix is a rectangular array of real or complex numbers arranged in an orderly table of rows and columns.

The individual numbers in a matrix are called the elements of the matrix. Each matrix element is equipped with a pair of indices, the first one referring to the row and the second one to the column in which the matrix element is located. For example, the matrix element a_{ij} appears in the ith row and the jth column. The total number of elements in a matrix is equal to the total number of rows times the total number of columns. Thus, a rectangular matrix with n rows and m columns will contain $n \times m$ elements. If $n = m$, the matrix is known as a square matrix and it will contain n^2 matrix elements.

EXAMPLE 2-1:

$$2 \times 2 \text{ matrix:} \qquad A = \begin{bmatrix} 7 & 9 \\ 5 & 4 \end{bmatrix} \tag{2-1}$$

$$2 \times 3 \text{ matrix:} \qquad A = \begin{bmatrix} 8 & 5 & 13 \\ 3 & 9 & 7 \end{bmatrix} \tag{2-2}$$

$$n \times m \text{ matrix:} \qquad A = \begin{bmatrix} a_{11} & a_{12} & \cdots & a_{1m} \\ a_{21} & a_{22} & \cdots & a_{2m} \\ \cdot & \cdot & & \cdot \\ \cdot & \cdot & & \cdot \\ \cdot & \cdot & & \cdot \\ a_{n1} & a_{n2} & \cdots & a_{nm} \end{bmatrix} \tag{2-3}$$

Indicial notation

In carrying out computations involving $n \times m$ matrices such as Eq. (2-3), it is frequently desirable to avoid having to write out the entire $n \times m$ array. Thus, we could symbolize the $n \times m$ matrix A in the form

$$A = (a_{ij}) = \begin{bmatrix} a_{11} & a_{12} & \cdots & a_{1m} \\ \cdot & \cdot & & \cdot \\ \cdot & \cdot & & \cdot \\ \cdot & \cdot & & \cdot \\ a_{n1} & a_{n2} & \cdots & a_{nm} \end{bmatrix} \tag{2-4}$$

$i = 1,2, \ldots ,n$ and $j = 1,2, \ldots ,m$. The notation becomes even more compact if we simply drop the parentheses around (a_{ij}) and write

$$A = a_{ij} = \begin{bmatrix} a_{11} & a_{12} & \cdots & a_{1m} \\ \cdot & \cdot & & \cdot \\ \cdot & \cdot & & \cdot \\ \cdot & \cdot & & \cdot \\ a_{n1} & a_{n2} & \cdots & a_{nm} \end{bmatrix} \tag{2-5}$$

$i = 1,2, \ldots ,n$ and $j = 1,2, \ldots ,m$. There is one feature of this notation which should be carefully noted. Although the symbol a_{ij} stands for the entire $n \times m$ matrix A, it also stands for a general element of this matrix, namely the element appearing in the ith row and jth column. The rule is that if one wishes to use a_{ij} to represent a specific matrix element rather than the whole matrix, then i and j are given specific numerical values. The same convention applies to vectors. For example, an n-dimensional vector such as

$$\mathbf{A} = (a_1, a_2, \ldots ,a_n) \tag{2-6a}$$

can also be written as

$$\mathbf{A} = a_i = (a_1, a_2, \ldots ,a_n) \tag{2-6b}$$

$i = 1,2, \ldots ,n$. Here a_i stands for the ordered set of n numbers constituting the vector $\mathbf{A}$. However, a_i also stands for the ith component of vector $\mathbf{A}$. The rule is that if one wishes to use a_i to represent a specific component of $\mathbf{A}$, then i is assigned the appropriate numerical value. For example,

$$a_i \qquad i = 1,2,3$$

represents a three-dimensional vector and a_2 represents the second component of the vector a_i. Using the indicial notation, the formula for vector addition (1-17) becomes

$$c_i = a_i + b_i \qquad i = 1,2, \ldots ,n \tag{2-7}$$

and the second component of the vector sum c_i is given by

$$c_2 = a_2 + b_2 \tag{2-8}$$

2-2 EQUALITY OF MATRICES AND NULL MATRICES

Two matrices A and B are equal if and only if their corresponding elements are equal. Thus

$A = B$ $\qquad$ if and only if

$$A_{ij} = B_{ij} \qquad \text{for every } i \text{ and } j \tag{2-9}$$

If all the elements of a matrix are zero, then it is called a "zero" or "null" matrix.

2-3 MATRIX OPERATIONS

Matrices can be added to, subtracted from, and multiplied by matrices. Matrices can also be multiplied by scalars. The following rules of operation apply:

Matrix addition

Two $n \times m$ matrices are added or subtracted by adding or subtracting their corresponding elements to form the $n \times m$ sum or difference matrix. Thus, if

$$A = a_{ij} \qquad i = 1,2, \ldots ,n \text{ and } j = 1,2, \ldots ,m$$

and

$$B = b_{ij} \qquad C = c_{ij}$$

then

$$C = A \pm B \qquad \text{means} \qquad c_{ij} = a_{ij} \pm b_{ij} \qquad (2\text{-}10)$$

EXAMPLE 2-2:

$$\begin{bmatrix} 2 & 3 & 4 \\ 5 & 7 & 0 \end{bmatrix} + \begin{bmatrix} 4 & 9 & 2 \\ 9 & 8 & 0 \end{bmatrix} = \begin{bmatrix} 6 & 12 & 6 \\ 14 & 15 & 0 \end{bmatrix}$$

Matrix multiplication

If λ is a scalar, then

$$B = \lambda A \qquad \text{means} \qquad b_{ij} = \lambda a_{ij} \qquad (2\text{-}11)$$

EXAMPLE 2-3:

$$3 \begin{bmatrix} 2 & 1 \\ 6 & 4 \end{bmatrix} = \begin{bmatrix} 6 & 3 \\ 18 & 12 \end{bmatrix}$$

There are two types of products which can be formed with a pair of matrices. They are known as the "matrix" product and the "direct" product.

Matrix product

The matrix product $C = AB$ of the matrices A and B is defined if and only if the number of columns in A is equal to the number of rows in B. If this is the case, then the matrices A and B are called "conformable." If A is an $n \times s$ matrix and B is an $s \times m$ matrix, then A and B are conformable and their matrix product $C = AB$ is an $n \times m$ matrix formed according to the rule

$$c_{ij} = \sum_{k=1}^{s} a_{ik}b_{kj} \qquad i = 1,2, \ldots ,n \text{ and } j = 1,2, \ldots ,m \qquad (2\text{-}12)$$

Notice that the reverse product BA is not even defined because B is an $s \times m$ matrix and A is an $n \times s$ matrix. Thus B and A are not conformable in the *order* BA but they are conformable in the order AB. Consequently, $AB \neq BA$. Even if A and B are both square matrices so that they are conformable in either order, we still have $AB \neq BA$ in general. If A and B happen to have the special property that $AB = BA$, then they are said to "commute."

EXAMPLE 2-4:

$$\begin{bmatrix} 1 & 2 \\ 3 & 4 \end{bmatrix} \begin{bmatrix} 3 \\ 7 \end{bmatrix} = \begin{bmatrix} 1 \times 3 + 2 \times 7 \\ 3 \times 3 + 4 \times 7 \end{bmatrix} = \begin{bmatrix} 17 \\ 37 \end{bmatrix} \tag{2-13}$$

Here a 2×2 matrix times a 2×1 matrix yields a 2×1 matrix.

$$\begin{bmatrix} a_{11} & a_{12} \\ a_{21} & a_{22} \end{bmatrix} \begin{bmatrix} x_1 \\ x_2 \end{bmatrix} = \begin{bmatrix} a_{11}x_1 + a_{12}x_2 \\ a_{21}x_1 + a_{22}x_2 \end{bmatrix}$$

$$\begin{bmatrix} 1 & 2 \\ 3 & 4 \end{bmatrix} \begin{bmatrix} 3 & 2 \\ 7 & 3 \end{bmatrix} = \begin{bmatrix} 1 \times 3 + 2 \times 7 & 1 \times 2 + 2 \times 3 \\ 3 \times 3 + 4 \times 7 & 3 \times 2 + 4 \times 3 \end{bmatrix} \tag{2-14}$$

$$= \begin{bmatrix} 17 & 8 \\ 34 & 18 \end{bmatrix}$$

Here a 2×2 matrix times a 2×2 matrix yields a 2×2 matrix.

$$\begin{bmatrix} a_{11} & a_{12} \\ a_{21} & a_{22} \end{bmatrix} \begin{bmatrix} b_{11} & b_{12} \\ b_{21} & b_{22} \end{bmatrix} = \begin{bmatrix} a_{11}b_{11} + a_{12}b_{21} & a_{11}b_{12} + a_{12}b_{22} \\ a_{21}b_{11} + a_{22}b_{21} & a_{21}b_{12} + a_{22}b_{22} \end{bmatrix} \tag{2-15}$$

REMARK: A $1 \times m$ matrix consists of a single row with m columns and is in fact an ordered set of m numbers. Thus the matrix $[a_1, a_2, \ldots, a_m]$ is also a vector. It is referred to as a "row" vector. On the other hand, an $n \times 1$ column matrix consists of a single column with n rows and is in fact an ordered set of n numbers whose ordering is arranged vertically instead of horizontally. Thus the matrix

$$\begin{bmatrix} a_1 \\ a_2 \\ \cdot \\ \cdot \\ \cdot \\ a_n \end{bmatrix}$$

is also a vector. It is referred to as a "column" vector. Hence the rows of a matrix can be thought of as row vectors, and the columns of a matrix can be thought of as column vectors. For example, the scalar product of a $1 \times n$ row vector with a conformable $n \times 1$ column vector is written

$$[a_1, a_2, \ldots, a_n] \begin{bmatrix} b_1 \\ b_2 \\ \cdot \\ \cdot \\ \cdot \\ b_n \end{bmatrix} = a_1 b_1 + a_2 b_2 + \cdots + a_n b_n \tag{2-16}$$

The idea of row vectors and column vectors simplifies the computation of the matrix product (2-12). Consider Eq. (2-15). The first element in the first row of the product matrix is the scalar product of $[a_{11} \quad a_{12}]$ with $\begin{bmatrix} b_{11} \\ b_{12} \end{bmatrix}$. Thus the first element in the first row of the product matrix is formed by taking the dot product of the first row vector of the left-hand factor with the first column vector of the right-hand factor. Similarly, the first element of the second row of the product matrix is the dot product of the second row of the left-hand factor with the first column vector of the right-hand factor, and so on. Each column of the right-hand factor contributes one column to the product matrix. Each row of the left-hand factor contributes one row to the product matrix.

EXAMPLE 2-5:

$$[a_1 \cdots a_n] \begin{bmatrix} b_1 \\ b_2 \\ \cdot \\ \cdot \\ \cdot \\ b_n \end{bmatrix} = a_1 b_1 + \cdots + a_n b_n \tag{2-17}$$

is the product of a $1 \times n$ matrix with an $n \times 1$ matrix and is therefore a 1×1 matrix which is a scalar. The left-hand factor has one row so the product will have only one row, but since the right-hand factor has only one column, the product can have only one column. This means that the one row of the product can have only one element in it. Thus the product is a scalar. The rule can be shortened to "Each row gives a row; each column gives a column." Consider now the product of an $n \times 1$ matrix with a $1 \times n$ matrix. The product will have n rows and n columns and is thus an $n \times n$ matrix. In particular,

$$\begin{bmatrix} a_1 \\ a_2 \\ \cdot \\ \cdot \\ \cdot \\ a_n \end{bmatrix} [b_1 \quad b_2 \quad \cdots \quad b_n] = \begin{bmatrix} a_1 b_1 & a_1 b_2 & \cdots & a_1 b_n \\ a_2 b_1 & a_2 b_2 & \cdots & a_2 b_n \\ \cdot & \cdot & & \cdot \\ \cdot & \cdot & & \cdot \\ \cdot & \cdot & & \cdot \\ a_n b_1 & a_n b_2 & \cdots & a_n b_n \end{bmatrix} \tag{2-18}$$

Direct product

If A is an $n \times n$ matrix and B is an $m \times m$ matrix, then the direct product of A and B is written as

$$C = A \times B \tag{2-19}$$

where C is a matrix having nm rows and nm columns.

EXAMPLE 2-6: Let

$$A = \begin{bmatrix} a_{11} & a_{12} \\ a_{21} & a_{22} \end{bmatrix} \quad \text{and} \quad B = \begin{bmatrix} b_{11} & b_{12} \\ b_{21} & b_{22} \end{bmatrix}$$

Then, since A and B are each 2×2 matrices, $C = A \times B$ will be a 4×4 matrix and is formed according to the following rule:

$$C = A \times B = \begin{bmatrix} a_{11}B & a_{12}B \\ a_{21}B & a_{22}B \end{bmatrix} = \begin{bmatrix} a_{11}\begin{pmatrix} b_{11} & b_{12} \\ b_{21} & b_{22} \end{pmatrix} & a_{12}\begin{pmatrix} b_{11} & b_{12} \\ b_{21} & b_{22} \end{pmatrix} \\ a_{21}\begin{pmatrix} b_{11} & b_{12} \\ b_{21} & b_{22} \end{pmatrix} & a_{22}\begin{pmatrix} b_{11} & b_{12} \\ b_{21} & b_{22} \end{pmatrix} \end{bmatrix} \tag{2-20}$$

or

$$C = A \times B = \begin{bmatrix} a_{11}b_{11} & a_{11}b_{12} & a_{12}b_{11} & a_{12}b_{12} \\ a_{11}b_{21} & a_{11}b_{22} & a_{12}b_{21} & a_{12}b_{22} \\ a_{21}b_{11} & a_{21}b_{12} & a_{22}b_{11} & a_{22}b_{12} \\ a_{21}b_{21} & a_{21}b_{22} & a_{22}b_{21} & a_{22}b_{22} \end{bmatrix} \tag{2-21}$$

Clearly, the direct product is not commutative in general since

$$A \times B = \begin{bmatrix} a_{11}B & a_{12}B \\ a_{21}B & a_{22}B \end{bmatrix} \neq B \times A = \begin{bmatrix} b_{11}A & b_{12}A \\ b_{21}A & b_{22}A \end{bmatrix} \tag{2-22}$$

In the general case for which A is an $n \times n$ matrix and B an $m \times m$ matrix,

$$C = A \times B = \begin{bmatrix} a_{11}B & a_{12}B & \cdots & a_{1n}B \\ & & & \\ \cdot & \cdot & & \cdot \\ \cdot & \cdot & & \cdot \\ & & & \\ a_{n1}B & a_{n2}B & \cdots & a_{nn}B \end{bmatrix} \tag{2-23}$$

is an $nm \times nm$ matrix.

Partitioned matrices

If a matrix is divided into smaller submatrices the matrix is said to be "partitioned." For example, a square 3×3 matrix can be partitioned into four submatrices, as shown below:

$$A = \left[\begin{array}{cc|c} a_{11} & a_{12} & a_{13} \\ a_{21} & a_{22} & a_{23} \\ \hline a_{31} & a_{32} & a_{33} \end{array}\right] = \begin{bmatrix} b_{11} & b_{12} \\ b_{21} & b_{22} \end{bmatrix} \tag{2-24}$$

where

$$b_{11} = \begin{bmatrix} a_{11} & a_{12} \\ a_{21} & a_{22} \end{bmatrix} \quad b_{12} = \begin{bmatrix} a_{13} \\ a_{23} \end{bmatrix} \tag{2-24a}$$

$$b_{21} = [a_{31} \quad a_{32}] \quad b_{22} = a_{33}$$

The partitioning operation is useful in simplifying the evaluation of a matrix product. For example, let

$$A = \left[\begin{array}{cc|c} a_{11} & a_{12} & a_{13} \\ a_{21} & a_{22} & a_{23} \\ \hline a_{31} & a_{32} & a_{33} \end{array}\right] \quad C = \left[\begin{array}{cc|c} c_{11} & c_{12} & c_{13} \\ c_{21} & c_{22} & c_{23} \\ \hline c_{31} & c_{32} & c_{33} \end{array}\right] \tag{2-25}$$

and compute $AC = D$. The partitioned matrix A becomes

$$A = \begin{bmatrix} b_{11} & b_{12} \\ b_{21} & b_{22} \end{bmatrix} \tag{2-26}$$

as in (2-24), and the partitioned matrix C becomes

$$C = \begin{bmatrix} d_{11} & d_{12} \\ d_{21} & d_{22} \end{bmatrix} \tag{2-27}$$

Then

$$D = AC = \begin{bmatrix} b_{11} & b_{12} \\ b_{21} & b_{22} \end{bmatrix} \begin{bmatrix} d_{11} & d_{12} \\ d_{21} & d_{22} \end{bmatrix} \tag{2-28}$$

giving

$$D = \begin{bmatrix} b_{11}d_{11} + b_{12}d_{21} & b_{11}d_{12} + b_{12}d_{22} \\ b_{21}d_{11} + b_{22}d_{21} & b_{21}d_{12} + b_{22}d_{22} \end{bmatrix} \tag{2-29}$$

In obtaining (2-29) we treat each submatrix in (2-25) as a single matrix element. The final result is then obtained by using the rules for matrix products and matrix sums to evaluate the elements in (2-29).

2-4 DETERMINANTS

The $n \times n$ square matrix $A = a_{ij}$, $i,j = 1,2, \ldots ,n$, has an associated determinant which is denoted by any of the following symbols: $|A|$, $|a_{ij}|$, $\det |A|$, or $\det |a_{ij}|$. Thus

$$\det |A| = |a_{ij}| = \begin{vmatrix} a_{11} & a_{12} & \cdots & a_{1n} \\ \cdot & \cdot & & \cdot \\ \cdot & \cdot & & \cdot \\ \cdot & \cdot & & \cdot \\ a_{n1} & a_{n2} & \cdots & a_{nn} \end{vmatrix} \tag{2-30}$$

Minors and cofactors

The cofactor of the element a_{ij} in the determinant (2-30) is the signed minor of a_{ij}. The minor of the element a_{ij} in $\det |a_{ij}|$ is the determinant which remains after striking out the ith row and jth column. The signed minor is then $(-1)^{i+j}$ times this minor. The signed minor or cofactor of a_{ij} will be denoted by A^{ij}.

EXAMPLE 2-7:

$$\begin{vmatrix} a_{11} & a_{12} & a_{13} \\ a_{21} & a_{22} & a_{23} \\ a_{31} & a_{32} & a_{33} \end{vmatrix} \tag{2-31}$$

The signed minor or cofactor of a_{11} is

$$A^{11} = (-1)^2 \begin{vmatrix} a_{22} & a_{23} \\ a_{32} & a_{33} \end{vmatrix}$$

The signed minor or cofactor of a_{12} is

$$A^{12} = (-1)^3 \begin{vmatrix} a_{21} & a_{23} \\ a_{31} & a_{33} \end{vmatrix}$$

The signed minor or cofactor of a_{13} is

$$A^{13} = (-1)^4 \begin{vmatrix} a_{21} & a_{22} \\ a_{31} & a_{32} \end{vmatrix}$$

A determinant is evaluated by expanding it in terms of its cofactors. This procedure is known as a "Laplace development" and is given by

$$\det |A| = \sum_{j=1}^{n} a_{ij} A^{ij} \tag{2-32}$$

In applying Eq. (2-32) we think of i as taking a fixed numerical value corresponding to a fixed row of the matrix. Thus Eq. (2-32) is most accurately described as the expansion of $\det |A|$ in cofactors of the ith row of A where i is a fixed number between 1 and n. For example, the expansion of Eq. (2-32) in terms of cofactors of the first row of A is given by

$$\det |A| = a_{11} A^{11} + a_{12} A^{12} + a_{13} A^{13} \tag{2-33}$$

The student should verify that

$$\sum_{j=1}^{n} a_{ij} A^{kj} = 0 \qquad i \neq k \tag{2-34}$$

The significance of Eq. (2-34) is that if one uses the elements of the ith row of $|A|$ for a Laplace development but replaces all the cofactors of the elements in the ith row by the cofactors of the elements in some other row, say the kth row, then the Laplace development vanishes. The student should verify that $\det |A| = 0$ if:

1. All elements of a row are zero.
2. A pair of rows (or a pair of columns) are equal.
3. The elements of one row (column) are a fixed multiple of another row (column).

It should also be verified that:

4. The value of a determinant changes sign if two rows (or columns) are interchanged.
5. The value of a determinant remains fixed if rows and columns are interchanged.
6. Multiplying each element of a given row (column) by the same constant factor multiplies the value of the determinant by this same factor.

Rank of a matrix

If A is a square matrix and $\det |A| = 0$, then A is singular. If A is not a square matrix, then $\det |A|$ is undefined. Thus all nonsquare matrices are singular by definition. For a given matrix A one can consider all possible partitions into submatrices. Those submatrices which are square will have subdeterminants. If at least one $r \times r$ subdeterminant does not vanish and all subdeterminants with more than r rows and r columns do vanish, then A is said to be of rank r. Thus, if A is a singular $n \times n$ matrix of rank r, then $r < n$. If A is nonsingular, then $r = n$.

2-5 SPECIAL MATRICES

Unit matrix

The unit matrix I has the property that $IA = AI = A$ for any matrix A. The matrix I has unity for elements along the main diagonal. All other elements vanish. The unit matrix is symbolized by the Kronecker delta

$$I = \delta_{ij} \tag{2-35}$$

where

$$\delta_{ij} = \begin{cases} 1 & i = j \\ 0 & i \neq j \end{cases} \tag{2-36}$$

Diagonal matrices

A matrix whose only nonvanishing components are on the main diagonal is referred to as a "diagonal" matrix

$$D = D_i \delta_{ij} \tag{2-37}$$

Diagonal matrices have the property of commuting with one another. Thus, if $D = D_i \delta_{ij}$ and $E = E_i \delta_{ij}$, then

$$DE = \sum_{k=1}^{n} D_k \delta_{ik} E_k \delta_{kj} = D_i E_i \delta_{ij}$$

$$ED = \sum_{k=1}^{n} E_k \delta_{ik} D_k \delta_{kj} = E_i D_i \delta_{ij}$$

giving $DE = ED$. A matrix which is of the form λI where λ is a scalar and I is the unit matrix is called a "scalar" matrix. If two matrices, one of which is diagonal and nonscalar, commute, then the other matrix is not necessarily diagonal. (Example?)

Trace of a square matrix

The trace of a square $n \times n$ matrix $A = a_{ij}$ defined as

$$\text{Tr } (A) = \sum_{k=1}^{n} a_{kk} \tag{2-38}$$

is thus the sum of the elements on the main diagonal of A. If A and

B are square matrices, then

$$\mathrm{Tr}\,(AB) = \sum_{i=1}^{n} \sum_{k=1}^{n} a_{ik}b_{ki} = \mathrm{Tr}\,(BA) \qquad (2\text{-}39)$$

Notice also that

$$A \times B = \begin{bmatrix} a_{11}B & a_{12}B & \cdots & a_{1n}B \\ \cdot & \cdot & & \cdot \\ \cdot & \cdot & & \cdot \\ \cdot & \cdot & & \cdot \\ a_{n1}B & a_{n2}B & \cdots & a_{nn}B \end{bmatrix}$$

yields

$$\mathrm{Tr}\,(A \times B) = a_{11}\,\mathrm{Tr}\,(B) + a_{22}\,\mathrm{Tr}\,(B) + \cdots + a_{nn}\,\mathrm{Tr}\,(B)$$

or

$$\mathrm{Tr}\,(A \times B) = \mathrm{Tr}\,(A) \cdot \mathrm{Tr}\,(B) \qquad (2\text{-}40)$$

Transpose of an arbitrary matrix

The transpose of the matrix $A = a_{ij}$ is $A^T = a_{ji}$ and is formed by interchanging the rows and columns in A. If A is an $n \times s$ matrix and B is an $s \times m$ matrix, then $C = AB$ is an $n \times m$ matrix. However, A^T will be an $s \times n$ matrix and B^T will be an $m \times s$ matrix. Therefore, A^T and B^T are conformable only in the order $B^T A^T$, yielding an $m \times n$ matrix. This is the basis of the important:

Reversal rule for matrix products

The transpose of a matrix product is equal to the product of the transposed factors taken in the reverse order.

$$C = AB \qquad C^T = B^T A^T \qquad (2\text{-}41)$$

$$Z = ABCD \cdots Y \qquad Z^T = Y^T \cdots D^T C^T B^T A^T \qquad (2\text{-}42)$$

Cofactor matrix

If $A = a_{ij}$ is a square matrix, then $A^C = A^{ij}$ is called the cofactor matrix of A. The matrix element A^{ij} of A^C is the cofactor of the element a_{ij} in the determinant $|a_{ij}|$.

EXAMPLE 2-8:

$$A = \begin{bmatrix} a_{11} & a_{12} \\ a_{21} & a_{22} \end{bmatrix} \qquad A^C = \begin{bmatrix} a_{22} & -a_{21} \\ -a_{12} & a_{11} \end{bmatrix} \qquad (2\text{-}43)$$

Adjoint of a square matrix

The adjoint of a square matrix is defined as the transpose of its cofactor matrix and is written as A^{CT}. The student should verify that

$$A^{CT} = A^{TC} \tag{2-44}$$

Recalling the Laplace development of det $|A|$ discussed in Sec. 2-4,

$$\det |A|\ \delta_{ik} = \sum_{j=1}^{n} a_{ij}A^{kj} \tag{2-45}$$

let

$$B_{jk} = A^{kj} \tag{2-46}$$

Then

$$\det |A|\ \delta_{ik} = \sum_{j=1}^{n} a_{ij}B_{jk} = C_{ik} \tag{2-47}$$

is recognized as a matrix product. Notice that the matrix $B = B_{jk}$ has as its first row, the first column of A^{kj}, and as its second row, the second column of A^{kj}, and so on. Therefore, $B = B_{jk}$ is the transpose of the cofactor matrix A^{kj}, and we can write

$$B = A^{CT} \tag{2-48}$$

so that Eq. (2-47) becomes

$$I \det |A| = AB = AA^{CT} \tag{2-49}$$

where $I = \delta_{ik}$ is the unit matrix. The expression (2-49) is important because it leads to the concept of the inverse of a square matrix.

Inverse of a square matrix

If A is a nonsingular square matrix, then det $|A| \neq 0$, and Eq. (2-49) can be written in the form

$$A \left[\frac{A^{CT}}{\det |A|} \right] = I \tag{2-50}$$

When the product of two factors is unity, it is customary to call one the "reciprocal" of the other. Thus we define

$$A^{-1} = \frac{A^{CT}}{|A|} \tag{2-51}$$

as the inverse of matrix A. Then

$$AA^{-1} = I \tag{2-52}$$

However, the Laplace development (2-45) gives the expansion of det $|A|$ in terms of the cofactors of the ith *row*, when $k = i$. It is also possible to expand det $|A|$ in terms of cofactors of the ith column, and in fact

$$\det |A|\ \delta_{ik} = \sum_{j=1}^{n} a_{ij}A^{kj} = \sum_{j=1}^{n} a_{ji}A^{jk} \tag{2-53}$$

If we let

$$B = b_{ij} = a_{ji} \tag{2-54}$$

then the last term of Eq. (2-53) is recognized as a matrix product. Thus

$$\det |A| \, \delta_{ik} = \sum_{j=1}^{n} b_{ij} A^{jk} = C_{ik} \tag{2-55}$$

Now we notice that the matrix $B = b_{ij}$ has as its first row, the first column of $A = a_{ij}$, and as its second row, the second column of A, and so on. Thus $B = b_{ij}$ is the transpose of the matrix a_{ij}, and we can write

$$B = A^T \tag{2-56}$$

so that Eq. (2-55) becomes

$$I \det |A| = A^T A^C \tag{2-57}$$

If we now employ the reversal rule (2-42), noting that

$$A^{TT} = A \tag{2-58}$$

and that

$$(I \det |A|)^T = I \det |A| \tag{2-59}$$

we obtain

$$I \det |A| = A^{CT} A \tag{2-60}$$

Thus, comparing with Eq. (2-49), we find

$$A A^{CT} = A^{CT} A \tag{2-61}$$

which shows that A commutes with the transpose of its own cofactor matrix. Also, Eq. (2-60) gives

$$A^{-1} A = A A^{-1} = I \tag{2-62}$$

when $|A|$ is nonsingular.

Reversal rule for the inverse of a matrix product

For a pair of matrices,

$$(AB)^{-1} = B^{-1} A^{-1} \tag{2-63}$$

and, in general,

$$(ABC \cdots Z)^{-1} = (Z^{-1} \cdots C^{-1} B^{-1} A^{-1}) \tag{2-64}$$

Consider the identity

$$BB^{-1} A^{-1} A = I$$

Multiplication on the left by A and on the right by B yields

$$ABB^{-1} A^{-1} AB = AB$$

Finally, multiplying both sides by $(AB)^{-1}$ gives either

$$ABB^{-1} A^{-1} = I \qquad \text{or} \qquad B^{-1} A^{-1} AB = I$$

both of which imply

$$(AB)^{-1} = B^{-1} A^{-1}$$

A simple extension of this argument suffices to prove Eq. (2-64).

Complex matrices

Matrices occurring in physical problems frequently have matrix elements which are complex numbers.

EXAMPLE 2-9:

$$A = \begin{bmatrix} 2 + 3i & 4 - 5i \\ 3 & 4i \end{bmatrix}$$

The complex conjugate of matrix A is written as $\bar{A}$ and is defined by

$$\bar{A} = \begin{bmatrix} 2 - 3i & 4 + 5i \\ 3 & -4i \end{bmatrix}$$

In general, the complex conjugate of a matrix is formed by replacing each element of the original matrix by its complex conjugate element. If

$$A = a_{ij} \tag{2-65}$$

then

$$\bar{A} = \bar{a}_{ij} \tag{2-66}$$

where $\bar{a}_{12}$ represents the complex conjugate of a_{12}, and so on. The student should verify that if

$$X = ABC \cdots W \tag{2-67}$$

then

$$\bar{X} = \bar{A}\bar{B}\bar{C} \cdots \bar{W} \tag{2-68}$$

Thus the complex conjugation does not reverse the order of the factors in a matrix product.

Hermitian conjugate matrix

Taking the complex conjugate of a matrix and transposing the result yields a new matrix called the "Hermitian conjugate" of the original. The Hermitian conjugate of A is denoted by A^* and is defined as

$$A^* = (\bar{A})^T = (\overline{A^T}) = \bar{A}^T \tag{2-69}$$

When $A = a_{ij}$, then $A^* = \bar{a}_{ji}$. It follows from Eqs. (2-67) and (2-42) that if

$$X = ABC \cdots W \tag{2-70}$$

then

$$X^* = W^* \cdots C^*B^*A^* \tag{2-71}$$

2-6 SYSTEMS OF LINEAR EQUATIONS

Consider the following system of linear equations:

$$a_{11}x_1 + a_{12}x_2 + \cdots + a_{1m}x_m = c_1$$
$$a_{21}x_1 + a_{22}x_2 + \cdots + a_{2m}x_m = c_2$$

$$\cdot \qquad\qquad\qquad \cdot$$
$$\cdot \qquad\qquad\qquad \cdot \qquad\qquad\qquad (2\text{-}72)$$
$$\cdot \qquad\qquad\qquad \cdot$$

$$a_{n1}x_1 + a_{n2}x_2 + \cdots + a_{nm}x_m = c_n$$

If $n < m$, then there are fewer equations than unknowns, and the system is called "underdetermined." If $n > m$, then there are more equations than unknowns, and the system is said to be "overdetermined." We shall confine ourselves here to a discussion of systems in which there are as many equations as unknowns, so that $n = m$, in which case the system (2-72) is called "well determined."

When the system (2-72) is well determined, its solution is easily written down by matrix methods. Let

$$A = \begin{bmatrix} a_{11} & a_{12} & \cdots & a_{1n} \\ a_{21} & a_{22} & \cdots & a_{2n} \\ \cdot & \cdot & & \cdot \\ \cdot & \cdot & & \cdot \\ \cdot & \cdot & & \cdot \\ a_{n1} & a_{n2} & \cdots & a_{nn} \end{bmatrix} \qquad (2\text{-}73)$$

$$X = \begin{bmatrix} x_1 \\ x_2 \\ \cdot \\ \cdot \\ \cdot \\ x_n \end{bmatrix} \qquad (2\text{-}74)$$

$$C = \begin{bmatrix} c_1 \\ c_2 \\ \cdot \\ \cdot \\ \cdot \\ c_n \end{bmatrix} \qquad (2\text{-}75)$$

and consider the problem of finding the column vector X which satisfies the *inhomogeneous* matrix equation

$$AX = C \qquad (2\text{-}76)$$

The corresponding *homogeneous* problem is to find the column vector X which satisfies

$$AX = 0 \qquad (2\text{-}77)$$

where

$$0 = \begin{bmatrix} 0 \\ 0 \\ \cdot \\ \cdot \\ \cdot \\ 0 \end{bmatrix} \qquad (2\text{-}78)$$

If the square $n \times n$ matrix is of rank n, then its determinant is non-singular, and the solution of Eq. (2-76) is given by

$$X = A^{-1}C = \frac{A^{CT}}{|A|} C \qquad (2\text{-}79)$$

Since

$$A^{CT} = \begin{bmatrix} A^{11} & A^{21} & \cdots & A^{n1} \\ A^{12} & A^{22} & \cdots & A^{n2} \\ \cdot & \cdot & & \cdot \\ \cdot & \cdot & & \cdot \\ \cdot & \cdot & & \cdot \\ A^{1n} & A^{2n} & \cdots & A^{nn} \end{bmatrix} \qquad (2\text{-}80)$$

the ith component of the column vector X is given by

$$X_i = \frac{1}{|A|} \sum_{k=1}^{n} c_k A^{ki} \qquad (2\text{-}81)$$

$i = 1,2, \ldots ,n$. Comparison of Eq. (2-81) with Eq. (2-32) shows that $\sum_{k=1}^{n} c_k A^{ki}$ represents the expansion of det $|A|$ in terms of cofactors of the ith column. However, the elements $a_{1i}, a_{2i}, \ldots , a_{ni}$ in the ith column of det $|A|$ are replaced by $c_1, c_2, \ldots , c_n$ in Eq. (2-81). Equation (2-81) is called "Cramer's rule."

EXAMPLE 2-10:

$$\begin{bmatrix} a_{11} & a_{12} \\ a_{21} & a_{22} \end{bmatrix} \begin{bmatrix} x_1 \\ x_2 \end{bmatrix} = \begin{bmatrix} c_1 \\ c_2 \end{bmatrix}$$

$$x_1 = \frac{\begin{vmatrix} c_1 & a_{12} \\ c_2 & a_{22} \end{vmatrix}}{\begin{vmatrix} a_{11} & a_{12} \\ a_{21} & a_{22} \end{vmatrix}} \qquad x_2 = \frac{\begin{vmatrix} a_{11} & c_1 \\ a_{21} & c_2 \end{vmatrix}}{\begin{vmatrix} a_{11} & a_{12} \\ a_{21} & a_{22} \end{vmatrix}}$$

Let us now turn our attention to the homogeneous problem (2-77). If $|A| \neq 0$, then the only solution of Eq. (2-77) is the trivial one, $x_1 = 0$, $x_2 = 0$, $\ldots$, $x_n = 0$. Thus, a necessary condition for the homogeneous system (2-77) to have a nontrivial solution is that $|A| = 0$. (The condition is not sufficient since it is possible that all the elements of matrix A are themselves zero.) Thus, if A is an $n \times n$ matrix, then the homogeneous problem (2-77) has a nontrivial solution only if the rank of matrix A is less than n.

This type of problem occurs frequently in physics, particularly in the computation of natural modes of vibration.

Parametric solution of $AX = 0$

The solution of the problem

$$AX = 0 \qquad (2\text{-}82)$$

$$|A| = 0 \qquad (2\text{-}83)$$

is easily written in parametric form, using matrix notation. Let

$$X = A^{CT}Y \qquad (2\text{-}84)$$

where Y is an arbitrary n-dimensional column vector. Then

$$AX = AA^{CT}Y \qquad (2\text{-}85)$$

but Eq. (2-83) together with Eq. (2-49) gives $AA^{CT} = 0$; thus

$$AX = AA^{CT}Y = 0 \qquad (2\text{-}86)$$

proving that Eq. (2-84) is a solution of Eqs. (2-82) and (2-83). The column vector Y in Eq. (2-84) parameterizes the solution. Choose

$$Y = \begin{bmatrix} Y_1 \\ 0 \\ \cdot \\ \cdot \\ \cdot \\ 0 \end{bmatrix} \qquad (2\text{-}87)$$

so that the column vector Y has only a single nonzero component. Then Eq. (2-84) becomes

$$\begin{bmatrix} x_1 \\ x_2 \\ \cdot \\ \cdot \\ \cdot \\ x_n \end{bmatrix} = \begin{bmatrix} A^{11} & A^{21} & \cdots & A^{n1} \\ A^{12} & A^{22} & \cdots & A^{n2} \\ \cdot & \cdot & & \cdot \\ \cdot & \cdot & & \cdot \\ \cdot & \cdot & & \cdot \\ A^{1n} & A^{2n} & \cdots & A^{nn} \end{bmatrix} \begin{bmatrix} Y_1 \\ 0 \\ \cdot \\ \cdot \\ \cdot \\ 0 \end{bmatrix} \qquad (2\text{-}88)$$

which gives

$$x_1 = A^{11}Y_1,\ x_2 = A^{12}Y_1,\ \ldots,\ x_n = A^{1n}Y_1 \qquad (2\text{-}89)$$

We can now eliminate the parameter Y_1. The result is

$$\frac{x_1}{x_n} = \frac{A^{11}}{A^{1n}},\ \frac{x_2}{x_n} = \frac{A^{12}}{A^{1n}},\ \cdots,\ \frac{x_{n-1}}{x_n} = \frac{A^{1n-1}}{A^{1n}} \qquad (2\text{-}90)$$

The result (2-90) requires that the component x_n appearing in the denominator of each ratio in (2-90) be nonzero and hence that $A^{1n} \neq 0$. If $x_n = 0$, then we simply use another component of X, say x_k, to form

$$\frac{x_1}{x_k} = \frac{A^{11}}{A^{1k}} \qquad \frac{x_2}{x_k} = \frac{A^{12}}{A^{1k}}$$

and so on. If it is impossible to find an $x_k \neq 0$ for any k between 1 and n, then all the cofactors A^{ij} must vanish, and the homogeneous problem [Eqs. (2-82) and (2-83)] has only the trivial solution $x_1 = 0$, $x_2 = 0, \ldots, x_n = 0$. The significance of (2-90) is that when the homogeneous problem (2-82) and (2-83) has a nontrivial solution given by vector X, only the ratios of the components of this vector are fixed. Thus, the magnitude of one component of X can be arbitrarily assigned and the others determined immediately in terms of it by (2-90). A normalization condition, for example $X^T X = 1$, would remove this last remaining degree of freedom, so that a nontrivial solution of

$$AX = 0 \qquad |A| = 0$$

satisfying in addition the condition

$$X^T X = 1$$

is unique.

REMARK: Suppose that A is a nonsingular $n \times n$ matrix. What can be said about $|A^{CT}|$? To answer this question, it is necessary to know how to multiply two determinants together. Multiplication of determinants is expressible in terms of the determinant of the product of their associated matrices. Thus, let $|A|$ and $|B|$ be the determinants associated with the square matrices A and B.

RULE: $|A|\,|B| = |AB|$

The determinant of the product of two matrices is equal to the product of their determinants. (Verify!) Now, recalling Eq. (2-49),

$$I|A| = AA^{CT} \tag{2-91}$$

we notice that the left-hand side of Eq. (2-91) is a diagonal $n \times n$ matrix with $|A|$ for each diagonal matrix element. Hence $\det |I|A|| = |A|^n$, and we have

$$|A|^n = |I|A|| = |AA^{CT}| = |A|\,|A^{CT}| \tag{2-92}$$

so that

$$|A^{CT}| = |A|^{n-1} \tag{2-93}$$

2-7 LINEAR OPERATORS

The $n \times n$ matrix A operating on an $n \times 1$ column vector X produces a new $n \times 1$ column vector $Y = AX$. If k is scalar and if X and Z are both $n \times 1$ column vectors, then matrix multiplication has the properties

$$\begin{aligned} A(kX) &= k(AX) \\ A(X + Z) &= AX + AZ \end{aligned} \tag{2-94}$$

The fact that A manufactures a "new" vector Y out of an "old" vector X is the basis for referring to A as an operator. The properties expressed by Eqs. (2-94) define A to be a linear operator.

Geometric interpretation

The effect of the operator A on the vector X is to change both the direction and the magnitude of X. Thus the vector $Y = AX$ points in a direction different from that of X and has a length different from that of X. In the preceding discussion it is assumed that the components of both X and Y are determined by projecting them along the *same* set of rectangular Cartesian coordinate axes.

Similarity transformations

Now imagine three distinct fixed points O, P_1, P_2 embedded in three-dimensional space (Fig. 2-1). We shall call the vector from O to P_1, $\mathbf{OP}_1$, and the vector from O to P_2, $\mathbf{OP}_2$. We now erect a set of three-dimensional Cartesian coordinates centered at the point O and referred to as frame I. In frame I we have $\mathbf{OP}_1 = X$ and $\mathbf{OP}_2 = Y$. Suppose that an operator A *also thought of as being associated with frame I* transforms the vector X in frame I into the vector Y in frame I according to the equation

$$Y = AX \tag{2-95}$$

Let frame I be rotated into a new position, keeping the origin of coordinates fixed at O and leaving the points P_1 and P_2 fixed in space. Frame I in its new position is called frame II. Notice that the vectors $\mathbf{OP}_1$ and $\mathbf{OP}_2$ have been unaffected by this procedure, since the three points O, P_1, and P_2 have remained fixed in space. However, the projections of $\mathbf{OP}_1$ and $\mathbf{OP}_2$ on the coordinate axes of frame II will have different numerical values from those which they had when projected along the coordinate axes of frame I. Thus in frame II we write $\mathbf{OP}_1 = X'$ and $\mathbf{OP}_2 = Y'$. We now want to find an operator A' *associated with frame II* which transforms the vector X' in frame II into the vector Y' in frame II according to

$$Y' = A'X' \tag{2-96}$$

The operator A' in frame II is called similar to the operator A in frame I. Thus A' sends $\mathbf{OP}_1$ expressed in frame II into $\mathbf{OP}_2$ expressed in frame II, while A does the same thing in frame I. In order to compute the operator A' we need to know the relationship between the components of both $\mathbf{OP}_1$ and $\mathbf{OP}_2$ expressed in frame I and the components of $\mathbf{OP}_1$ and $\mathbf{OP}_2$ expressed in frame II. This information is given in the form of a transformation of coordinates expressed by a nonsingular matrix S. Thus

$$X = SX' \tag{2-97}$$

$$Y = SY' \tag{2-98}$$

and

$$Y = AX \tag{2-99}$$

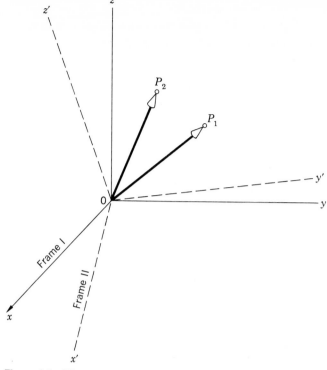

Figure 2-1 The vectors $O\mathbf{P}_1$ and $O\mathbf{P}_2$ are fixed in space, but they have different projections along the coordinate axes of frames I and II.

becomes

$$SY' = ASX' \tag{2-100}$$

Since $|S| \neq 0$ by hypothesis, S^{-1} exists and

$$Y' = S^{-1}ASX' \tag{2-101}$$

Thus

$$Y' = A'X'$$

if

$$A' = S^{-1}AS \tag{2-102}$$

The similar matrices A' and A are connected by Eq. (2-102), which is known as a similarity transformation. Notice that

$$\det |A'| = \det |S^{-1}AS| = \det |SS^{-1}| \det |A| = \det |A| \tag{2-103}$$

and

$$\mathrm{Tr}\,(A') = \mathrm{Tr}\,(S^{-1}AS) = \mathrm{Tr}\,(SS^{-1}A) = \mathrm{Tr}\,(A) \tag{2-104}$$

where we have employed Eq. (2-39) to obtain Eq. (2-104). Then, if A' and A are similar matrices, $|A'| = |A|$ and $\mathrm{Tr}\,(A') = \mathrm{Tr}\,(A)$.

Unitary operators

Matrix operators which leave the magnitude of a vector unaltered are called "unitary" operators. Thus, if

$$Y = AX$$

the square of the magnitude of Y is given by

$$|Y|^2 = Y^*Y$$

where Y^* is the Hermitian conjugate of Y. We have, using Eq. (2-71),

$$Y^* = X^*A^* \qquad \text{and} \qquad Y^*Y = X^*A^*AX$$

The condition $|Y|^2 = |X|^2$ then requires

$$A^*A = I \tag{2-105}$$

or

$$A^{-1} = A^* \tag{2-106}$$

Matrices satisfying Eq. (2-106) are unitary.

Orthogonal operators

A matrix operator with purely real matrix elements which leaves the magnitude of a vector with purely real components unaltered is called "orthogonal." Thus, if

$$Y = AX$$

then

$$|Y|^2 = Y^T Y$$

and using Eq. (2-42),

$$Y^T = X^T A^T$$

so that

$$|Y|^2 = Y^T Y = X^T A^T A X$$

The condition $|Y|^2 = |X|^2$ requires

$$A^T A = I \tag{2-107}$$

or

$$A^{-1} = A^T \tag{2-108}$$

Matrices satisfying Eq. (2-108) are orthogonal.

REMARK: A similarity transformation (2-102) in which the S matrix is unitary is called a "unitary" transformation. If A is a real matrix and S is an orthogonal matrix, then Eq. (2-102) is called an "orthogonal" transformation.

Hermitian operators

An operator is called "Hermitian" (or self-conjugate or self-adjoint) if

$$A = A^* \qquad (2\text{-}109)$$

If A has only real matrix elements, Eq. (2-109) reduces to

$$A = A^T \qquad (2\text{-}110)$$

If an operator A is both Hermitian and unitary, then

$$A = A^* = A^{-1} \qquad (2\text{-}111)$$

which reduces to

$$A = A^T = A^{-1} \qquad (2\text{-}112)$$

for real orthogonal operators. Thus, the matrices characterizing self-adjoint orthogonal operators must be symmetric.

REMARK: Hermitian unitary operators and symmetric orthogonal operators must satisfy

$$A = A^{-1} \qquad \text{or} \qquad A^2 = I$$

Thus

$$|A|^2 = 1 \qquad |A| = \pm 1$$

If $|A| = +1$, then the operator A corresponds to a pure rotation. If $|A| = -1$, then A corresponds to a rotation followed by a reflection (or vice versa) or a pure reflection.

2-8 EIGENVALUE PROBLEMS

We have seen that a matrix usually alters both the direction and the magnitude of a column vector upon which it operates. There are, however, certain vectors associated with a given matrix which have the property that only their magnitudes are altered by the matrix while their directions remain unchanged. Such vectors are called the "eigenvectors" or the "characteristic vectors" of the matrix. These vectors are the solutions of the following eigenvalue problem,

$$Ax = \lambda x \qquad (2\text{-}113)$$

The complex number λ is called the "eigenvalue" associated with the eigenvector x. Let

$$y = Ax = \lambda x \qquad (2\text{-}114)$$

Then

$$y^*y = x^*\lambda^*\lambda x = (\lambda\lambda^*)(x^*x) \qquad (2\text{-}115)$$

and since

$$y^*y = |y|^2 \qquad x^*x = |x|^2 \qquad \text{and} \qquad \lambda^*\lambda = |\lambda|^2$$

we find

$$|y|^2 = |Ax|^2 = |\lambda|^2|x|^2 \tag{2-116}$$

Therefore the magnitude $|\lambda|$ of the complex eigenvalue λ determines the contraction or extension of x that arises when A operates upon x. Notice that if

$$\lambda = a + ib \tag{2-117}$$

then

$$|\lambda| = + (a^2 + b^2)^{1/2} \tag{2-118}$$

is a positive real number.

There are two parts to every eigenvalue problem. Part 1 is to compute the eigenvalues λ given the matrix A. Part 2 is to compute an eigenvector x for each previously computed eigenvalue λ. If Eq. (2-113) is written as

$$Ax = \lambda Ix \tag{2-119}$$

the eigenvalue problem becomes

$$(A - \lambda I)x = 0 \tag{2-120}$$

Recalling the discussions in Sec. 2-6,

$$\det |A - \lambda I| = 0 \tag{2-121}$$

is a necessary condition for a nontrivial solution of Eq. (2-120). Equation (2-121) is the eigenvalue equation or characteristic-value equation associated with the eigenvalue problem (2-120).

EXAMPLE 2-11:

$$
\det |A - \lambda I| =
\begin{vmatrix}
a_{11} - \lambda & a_{12} & \cdots & a_{1n} \\
a_{21} & a_{22} - \lambda & \cdots & a_{2n} \\
\vdots & \vdots & & \vdots \\
a_{n1} & a_{n2} & \cdots & a_{nn} - \lambda
\end{vmatrix}
= 0 \tag{2-122}
$$

is the eigenvalue equation associated with an $n \times n$ matrix $A = a_{ij}$. In indicial form determinant (2-122) becomes

$$\det |A - \lambda I| = \det |a_{ij} - \lambda \delta_{ij}| = 0 \tag{2-123}$$

The eigenvalue equation for λ given by (2-122) becomes, on expanding the determinant (2-122),

$$\lambda^n + a_1 \lambda^{n-1} + a_2 \lambda^{n-2} + \cdots + a_n = 0 \tag{2-124}$$

where each cofficient $a_1, a_2, \ldots, a_n$ is some function of the matrix elements $a_{11}, a_{12}, \ldots, a_{ij}$ of A. The n-complex roots of Eq. (2-124), $\lambda_1, \lambda_2, \ldots, \lambda_n$, are the eigenvalues of matrix A. These eigenvalues are not necessarily all different, and it should be remembered that complex eigenvalues can be purely real or purely imaginary.

The set of n, not necessarily distinct, eigenvalues of the operator A is called the "spectrum" of A. The eigenvalue equation (2-124) can be written in the form

$$(\lambda - \lambda_1)(\lambda - \lambda_2) \cdots (\lambda - \lambda_n) = 0 \qquad (2\text{-}125)$$

Expansion of Eq. (2-125) and comparison with Eq. (2-124) gives

$$a_1 = -(\lambda_1 + \lambda_2 + \cdots + \lambda_n) \qquad (2\text{-}126)$$

$$a_2 = (\lambda_1\lambda_2 + \lambda_1\lambda_3 + \cdots + \lambda_{n-1}\lambda_n) \qquad (2\text{-}127)$$

$$a_3 = -(\lambda_1\lambda_2\lambda_3 + \cdots + \lambda_{n-2}\lambda_{n-1}\lambda_n) \qquad (2\text{-}128)$$

$$\cdots \cdots \cdots \cdots \cdots \cdots \cdots \cdots$$

$$a_n = (-1)^n \lambda_1\lambda_2\lambda_3 \cdots \lambda_n \qquad (2\text{-}129)$$

Effect of a similarity transformation on the spectrum of an operator

Let the operators A and A' be related by the similarity transformation

$$A' = S^{-1}AS \qquad (2\text{-}130)$$

Then

$$A = SA'S^{-1} \qquad (2\text{-}131)$$

and

$$A - \lambda I = SA'S^{-1} - \lambda I = S(A' - \lambda I)S^{-1} \qquad (2\text{-}132)$$

which gives

$$\det |A - \lambda I| = \det |S(A' - \lambda I)S^{-1}| = \det |SS^{-1}| \det |A' - \lambda I|$$

Hence

$$\det |A - \lambda I| = \det |A' - \lambda I| \qquad (2\text{-}133)$$

It follows from Eq. (2-133) that if λ is an eigenvalue of A, then it is also an eigenvalue of A' (and vice versa). Thus A and A' have the *same* eigenvalues. This is what is meant when one says that the spectrum of an operator is invariant under a similarity transformation.

REMARK: Suppose that A' is a diagonal matrix:

$$A' = \begin{bmatrix} \lambda_1 & 0 & \cdots & 0 \\ 0 & \lambda_2 & \cdots & 0 \\ \cdot & \cdot & & \cdot \\ \cdot & \cdot & & \cdot \\ \cdot & \cdot & & \cdot \\ 0 & 0 & \cdots & \lambda_n \end{bmatrix}$$

Then

$$\det |A' - \lambda I| = \prod_{i=1}^{n} (\lambda - \lambda_i) = 0$$

and the eigenvalues of A' are just the elements appearing on the main diagonal of A'. If A is not a diagonal matrix but is related to A' by the similarity transformation

$$A' = S^{-1}AS$$

then the eigenvalues of A are the same as those of A', namely $\lambda_1, \lambda_2, \ldots, \lambda_n$. However, $\lambda_1, \lambda_2, \ldots, \lambda_n$ are also the roots of Eq. (2-124). Thus, taking note of Eqs. (2-103) and (2-104), we see that Eqs. (2-126) and (2-129) become

$$a_1 = -\operatorname{Tr}(A) \tag{2-134}$$

and

$$a_n = (-1)^n \det |A| \tag{2-135}$$

2-9 DIAGONALIZATION OF MATRICES

Consider the problem of finding a nonsingular matrix S which reduces a given matrix A to diagonal form under the similarity transformation

$$A' = S^{-1}AS \tag{2-136}$$

It is shown in textbooks on matrix theory that such a problem can always be solved for any matrix A which satisfies the condition

$$A^*A = AA^* \tag{2-137}$$

In particular, if $A = A^*$ or $A^* = A^{-1}$, then A will satisfy Eq. (2-137). Therefore, Hermitian and unitary matrices can always be diagonalized by a similarity transformation.

CASE I: *Eigenvalues of A are all different.* Let A be an $n \times n$ matrix that satisfies Eq. (2-137), and suppose that all the n eigenvalues $\{\lambda_1, \lambda_2, \ldots, \lambda_n\}$ of A are different. We shall prove that the diagonalizing matrix S in Eq. (2-136) is just the matrix whose column vectors are the eigenvectors of A, and we shall prove that the diagonal elements of A' are exactly the eigenvalues of A. Thus let

$$A' = S^{-1}AS = \begin{bmatrix} \mu_1 & 0 & \cdots & 0 \\ 0 & \mu_2 & \cdots & 0 \\ \cdot & \cdot & & \cdot \\ \cdot & \cdot & & \cdot \\ \cdot & \cdot & & \cdot \\ 0 & \cdots & \cdots & \mu_n \end{bmatrix} \tag{2-138}$$

and let

$$S = \begin{bmatrix} s_{11} & s_{12} & \cdots & s_{1k} & \cdots & s_{1n} \\ s_{21} & s_{22} & \cdots & s_{2k} & \cdots & s_{2n} \\ \cdot & \cdot & & \cdot & & \cdot \\ \cdot & \cdot & & \cdot & & \cdot \\ \cdot & \cdot & & \cdot & & \cdot \\ s_{n1} & s_{n2} & \cdots & s_{nk} & \cdots & s_{nn} \end{bmatrix} \tag{2-139}$$

Writing out (2-138) gives

$$
\begin{bmatrix}
a_{11} & a_{12} & \cdots & a_{1k} & \cdots & a_{1n} \\
a_{21} & a_{22} & \cdots & a_{2k} & \cdots & a_{2n} \\
\cdot & \cdot & & \cdot & & \cdot \\
\cdot & \cdot & & \cdot & & \cdot \\
\cdot & \cdot & & \cdot & & \cdot \\
a_{n1} & a_{n2} & \cdots & a_{nk} & \cdots & a_{nn}
\end{bmatrix}
\begin{bmatrix}
s_{11} & s_{12} & \cdots & s_{1k} & \cdots & s_{1n} \\
s_{21} & s_{22} & \cdots & s_{2k} & \cdots & s_{2n} \\
\cdot & \cdot & & \cdot & & \cdot \\
\cdot & \cdot & & \cdot & & \cdot \\
\cdot & \cdot & & \cdot & & \cdot \\
s_{n1} & s_{n2} & \cdots & s_{nk} & \cdots & s_{nn}
\end{bmatrix}
$$

$$
=
\begin{bmatrix}
s_{11} & s_{12} & \cdots & s_{1k} & \cdots & s_{1n} \\
s_{21} & s_{22} & \cdots & s_{2k} & \cdots & s_{2n} \\
\cdot & \cdot & & \cdot & & \cdot \\
\cdot & \cdot & & \cdot & & \cdot \\
\cdot & \cdot & & \cdot & & \cdot \\
s_{n1} & s_{n2} & \cdots & s_{nk} & \cdots & s_{nn}
\end{bmatrix}
\begin{bmatrix}
\mu_1 & 0 & \cdots & 0 \\
0 & \mu_2 & \cdots & 0 \\
\cdot & & & \cdot \\
\cdot & & & \cdot \\
\cdot & & & \cdot \\
0 & 0 & \cdots & \mu_n
\end{bmatrix}
\qquad (2\text{-}140)
$$

Notice that the product of A and the kth column vector on the left side of matrix (2-140) is equal to the product of S and the kth column vector on the right side of (2-140). In other words,

$$
\begin{bmatrix}
a_{11} & a_{12} & \cdots & a_{1k} & \cdots & a_{1n} \\
a_{21} & a_{22} & \cdots & a_{2k} & \cdots & a_{2n} \\
\cdot & \cdot & & \cdot & & \cdot \\
\cdot & \cdot & & \cdot & & \cdot \\
\cdot & \cdot & & \cdot & & \cdot \\
a_{n1} & a_{n2} & \cdots & a_{nk} & \cdots & a_{nn}
\end{bmatrix}
\begin{bmatrix}
s_{1k} \\
s_{2k} \\
\cdot \\
\cdot \\
\cdot \\
s_{nk}
\end{bmatrix}
=
\begin{bmatrix}
\mu_k s_{1k} \\
\mu_k s_{2k} \\
\cdot \\
\cdot \\
\cdot \\
\mu_k s_{nk}
\end{bmatrix}
= \mu_k
\begin{bmatrix}
s_{1k} \\
s_{2k} \\
\cdot \\
\cdot \\
\cdot \\
s_{nk}
\end{bmatrix}
$$

$$(2\text{-}141)$$

If the kth column vector of S is written as $\mathbf{s}_k$, then matrix (2-141) becomes

$$A\mathbf{s}_k = \mu_k \mathbf{s}_k \qquad (2\text{-}142)$$

and this is equivalent to

$$\{A - \mu_k I\}\mathbf{s}_k = 0 \qquad (2\text{-}143)$$

In order for the linear homogeneous system (2-143) to have a non-trivial solution, μ_k must be a root of the secular equation

$$|A - \mu I| = 0 \qquad (2\text{-}144)$$

Hence the μ_k's are the n distinct eigenvalues $\lambda_1, \lambda_2, \ldots, \lambda_n$ of A, and we can number them so that $\lambda_1 = \mu_1, \lambda_2 = \mu_2, \ldots, \lambda_k = \mu_k, \ldots, \lambda_n = \mu_n$. To compute the n eigenvectors $\mathbf{s}_1, \mathbf{s}_2, \ldots, \mathbf{s}_n$ let

$$B_k = \{A - \lambda_k I\} \qquad (2\text{-}145)$$

Then the kth (column) eigenvector is the nontrivial solution of the homogeneous system

$$B_k \mathbf{s}_k = 0 \qquad (2\text{-}146)$$

This solution can be obtained explicitly by means of the technique introduced in Eqs. (2-82) to (2-90). It is given by

$$\mathbf{s}_k = B_k{}^{CT} Y_k \qquad k = 1, 2, \ldots, n \qquad (2\text{-}147)$$

where Y_k is an arbitrary parametric column vector, and $B_k{}^{CT}$ is the transposed cofactor matrix of B_k. Formula (2-147) provides us with all the n column vectors forming S.

It remains for us to show that S^{-1} exists. Suppose that S^{-1} does not exist. Then S is singular and $|S| = 0$. As a result, the column vectors s_k appearing in S must be linearly dependent, and thus there must be a set of constants $c_1, c_2, \ldots, c_n$, not all zero, such that

$$c_1 s_1 + c_2 s_2 + \cdots + c_n s_n = 0 \qquad (2\text{-}148)$$

Suppose that the first k c's do not vanish; then

$$c_1 s_1 + c_2 s_2 + \cdots + c_k s_k = 0 \qquad k \le n \qquad (2\text{-}149)$$

where none of the c's or s_k's in Eq. (2-149) are zero. The eigenvalue equation (2-142) gives us

$$A^q s_r = \lambda_r{}^q s_r \qquad q = 1,2, \ldots$$

and if Eq. (2-149) is now multiplied successively $k - 1$ times by A and the result written down each time, the system

$$c_1 s_1 + c_2 s_2 + \cdots + c_k s_k = 0$$
$$c_1 \lambda_1 s_1 + c_2 \lambda_2 s_2 + \cdots + c_k \lambda_k s_k = 0$$
$$\cdots \cdots \cdots \cdots \cdots \cdots \cdots \cdots \qquad (2\text{-}150)$$
$$c_1 \lambda_1{}^{k-1} s_1 + c_2 \lambda_2{}^{k-1} s_2 + \cdots + c_k \lambda_k{}^{k-1} s_k = 0$$

is obtained. Since none of the c's or s_r's vanish, the system (2-150) can be satisfied only if

$$\Delta = \begin{vmatrix} 1 & 1 & \cdots & 1 \\ \lambda_1 & \lambda_2 & \cdots & \lambda_k \\ \lambda_1{}^2 & \lambda_2{}^2 & \cdots & \lambda_k{}^2 \\ \cdot & \cdot & & \cdot \\ \cdot & \cdot & & \cdot \\ \cdot & \cdot & & \cdot \\ \lambda_1{}^{k-1} & \lambda_2{}^{k-1} & \cdots & \lambda_k{}^{k-1} \end{vmatrix} = 0 \qquad (2\text{-}151)$$

The determinant (2-151) is called the "Vandermondian," and its value can be shown to be

$$\Delta = \begin{vmatrix} 1 & 1 & \cdots & 1 \\ \lambda_1 & \lambda_2 & \cdots & \lambda_k \\ \lambda_1{}^2 & \lambda_2{}^2 & \cdots & \lambda_k{}^2 \\ \cdot & \cdot & & \cdot \\ \cdot & \cdot & & \cdot \\ \cdot & \cdot & & \cdot \\ \lambda_1{}^{k-1} & \lambda_2{}^{k-1} & \cdots & \lambda_k{}^{k-1} \end{vmatrix} = \prod_{i>j} (\lambda_i - \lambda_j)$$
$$= (\lambda_k - \lambda_{k-1})(\lambda_k - \lambda_{k-2}) \cdots (\lambda_{k-1} - \lambda_{k-2})(\lambda_{k-1} - \lambda_{k-3})$$
$$\cdots (\lambda_2 - \lambda_1) \qquad (2\text{-}152)$$

This is never zero if the λ's are all different; hence $|S|$ cannot equal zero and S^{-1} must exist. This proves that a matrix A, whose eigenvalues are all distinct, can always be diagonalized by a similarity transformation accomplished with a matrix S whose column vectors are the eigenvectors of A. The diagonal elements of $A' = S^{-1}AS$ are exactly the eigenvalues of A.

CASE II: *Matrices with repeated eigenvalues.* If the eigenvalues of a matrix are not all different, then it may not be possible to reduce the matrix to diagonal form. However, a sufficient condition on A, which guarantees that it can be diagonalized, is given in (2-137). Equation (2-137) states that any matrix which commutes with its Hermitian adjoint can always be diagonalized. In particular, Hermitian and unitary matrices can always be diagonalized, regardless of whether their eigenvalues are all different or not.

The matrix S which diagonalizes A is still constructed by choosing the n linearly independent eigenvectors of A as the column vectors of S. The real problem is to find these n linearly independent eigenvectors when the n eigenvalues of A are no longer all different. For example, suppose that $\lambda = \lambda_p$ is a k-fold eigenvalue of A. We shall *define a generalized eigenvector* $s_p{}^{(k)}$ *of rank* k, and associated with $\lambda = \lambda_p$, by the statement that

$$\{A - \lambda_p I\}^{k-1} s_p{}^{(k)} \neq 0 \tag{2-153}$$

and

$$\{A - \lambda_p I\}^k s_p{}^{(k)} = 0 \tag{2-154}$$

Now consider the $k - 1$ vectors

$$s_p{}^{(1)} = \{A - \lambda_p I\}^{k-1} s_p{}^{(k)} \tag{2-155}$$

$$s_p{}^{(2)} = \{A - \lambda_p I\}^{k-2} s_p{}^{(k)} \tag{2-156}$$

$$\cdot \qquad \cdot \qquad \cdot$$
$$\cdot \qquad \cdot \qquad \cdot$$
$$\cdot \qquad \cdot \qquad \cdot$$

$$s_p{}^{(k-1)} = \{A - \lambda_p I\} s_p{}^{(k)} \tag{2-157}$$

or, in general,

$$s_p{}^{(j)} = \{A - \lambda_p I\}^{k-j} s_p{}^{(k)} \qquad j = 1,2, \ldots ,(k - 1) \tag{2-158}$$

We will show that the vector $s_p{}^{(j)}$ is a generalized eigenvector of rank j and corresponds to $\lambda = \lambda_p$. To see this, one notes that

$$\{A - \lambda_p I\}^{j-1} s_p{}^{(j)} = \{A - \lambda_p I\}^{j-1}\{A - \lambda_p I\}^{k-j} s_p{}^{(k)} \tag{2-159}$$

Hence

$$\{A - \lambda_p I\}^{j-1} s_p{}^{(j)} = \{A - \lambda_p I\}^{k-1} s_p{}^{(k)} \neq 0 \tag{2-160}$$

while

$$\{A - \lambda_p I\}^j s_p{}^{(j)} = \{A - \lambda_p I\}^k s_p{}^{(k)} = 0 \tag{2-161}$$

This proves that $s_p{}^{(j)}$ is a generalized eigenvector of rank j. Furthermore, generalized eigenvectors of different ranks must be linearly independent. To see why this must be true, consider the set of k

generalized eigenvectors

$$\{s_p{}^{(1)},\ s_p{}^{(2)},\ \ldots\ ,\ s_p{}^{(k)}\} \tag{2-162}$$

We see immediately that no $s_p{}^{(j)}$ can be a linear combination of the preceding s_p's; otherwise there are numbers $c_1, c_2, \ldots, c_{j-1}$, not all of which are zero, such that

$$s_p{}^{(j)} = c_1 s_p{}^{(j-1)} + c_2 s_p{}^{(j-2)} + \cdots + c_{j-1} s_p{}^{(1)} \tag{2-163}$$

Operating on Eq. (2-163) with $\{A - \lambda_p I\}^{j-1}$ would then give us

$$\{A - \lambda_p I\}^{j-1} s_p{}^{(j)} = \mathbf{0} \tag{2-164}$$

contradicting (2-160). It follows that $\{s_p{}^{(1)},\ s_p{}^{(2)},\ \ldots\ ,\ s_p{}^{(k)}\}$ is a linearly independent set of vectors; otherwise there are numbers $c_1, c_2, \ldots, c_k$, not all of which are zero, such that

$$c_1 s_p{}^{(1)} + c_2 s_p{}^{(2)} + \cdots + c_k s_p{}^{(k)} = \mathbf{0} \tag{2-165}$$

If Eq. (2-165) holds when the c's are not all zero, then there must be a largest integer j for which $c_j \neq 0$, and it becomes possible to solve (2-165) for $s_p{}^{(j)}$ as a linear combination of the *preceding* s_p's. This contradicts our result that $s_p{}^{(j)}$ is not expressible as a linear combination of preceding s_p's. Consequently, (2-165) can hold only if all the c's are zero. This establishes the linear independence of the s_p's.

EXAMPLE 2-12: Consider the matrix

$$A = \begin{bmatrix} 3 & 0 & 1 \\ 0 & 2 & 0 \\ 1 & 0 & 3 \end{bmatrix} \tag{2-166}$$

The eigenvalue equation is

$$|A - \lambda I| = \begin{vmatrix} 3 - \lambda & 0 & 1 \\ 0 & 2 - \lambda & 0 \\ 1 & 0 & 3 - \lambda \end{vmatrix} = 0 \tag{2-167}$$

or

$$|A - \lambda I| = -1(\lambda^3 - 8\lambda^2 + 20\lambda - 16) = -1(\lambda - 2)^2(\lambda - 4) = 0 \tag{2-168}$$

Thus, $\lambda_1 = \lambda_2 = 2$ is an eigenvalue of multiplicity 2, while $\lambda_3 = 4$ is an eigenvalue of multiplicity 1. Since $A = A^*$, A is Hermitian. Therefore A satisfies Eq. (2-137) and can be diagonalized. We find

$$(A - 2I) = \begin{bmatrix} 1 & 0 & 1 \\ 0 & 0 & 0 \\ 1 & 0 & 1 \end{bmatrix} \tag{2-169}$$

$$(A - 2I)^2 = 2\begin{bmatrix} 1 & 0 & 1 \\ 0 & 0 & 0 \\ 1 & 0 & 1 \end{bmatrix} \tag{2-170}$$

$$(A - 4I) = \begin{bmatrix} -1 & 0 & 1 \\ 0 & -2 & 0 \\ 1 & 0 & -1 \end{bmatrix} \tag{2-171}$$

Now suppose that we attempt to construct the generalized eigenvector of rank 2 which is associated with the double root $\lambda_1 = \lambda_2 = 2$. If $s_1^{(2)}$ is such a column vector, then from expressions (2-153) and (2-154)

$$(A - 2I)^2 s_1^{(2)} = 0 \tag{2-172}$$

while

$$(A - 2I) s_1^{(2)} = s_1^{(1)} \neq 0 \tag{2-173}$$

However, Eqs. (2-169) and (2-170) show that

$$(A - 2I)^2 = 2(A - 2I) \tag{2-174}$$

Consequently, (2-172) and (2-173) cannot hold simultaneously for our *particular* choice of A. Nevertheless, it is still possible to find two *linearly independent* eigenvectors associated with the double root $\lambda_1 = \lambda_2 = 2$ of Eq. (2-168). One eigenvector is found using

$$(A - 2I) s_1 = 0 \tag{2-175}$$

This has a solution

$$s_1 = \begin{bmatrix} Y \\ 0 \\ -Y \end{bmatrix} \tag{2-176}$$

for any Y. Notice that s_1 is unique only to within a scale factor c since

$$(A - 2I) c s_1 = 0 \tag{2-177}$$

for any constant c. In other words, the solution

$$s_1 = \begin{bmatrix} -Y \\ 0 \\ Y \end{bmatrix} \tag{2-178}$$

is just as good as (2-176). A second linearly independent eigenvector associated with $\lambda_1 = \lambda_2 = 2$ can be obtained by noticing that

$$(A - 2I) s_2 = 0 \tag{2-179}$$

is satisfied by

$$s_2 = \begin{bmatrix} 0 \\ Z \\ 0 \end{bmatrix} \tag{2-180}$$

for any value of Z. Obviously, s_1 and s_2 are linearly independent since they are orthogonal to each other. Finally,

$$(A - 4I) s_3 = 0 \tag{2-181}$$

is satisfied by any column vector of the form

$$s_3 = \begin{bmatrix} X \\ 0 \\ X \end{bmatrix} \tag{2-182}$$

and s_3 is orthogonal to both s_2 and s_1.

The matrix S whose column vectors are formed from s_1, s_2, and s_3 is given by

$$S = \begin{bmatrix} Y & 0 & X \\ 0 & Z & 0 \\ -Y & 0 & X \end{bmatrix} \tag{2-183}$$

Since the column vectors in (2-183) are all perpendicular to one another, $|S| \neq 0$ and S^{-1} exists. Furthermore, since each column eigenvector in (2-183) is determined only to within a constant scale factor, it is convenient to choose these scale factors so that the length of each column vector in (2-183) is unity. Then

$$S = \begin{bmatrix} \dfrac{1}{\sqrt{2}} & 0 & \dfrac{1}{\sqrt{2}} \\ 0 & 1 & 0 \\ \dfrac{-1}{\sqrt{2}} & 0 & \dfrac{1}{\sqrt{2}} \end{bmatrix} \tag{2-184}$$

and

$$S^{-1}AS = \begin{bmatrix} \dfrac{1}{\sqrt{2}} & 0 & \dfrac{-1}{\sqrt{2}} \\ 0 & 1 & 0 \\ \dfrac{1}{\sqrt{2}} & 0 & \dfrac{1}{\sqrt{2}} \end{bmatrix} \begin{bmatrix} 3 & 0 & 1 \\ 0 & 2 & 0 \\ 1 & 0 & 3 \end{bmatrix} \begin{bmatrix} \dfrac{1}{\sqrt{2}} & 0 & \dfrac{1}{\sqrt{2}} \\ 0 & 1 & 0 \\ \dfrac{-1}{\sqrt{2}} & 0 & \dfrac{1}{\sqrt{2}} \end{bmatrix}$$

$$= \begin{bmatrix} \dfrac{1}{\sqrt{2}} & 0 & \dfrac{-1}{\sqrt{2}} \\ 0 & 1 & 0 \\ \dfrac{1}{\sqrt{2}} & 0 & \dfrac{1}{\sqrt{2}} \end{bmatrix} \begin{bmatrix} \dfrac{2}{\sqrt{2}} & 0 & \dfrac{4}{\sqrt{2}} \\ 0 & 2 & 0 \\ \dfrac{-2}{\sqrt{2}} & 0 & \dfrac{4}{\sqrt{2}} \end{bmatrix} = \begin{bmatrix} 2 & 0 & 0 \\ 0 & 2 & 0 \\ 0 & 0 & 4 \end{bmatrix} \tag{2-185}$$

as expected.

REMARK: If λ_k is an eigenvalue of A of multiplicity m_k, then Eqs. (2-103) and (2-104) give

$$\text{Tr } (A) = \sum_{k=1}^{r} m_k \lambda_k \tag{2-186}$$

$$\det |A| = \prod_{k=1}^{r} \lambda_k{}^{m_k} \tag{2-187}$$

$$\sum_{k=1}^{r} m_k = n \tag{2-188}$$

where A is an $n \times n$ matrix which satisfies Eq. (2-137) and has a total of $r \leq n$ different eigenvalues.

2-10 SPECIAL PROPERTIES OF HERMITIAN MATRICES

Hermitian matrices have two special properties which make them important in physical problems. These are that the eigenvalues of a Hermitian matrix are all real and that the eigenvectors corresponding to different eigenvalues are orthogonal.

Thus if

$$A S_k = \lambda_k S_k \qquad (2\text{-}189)$$

$$S_k^* A S_k = \lambda_k |S_k|^2 \qquad (2\text{-}190)$$

$$S_k^* A^* S_k = \bar{\lambda}_k |S_k|^2 \qquad (2\text{-}191)$$

or

$$S_k^* (A - A^*) S_k = (\lambda_k - \bar{\lambda}_k) |S_k|^2 \qquad (2\text{-}192)$$

Since $A = A^*$ and $|S_k|^2 > 0$ $\qquad (2\text{-}193)$

$$\lambda_k = \bar{\lambda}_k \qquad (2\text{-}194)$$

shows that the eigenvalues of a Hermitian matrix are real.

We also have, using Eq. (2-189),

$$S_j^* A S_k = \lambda_k S_j^* S_k \qquad (2\text{-}195)$$

and

$$S_k^* A S_j = \lambda_j S_k^* S_j \qquad (2\text{-}196)$$

Thus

$$S_j^* (A - A^*) S_k = (\lambda_k - \bar{\lambda}_j) S_j^* S_k \qquad (2\text{-}197)$$

and since $A = A^*$ and $\lambda_j = \bar{\lambda}_j$,

$$(\lambda_k - \lambda_j) S_j^* S_k = 0 \qquad (2\text{-}198)$$

Then if $\lambda_k \neq \lambda_j$,

$$S_j^* S_k = 0 \qquad (2\text{-}199)$$

which proves that the eigenvectors of a Hermitian matrix, belonging to different eigenvalues, are orthogonal.

2-11 TENSOR ALGEBRA

We have seen that an ordered set of n numbers can be written as a column vector or as a row vector, and that an ordered set of n^2 numbers can be written as a square matrix. However, if we were to represent an ordered set of n^3 numbers in matrix form, the resulting matrix would be cubic and would occupy three spatial dimensions! Operations with such solid matrices would be clumsy, to say the least.

Tensor algebra does two things for us: the first and perhaps most important of these is that it permits us to represent ordered sets of n, n^2, n^3, or for that matter n^r, numbers on a flat piece of paper in *a manner sufficiently detailed to be computationally useful.* Secondly, the tensor formalism provides a means of giving a precise definition of invariance.

Notation

The heart of tensor algebra is the indicial notation already introduced in Sec. 2-1 in connection with matrices. The student will recall that the "hard part" of this notation lies in getting accustomed to the idea that the symbol a_{ij} represents an entire set of n^2 numbers when i and j are thought of as running from 1 to n, and that a_{ij} also represents a *particular element* of the set of n^2 elements when i and j are thought of as having *particular numerical values*, say $i = 1, j = 3$.

It proves useful to be able to use superscripts as well as subscripts in manufacturing tensors. Thus, the symbol a^{ij} represents a set of n^2 elements when i and j run from 1 to n just as a_{ij} does. In general, these two sets of n^2 elements are not equal, so that $a_{ij} \neq a^{ij}$. In fact, one can also represent a set of n^2 elements with a symbol like $a_j{}^i$, and $a_j{}^i \neq a^{ij} \neq a_{ij}$.

Tensors with *superscripts* are called *contravariant* tensors, while tensors with *subscripts* are called *covariant* tensors. Those tensors which have both superscripts and subscripts are called *mixed* tensors.

The *rank* of a *covariant* tensor is the *number* of *subscripts* which it has. Thus, a_{ij} is a covariant tensor of rank 2. Similarly, the *rank* of a *contravariant* tensor is equal to the *number* of *superscripts* which it has, so that a^{ij} is a contravariant tensor of rank 2. The tensor $a_j{}^i$ is a mixed tensor of covariant rank 1 and contravariant rank 1. A tensor of rank 0 is a scalar, and a tensor of rank 1 is a vector. In tensor algebra it is usual to assume that each sub- or superscript ranges over the same set of values; thus, $i = 1,2, \ldots ,n, j = 1,2, \ldots ,n$ in a_{ij}, etc. Hence a second-rank tensor is the analogue of a *square* matrix. Notice that a tensor with s superscripts and r subscripts, each of which ranges over the set of numbers from 1 to n, represents a set containing n^{r+s} elements.

EXAMPLE 2-13:

$$A^{i_1 i_2 \cdots i_s}_{j_1 j_2 \cdots j_r} \qquad \begin{array}{l} (i_1 = 1, \ldots ,n) \ldots (i_s = 1, \ldots ,n) \\ (j_1 = 1, \ldots ,n) \ldots (j_r = 1, \ldots ,n) \end{array}$$

represents a set of n^{r+s} elements and $A^{137 \cdots 6}_{485 \cdots 12}$ represents a particular element of the set.

2-12 TENSOR OPERATIONS

Tensors can be added to, subtracted from, and multiplied by tensors. The result of each such operation is another tensor.

Addition

$$C^{i_1 i_2 \cdots i_s}_{j_1 j_2 \cdots j_r} = A^{i_1 i_2 \cdots i_s}_{j_1 j_2 \cdots j_r} + B^{i_1 i_2 \cdots i_s}_{j_1 j_2 \cdots j_r} \tag{2-200}$$

Notice that the covariant and contravariant ranks of each tensor in Eq. (2-200) are the same.

Multiplication: outer product

The outer product of the tensor $A_j{}^i$ and the tensor B_{rs}^k is defined as

$$C_{jrs}^{ik} = A_j{}^i B_{rs}^k \qquad i,j,k,r,s = 1,2, \ldots ,n \tag{2-201}$$

The mixed tensor C_{jrs}^{ik} is of covariant rank 3 and contravariant rank 2, and thus it represents a set of n^5 elements. The element C_{379}^{12} of C_{jrs}^{ik} is the arithmetical product of the element $A_3{}^1$ of $A_j{}^i$ and the element B_{79}^2 of B_{rs}^k. In defining the outer product as in Eq. (2-201), one must be careful to keep each particular suffix at the same level on both sides of the equation.

Contraction

We now introduce an operation known as "contraction." It consists of replacing one superscript and one subscript of a mixed tensor by a single letter and then summing on this letter. For example, to contract the tensor $A_j{}^i$ we replace both i and j by the letter k and then sum on k; thus

$$\text{Contraction of } A_j{}^i = \sum_{k=1}^{n} A_k{}^k \tag{2-202}$$

Summation convention

In order to simplify the writing of tensor equations involving contractions, it is desirable to avoid having to write a summation sign for each contracted index. We avoid this by agreeing to *sum* each repeated index in a tensor equation over its full range of values. For example, if $i = 1,2,3$ and $j = 1,2,3$,

$$A_k{}^k = A_i{}^i = A_j{}^j = A_1{}^1 + A_2{}^2 + A_3{}^3$$

$$A_i A_i = A_1{}^2 + A_2{}^2 + A_3{}^2$$

$$A^i A_i = A^1 A_1 + A^2 A_2 + A^3 A_3$$

$$A_{kk} = A_{11} + A_{22} + A_{33}$$

$$A_{ij} X_i X_j = A_{11} X_1{}^2 + A_{22} X_2{}^2 + A_{33} X_3{}^2 + (A_{12} + A_{21}) X_1 X_2$$
$$+ (A_{13} + A_{31}) X_1 X_3 + (A_{23} + A_{32}) X_2 X_3$$

$$A_{kj}^k = A_{1j}^1 + A_{2j}^2 + A_{3j}^3$$

Inner product

To form the inner product of two tensors, we first form the outer product of the two tensors and then perform a contraction involving a superscript of one tensor and a subscript of the other tensor. For example, one inner product of two tensors $A_j{}^i$ and B_{kr} is

$$C_{jr} = A_j{}^k B_{kr} = A_j{}^1 B_{1r} + A_j{}^2 B_{2r} + A_j{}^3 B_{3r} \tag{2-203}$$

and the other inner product is

$$D_{jk} = A_j{}^r B_{kr} = A_j{}^1 B_{k1} + A_j{}^2 B_{k2} + A_j{}^3 B_{k3} \tag{2-204}$$

Because of the possibility of contracting different indices, the inner product of a pair of tensors is not always unique, as illustrated in Eqs. (2-203) and (2-204).

2-13 TRANSFORMATION PROPERTIES OF TENSORS

It is clear that a tensor of rank 2 such as A_{ij} is a set containing n^2 elements. What we have not emphasized so far is that *not every set* of n^2 elements is a tensor of second rank. The feature of a set of n^2 elements which makes it a tensor of rank 2 is its behavior under a transformation of coordinates. We shall illustrate this idea by considering some special examples.

Consider the set of n functions of the variables x^1, x^2, and x^3.

$$\{a_1(x^1,x^2,x^3),\ a_2(x^1,x^2,x^3),\ \ldots\ ,\ a_n(x^1,x^2,x^3)\} \tag{2-205}$$

The ordered set of n functions (2-205) is a vector according to the definition given in Sec. 1-1. We are about to see what properties each of the n functions in (2-205) must have for Eq. (2-205) to be a tensor of rank 1 also. Consider a y coordinate system (y^1,y^2,y^3) related to the x coordinate system (x^1,x^2,x^3) by a set of equations known as a transformation of coordinates,

$$y^1 = f^1(x^1,x^2,x^3)$$
$$y^2 = f^2(x^1,x^2,x^3) \tag{2-206}$$
$$y^3 = f^3(x^1,x^2,x^3)$$

The three functions f^1, f^2, and f^3 are single-valued and differentiable for some domain of values of x^1, x^2, and x^3. The transformation (2-206) is to be invertible so that

$$x^1 = h^1(y^1,y^2,y^3)$$
$$x^2 = h^2(y^1,y^2,y^3) \tag{2-207}$$
$$x^3 = h^3(y^1,y^2,y^3)$$

where h^1, h^2, and h^3 are also single-valued and differentiable.

If the coordinate transformation is linear, then in matrix form Eqs. (2-206) become

$$y = Ax \tag{2-208}$$

and in order that A^{-1} be well defined we would need det $|A| \neq 0$. However, in indicial form, using the summation convention, Eq. (2-208) becomes

$$y^i = a_j{}^i x^j \qquad i,j = 1,2,3 \tag{2-209}$$
$$a_j{}^i = \frac{\partial y^i}{\partial x^j} \tag{2-210}$$

and thus

$$\det |A| = \det \left| \frac{\partial y^i}{\partial x^j} \right| \neq 0 \tag{2-211}$$

is the condition for A^{-1} to exist.

The expression

$$J = \det \left| \frac{\partial y^i}{\partial x^j} \right| \qquad (2\text{-}212)$$

is known as the Jacobian of transformation from x^1, x^2, x^3 to y^1, y^2, y^3. The transformation (2-206) which must include a linear transformation as a special case, must have a nonvanishing Jacobian in order that it be invertible.

We now think of an abstract entity which is represented in the x coordinate system by the ordered set of n functions $\{a_1(x^1,x^2,x^3),$ . . . , $a_n(x^1,x^2,x^3)\}$.

If the entity also has a representation in the y coordinate system as an ordered set of n functions

$$\{b_1(y^1,y^2,y^3), \ . \ . \ . \ , b_n(y^1,y^2,y^3)\}$$

and if the components of the two representations are related according to the:

Covariant transformation law

$$b_i(y^1,y^2,y^3) = a_j(x^1,x^2,x^3) \frac{\partial x^j}{\partial y^i} \qquad i = 1,2,3 \qquad (2\text{-}213)$$

then the abstract entity is called a "covariant tensor" of rank 1. We say that $a_i(x^1,x^2,x^3) = \{a_1(x^1,x^2,x^3), \ . \ . \ . \ , a_n(x^1,x^2,x^3)\}$ is the representation of a covariant tensor of rank 1 in the x coordinate system while $b_i(y^1,y^2,y^3) = \{b_1(y^1,y^2,y^3), \ . \ . \ . \ , b_n(y^1,y^2,y^3)\}$ is the representation of the *same* covariant tensor of rank 1 in the y coordinate system.

In computing the right side of Eq. (2-213) we must use Eqs. (2-207), the inverted form of the transformation of coordinates given by Eqs. (2-206).

REMARK: In applications it is common to overlook the distinction between a tensor and the representation of a tensor in a given coordinate system. Thus, one refers to the set

$$a_i(x^1,x^2,x^3) = \{a_1(x^1,x^2,x^3), \ . \ . \ . \ , a_n(x^1,x^2,x^3)\}$$

as a covariant tensor provided Eq. (2-213) holds, although $a_i(x^1,x^2,x^3)$ is more accurately described as the *representation* of a covariant tensor in the x coordinate system.

Contravariant transformation law

$$b^i(y^1,y^2,y^3) = a^j(x^1,x^2,x^3) \frac{\partial y^i}{\partial x^j} \qquad (2\text{-}214)$$

If an ordered set of n functions $a^i(x^1,x^2,x^3)$ transforms according to Eq. (2-214), then we say that $a^i(x^1,x^2,x^3)$ is a contravariant tensor of rank 1.

The covariant transformation law for tensors of rank 2 becomes

$$b_{ij}(y^1,y^2,y^3) = a_{kr}(x^1,x^2,x^3) \frac{\partial x^k}{\partial y^i} \frac{\partial x^r}{\partial y^j} \qquad (2\text{-}215)$$

while contravariant tensors of rank 2 transform according to

$$b^{ij}(y^1,y^2,y^3) = a^{kr}(x^1,x^2,x^3) \frac{\partial y^i}{\partial x^k} \frac{\partial y^j}{\partial x^r} \qquad (2\text{-}216)$$

For a mixed tensor of rank 2 the transformation law is

$$b_j{}^i(y^1,y^2,y^3) = a_r{}^k(x^1,x^2,x^3) \frac{\partial y^i}{\partial x^k} \frac{\partial x^r}{\partial y^j} \qquad (2\text{-}217)$$

Scalar transformation law

A single function $a(x^1,x^2,x^3)$ is called a "scalar" function or an invariant, provided that it transforms according to the law

$$b(y^1,y^2,y^3) = a(x^1,x^2,x^3) \qquad (2\text{-}218)$$

where $x^1 = h^1(y^1,y^2,y^3)$

$$x^2 = h^2(y^1,y^2,y^3)$$

$$x^3 = h^3(y^1,y^2,y^3)$$

Invariance of tensor equations

As we have mentioned in Sec. 2-11, the tensor formalism gives a means of treating the concept of invariance in a precise way. One feels intuitively that the laws of nature should not depend on the particular coordinate system used to represent the physical quantities involved. A more quantitative statement of this idea is that if a law of nature can be expressed as an equation, and if this equation holds in one coordinate system, then it should hold in all coordinate systems. This is precisely the property which tensor equations have, as we shall now show. Consider, for example, a tensor represented by $A_{qr}^p(x^1,x^2,x^3)$ in the x coordinate system. Suppose that

$$A_{qr}^p(x^1,x^2,x^3) = 0 \qquad (2\text{-}219)$$

which is interpreted to say that in the x coordinate system each component of the tensor A_{qr}^p vanishes. We must show that

$$B_{qr}^p(y^1,y^2,y^3) = 0 \qquad (2\text{-}220)$$

provided that $B_{qr}^p(y^1,y^2,y^3)$ represents in the y coordinate system the *same tensor* represented by $A_{qr}^p(x^1,x^2,x^3)$ in the x coordinate system. Then Eq. (2-220) follows immediately from the transformation law for tensors. Thus

$$B_{rq}^p(y^1,y^2,y^3) = A_{jk}^i(x^1,x^2,x^3) \frac{\partial y^p}{\partial x^i} \frac{\partial x^j}{\partial y^q} \frac{\partial x^k}{\partial y^r} = 0 \qquad (2\text{-}221)$$

as a result of Eq. (2-219).

Now let C_{jk}^i and D_{jk}^i be the representations of two tensors in the x coordinate system, and suppose that

$$C_{jk}^i = D_{jk}^i \qquad (2\text{-}222)$$

in the x coordinate system.

Then by the previous consideration

$$A_{jk}^i(x^1,x^2,x^3) = C_{jk}^i - D_{jk}^i \qquad (2\text{-}223)$$

is a tensor which vanishes in the x coordinate system, and therefore

$$B_{jk}^i(y^1,y^2,y^3) = 0 \qquad (2\text{-}224)$$

where B_{jk}^i is the representation, in the y coordinate system, of $A_{jk}^i = C_{jk}^i - D_{jk}^i$. Thus, if the tensor equation (2-222) holds in the x coordinate system, then it must also hold in the y coordinate system, provided that we first transform $C_{jk}^i(x^1,x^2,x^3)$ and $D_{jk}^i(x^1,x^2,x^3)$ into the y coordinate system using the appropriate transformation law.

In physics, the formulation of a physical law as a tensor equation is called a "covariant" formulation. A physical law given in covariant form, for example the vanishing of a certain tensor, has the same form in all coordinate systems. In this sense the word covariant means just tensor, rather than tensor without superscripts.

2-14 SPECIAL TENSORS

Symmetric tensors

If interchanging a pair of covariant or contravariant indices leaves a tensor unchanged, then the tensor is said to be "symmetric" in those indices.

EXAMPLE 2-14:

$$g_{ij} = g_{ji} \qquad \begin{array}{l} i = 1,2, \ldots ,n \\ j = 1,2, \ldots ,n \end{array}$$

implies that g_{ij} is a symmetric tensor. Notice that a symmetric tensor of rank 2 has $\frac{1}{2}n(n+1)$ independent components.

Antisymmetric or skew-symmetric tensors

If interchanging a pair of covariant or contravariant indices changes the sign of a tensor, then the tensor is said to be "antisymmetric" or "skew-symmetric" in those indices.

EXAMPLE 2-16:

$$g_{ij} = -g_{ji} \qquad \begin{array}{l} i = 1,2, \ldots ,n \\ j = 1,2, \ldots ,n \end{array}$$

implies that g_{ij} is an antisymmetric tensor. Notice that an antisymmetric tensor has $\frac{1}{2}n(n-1)$ independent components.

Any second-rank tensor which has n^2 components can be written as the sum of a symmetric part with $\frac{1}{2}n(n + 1)$ independent components and an antisymmetric part with $\frac{1}{2}n(n - 1)$ independent components, as follows:

$$g_{ij} = \tfrac{1}{2}(g_{ij} + g_{ji}) + \tfrac{1}{2}(g_{ij} - g_{ji})$$

The metric tensor

In a three-dimensional Euclidean space the infinitesimal distance ds between two points is given by

$$ds^2 = dx^k\, dx^k = (dx^1)^2 + (dx^2)^2 + (dx^3)^2 \tag{2-225}$$

Using Eqs. (2-207),

$$dx^k = \frac{\partial h^k}{\partial y^i}\, dy^i \qquad \begin{array}{l} k = 1,2,3 \\ i = 1,2,3 \end{array}$$

so that the formula for the square of the element of arc in the y coordinate system becomes

$$ds^2 = g_{ij}(y^1,y^2,y^3)\, dy^i\, dy^j \tag{2-226}$$

where

$$g_{ij}(y^1,y^2,y^3) = \frac{\partial h^k}{\partial y^i}\frac{\partial h^k}{\partial y^j} \qquad \begin{array}{l} i = 1,2,3 \\ j = 1,2,3 \end{array} \tag{2-227}$$

is called the "metric tensor" in the y coordinate system. The metric tensor is obviously a symmetric tensor of rank 2, and therefore it can have up to six independent components in a three-dimensional space. The metric tensor is very important because all the metric properties of space are completely determined by it. If the components of the metric tensor are not all constant in a given coordinate system, then the given system of coordinates is called "curvilinear." If in the given system of coordinates $g_{ij} = 0$ when $i \neq j$, then the system is called an "orthogonal" coordinate system.

The associated metric tensor

Consider

$$g = \det |g_{ij}| \tag{2-228}$$

and let

$$G^{ij} = \text{cofactor of } g_{ij} \text{ in } \det |g_{ij}| \tag{2-229}$$

It can be shown that

$$g^{ij} = \frac{G^{ij}}{g} \tag{2-230}$$

is a symmetric contravariant tensor of rank 2. The tensor g^{ij} is called the "associated" metric tensor. It follows from Eqs. (2-32) and (2-34) that

$$g^{ij}g_{ik} = \delta_k{}^j \tag{2-231}$$

where

$$\delta_k{}^i = \begin{cases} 1 & j = k \\ 0 & j \neq k \end{cases}$$

is the mixed Kronecker tensor.

2-15 PROBLEMS AND APPLICATIONS

1. Let $A = \begin{bmatrix} 3 & 4 & 5 \\ 1 & 3 & 7 \\ 9 & 8 & 2 \end{bmatrix}$ $B = \begin{bmatrix} 5 & 3 & 1 \\ 4 & 3 & 2 \\ 1 & 6 & 5 \end{bmatrix}$

and compute $A + B$, AB, BA, det $|A|$, det $|B|$, A^{-1}, and B^{-1}. Verify that $AA^{-1} = A^{-1}A = I$.

2. Let $\sigma_x = \begin{bmatrix} 0 & 1 \\ 1 & 0 \end{bmatrix}$, $\sigma_y = \begin{bmatrix} 0 & -i \\ i & 0 \end{bmatrix}$, and $\sigma_z = \begin{bmatrix} 1 & 0 \\ 0 & -1 \end{bmatrix}$ where

$i = \sqrt{-1}$, and verify the following relations:

$$\sigma_x\sigma_y + \sigma_y\sigma_x = 0 \qquad \sigma_x\sigma_y - \sigma_y\sigma_x = 2i\sigma_z \qquad \sigma_x{}^2 = \sigma_y{}^2 = \sigma_z{}^2 = I$$

3. Compute the direct products

$$\sigma_x x \sigma_x \qquad \sigma_x x \sigma_y \qquad \sigma_x x \sigma_z \qquad \sigma_z x I$$

and evaluate

$$(\sigma_x x \sigma_z)(\sigma_x x \sigma_y) + (\sigma_y x \sigma_x)(\sigma_x x \sigma_x)$$

$$(\sigma_x x \sigma_x)(\sigma_z x I) + (\sigma_z x)I(\sigma_x x \sigma_x)$$

$$(\sigma_x x \sigma_x)^2 \qquad (\sigma_x x \sigma_y)^2 \qquad (\sigma_x x \sigma_z)^2 \qquad (\sigma_z x I)^2$$

4. Write the linear system

$$2x + 3y = -4$$
$$3x - y = 1$$

in matrix form, and solve it by computing the inverse matrix. Do the same for

$$3x - y - z = 2$$
$$x - 2y - 3z = 0$$
$$4x + y + 2z = 4$$

and

$$3x + y + 2z = 3$$
$$2x - 3y - z = -3$$
$$x + 2y + z = 4$$

5. Solve the singular system

$$x - y + z = 0$$
$$2x + 3y + z = 0$$
$$3x + 2y + 2z = 0$$

by the parametric method.

6. Given the matrix

$$A = \begin{bmatrix} 1 & 0 & 6 \\ 0 & -2 & 0 \\ 6 & 0 & 6 \end{bmatrix}$$

find the adjoint matrix and the inverse matrix. Compute the eigenvectors of A normalized to unity and show that they are orthogonal. Show by direct computation that the matrix $S^{-1}AS$ is diagonal where S is the matrix whose columns are the eigenvectors of A.

7. If H is any Hermitian operator, show that e^{iH} is a unitary operator. *Hint:* Use the power-series definition of the exponential function to define the exponential of a matrix.

8. Compute the matrix which reduces

$$A = \begin{bmatrix} 2 & 4 & -6 \\ 4 & 2 & -6 \\ -6 & -6 & -15 \end{bmatrix}$$

to diagonal form. Compute Tr (A) and det $|A|$.

9. Find the matrix S which diagonalizes

$$A = \begin{bmatrix} 2 & 0 & 1 \\ 0 & 1 & 0 \\ 1 & 0 & 2 \end{bmatrix}$$

and compute Tr (A) and det $|A|$.

10. Show that the matrix

$$A = \begin{bmatrix} \cos\theta & \sin\theta & 0 \\ -\sin\theta & \cos\theta & 0 \\ 0 & 0 & 1 \end{bmatrix}$$

is orthogonal, satisfies $|A| = 1$, and that the matrix equation

$$y = Ax$$

represents a rotation of coordinates.

11. Let (x^1, x^2, x^3) be a rectangular Cartesian coordinate system. Introduce a transformation of coordinates to a curvilinear coordinate system (y^1, y^2, y^3) in which the metric tensor becomes $g_{ij}(y^1, y^2, y^3)$. Prove that the Jacobian, $J = \det \left| \dfrac{\partial y^i}{\partial x^j} \right|$, is related to the metric tensor by the equation

$$J^2 = \left| \frac{\partial y^i}{\partial x^j} \right|^2 = \det |g_{ij}|$$

12. Show that if the transformation

$$y^i = a_j^i x^j$$

is orthogonal, then the distinction between the covariant and contravariant transformation laws disappears.

13. A tensor is said to be "Cartesian" when the transformations involved are from one set of rectangular Cartesian coordinates to another. Prove that there is no distinction between covariant and contravariant Cartesian tensors.

14. Consider a rectangular Cartesian coordinate system (x^1,x^2,x^3) and consider the transformation to spherical coordinates

$$(y^1,y^2,y^3) = (r,\theta,\Phi)$$

$$x^1 = y^1 \sin y^2 \cos y^3$$

$$x^2 = y^1 \sin y^2 \sin y^3$$

$$x^3 = y^1 \cos y^2$$

Compute the components of the metric tensor $g_{ij}(y^1,y^2,y^3)$, and calculate $ds^2 = g_{ij}\, dy^i\, dy^j$.

15. Consider a rectangular Cartesian coordinate system (x^1,x^2,x^3), and consider the transformation to cylindrical coordinates

$$(y^1,y^2,y^3) = (r,\theta,z)$$

given by

$$x^1 = y^1 \cos y^2$$

$$x^2 = y^1 \sin y^2$$

$$x^3 = y^3$$

Compute the metric tensor $g_{ij}(y^1,y^2,y^3)$ and the line element $ds^2 = g_{ij}\, dy^i\, dy^j$.

16. The Kronecker e symbol is e_{ijk} and has the following properties:

$e_{ijk} = 0$ if any two indices are alike

$e_{ijk} = +1$ if ijk is an even permutation of the numbers 123

$e_{ijk} = -1$ if ijk is an odd permutation of the numbers 123

Show that the cross product of a pair of Cartesian vectors A_i and B_i can be written as $\mathbf{C} = \mathbf{A} \times \mathbf{B}$ or as

$$C_i = e_{ijk}A_j B_k \qquad i,j,k = 1,2,3$$

using the summation convention.

17. Show that the magnitude of a vector A^i is given by

$$|\mathbf{A}|^2 = g_{ij}A^i A^j$$

and that the inner product of a pair of vectors A^i and B^i is given by

$$\mathbf{A} \cdot \mathbf{B} = g_{ij}A^i B^j$$

Hint: Start with an orthogonal Cartesian coordinate system in which $g_{ij} = \delta_{ij}$, and use the invariant properties of tensor equations together with a transformation to curvilinear coordinates.

18. The tensors g_{ij} and g^{ij} raise and lower the indices of tensors with which they form an inner product thus:

$$A_i = g_{ij}A^j \qquad A^i = g^{ij}A_j$$

Show that

$$|\mathbf{A}|^2 = g^{ij}A_i A_j = g_{ij}A^i A^j$$

$$\mathbf{A} \cdot \mathbf{B} = g^{ij}A_i B_j = g_{ij}A^i B^j$$

19. If $g_{ij} = 0$ for $i \neq j$, prove that

$$g^{11} = \frac{1}{g_{11}} \qquad g^{22} = \frac{1}{g_{22}} \qquad g^{33} = \frac{1}{g_{33}}$$

$$g^{23} = g^{12} = g^{13} = 0$$

20. If $y^i = f^i(x^1, x^2, x^3)$, $i = 1, 2, 3$, show that dy^i transforms like a contravariant vector. If $V = V(x^1, x^2, x^3)$, show that $\partial V / \partial x^i$ transforms like a covariant vector.

vector calculus

3-1 ORDINARY VECTOR DIFFERENTIATION

Let us recall the definition of a vector as given by Eq. (1-11):

$$\mathbf{A} = (a_1, a_2, \ldots, a_n) \tag{3-1}$$

The derivative of $\mathbf{A}$ is a new vector defined by

$$\frac{d\mathbf{A}}{dt} = \left(\frac{da_1}{dt}, \frac{da_2}{dt}, \ldots, \frac{da_n}{dt} \right) \tag{3-2}$$

If we employ the expansion procedure of Sec. 1-4, then Eqs. (3-1) and (3-2) take the form

$$\mathbf{A} = \sum_{k=1}^{n} a_k(t) \mathbf{e}_k \tag{3-3}$$

$$\frac{dA}{dt} = \sum_{k=1}^{n} \frac{da_k}{dt} \mathbf{e}_k \tag{3-4}$$

Notice that the operation of differentiation does not affect the base vectors $\mathbf{e}_k$ because they are constant vectors.

Using the definitions given in Chap. 1 together with Eqs. (3-3) and (3-4), the student can easily verify the following identities:

$$\frac{d}{dt}(\mathbf{A} \cdot \mathbf{B}) = \frac{d\mathbf{A}}{dt} \cdot \mathbf{B} + \mathbf{A} \cdot \frac{d\mathbf{B}}{dt} \tag{3-5}$$

$$\frac{d}{dt}(\mathbf{A} \times \mathbf{B}) = \frac{d\mathbf{A}}{dt} \times \mathbf{B} + \mathbf{A} \times \frac{d\mathbf{B}}{dt} \tag{3-6}$$

$$\frac{d}{dt}(k\mathbf{A}) = \frac{dk}{dt} \mathbf{A} + k \frac{d\mathbf{A}}{dt} \tag{3-7}$$

EXAMPLE 3-1: Consider the kinetic energy of a particle of mass m moving with a velocity vector $\mathbf{v} = \mathbf{v}(t)$:

$$E(t) = \tfrac{1}{2}m(\mathbf{v} \cdot \mathbf{v}) = \tfrac{1}{2}m\mathbf{v}^2$$

If the motion is such that the kinetic energy is conserved, then $dE/dt = 0$. Hence

$$\mathbf{v} \cdot \frac{d\mathbf{v}}{dt} = 0$$

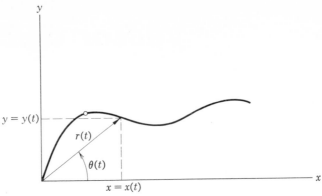

Figure 3-1 Motion of a particle along a plane curve.

This says that the instantaneous acceleration of the particle $d\mathbf{v}/dt$ is either zero or is perpendicular to the velocity vector $\mathbf{v}$.

EXAMPLE 3-2: Consider a particle moving in the x, y plane so that its coordinates are $x = x(t)$ and $y = y(t)$. Its position, velocity, and acceleration vectors become

$$\mathbf{r} = x(t)\mathbf{e}_x + y(t)\mathbf{e}_y$$

$$\mathbf{v} = \frac{d\mathbf{r}}{dt} = \frac{dx}{dt}\,\mathbf{e}_x + \frac{dy}{dt}\,\mathbf{e}_y$$

$$\mathbf{a} = \frac{d^2\mathbf{r}}{dt^2} = \frac{d^2x}{dt^2}\,\mathbf{e}_x + \frac{d^2y}{dt^2}\,\mathbf{e}_y$$

Suppose that we now introduce a polar coordinate system (r,θ). Let the instantaneous position of the particle in polar coordinates be given by $r = r(t)$ and $\theta = \theta(t)$.

The polar and rectangular coordinates are related by the transformation equations

$$x = r\cos\theta \qquad y = r\sin\theta$$

The position vector $\mathbf{r}$ of the particle now becomes

$$\mathbf{r} = r(\cos\theta\,\mathbf{e}_x + \sin\theta\,\mathbf{e}_y)$$

We shall let

$$\mathbf{e}_r = \cos\theta\,\mathbf{e}_x + \sin\theta\,\mathbf{e}_y$$

Notice that

$$|\mathbf{e}_r| = 1$$

and that the vector $\mathbf{e}_r$ makes an angle θ with the x axis of the (x,y) coordinate system. We can now write the position, velocity, and

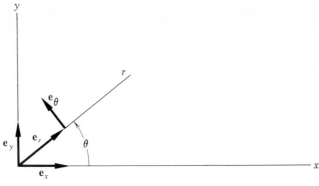

$$\mathbf{e}_r = \cos\theta\,\mathbf{e}_x + \sin\theta\,\mathbf{e}_y$$
$$\mathbf{e}_\theta = -\sin\theta\,\mathbf{e}_y + \cos\theta\,\mathbf{e}_x$$

Figure 3-2 Base vectors in plane rectangular and plane polar coordinates.

acceleration vectors of the particle as

$$\mathbf{r} = r\mathbf{e}_r$$

$$\mathbf{v} = \frac{d\mathbf{r}}{dt} = \frac{dr}{dt}\,\mathbf{e}_r + r\,\frac{d\mathbf{e}_r}{dt}$$

$$\mathbf{a} = \frac{d^2\mathbf{r}}{dt^2} = \frac{d^2 r}{dt^2}\,\mathbf{e}_r + 2\,\frac{dr}{dt}\frac{d\mathbf{e}_r}{dt} + r\,\frac{d^2\mathbf{e}_r}{dt^2}$$

Notice that we have had to differentiate the vector $\mathbf{e}_r$. This is because even though $\mathbf{e}_r$ has a constant unit magnitude, its direction changes with time, since $\theta = \theta(t)$ occurs in its definition. The base vectors $\mathbf{e}_x$ and $\mathbf{e}_y$, on the other hand, do not change in direction or magnitude.

We can write

$$\frac{d\mathbf{e}_r}{dt} = \frac{d\theta}{dt}\frac{d\mathbf{e}_r}{d\theta}$$

using the "chain rule" of differential calculus. Then $\mathbf{e}_\theta$ is defined by

$$\mathbf{e}_\theta = \frac{d\mathbf{e}_r}{d\theta} = -\sin\theta\,\mathbf{e}_x + \cos\theta\,\mathbf{e}_y$$

and we notice that $|\mathbf{e}_\theta| = 1$ while $\mathbf{e}_r \cdot \mathbf{e}_\theta = 0$. Therefore, $\mathbf{e}_\theta$ is a unit vector perpendicular to $\mathbf{e}_r$. The vector $\mathbf{e}_\theta$ makes an angle θ with the y axis. Using the properties of the sine and cosine, we find

$$\frac{d\mathbf{e}_r}{d\theta} = \mathbf{e}_\theta \qquad \frac{d\mathbf{e}_\theta}{d\theta} = -\mathbf{e}_r$$

Then

$$\frac{d\mathbf{e}_r}{dt} = \frac{d\theta}{dt}\,\mathbf{e}_\theta$$

$$\frac{d^2\mathbf{e}_r}{dt^2} = \frac{d^2\theta}{dt^2}\,\mathbf{e}_\theta + \frac{d\theta}{dt}\frac{d\mathbf{e}_\theta}{dt}$$

and

$$\frac{d\mathbf{e}_\theta}{dt} = \frac{d\theta}{dt}\frac{d\mathbf{e}_\theta}{d\theta} = -\frac{d\theta}{dt}\mathbf{e}_r$$

so that

$$\frac{d^2\mathbf{e}_r}{dt} = \frac{d^2\theta}{dt^2}\mathbf{e}_\theta - \left(\frac{d\theta}{dt}\right)^2 \mathbf{e}_r$$

giving finally

$$\mathbf{r} = r\mathbf{e}_r$$

$$\mathbf{v} = \frac{d\mathbf{r}}{dt} = \frac{dr}{dt}\mathbf{e}_r + r\frac{d\theta}{dt}\mathbf{e}_\theta$$

$$\mathbf{a} = \frac{d^2\mathbf{r}}{dt^2} = \left[\frac{d^2r}{dt^2} - r\left(\frac{d\theta}{dt}\right)^2\right]\mathbf{e}_r + \left(r\frac{d^2\theta}{dt^2} + 2\frac{dr}{dt}\frac{d\theta}{dt}\right)\mathbf{e}_\theta$$

The pair of vectors $\mathbf{e}_r$ and $\mathbf{e}_\theta$ form a complete set for the expansion of two-dimensional plane vectors, just as the vectors $\mathbf{e}_x$ and $\mathbf{e}_y$ do. However, the directions of $\mathbf{e}_r$ and $\mathbf{e}_\theta$ are not, in general, constant, while those of $\mathbf{e}_x$ and $\mathbf{e}_y$ are constant.

EXAMPLE 3-3: We shall again consider a particle moving in a plane, so that its instantaneous position is given by $x = x(t)$ and $y = y(t)$. During a time interval dt the particle moves a distance ds such that

$$ds^2 = \left[\left(\frac{dx}{dt}\right)^2 + \left(\frac{dy}{dt}\right)^2\right]dt^2$$

The instantaneous speed of the particle is

$$v = \frac{ds}{dt}$$

and we can write the position, velocity, and acceleration vectors of the particle as

$$\mathbf{r} = \mathbf{r}(t)$$

$$\mathbf{v} = \frac{d\mathbf{r}}{dt} = \frac{ds}{dt}\frac{d\mathbf{r}}{ds} = v\frac{d\mathbf{r}}{ds}$$

$$\mathbf{a} = \frac{d^2\mathbf{r}}{dt^2} = \frac{d^2s}{dt^2}\frac{d\mathbf{r}}{ds} + \left(\frac{ds}{dt}\right)^2\frac{d^2\mathbf{r}}{ds^2}$$

The vector

$$\mathbf{T} = \frac{d\mathbf{r}}{ds}$$

must be tangent to the path along which the particle moves, since

$$d\mathbf{r} = \mathbf{T}\,ds$$

represents the infinitesimal displacement experienced by the particle during the time interval dt.

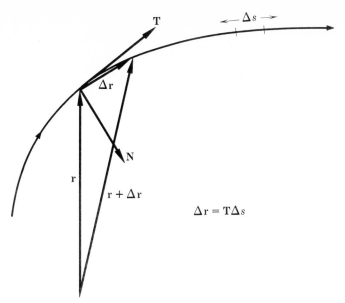

Figure 3-3 The intrinsic (**T,N**) base vectors carried with a moving particle.

On the other hand,
$$\mathbf{r} = x\mathbf{e}_x + y\mathbf{e}_y$$
$$d\mathbf{r} = dx\mathbf{e}_x + dy\mathbf{e}_y$$
$$d\mathbf{r} \cdot d\mathbf{r} = (dx)^2 + (dy)^2 = ds^2$$
and
$$\frac{d\mathbf{r}}{ds} \cdot \frac{d\mathbf{r}}{ds} = \mathbf{T} \cdot \mathbf{T} = 1$$

This shows that **T** is a unit vector tangent to the path of the particle at its instantaneous position. Differentiation of $\mathbf{T} \cdot \mathbf{T} = 1$ gives

$$\mathbf{T} \cdot \frac{d\mathbf{T}}{ds} = 0$$

which means that $d\mathbf{T}/ds$ is perpendicular to **T**, provided that the path is not a straight line.

We define

$$\frac{d\mathbf{T}}{ds} = k\mathbf{N}$$

where $|\mathbf{N}| = 1$ and $\mathbf{N} \cdot \mathbf{T} = 0$. The parameter k is called the "curvature" of the path, and its absolute value is equal to the magnitude of $d\mathbf{T}/ds$,

$$|k| = \left| \frac{d\mathbf{T}}{ds} \right|$$

The direction of $d\mathbf{T}/ds$ always points toward the concave side of the curve. For example, if a particle moves along a circular path, then $d\mathbf{T}/ds$ points toward the center of the circle. The reciprocal of the curvature, $r = 1/k$, is called the "radius of curvature." For a circular path, the radius of curvature is just the radius of the circle. The $(\mathbf{T},\mathbf{N})$ coordinate system associated with the path, $x = x(t)$, $y = y(t)$, is called the "intrinsic" coordinate system, and in this coordinate system the position, velocity, and acceleration vectors become

$$\mathbf{r} = \mathbf{r}(t)$$

$$\mathbf{v} = \frac{d\mathbf{r}}{dt} = \frac{ds}{dt}\,\mathbf{T}$$

$$\mathbf{a} = \frac{d\mathbf{v}}{dt} = \frac{d^2s}{dt^2}\,\mathbf{T} + k\left(\frac{ds}{dt}\right)^2\mathbf{N}$$

where $k = 1/r$ is the curvature.

3-2 PARTIAL VECTOR DIFFERENTIATION

Let x, y, z be the axes of a rectangular Cartesian coordinate system. Let $\mathbf{r} = (x,y,z)$ represent the position vector of an arbitrary point in this coordinate system. Suppose that there is a scalar function f which assigns a numerical value to each point in space. We shall then write

$$f = f(x,y,z) \tag{3-8}$$

or, in more compact form,

$$f = f(\mathbf{r}) \tag{3-9}$$

The values of f associated with all the points in space constitute a scalar field. If there is a vector function which assigns a vector to each point in space, then we write

$$\mathbf{A} = \mathbf{A}(x,y,z) \tag{3-10}$$

or, in more compact form,

$$\mathbf{A} = \mathbf{A}(\mathbf{r}) \tag{3-11}$$

The values of $\mathbf{A}$ associated with all the points in space constitute a vector field.

In physics, it is frequently necessary to consider scalar and vector fields which vary with a parameter such as time t. We then write

$$f = f(\mathbf{r},t) \tag{3-12}$$

$$\mathbf{A} = \mathbf{A}(\mathbf{r},t) \tag{3-13}$$

The temperature and pressure in a fluid are examples of scalar fields, while electric, magnetic, and gravitational fields are vector fields.

The gradient of a scalar field

If the partial derivatives of $f(x,y,z)$ exist and are continuous throughout some region of space, then in such a region the differential of f is given by

$$df = \frac{\partial f}{\partial x}\,dx + \frac{\partial f}{\partial y}\,dy + \frac{\partial f}{\partial z}\,dz \tag{3-14}$$

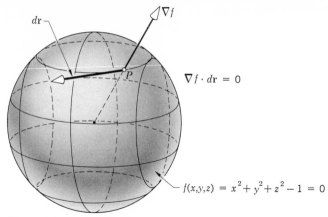

Figure 3-4 Geometric interpretation of the gradient of $f(x,y,z)$.

Notice that Eq. (3-14) may be regarded as the scalar product of two vectors

$$df = \left(\frac{\partial f}{\partial x}, \frac{\partial f}{\partial y}, \frac{\partial f}{\partial z}\right) \cdot (dx, dy, dz) \tag{3-15}$$

or

$$df = \left(\mathbf{e}_x \frac{\partial f}{\partial x} + \mathbf{e}_y \frac{\partial f}{\partial y} + \mathbf{e}_z \frac{\partial f}{\partial z}\right) \cdot (\mathbf{e}_x\, dx + \mathbf{e}_y\, dy + \mathbf{e}_z\, dz) \tag{3-16}$$

The operator

$$\boldsymbol{\nabla} = \mathbf{e}_x \frac{\partial}{\partial x} + \mathbf{e}_y \frac{\partial}{\partial y} + \mathbf{e}_z \frac{\partial}{\partial z} \tag{3-17}$$

is called the "del" or "gradient" operator, and the expression

$$\boldsymbol{\nabla} f = \operatorname{grad} f = \left(\mathbf{e}_x \frac{\partial}{\partial x} + \mathbf{e}_y \frac{\partial}{\partial y} + \mathbf{e}_z \frac{\partial}{\partial z}\right) f \tag{3-18}$$

is known as the gradient of f or simply del f.

The differential of f can then be written as

$$df = \boldsymbol{\nabla} f \cdot d\mathbf{r} \tag{3-19}$$

since

$$\mathbf{r} = \mathbf{e}_x x + \mathbf{e}_y y + \mathbf{e}_z z$$

and

$$d\mathbf{r} = \mathbf{e}_x\, dx + \mathbf{e}_y\, dy + \mathbf{e}_z\, dz$$

Geometric interpretation of the $\boldsymbol{\nabla}$ operator

The equation $f(x,y,z) = 0$ is the equation of a surface in space. For example, $x^2 + y^2 + z^2 - 1 = 0$ is the equation of a spherical surface of unit radius. For points on the surface, $f(x,y,z) = 0$, we have $df = 0$, and therefore

$$\boldsymbol{\nabla} f \cdot d\mathbf{r} = 0 \tag{3-20}$$

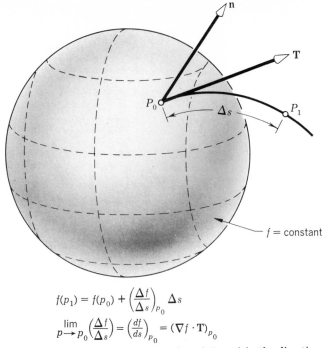

$$f(p_1) = f(p_0) + \left(\frac{\Delta f}{\Delta s}\right)_{p_0} \Delta s$$

$$\lim_{p \to p_0} \left(\frac{\Delta f}{\Delta s}\right) = \left(\frac{df}{ds}\right)_{p_0} = (\nabla f \cdot \mathbf{T})_{p_0}$$

Figure 3-5   The directional derivative of $f(x,y,z)$ in the direction **T**.

as a result of Eq. (3-19). We now choose P to be any point on the surface $f(x,y,z) = 0$, and we hold P fixed throughout our discussion. Let $d\mathbf{r}$ represent any infinitesimal displacement vector which begins at P and is *tangent* to the surface $f(x,y,z) = 0$ at the point P. Equation (3-20) then states that ∇f must be perpendicular to this particular infinitesimal displacement vector $d\mathbf{r}$. However, $d\mathbf{r}$ is *arbitrary*, subject only to the restriction that it be *tangent* to the surface at P. We therefore conclude that ∇f is normal to the surface $f = 0$ at any point on the surface.

The directional derivative

Consider an arbitrary point P in space, and let the partial derivatives of f be computed at P. We no longer constrain the infinitesimal displacement vector $d\mathbf{r}$ at P to be tangent to the surface $f = 0$, but instead allow it to point in any direction in space, keeping only its tail end fixed at P.

Let **T** be a unit vector pointing in the direction of $d\mathbf{r}$ and set $|d\mathbf{r}| = ds$. Then

$$d\mathbf{r} = \mathbf{T} \, ds \qquad |\mathbf{T}| = 1$$

and

$$df = \nabla f \cdot \mathbf{T} \, ds$$

gives

$$\frac{df}{ds} = \nabla f \cdot \mathbf{T} \tag{3-21}$$

The ordinary derivative df/ds is called the "directional" derivative of f in the direction $\mathbf{T}$.

Notice that f increases most rapidly when the direction $\mathbf{T}$ of $d\mathbf{r}$ is parallel to ∇f since

$$\nabla f \cdot \mathbf{T} = |\nabla f| \cos (\mathbf{T}, \nabla f)$$

The divergence of a vector field

The divergence of a vector field is defined as the scalar product of the ∇ operator with the field. Thus, given

$$\mathbf{A} = A_x \mathbf{e}_x + A_y \mathbf{e}_y + A_z \mathbf{e}_z \tag{3-22}$$

$$\nabla \cdot \mathbf{A} = \operatorname{div} \mathbf{A} = \frac{\partial A_x}{\partial x} + \frac{\partial A_y}{\partial y} + \frac{\partial A_z}{\partial z} \tag{3-23}$$

The Laplacian of a scalar or a vector field

The Laplacian of scalar function f is defined by

$$\nabla^2 f = \frac{\partial^2 f}{\partial x^2} + \frac{\partial^2 f}{\partial y^2} + \frac{\partial^2 f}{\partial z^2} \tag{3-24}$$

If

$$\mathbf{A} = A_x \mathbf{e}_x + A_y \mathbf{e}_y + A_z \mathbf{e}_z \tag{3-25}$$

then the Laplacian of $\mathbf{A}$ is defined by

$$\nabla^2 \mathbf{A} = \mathbf{e}_x \nabla^2 A_x + \mathbf{e}_y \nabla^2 A_y + \mathbf{e}_z \nabla^2 A_z \tag{3-26}$$

Notice that for a scalar function

$$\nabla^2 f = \nabla \cdot \nabla f = \operatorname{div} \operatorname{grad} f \tag{3-27}$$

The curl of a vector field

If

$$\mathbf{A} = A_x \mathbf{e}_x + A_y \mathbf{e}_y + A_z \mathbf{e}_z \tag{3-28}$$

then the curl of $\mathbf{A}$ is defined by

$$\nabla \times \mathbf{A} = \operatorname{curl} \mathbf{A} = \det \begin{vmatrix} \mathbf{e}_x & \mathbf{e}_y & \mathbf{e}_z \\ \dfrac{\partial}{\partial x} & \dfrac{\partial}{\partial y} & \dfrac{\partial}{\partial z} \\ A_x & A_y & A_z \end{vmatrix} \tag{3-29}$$

or

$$\nabla \times \mathbf{A} = \mathbf{e}_x \left(\frac{\partial A_z}{\partial y} - \frac{\partial A_y}{\partial z} \right) + \mathbf{e}_y \left(\frac{\partial A_x}{\partial z} - \frac{\partial A_z}{\partial x} \right)$$
$$+ \mathbf{e}_z \left(\frac{\partial A_y}{\partial x} - \frac{\partial A_x}{\partial y} \right) \tag{3-30}$$

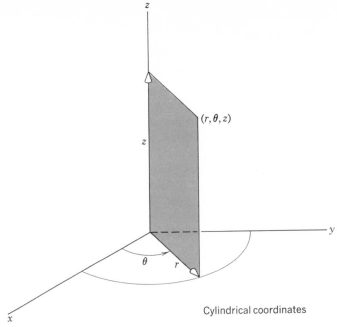

(r,θ,z)

Cylindrical coordinates

Figure 3-5a Cylindrical coordinates.

REMARK: The student should verify that by using Eq. (3-30) twice, one obtains the identity

$$\nabla \times \nabla \times \mathbf{A} = \nabla\nabla \cdot \mathbf{A} - \nabla^2\mathbf{A} \qquad (3\text{-}31)$$

The expression (3-31) defines the Laplacian of a vector even if the vector is *not* expressed in rectangular Cartesian coordinates.

3-3 VECTOR OPERATIONS IN CYLINDRICAL AND SPHERICAL COORDINATE SYSTEMS

The gradient, divergence, and curl operators have an invariant meaning independent of the coordinate system in which they are expressed. These operators acquire particularly simple forms in the rectangular Cartesian coordinate system used in Sec. 3-2. Their corresponding forms in cylindrical and spherical coordinate systems can be obtained by straightforward use of the chain rule of differential calculus.

EXAMPLE 3-4: *Cylindrical Coordinates* (r,θ,z). The cylindrical coordinates (r,θ,z) of a point are related to the rectangular Cartesian coordinates (x,y,z) of the same point by the following transformation of coordinates:

$$x = r \cos \theta \qquad (3\text{-}32)$$

$$y = r \sin \theta \qquad (3\text{-}33)$$

$$z = z \qquad (3\text{-}34)$$

Suppose that we have a scalar function $f = f(x,y,z)$ which depends on x, y, and z and that we set $x = r \cos \theta$, $y = r \sin \theta$, $z = z$, in f. Now f will be a function of r, θ, and z. In order to calculate $\partial f/\partial x$ and $\partial f/\partial y$ we apply the chain rule of differential calculus:

$$\frac{\partial f}{\partial x} = \frac{\partial f}{\partial r}\frac{\partial r}{\partial x} + \frac{\partial f}{\partial \theta}\frac{\partial \theta}{\partial x} \tag{3-35}$$

$$\frac{\partial f}{\partial y} = \frac{\partial f}{\partial r}\frac{\partial r}{\partial y} + \frac{\partial f}{\partial \theta}\frac{\partial \theta}{\partial y} \tag{3-36}$$

From Eqs. (3-32) to (3-24) we have

$$r^2 = x^2 + y^2 \tag{3-37}$$

$$\theta = \tan^{-1}\frac{y}{x} \tag{3-38}$$

and consequently

$$\frac{\partial r}{\partial x} = \cos \theta \qquad \frac{\partial r}{\partial y} = \sin \theta \tag{3-39}$$

$$\frac{\partial \theta}{\partial x} = \frac{-\sin \theta}{r} \qquad \frac{\partial \theta}{\partial y} = \frac{\cos \theta}{r} \tag{3-40}$$

Therefore

$$\frac{\partial f}{\partial x} = \cos \theta \frac{\partial f}{\partial r} - \frac{\sin \theta}{r}\frac{\partial f}{\partial \theta} \tag{3-41}$$

$$\frac{\partial f}{\partial y} = \sin \theta \frac{\partial f}{\partial r} + \frac{\cos \theta}{r}\frac{\partial f}{\partial \theta} \tag{3-42}$$

In Example 3-2 we obtained the following expressions for the unit base vectors in the r and θ directions:

$$\mathbf{e}_r = \cos \theta \, \mathbf{e}_x + \sin \theta \, \mathbf{e}_y \tag{3-43}$$

$$\mathbf{e}_\theta = -\sin \theta \, \mathbf{e}_x + \cos \theta \, \mathbf{e}_y \tag{3-44}$$

We can solve Eqs. (3-43) and (3-44) for $\mathbf{e}_x$ and $\mathbf{e}_y$ obtaining

$$\mathbf{e}_x = \cos \theta \, \mathbf{e}_r - \sin \theta \, \mathbf{e}_\theta \tag{3-45}$$

$$\mathbf{e}_y = \sin \theta \, \mathbf{e}_r + \cos \theta \, \mathbf{e}_\theta \tag{3-46}$$

The gradient of a scalar in rectangular Cartesian coordinates is

$$\nabla f = \frac{\partial f}{\partial x}\mathbf{e}_x + \frac{\partial f}{\partial y}\mathbf{e}_y + \frac{\partial f}{\partial z}\mathbf{e}_z \tag{3-47}$$

and on substituting Eqs. (3-41), (3-42), (3-45), and (3-46) into Eq. (3-47), we obtain

$$\nabla f = \frac{\partial f}{\partial r}\mathbf{e}_r + \frac{1}{r}\frac{\partial f}{\partial \theta}\mathbf{e}_\theta + \frac{\partial f}{\partial z}\mathbf{e}_z \tag{3-48}$$

as the gradient of a scalar function written in cylindrical coordinates.

Next we shall obtain a formula for the divergence of a vector expressed in cylindrical coordinates. A given vector, say $\mathbf{A}$, can be expressed in both cylindrical and rectangular Cartesian coordinates. Since there is only one vector, but there are two different representations, we must have

$$\mathbf{A} = A_x\mathbf{e}_x + A_y\mathbf{e}_y + A_z\mathbf{e}_z = A_r\mathbf{e}_r + A_\theta\mathbf{e}_\theta + A_z\mathbf{e}_z \qquad (3\text{-}49)$$

and consequently from Eqs. (3-43), (3-44), and (3-49),

$$A_x = A_r \cos \theta - A_\theta \sin \theta \qquad (3\text{-}50)$$

$$A_y = A_r \sin \theta + A_\theta \cos \theta \qquad (3\text{-}51)$$

$$A_z = A_z \qquad (3\text{-}52)$$

Using Eqs. (3-41) and (3-42), we can write

$$\frac{\partial A_x}{\partial x} = \cos \theta \frac{\partial A_x}{\partial r} - \frac{\sin \theta}{r} \frac{\partial A_x}{\partial \theta} \qquad (3\text{-}53)$$

$$\frac{\partial A_y}{\partial y} = \sin \theta \frac{\partial A_y}{\partial r} + \frac{\cos \theta}{r} \frac{\partial A_y}{\partial \theta} \qquad (3\text{-}54)$$

and since

$$\nabla \cdot \mathbf{A} = \frac{\partial A_x}{\partial x} + \frac{\partial A_y}{\partial y} + \frac{\partial A_z}{\partial z} \qquad (3\text{-}55)$$

we find on substituting Eqs. (3-50) and (3-51) into (3-53) and (3-54) that

$$\nabla \cdot \mathbf{A} = \frac{\partial A_r}{\partial r} + \frac{A_r}{r} + \frac{1}{r} \frac{\partial A_\theta}{\partial \theta} + \frac{\partial A_z}{\partial z} \qquad (3\text{-}56)$$

or

$$\nabla \cdot \mathbf{A} = \frac{1}{r} \frac{\partial}{\partial r} (rA_r) + \frac{1}{r} \frac{\partial A_\theta}{\partial \theta} + \frac{\partial A_z}{\partial z} \qquad (3\text{-}57)$$

It is now an easy matter to calculate the Laplacian of a scalar function in cylindrical coordinates since

$$\nabla^2 f = \nabla \cdot (\nabla f) \qquad (3\text{-}58)$$

The result is that

$$\nabla^2 f = \frac{1}{r} \frac{\partial}{\partial r} \left(r \frac{\partial f}{\partial r} \right) + \frac{1}{r^2} \frac{\partial^2 f}{\partial \theta^2} + \frac{\partial^2 f}{\partial z^2} \qquad (3\text{-}59)$$

The same technique applied to Eq. (3-30) suffices to show that in cylindrical coordinates

$$\nabla \times \mathbf{A} = \left(\frac{1}{r} \frac{\partial A_z}{\partial \theta} - \frac{\partial A_\theta}{\partial z} \right) \mathbf{e}_r + \left(\frac{\partial A_r}{\partial z} - \frac{\partial A_z}{\partial r} \right) \mathbf{e}_\theta$$
$$+ \left[\frac{1}{r} \frac{\partial}{\partial r} (rA_\theta) - \frac{1}{r} \frac{\partial A_r}{\partial \theta} \right] \mathbf{e}_z \qquad (3\text{-}60)$$

EXERCISE: Derive Eq. (3-60) from Eq. (3-30) by the method illustrated here.

EXAMPLE 3-5: *Spherical Coordinates* (R,θ,ϕ). The spherical coordinates (R,θ,ϕ) of a point are related to the rectangular Cartesian coordinates (x,y,z) of the same point by the transformation of coordinates:

$$x = R \sin \theta \cos \phi \qquad (3\text{-}61)$$

$$y = R \sin \theta \sin \phi \qquad (3\text{-}62)$$

$$z = R \cos \theta \qquad (3\text{-}63)$$

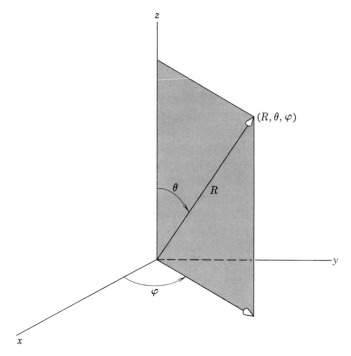

Spherical coordinates

Figure 3-5b Spherical coordinates.

Here R is the radial distance of a given point from the origin of coordinates, θ is the colatitude of the point, as measured from the z axis, and ϕ is the longitude of the point measured from the x axis, in the x, y plane. The transformation of coordinates (3-61) to (3-63) can be considered as the result of two consecutive transformations:

$$x = r \cos \phi \tag{3-64}$$

$$y = r \sin \phi \tag{3-65}$$

and

$$z = R \cos \theta \tag{3-66}$$

$$r = R \sin \theta \tag{3-67}$$

both of which have the *same form* as the transformation (3-32) and (3-33) from rectangular to cylindrical coordinates. Therefore we can write down the gradient, divergence, Laplacian, and curl operators in spherical coordinates by applying the results of Example 3-4 *twice* in succession. For example, the gradient of a scalar transforms according to

$$\boldsymbol{\nabla}f = \frac{\partial f}{\partial x}\,\mathbf{e}_x + \frac{\partial f}{\partial y}\,\mathbf{e}_y + \frac{\partial f}{\partial z}\,\mathbf{e}_z = \frac{\partial f}{\partial r}\,\mathbf{e}_r + \frac{1}{r}\frac{\partial f}{\partial \phi}\,\mathbf{e}_\phi + \frac{\partial f}{\partial z}\,\mathbf{e}_z \tag{3-68}$$

under the first set of transformations (3-64) and (3-65). Applying the second set of transformations (3-66) and (3-67) to

$$\frac{\partial f}{\partial r} \mathbf{e}_r + \frac{\partial f}{\partial z} \mathbf{e}_z$$

yields

$$\frac{\partial f}{\partial r} \mathbf{e}_r + \frac{\partial f}{\partial z} \mathbf{e}_z = \frac{\partial f}{\partial R} \mathbf{e}_R + \frac{1}{R} \frac{\partial f}{\partial \theta} \mathbf{e}_\theta \qquad (3\text{-}69)$$

The remaining term in Eq. (3-68) transforms as

$$\frac{1}{r} \frac{\partial f}{\partial \phi} \mathbf{e}_\phi = \frac{1}{R \sin \theta} \frac{\partial f}{\partial \phi} \mathbf{e}_\phi \qquad (3\text{-}70)$$

and therefore

$$\nabla f = \frac{\partial f}{\partial R} \mathbf{e}_R + \frac{1}{R} \frac{\partial f}{\partial \theta} \mathbf{e}_\theta + \frac{1}{R \sin \theta} \frac{\partial f}{\partial \phi} \mathbf{e}_\phi \qquad (3\text{-}71)$$

gives the gradient of a scalar function expressed in spherical coordinates.

To compute

$$\nabla \cdot \mathbf{A} = \frac{\partial A_x}{\partial x} + \frac{\partial A_y}{\partial y} + \frac{\partial A_z}{\partial z} \qquad (3\text{-}72)$$

in spherical coordinates we observe that under the first set of transformations (3-64) and (3-65)

$$\nabla \cdot \mathbf{A} = \frac{\partial A_r}{\partial r} + \frac{A_r}{r} + \frac{1}{r} \frac{\partial A_\phi}{\partial \phi} + \frac{\partial A_z}{\partial z} \qquad (3\text{-}73)$$

The second set of transformations (3-66) and (3-67) can now be applied to $\partial A_r / \partial r + \partial A_z / \partial z$ in Eq. (3-73) to give

$$\frac{\partial A_r}{\partial r} + \frac{\partial A_z}{\partial z} = \frac{\partial A_R}{\partial R} + \frac{A_R}{R} + \frac{1}{R} \frac{\partial A_\theta}{\partial \theta} \qquad (3\text{-}74)$$

Equation (3-73) then becomes

$$\nabla \cdot \mathbf{A} = \frac{\partial A_R}{\partial R} + \left(\frac{A_R}{R} + \frac{A_r}{r} \right) + \frac{1}{R} \frac{\partial A_\theta}{\partial \theta} + \frac{1}{R \sin \theta} \frac{\partial A_\phi}{\partial \phi} \qquad (3\text{-}75)$$

To evaluate $A_R / R + A_r / r$ we note that since

$$\mathbf{r} = x \mathbf{e}_x + y \mathbf{e}_y + z \mathbf{e}_z$$

Eqs. (3-61) to (3-63) yield

$$\mathbf{e}_R = \sin \theta \cos \phi \, \mathbf{e}_x + \sin \theta \sin \phi \, \mathbf{e}_y + \cos \theta \, \mathbf{e}_z \qquad (3\text{-}76)$$

for the unit base vector in the radial direction. The unit base vector in the θ direction is called $\mathbf{e}_\theta$. It must be perpendicular to $\mathbf{e}_R$, and it must lie in the R, θ plane. Since $\mathbf{e}_R \cdot \mathbf{e}_R = 1$, we have $\mathbf{e}_R \cdot d\mathbf{e}_R / d\theta = 0$, and consequently we choose

$$\mathbf{e}_\theta = \frac{d\mathbf{e}_R}{d\theta} \qquad (3\text{-}77)$$

to give

$$\mathbf{e}_\theta = \cos \theta \cos \phi \, \mathbf{e}_x + \cos \theta \sin \phi \, \mathbf{e}_y - \sin \theta \, \mathbf{e}_z \qquad (3\text{-}78)$$

The unit base vector $\mathbf{e}_\phi$ in the ϕ direction is perpendicular to $\mathbf{e}_r$ and is given by

$$\mathbf{e}_\phi = -\sin\phi\,\mathbf{e}_x + \cos\phi\,\mathbf{e}_y \tag{3-79}$$

An arbitrary vector $\mathbf{A}$ can be represented in cylindrical or spherical coordinates, thus:

$$\mathbf{A} = A_r\mathbf{e}_r + A_z\mathbf{e}_z = A_R\mathbf{e}_R + A_\theta\mathbf{e}_\theta + A_\phi\mathbf{e}_\phi \tag{3-80}$$

where

$$\mathbf{e}_r = \cos\phi\,\mathbf{e}_x + \sin\phi\,\mathbf{e}_y \tag{3-81}$$

Also, we can write Eqs. (3-76) and (3-78) as

$$\mathbf{e}_R = \sin\theta\,\mathbf{e}_r + \cos\theta\,\mathbf{e}_z \tag{3-82}$$

$$\mathbf{e}_\theta = \cos\theta\,\mathbf{e}_r - \sin\theta\,\mathbf{e}_z \tag{3-83}$$

From Eq. (3-80),

$$A_R = A_r(\mathbf{e}_r \cdot \mathbf{e}_R) + A_z(\mathbf{e}_z \cdot \mathbf{e}_R) \tag{3-84}$$
$$A_\theta = A_r(\mathbf{e}_r \cdot \mathbf{e}_\theta) + A_z(\mathbf{e}_z \cdot \mathbf{e}_\theta)$$

and with the aid of Eqs. (3-82) and (3-83),

$$(\mathbf{e}_r \cdot \mathbf{e}_R) = \sin\theta \qquad (\mathbf{e}_z \cdot \mathbf{e}_R) = \cos\theta \tag{3-85}$$

$$(\mathbf{e}_r \cdot \mathbf{e}_\theta) = \cos\theta \qquad (\mathbf{e}_z \cdot \mathbf{e}_\theta) = -\sin\theta \tag{3-86}$$

so that

$$A_R = \sin\theta\,A_r + \cos\theta\,A_z \tag{3-87}$$

$$A_\theta = \cos\theta\,A_r - \sin\theta\,A_z \tag{3-88}$$

Eliminating A_z between Eqs. (3-87) and (3-88) yields

$$\sin\theta\,A_R + \cos\theta\,A_\theta = A_r \tag{3-89}$$

Hence

$$\frac{A_r}{r} = \frac{A_R}{R} + \frac{A_\theta}{R}\frac{\cos\theta}{\sin\theta} \tag{3-90}$$

Returning to Eq. (3-75), we have

$$\frac{A_R}{R} + \frac{A_r}{r} = \frac{2A_R}{R} + \frac{A_\theta}{R}\frac{\cos\theta}{\sin\theta} \tag{3-91}$$

and therefore

$$\boldsymbol{\nabla}\cdot\mathbf{A} = \frac{\partial A_R}{\partial R} + \frac{2A_R}{R} + \frac{1}{R}\frac{\partial A_\theta}{\partial\theta} + \frac{A_\theta}{R}\frac{\cos\theta}{\sin\theta} + \frac{1}{R\sin\theta}\frac{\partial A_\phi}{\partial\phi} \tag{3-92}$$

or

$$\boldsymbol{\nabla}\cdot\mathbf{A} = \frac{1}{R^2}\frac{\partial}{\partial R}(R^2 A_R) + \frac{1}{R\sin\theta}\frac{\partial}{\partial\theta}(\sin\theta\,A_\theta)$$
$$+ \frac{1}{R\sin\theta}\frac{\partial A_\phi}{\partial\phi} \tag{3-93}$$

It is now an easy matter to compute the Laplacian in spherical coordinates, since

$$\nabla^2 f = \boldsymbol{\nabla}\cdot(\boldsymbol{\nabla}f) \tag{3-94}$$

We find

$$\nabla^2 f = \frac{1}{R^2} \frac{\partial}{\partial R} \left(R^2 \frac{\partial f}{\partial R} \right) + \frac{1}{R^2 \sin \theta} \frac{\partial}{\partial \theta} \left(\sin \theta \frac{\partial f}{\partial \theta} \right)$$
$$+ \frac{1}{R^2 \sin^2 \theta} \frac{\partial^2 f}{\partial \phi^2} \qquad (3\text{-}95)$$

The curl can be treated in the same way, and the student should show that

$$\nabla \times \mathbf{A} = \frac{1}{R \sin \theta} \left[\frac{\partial}{\partial \theta} (\sin \theta \, A_\phi) - \frac{\partial A_\theta}{\partial \phi} \right] \mathbf{e}_R + \frac{1}{R \sin \theta} \left[\frac{\partial A_R}{\partial \phi} \right.$$
$$\left. - \sin \theta \frac{\partial}{\partial R} (RA_\phi) \right] \mathbf{e}_\theta + \frac{1}{R} \left[\frac{\partial}{\partial R} (RA_\theta) - \frac{\partial A_R}{\partial \theta} \right] \mathbf{e}_\phi \qquad (3\text{-}96)$$

REMARK: The relationship between the components of a given vector in rectangular Cartesian coordinates and the components of the same vector expressed in cylindrical or spherical coordinates can easily be written in matrix form. For cylindrical coordinates

$$\begin{bmatrix} A_r \\ A_\theta \\ A_z \end{bmatrix} = \begin{bmatrix} \cos \theta & \sin \theta & 0 \\ -\sin \theta & \cos \theta & 0 \\ 0 & 0 & 1 \end{bmatrix} \begin{bmatrix} A_x \\ A_y \\ A_z \end{bmatrix} \qquad (3\text{-}97)$$

while for spherical coordinates

$$\begin{bmatrix} A_r \\ A_\theta \\ A_\phi \end{bmatrix} = \begin{bmatrix} \sin \theta \cos \phi & \sin \theta \sin \phi & \cos \theta \\ \cos \theta \cos \phi & \cos \theta \sin \phi & -\sin \theta \\ -\sin \phi & \cos \phi & 0 \end{bmatrix} \begin{bmatrix} A_x \\ A_y \\ A_z \end{bmatrix} \qquad (3\text{-}98)$$

3-4 DIFFERENTIAL VECTOR IDENTITIES

There are a large number of differential vector identities which are important in physics. We shall list them, starting with the most important ones first. The student should verify them in Cartesian coordinates and then memorize them.

$$\nabla \cdot (\nabla \times \mathbf{A}) = 0 \qquad (3\text{-}99)$$

$$\nabla \times (\nabla f) = 0 \qquad (3\text{-}100)$$

$$\nabla \cdot (\mathbf{A} \times \mathbf{B}) = \mathbf{B} \cdot (\nabla \times \mathbf{A}) - \mathbf{A} \cdot (\nabla \times \mathbf{B}) \qquad (3\text{-}101)$$

$$\nabla \times (\mathbf{A} \times \mathbf{B}) = (\mathbf{B} \cdot \nabla)\mathbf{A} - (\mathbf{A} \cdot \nabla)\mathbf{B} + (\nabla \cdot \mathbf{B})\mathbf{A} - (\nabla \cdot \mathbf{A})\mathbf{B}$$
$$(3\text{-}102)$$

$$\nabla(\mathbf{A} \cdot \mathbf{B}) = (\mathbf{B} \cdot \nabla)\mathbf{A} + (\mathbf{A} \cdot \nabla)\mathbf{B} + \mathbf{A} \times (\nabla \times \mathbf{B}) + \mathbf{B} \times (\nabla \times \mathbf{A})$$
$$(3\text{-}103)$$

$$\nabla \cdot (f\mathbf{A}) = (\nabla f) \cdot \mathbf{A} + f(\nabla \cdot \mathbf{A}) \qquad (3\text{-}104)$$

$$\nabla \times (f\mathbf{A}) = (\nabla f) \times \mathbf{A} + f(\nabla \times \mathbf{A}) \qquad (3\text{-}105)$$

$$\nabla \times \nabla \times \mathbf{A} = \nabla \nabla \cdot \mathbf{A} - \nabla^2 \mathbf{A} \qquad (3\text{-}106)$$

$$\nabla \cdot \mathbf{r} = 3 \qquad (3\text{-}107)$$

$$\nabla \times \mathbf{r} = 0 \qquad (3\text{-}108)$$

$$(\mathbf{A} \cdot \nabla)\mathbf{r} = \mathbf{A} \qquad (3\text{-}109)$$

$$\frac{d\mathbf{A}}{dt} = \left(\frac{d\mathbf{r}}{dt} \cdot \nabla\right)\mathbf{A} + \frac{\partial \mathbf{A}}{\partial t} \qquad (3\text{-}110)$$

$$\frac{df}{dt} = \left(\frac{d\mathbf{r}}{dt} \cdot \nabla\right)f + \frac{\partial f}{\partial t} \qquad (3\text{-}111)$$

$$\nabla(fg) = f\,\nabla g + g\,\nabla f \qquad (3\text{-}112)$$

$$\nabla \cdot (f\,\nabla g) = f\,\nabla^2 g + \nabla f \cdot \nabla g \qquad (3\text{-}113)$$

$$\nabla \cdot \{f\,\nabla g - g\,\nabla f\} = (f\,\nabla^2 g - g\,\nabla^2 f) \qquad (3\text{-}114)$$

$$\nabla r = \frac{\mathbf{r}}{|\mathbf{r}|} \qquad (3\text{-}115)$$

where $\mathbf{r} = x\mathbf{e}_x + y\mathbf{e}_y + z\mathbf{e}_z$.

$$\nabla(r^n) = nr^{n-2}\mathbf{r} \qquad (3\text{-}116)$$

$$\nabla\left(\frac{f}{g}\right) = \frac{1}{g^2}(g\,\nabla f - f\,\nabla g) \qquad (3\text{-}117)$$

where f and g are scalar fields.

$$\nabla \cdot \left(\frac{\mathbf{r}}{|r|^3}\right) = \nabla \cdot \nabla\left(\frac{-1}{r}\right) = \nabla^2\left(\frac{-1}{r}\right) = 0 \qquad r \neq 0 \qquad (3\text{-}118)$$

REMARK: The verification of the identities (3-99) to (3-118) can be simplified in some cases by an intelligent use of the principle of linearity. It can be assumed that any pair of vectors entering into an identity will be either linearly independent or linearly dependent. This observation permits us to simplify the choice of vectors used in verifying an identity. We can consider an identity verified if we can verify it for a linearly independent pair of vectors and for a linearly dependent pair of vectors.

This idea is employed in the following way: If the two vectors chosen are linearly independent, then the Schmidt process discussed in Chap. 1 permits us to choose an orthogonal pair of vectors. As an example, consider identity (3-102).

Let

$$\mathbf{A} = A_x\mathbf{e}_x$$

$$\mathbf{B} = B_y\mathbf{e}_y$$

$$\mathbf{A} \times \mathbf{B} = (A_xB_y)\mathbf{e}_z$$

$$\nabla \times (\mathbf{A} \times \mathbf{B}) = \mathbf{e}_x\frac{\partial}{\partial y}(A_xB_y) - \mathbf{e}_y\frac{\partial}{\partial x}(A_xB_y)$$

$$\mathbf{B} \cdot \nabla = B_y\frac{\partial}{\partial y}$$

$$\mathbf{A} \cdot \nabla = A_x\frac{\partial}{\partial x}$$

$$\nabla \cdot \mathbf{B} = \frac{\partial B_y}{\partial y}$$

$$\nabla \cdot \mathbf{A} = \frac{\partial A_x}{\partial x}$$

$(\mathbf{B} \cdot \nabla)\mathbf{A} - (\mathbf{A} \cdot \nabla)\mathbf{B} + (\nabla \cdot \mathbf{B})\mathbf{A} - (\nabla \cdot \mathbf{A})\mathbf{B}$

$$= \mathbf{e}_z B_y \frac{\partial A_x}{\partial y} - \mathbf{e}_y A_x \frac{\partial B_y}{\partial x} + \mathbf{e}_z A_x \frac{\partial B_y}{\partial y} - \mathbf{e}_y B_y \frac{\partial A_x}{\partial x}$$

$$= \mathbf{e}_z \left(B_y \frac{\partial A_x}{\partial y} + A_x \frac{\partial B_y}{\partial y} \right) - \mathbf{e}_y \left(A_x \frac{\partial B_y}{\partial x} + B_y \frac{\partial A_x}{\partial x} \right)$$

$$= \mathbf{e}_z \frac{\partial}{\partial y} (A_x B_y) - \mathbf{e}_z \frac{\partial}{\partial x} (A_x B_y)$$

$$= \nabla \times (\mathbf{A} \times \mathbf{B})$$

This proves Eq. (3-102) for linearly independent vectors.

For the linearly dependent case, let

$\mathbf{B} = f\mathbf{A}$

Then

$\mathbf{A} \times \mathbf{B} = 0$

and

$\nabla \times (\mathbf{A} \times \mathbf{B}) = 0$

Suppose that

$\mathbf{A} = A_x \mathbf{e}_x$

a condition which can always be achieved by a suitable rotation of coordinates. Then

$$\mathbf{B} = (fA_x)\mathbf{e}_x$$

$\mathbf{B} \cdot \nabla = fA_x \dfrac{\partial}{\partial x}$

$\mathbf{A} \cdot \nabla = A_x \dfrac{\partial}{\partial x}$

$\nabla \cdot \mathbf{B} = \dfrac{\partial}{\partial x} (fA_x)$

$\nabla \cdot \mathbf{A} = \dfrac{\partial A_x}{\partial x}$

$(\mathbf{B} \cdot \nabla)\mathbf{A} - (\mathbf{A} \cdot \nabla)\mathbf{B} + (\nabla \cdot \mathbf{B})\mathbf{A} - (\nabla \cdot \mathbf{A})\mathbf{B}$

$$= \mathbf{e}_x fA_x \frac{\partial A_x}{\partial x} - \mathbf{e}_x A_x \frac{\partial}{\partial x} (fA_x) + \mathbf{e}_x A_x \frac{\partial}{\partial x} (fA_x) - \mathbf{e}_x fA_x \frac{\partial A_x}{\partial x}$$

$$= 0$$

This proves Eq. (3-102) for linearly dependent vectors. Thus (3-102) has been verified for any pair of vectors.

3-5 VECTOR INTEGRATION OVER A CLOSED SURFACE

Consider a cube together with a rectangular set of Cartesian coordinates. Choose the coordinate system so that the faces of the cube are perpendicular to the coordinate axes, and place the origin of coordi-

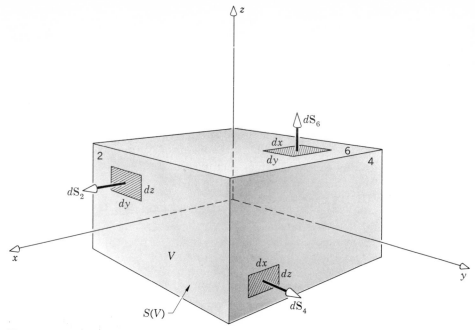

Figure 3-6 Cube of volume V and surface $S(V)$.

nates inside the cube. The cube has six faces labeled 1 through 6. We can represent an element of surface area on any one of the six faces as a vector quantity. The direction of this vector quantity is that of the *outward normal* to the particular face in question. Thus, the six elements of surface area associated with the cube are written

$$dS_1 = -e_x \, dy \, dz \qquad dS_2 = e_x \, dy \, dz \qquad (3\text{-}119)$$

$$dS_3 = -e_y \, dx \, dz \qquad dS_4 = e_y \, dx \, dz \qquad (3\text{-}120)$$

$$dS_5 = -e_z \, dx \, dy \qquad dS_6 = e_z \, dx \, dy \qquad (3\text{-}121)$$

where e_x, e_y, and e_z are the base vectors of the rectangular coordinate system centered in the cube.

We are going to prove that if $A = A(x,y,z)$ is such that $\partial A/\partial x$ is integrable over V, then

$$\iiint_V \frac{\partial A}{\partial x} \, dx \, dy \, dz = \iint_{S(V)} (e_x \cdot dS) A \qquad (3\text{-}122)$$

Here V denotes the volume enclosed by the cube, and $S(V)$ represents the total surface area of the cube (Fig. 3-6). At any point within a square face of the cube, dS is directed along the *outward normal* to the surface and represents the element of area about the point.

proof: Consider the right side of Eq. (3-122),

$$\iint_{S(V)} (e_x \cdot dS) A = \sum_{k=1}^{6} \iint_{S_k} (e_x \cdot dS_k) A \qquad (3\text{-}123)$$

where

$$S(V) = \sum_{k=1}^{6} S_k \qquad (3\text{-}124)$$

Equation (3-124) states that the total boundary surface of the cube is the sum of the six surfaces which form the sides of the cube.

Equation (3-123) is a consequence of (3-124) and the fact that integration is a linear operation. It means that the integral of $(\mathbf{e}_x \cdot d\mathbf{S})A$, taken over a closed surface consisting of several disjoint pieces, is equal to the sum of the integrals of $(\mathbf{e}_x \cdot d\mathbf{S})A$ obtained by integrating separately over each piece.

As a result of Eqs. (3-119) to (3-121),

$$\iint_{S(V)} (\mathbf{e}_x \cdot d\mathbf{S})A = \iint_{S_1} (\mathbf{e}_x \cdot d\mathbf{S}_1)A_1 + \iint_{S_2} (\mathbf{e}_x \cdot d\mathbf{S}_2)A_2 \qquad (3\text{-}125)$$

and from Eqs. (3-119),

$$\iint_{S(V)} (\mathbf{e}_x \cdot d\mathbf{S})A = \iint_{S_2} A_2 \, dy \, dz - \iint_{S_1} A_1 \, dy \, dz \qquad (3\text{-}126)$$

If the equation of S_2 is $x = x_2 = $ constant and the equation of S_1 is $x = x_1 = $ constant, then the value A_2 of A on S_2 becomes

$$A_2 = A(x_2,y,z) \qquad (3\text{-}127)$$

while

$$A_1 = A(x_1,y,z) \qquad (3\text{-}128)$$

Hence Eq. (3-126) becomes

$$\iint_{S(V)} (\mathbf{e}_x \cdot d\mathbf{S})A = \iint_{S_2} A(x_2,y,z) \, dy \, dz - \iint_{S_1} A(x_1,y,z) \, dy \, dz$$
$$(3\text{-}129)$$

Since we are dealing with a cube, the areas of faces S_1 and S_2 are equal. Therefore, the limits of integration over y and z will be the same for each term in Eq. (3-129). We shall indicate this by letting $S_1 = S_2 = S$, where S represents any cross-sectional area of the cube perpendicular to the x axis. Then Eq. (3-129) becomes

$$\iint_{S(V)} (\mathbf{e}_x \cdot d\mathbf{S})A = \iint_{S} A(x_2,y,z) \, dy \, dz - \iint_{S} A(x_1,y,z) \, dy \, dz$$
$$(3\text{-}130)$$

On the other hand,

$$\iiint_{V} \frac{\partial A}{\partial x} \, dx \, dy \, dz = \iint_{S} dy \, dz \int_{x_1}^{x_2} \frac{\partial A}{\partial x} \, dx \qquad (3\text{-}131)$$

gives

$$\iiint_{V} \frac{\partial A}{\partial x} \, dx \, dy \, dz = \iint_{S} A(x_2,y,z) \, dy \, dz$$
$$- \iint_{S} A(x_1,y,z) \, dy \, dz \qquad (3\text{-}132)$$

and therefore

$$\iiint_V \frac{\partial A}{\partial x}\, dx\, dy\, dz = \iint_{S(V)} (\mathbf{e}_x \cdot d\mathbf{S}) A \qquad (3\text{-}133)$$

which was to be proved.

Generalization

The result obtained in Eq. (3-133) applies not only to a cube but also to a solid of any shape. We shall not prove this here, although the proof is quite straightforward. The basic idea is that a solid of arbitrary shape can be divided into a large number of small cubes, and Eq. (3-133) can then be applied to each cube. Surface integral contributions from adjacent cube faces will cancel one another, because the outward normals to adjacent faces are antiparallel. We then add up the contributions from each cube while allowing their size to become infinitesimal and their number to increase without bound. In the limit, we obtain Eq. (3-133) again. Now V is the volume of the arbitrary solid, $S(V)$ is its total boundary surface, and $d\mathbf{S}$ is the element of area directed along the outward normal at any point on $S(V)$.

REMARK: If we define

$$dS_x = \mathbf{e}_x \cdot d\mathbf{S} \qquad (3\text{-}134)$$

and

$$dV = dx\, dy\, dz$$

then Eq. (3-133) becomes

$$\iiint_V \frac{\partial A}{\partial x}\, dV = \iint_{S(V)} dS_x A \qquad (3\text{-}135)$$

It is customary to make the notation even more compact by writing Eq. (3-135) as

$$\int_V \frac{\partial A}{\partial x}\, dV = \int_{S(V)} dS_x A \qquad (3\text{-}136)$$

Mnemonic devices

A mnemonic device is a scheme designed to aid one in remembering complicated mathematical expressions. A single such device becomes very useful if it helps one to remember a large number of formulas, since then it is necessary to remember only one mnemonic device in order to recall several formulas.

EXAMPLE 3-6: Consider the following mnemonic equation:

$$\frac{\partial}{\partial x} = \frac{dS_x}{dV} \qquad (3\text{-}137)$$

We interpret Eq. (3-137) by multiplying both sides *from the right* with an arbitrary scalar function.

Then

$$\frac{\partial A}{\partial x} = \frac{dS_x}{dV} A \qquad (3\text{-}138)$$

and treating dS_x/dV as though it were a fraction gives

$$\frac{\partial A}{\partial x} dV = dS_x A \qquad (3\text{-}139)$$

Therefore

$$\int_V \frac{\partial A}{\partial x} dV = \int_{S(V)} dS_x A$$

3-6 THE DIVERGENCE THEOREM

An application of Eq. (3-122) to the components A_x, A_y, and A_z of

$$\mathbf{A} = A_x\mathbf{e}_x + A_y\mathbf{e}_y + A_z\mathbf{e}_z \qquad (3\text{-}140)$$

gives

$$\int_V \frac{\partial A_x}{\partial x} dV = \int_{S(V)} d\mathbf{S} \cdot A_x\mathbf{e}_x \qquad (3\text{-}141)$$

$$\int_V \frac{\partial A_y}{\partial y} dV = \int_{S(V)} d\mathbf{S} \cdot A_y\mathbf{e}_y \qquad (3\text{-}142)$$

$$\int_V \frac{\partial A_z}{\partial z} dV = \int_{S(V)} d\mathbf{S} \cdot A_z\mathbf{e}_z \qquad (3\text{-}143)$$

and on adding Eqs. (3-141) through (3-143), we obtain

$$\int_V \nabla \cdot \mathbf{A}\, dV = \int_{S(V)} d\mathbf{S} \cdot \mathbf{A} \qquad (3\text{-}144)$$

which is known as the "divergence theorem." The divergence theorem relates the volume integral of the divergence of a vector field to the surface integral of its normal component.

Using Eq. (3-144), we are now in a position to obtain a physical interpretation of the meaning of the divergence of a vector field. The surface integral on the right-hand side of Eq. (3-144) is called the flux of vector $\mathbf{A}$,

$$\Phi(\mathbf{A}) = \int_{S(V)} d\mathbf{S} \cdot \mathbf{A} \qquad (3\text{-}145)$$

It follows from the left-hand side of Eq. (3-144) that the dimensions of $\nabla \cdot \mathbf{A}$ must be flux per unit volume or flux density. Thus we say that $\nabla \cdot \mathbf{A}$ is the flux density or flux per unit volume associated with the field $\mathbf{A}$.

When this idea is to be emphasized, Eq. (3-144) is usually written as

$$\nabla \cdot \mathbf{A} = \lim_{\Delta V \to 0} \frac{\int_{S(\Delta V)} d\mathbf{S} \cdot \mathbf{A}}{\Delta V} \qquad (3\text{-}146)$$

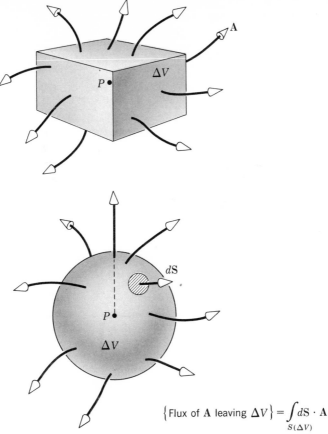

$$\left\{ \text{Flux of A leaving } \Delta V \right\} = \int_{S(\Delta V)} d\mathbf{S} \cdot \mathbf{A}$$

Figure 3-7 The divergence of **A** at P is computed by enclosing P in a small volume ΔV and then computing the ratio of the flux of **A** to the enclosed volume as $\Delta V \to 0$.

which means that for any point P we compute the divergence of **A** at P by enclosing P in a small volume and then computing the ratio of the flux to the volume as the volume element shrinks to zero (Fig. 3-7). The limit, if it exists, is the divergence of **A** at P. If **A** represents the velocity field of a fluid bounded by a surface $S(V)$, then the flux $\Phi(\mathbf{A})$ is the volume of fluid crossing the surface $S(V)$ per unit time. A positive flux means that fluid is leaving the region of space bounded by $S(V)$, while a negative flux means that fluid is entering that region. In the first case we say that there are sources present inside $S(V)$, while in the second case we say that there are sinks present. The divergence of **A** represents the volume of fluid produced or destroyed per unit volume of space per unit time inside $S(V)$. Thus, the divergence of **A** is the source or sink density inside $S(V)$. If the flux of **A** is zero, then either no fluid crosses the surface $S(V)$, or as much enters as leaves. If $\nabla \cdot \mathbf{A} = 0$ throughout some volume of the fluid, then the field **A** is said to be solenoidal in that volume, and there can be no sources or sinks present.

3-7 THE GRADIENT THEOREM

Using Eq. (3-122) and observing that e_x, e_y, and e_z are constant vectors, we can write

$$\int_V e_x \frac{\partial A}{\partial x} dV = \int_{S(V)} e_x (dS \cdot e_x) A \tag{3-147}$$

$$\int_V e_y \frac{\partial A}{\partial y} dV = \int_{S(V)} e_y (dS \cdot e_y) A \tag{3-148}$$

$$\int_V e_z \frac{\partial A}{\partial z} dV = \int_{S(V)} e_z (dS \cdot e_z) A \tag{3-149}$$

which upon addition gives

$$\int_V \nabla A \, dV = \int_{S(V)} dS \, A \tag{3-150}$$

where

$$dS = n \, dS = e_x (dS \cdot e_x) + e_y (dS \cdot e_y) + e_z (dS \cdot e_z) \tag{3-151}$$

or

$$dS = n \, dS = e_x \, dS_x + e_y \, dS_y + e_z \, dS_z \tag{3-152}$$

Here **n** is the unit outward normal to $S(V)$ at any point on $S(V)$.

3-8 THE CURL THEOREM

An application of Eq. (3-122) yields

$$\int_V \left(\frac{\partial A_z}{\partial y} - \frac{\partial A_y}{\partial z} \right) dV = \int_{S(V)} dS_y A_z - dS_z A_y \tag{3-153}$$

$$\int_V \left(\frac{\partial A_x}{\partial z} - \frac{\partial A_z}{\partial x} \right) dV = \int_{S(V)} dS_z A_x - dS_x A_z \tag{3-154}$$

$$\int_V \left(\frac{\partial A_y}{\partial x} - \frac{\partial A_x}{\partial y} \right) dV = \int_{S(V)} dS_x A_y - dS_y A_x \tag{3-155}$$

and if we now write

$$dS = e_x \, dS_x + e_y \, dS_y + e_z \, dS_z \tag{3-156}$$

and

$$A = A_x e_x + A_y e_y + A_z e_z \tag{3-157}$$

then it follows from Eq. (3-29) that Eqs. (3-153) to (3-155) can be written as the single vector equation

$$\int_V (\nabla \times A) \, dV = \int_{S(V)} dS \times A \tag{3-158}$$

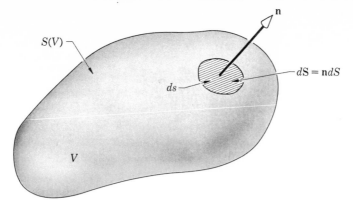

Figure 3-8 The domain of integration for the three-dimensional curl, divergence, and gradient theorems is a volume V enclosed by a surface $S(V)$. On $S(V)$, the directed element of surface area is $d\mathbf{S} = \mathbf{n}\, dS$.

where

$$d\mathbf{S} \times \mathbf{A} = \mathbf{n} \times \mathbf{A}\, dS \tag{3-159}$$

or

$$d\mathbf{S} \times \mathbf{A} = \begin{vmatrix} \mathbf{e}_x & \mathbf{e}_y & \mathbf{e}_z \\ dS_x & dS_y & dS_z \\ A_x & A_y & A_z \end{vmatrix} \tag{3-160}$$

Notice that $d\mathbf{S} \times \mathbf{A}$ is tangent to the surface $S(V)$. Hence Eq. (3-158) relates the volume integral of the curl of a vector field to the surface integral of its tangential components.

REMARK: We have developed integral theorems for the divergence, gradient, and curl operations which all share a common property. They relate the values of a scalar or vector field on a *closed surface* in space to the partial derivatives of the field throughout the *volume* bounded by the surface. In a similar way we can develop integral theorems for the divergence, gradient, and curl which relate the values of a field on a *closed curve* in space to the partial derivatives of the field throughout the *surface* bounded by the curve.

3-9 VECTOR INTEGRATION OVER A CLOSED CURVE

Consider a square together with a rectangular set of Cartesian coordinates. Choose the coordinate system so that the sides of the square are perpendicular to the coordinate axes, and place the origin of coordinates inside the square. The square has four sides labeled 1 through 4. We can represent an element of arc on any one of the four sides as a vector quantity. The direction of this vector quantity is that of the outward normal to the particular side in question. Thus, the four elements of arc associated with the square are written

$$d\boldsymbol{\sigma}_1 = -\mathbf{e}_x\, dy \qquad d\boldsymbol{\sigma}_2 = \mathbf{e}_x\, dy \tag{3-161}$$

$$d\boldsymbol{\sigma}_3 = -\mathbf{e}_y\, dx \qquad d\boldsymbol{\sigma}_4 = \mathbf{e}_y\, dx \tag{3-162}$$

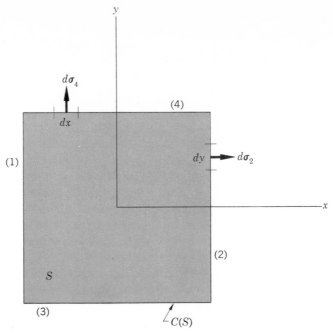

Figure 3-9 Square of surface area S and total boundary curve $C(S)$.

where $\mathbf{e}_x$ and $\mathbf{e}_y$ are the base vectors of the rectangular coordinate system centered in the square.

We are going to prove that if $A = A(x,y)$ is such that $\partial A/\partial x$ is integrable over S, then

$$\iint\limits_S \frac{\partial A}{\partial x}\, dx\, dy = \int_{C(S)} (\mathbf{e}_x \cdot d\mathbf{\sigma})A \tag{3-163}$$

Here S denotes the surface area enclosed by the square and $C(S)$ represents the total boundary of the square (Fig. 3-9). At any point on a side of the square (exclusive of the vertices), $d\mathbf{\sigma}$ is directed along the *outward normal* to the side and represents the element of arc about the point.

proof: Consider the right side of Eq. (3-163),

$$\int_{C(S)} (\mathbf{e}_x \cdot d\mathbf{\sigma})A = \sum_{k=1}^{4} \int_{C_k} (\mathbf{e}_x \cdot d\mathbf{\sigma})A \tag{3-164}$$

where

$$C(S) = \sum_{k=1}^{4} C_k \tag{3-165}$$

Equation (3-164) states that the total boundary curve of the square is the sum of the four lines which form the sides of the square.

Equation (3-164) is a consequence of Eq. (3-165) and the fact that integration is a linear operation. It means that the integral of

$(\mathbf{e}_x \cdot d\mathbf{\acute{o}})A$ taken over a closed curve consisting of several disjoint pieces is equal to the sum of the integrals of $(\mathbf{e}_x \cdot d\mathbf{\acute{o}})A$ obtained by integrating separately over each piece.

As a result of Eqs. (3-161) and (3-162), we have

$$\int_{C(S)} (\mathbf{e}_x \cdot d\mathbf{\acute{o}})A = \int_{C_1} (\mathbf{e}_x \cdot d\mathbf{\acute{o}}_1)A + \int_{C_2} (\mathbf{e}_x \cdot d\mathbf{\acute{o}}_2)A \qquad (3\text{-}166)$$

and from Eq. (3-161),

$$\int_{C(S)} (\mathbf{e}_x \cdot d\mathbf{\acute{o}})A = \int_{C_2} A_2 \, dy - \int_{C_1} A_1 \, dy \qquad (3\text{-}167)$$

If the equation of C_2 is $x = x_2 = $ constant and the equation of C_1 is $x = x_1 = $ constant, then the value A_2 of A on C_2 becomes

$$A_2 = A(x_2, y) \qquad (3\text{-}168)$$

while

$$A_1 = A(x_1, y) \qquad (3\text{-}169)$$

Hence Eq. (3-167) becomes

$$\int_{C(S)} (\mathbf{e}_x \cdot d\mathbf{\acute{o}})A = \int_{C_2} A(x_2, y) \, dy - \int_{C_1} A(x_1, y) \, dy \qquad (3\text{-}170)$$

Since we are dealing with a square, the lengths of sides C_1 and C_2 are equal. Therefore the limits of integration over y will be the same for each term in Eq. (3-170). We shall indicate this by letting $C_1 = C_2 = C$, where C represents the line of intersection of the square with any line parallel to the y axis. Then Eq. (3-170) becomes

$$\int_{C(S)} (\mathbf{e}_x \cdot d\mathbf{\acute{o}})A = \int_C A(x_2, y) \, dy - \int_C A(x_1, y) \, dy \qquad (3\text{-}171)$$

On the other hand,

$$\iint_S \frac{\partial A}{\partial x} \, dx \, dy = \int_C dy \int_{x_1}^{x_2} \frac{\partial A}{\partial x} \, dx \qquad (3\text{-}172)$$

gives

$$\iint_S \frac{\partial A}{\partial x} \, dx \, dy = \int_C A(x_2, y) \, dy - \int_C A(x_1, y) \, dy \qquad (3\text{-}173)$$

and therefore

$$\iint_S \frac{\partial A}{\partial x} \, dx \, dy = \int_{C(S)} (\mathbf{e}_x \cdot d\mathbf{\acute{o}})A \qquad (3\text{-}174)$$

which was to be proved.

Generalization

The result obtained in Eq. (3-174) can be generalized from a square to an area bounded by a curve of any shape. An area of any shape can be divided into a large number of small squares, and Eq. (3-174) can then be applied to each square. Line-integral contributions from the sides of adjacent squares will cancel one another because the outward normals to adjacent sides are antiparallel. We then add up

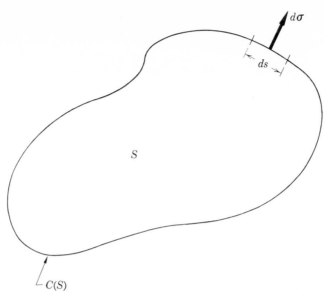

Figure 3-10 Plane lamina of area S and total boundary curve $C(S)$. The vector $d\boldsymbol{\sigma}$ is normal to $C(S)$ and points away from the interior of S. The magnitude $|d\boldsymbol{\sigma}| = ds$, where ds is the differential element of arc length along $C(S)$.

the contributions from each small square while allowing their size to shrink to zero and their number to increase without bound. In the limit we shall again obtain Eq. (3-174). Now S represents the area of the arbitrary surface, $C(S)$ is its total boundary curve, and $d\boldsymbol{\sigma}$ is the element of arc directed along the outward normal at any point on $C(S)$.

REMARK: If we define

$$d\sigma_x = \mathbf{e}_x \cdot d\boldsymbol{\sigma} \tag{3-175}$$

and

$$dS = dx\,dy \tag{3-176}$$

then Eq. (3-174) becomes

$$\iint_S \frac{\partial A}{\partial x}\,dS = \int_{C(S)} d\sigma_x A \tag{3-177}$$

To make the notation even more compact, we write Eq. (3-177) as

$$\int_S \frac{\partial A}{\partial x}\,dS = \int_{C(S)} d\sigma_x A \tag{3-178}$$

The mnemonic equation

$$\frac{\partial}{\partial x} = \frac{d\sigma_x}{dS} \tag{3-179}$$

then gives Eq. (3-178) if we interpret it as

$$\frac{\partial A}{\partial x} = \frac{d\sigma_x}{dS} A \tag{3-180}$$

$$\frac{\partial A}{\partial x} dS = d\sigma_x A \tag{3-181}$$

3-10 THE TWO-DIMENSIONAL DIVERGENCE THEOREM

An application of Eq. (3-163) to the components A_x and A_y of

$$\mathbf{A} = A_x\mathbf{e}_x + A_y\mathbf{e}_y \tag{3-182}$$

gives

$$\int_S \frac{\partial A_x}{\partial x} dS = \int_{C(S)} d\mathbf{\sigma} \cdot A_x\mathbf{e}_x \tag{3-183}$$

$$\int_S \frac{\partial A_y}{\partial y} dS = \int_{C(S)} d\mathbf{\sigma} \cdot A_y\mathbf{e}_y \tag{3-184}$$

and on adding Eqs. (3-183) and (3-184) we obtain

$$\int_S \mathbf{\nabla} \cdot \mathbf{A}\, dS = \int_{C(S)} d\mathbf{\sigma} \cdot \mathbf{A} \tag{3-185}$$

which is the two-dimensional divergence theorem. It relates the surface integral of the divergence of a vector field to the line integral of the normal component of the field around the boundary curve.

3-11 THE TWO-DIMENSIONAL GRADIENT THEOREM

Using Eq. (3-163) and noting that $\mathbf{e}_x$ and $\mathbf{e}_y$ are constant vectors, we can write

$$\int_S \mathbf{e}_x \frac{\partial A}{\partial x} dS = \int_{C(S)} \mathbf{e}_x(d\mathbf{\sigma} \cdot \mathbf{e}_x)A \tag{3-186}$$

$$\int_S \mathbf{e}_y \frac{\partial A}{\partial y} dS = \int_{C(S)} \mathbf{e}_y(d\mathbf{\sigma} \cdot \mathbf{e}_y)A \tag{3-187}$$

which upon addition gives

$$\int_S \mathbf{\nabla}A\, dS = \int_{C(S)} d\mathbf{\sigma}A \tag{3-188}$$

where

$$d\mathbf{\sigma} = \mathbf{n}\, d\sigma = \mathbf{e}_x(d\mathbf{\sigma} \cdot \mathbf{e}_x) + \mathbf{e}_y(d\mathbf{\sigma} \cdot \mathbf{e}_y) \tag{3-189}$$

or

$$d\mathbf{\sigma} = \mathbf{e}_x\, d\sigma_x + \mathbf{e}_y\, d\sigma_y \tag{3-190}$$

Here $\mathbf{n}$ is the unit outward normal to $C(S)$ at any point on $C(S)$, and $d\sigma$ is the element of arc length on $C(S)$.

An application of Eq. (3-163) yields

$$\int_S \left(\frac{\partial A_y}{\partial x} - \frac{\partial A_x}{\partial y} \right) dS = \int_{C(S)} d\sigma_x A_y - d\sigma_y A_x \tag{3-191}$$

and if we now write

$$d\boldsymbol{\sigma} = \mathbf{e}_x\, d\sigma_x + \mathbf{e}_y\, d\sigma_y = \mathbf{n}\, d\sigma \tag{3-192}$$

and

$$\mathbf{A} = A_x \mathbf{e}_x + A_y \mathbf{e}_y \tag{3-193}$$

then it follows from Eq. (3-29) that Eq. (3-191) can be written as the single vector equation,

$$\int_S \boldsymbol{\nabla} \times \mathbf{A}\, dS = \int_{C(S)} d\boldsymbol{\sigma} \times \mathbf{A} \tag{3-194}$$

where $d\boldsymbol{\sigma} \times \mathbf{A} = \mathbf{n} \times \mathbf{A}\, d\sigma$ (3-195)

or

$$d\boldsymbol{\sigma} \times \mathbf{A} = \begin{vmatrix} \mathbf{e}_x & \mathbf{e}_y & \mathbf{e}_z \\ d\sigma_x & d\sigma_y & 0 \\ A_x & A_y & 0 \end{vmatrix} \tag{3-196}$$

Let $\mathbf{e}_z$ be a constant unit vector perpendicular to the x, y plane in which $C(S)$ is located. Forming the scalar product of $\mathbf{e}_z$ with Eq. (3-194) gives

$$\int_S \mathbf{e}_z \cdot (\boldsymbol{\nabla} \times \mathbf{A})\, dS = \int_{C(S)} \mathbf{e}_z \cdot (d\boldsymbol{\sigma} \times \mathbf{A}) \tag{3-197}$$

and using Eq. (1-71), we obtain

$$\int_S \mathbf{e}_z \cdot (\boldsymbol{\nabla} \times \mathbf{A})\, dS = \int_{C(S)} (\mathbf{e}_z \times d\boldsymbol{\sigma}) \cdot \mathbf{A} \tag{3-198}$$

Notice that $\mathbf{e}_z$ is perpendicular to $d\boldsymbol{\sigma}$ at each point of the curve $C(S)$. Hence $\mathbf{e}_z \times d\boldsymbol{\sigma}$ is a vector which is tangent to the curve $C(S)$ at each point. Since

$$|\mathbf{e}_z \times d\boldsymbol{\sigma}| = |\mathbf{e}_z|\, |d\boldsymbol{\sigma}| = d\sigma \tag{3-199}$$

we see that the magnitude of $\mathbf{e}_z \times d\boldsymbol{\sigma}$ is equal to $d\sigma$, which is the differential of arc on $C(S)$. Thus

$$d\mathbf{r} = \mathbf{T}\, d\sigma = \mathbf{e}_z \times d\boldsymbol{\sigma} \tag{3-200}$$

represents an infinitesimal displacement vector tangent to $C(S)$. Insertion of Eq. (3-200) into Eq. (3-198) yields

$$\int_S \mathbf{e}_z \cdot (\boldsymbol{\nabla} \times \mathbf{A})\, dS = \int_{C(S)} \mathbf{A} \cdot d\mathbf{r} \tag{3-201}$$

Equation (3-201) provides a physical interpretation of the curl of a vector field. The right-hand integral in Eq. (3-201),

$$\psi(\mathbf{A}) = \int_{C(S)} \mathbf{A} \cdot d\mathbf{r} \tag{3-202}$$

is called the "circulation" of the vector field $\mathbf{A}$ around the closed curve $C(S)$. The circulation $\psi(\mathbf{A})$ is a measure of the rotation or

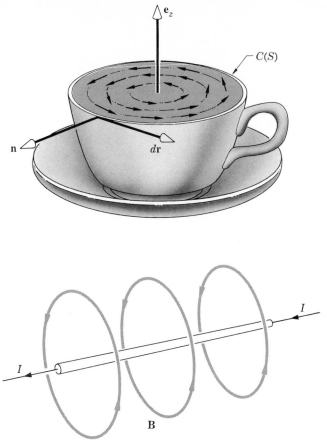

Figure 3-11 Coffee circulating around a coffee cup and a magnetic induction field **B** circulating around a current-carrying conductor.

vorticity associated with the field **A**. As an example, consider a cup of coffee which has just been stirred up. Suppose that **A** represents the velocity field of the coffee in the cup. Let $C(S)$ be the boundary curve of the cup. The outward normal **n** of the cup is a perfectly definite vector. Hence the direction of $d\mathbf{r}$ will be determined by whether we choose $\mathbf{e}_z$ to point out of or into the coffee at its top surface.

Suppose that we choose $\mathbf{e}_z$ to point out of the coffee at its top surface. The direction of $d\mathbf{r}$ is then counterclockwise looking down at the top of the coffee. A positive circulation $\psi(\mathbf{A})$ means that the coffee has been stirred into rotation in the counterclockwise direction, and a negative circulation means that the coffee is rotating in the clockwise direction. No circulation, $\psi(\mathbf{A}) = 0$, means either that the coffee has not been stirred or that it has come to rest. (The magnetic field surrounding a current-carrying conductor is another example of a vector field having a nonzero curl.)

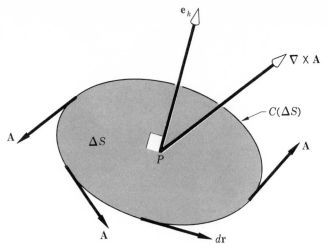

Figure 3-12 The curl of **A** at P is determined by computing the circulation of **A** around three mutually perpendicular infinitesimal disks intersecting at P.

We see from Eq. (3-201) that the component of curl **A** normal to a given plane must represent the circulation density, i.e., the circulation per unit surface area for that particular plane. The curl of **A**, however, is itself a vector; thus a knowledge of the circulation of **A** in only one plane involves only one component of the curl. To fully determine curl **A** at a point in space we must select three mutually perpendicular planes which intersect at the given point. The circulation is then computed about the point for all three planes as the three boundary curves shrink to zero. Then,

$$\mathbf{e}_k \cdot (\nabla \times \mathbf{A}) = \lim_{\Delta S \to 0} \frac{\int_{C(\Delta S)} \mathbf{A} \cdot d\mathbf{r}}{\Delta S} \qquad k = 1,2,3 \tag{3-203}$$

and

$$\nabla \times \mathbf{A} = \sum_{k=1}^{3} [\mathbf{e}_k \cdot (\nabla \times \mathbf{A})]\mathbf{e}_k \tag{3-204}$$

where $\mathbf{e}_k$ is the unit normal to the kth plane.

If **A** represents the velocity of a fluid, then $\mathbf{e}_k \cdot (\nabla \times \mathbf{A})$ represents the circulation created or destroyed per unit area per unit time in the plane perpendicular to $\mathbf{e}_k$. If $\nabla \times \mathbf{A} = 0$ throughout some volume of space, then the vector field **A** is said to be "irrotational" in that volume; otherwise we say that there are "sources" or "sinks" (or both) of vorticity present there.

REMARK: The student should carefully note that

$$\int_{S(V)} d\mathbf{S} \times \mathbf{A} = 0 = \int_V \nabla \times \mathbf{A} \, dV \tag{3-205}$$

does *not* imply that

$$\nabla \times \mathbf{A} = 0 \text{ throughout } V \tag{3-206}$$

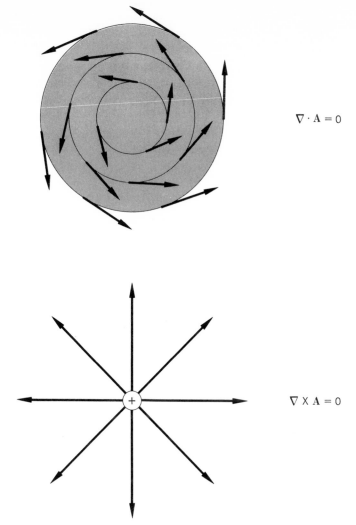

$$\nabla \cdot \mathbf{A} = 0$$

$$\nabla \times \mathbf{A} = 0$$

Figure 3-13 Solenoidal and irrotational vector fields.

It only implies that for each source of vorticity of given strength within V there is within V a sink of vorticity of equal strength. In order for

$$\int_V \boldsymbol{\nabla} \times \mathbf{A} \, dV = 0 \tag{3-207}$$

to imply

$$\boldsymbol{\nabla} \times \mathbf{A} = 0 \text{ throughout } V \tag{3-208}$$

Eq. (3-207) must hold for *any arbitrary volume contained within V.*
    In a similar way

$$\int_{S(V)} d\mathbf{S} \cdot \mathbf{A} = 0 = \int_V \boldsymbol{\nabla} \cdot \mathbf{A} \, dV \tag{3-209}$$

does not imply that

$$\boldsymbol{\nabla} \cdot \mathbf{A} = 0 \text{ throughout } V \tag{3-210}$$

It only implies that for each source of given strength which creates fluid inside V, there is a sink in V of equal strength which destroys fluid.

In order for

$$\int_V \nabla \cdot \mathbf{A} \, dV = 0 \qquad (3\text{-}211)$$

to imply

$$\nabla \cdot \mathbf{A} = 0 \text{ throughout } V \qquad (3\text{-}212)$$

Eq. (3-211) must hold for *any arbitrary volume contained within V.*

3-13 MNEMONIC OPERATORS

We have developed two sets of divergence, gradient, and curl theorems. They are easily remembered if we employ the following mnemonic operator equations:

$$\nabla = \frac{d\mathbf{S}}{dV} \qquad (3\text{-}213)$$

for operations involving the del operator and integration over a closed surface, and

$$\nabla = \frac{d\boldsymbol{\sigma}}{dS} \qquad (3\text{-}214)$$

for operations involving the del operator and integration around a closed curve.

If we note that

$$\nabla = \mathbf{e}_x \frac{\partial}{\partial x} + \mathbf{e}_y \frac{\partial}{\partial y} + \mathbf{e}_z \frac{\partial}{\partial z} \qquad (3\text{-}215)$$

then equating components in Eqs. (3-213) and (3-214) gives equations like

$$\frac{\partial}{\partial x} = \frac{dS_x}{dV} \qquad (3\text{-}216)$$

and

$$\frac{\partial}{\partial x} = \frac{d\sigma_x}{dS} \qquad (3\text{-}217)$$

which have already been introduced. To use Eqs. (3-213) and (3-214) we multiply them from the right with vector or scalar fields and treat dS/dV or $d\boldsymbol{\sigma}/dS$ as though they were fractions. For example,

$$\nabla = \frac{d\boldsymbol{\sigma}}{dS}$$

$$\nabla \times \mathbf{A} = \frac{d\boldsymbol{\sigma}}{dS} \times \mathbf{A}$$

$$\int_S \nabla \times \mathbf{A} \, dS = \int_{C(S)} d\boldsymbol{\sigma} \times \mathbf{A}$$

gives Eq. (3-194).

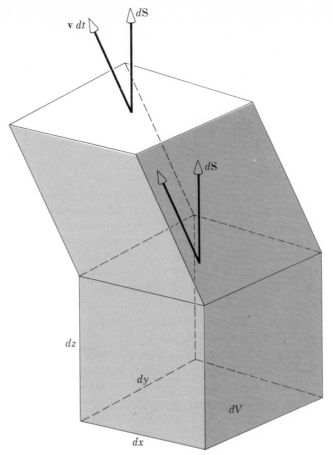

Figure 3-14 Change in volume of an infinitesimal cube.

3-14 KINEMATICS OF INFINITESIMAL VOLUME, SURFACE, AND LINE ELEMENTS

Consider an infinitesimal element of volume given by

$$dV = dx \, dy \, dz \tag{3-218}$$

Let one of the six faces of the infinitesimal cube dV be displaced through a distance

$$\mathbf{v} \, dt \tag{3-219}$$

while the other five faces remain fixed. If the surface element of the face which is displaced is given by $d\mathbf{S}$, then the volume swept out by $d\mathbf{S}$ as it moves through a displacement $\mathbf{v} \, dt$ forms a small parallelepiped of volume

$$(\mathbf{v} \, dt) \cdot (d\mathbf{S}) \tag{3-220}$$

The volume given by expression (3-220) represents the *change* in volume of the original infinitesimal cube (Fig. 3-14). Therefore, we write

$$d(dV) = d\mathbf{S} \cdot \mathbf{v}\, dt \tag{3-221}$$

However, Eq. (3-213) gives

$$d\mathbf{S} \cdot \mathbf{v}\, dt = (\boldsymbol{\nabla} \cdot \mathbf{v})\, dV\, dt \tag{3-222}$$

Hence

$$d(dV) = (\boldsymbol{\nabla} \cdot \mathbf{v})\, dV\, dt$$

or

$$\frac{d}{dt}(dV) = (\boldsymbol{\nabla} \cdot \mathbf{v})\, dV \tag{3-223}$$

Next let $d\mathbf{S}$ represent an element of surface area located in a plane and bounded by a plane curve of arbitrary shape. The direction of $d\mathbf{S}$ is normal to the plane, and we write

$$d\mathbf{S} = \mathbf{n}\, dS \tag{3-224}$$

where

$$|\mathbf{n}| = 1 \tag{3-225}$$

Let

$$d\mathbf{r} = \mathbf{T}\, ds \tag{3-226}$$
$$|\mathbf{T}| = 1$$

represent the local tangent displacement vector at any point of the curve which bounds $d\mathbf{S}$.

In the plane of $d\mathbf{S}$, let

$$d\boldsymbol{\sigma} = \mathbf{N}\, ds \tag{3-227}$$
$$|\mathbf{N}| = 1 \tag{3-228}$$
$$\mathbf{N} \cdot \mathbf{T} = 0 \tag{3-229}$$

where $d\boldsymbol{\sigma}$ points along the outward normal to any element of arc on the boundary of $d\mathbf{S}$. The unit vectors $(\mathbf{n},\mathbf{N},\mathbf{T})$ form a right-handed orthogonal system.

Thus,

$$\mathbf{n} \times \mathbf{N} = \mathbf{T} \tag{3-230}$$

and

$$\mathbf{N} \times \mathbf{T} = \mathbf{n} \tag{3-231}$$

Suppose that a portion of the boundary of $d\mathbf{S}$ represented by $d\mathbf{r}$ is displaced through a distance $\mathbf{v}\, dt$. The area swept out by $d\mathbf{r}$ as it moves through the displacement $\mathbf{v}\, dt$ forms an infinitesimal parallelogram whose edges are $\mathbf{v}\, dt$ and $d\mathbf{r}$. The directed area of this parallelogram is

$$(\mathbf{v}\, dt) \times d\mathbf{r} \tag{3-232}$$

The direction of the area in (3-232) is chosen to coincide with the direction of $d\mathbf{S}$ when $\mathbf{v}$ is parallel to $\mathbf{N}$ because then the area $d\mathbf{S}$

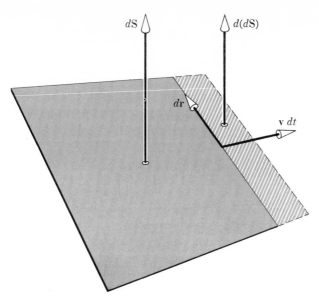

Figure 3-15 Change in a directed element of surface area.

expands. Hence the magnitude of $d\mathbf{S}$ must increase accordingly. The area given by (3-232) represents the *change* in the original infinitesimal area element $d\mathbf{S}$. Therefore we write

$$d(d\mathbf{S}) = (\mathbf{v}\,dt) \times d\mathbf{r} \tag{3-233}$$

However

$$d\mathbf{r} = \mathbf{n} \times d\boldsymbol{\sigma} \tag{3-234}$$

as a result of Eqs. (3-227), (3-230), and (3-226).
    Therefore,

$$d(d\mathbf{S}) = (\mathbf{v}\,dt) \times (\mathbf{n} \times d\boldsymbol{\sigma}) \tag{3-235}$$

or

$$d(d\mathbf{S}) = (\mathbf{v} \cdot d\boldsymbol{\sigma})\mathbf{n}\,dt - (\mathbf{v} \cdot \mathbf{n})\,d\boldsymbol{\sigma}\,dt \tag{3-236}$$

which gives

$$\frac{d}{dt}(d\mathbf{S}) = (\mathbf{v} \cdot d\boldsymbol{\sigma})\mathbf{n} - (\mathbf{v} \cdot \mathbf{n})\,d\boldsymbol{\sigma} \tag{3-237}$$

Using Eq. (3-214), then Eq. (3-237) becomes

$$\frac{d}{dt}(d\mathbf{S}) = (\boldsymbol{\nabla} \cdot \mathbf{v})\mathbf{n}\,dS - \boldsymbol{\nabla}(\mathbf{v} \cdot \mathbf{n})\,dS \tag{3-238}$$

and using Eq. (3-224),

$$\frac{d}{dt}(d\mathbf{S}) = (\boldsymbol{\nabla} \cdot \mathbf{v})\,d\mathbf{S} - \boldsymbol{\nabla}(\mathbf{v} \cdot \mathbf{n})\,dS \tag{3-239}$$

Finally, consider a line element

$$d\mathbf{r} = \mathbf{e}_x\,dx \tag{3-240}$$

Then

$$\mathbf{v} = \frac{d\mathbf{r}}{dt} = \mathbf{e}_x \frac{dx}{dt} = v_x \mathbf{e}_x \tag{3-241}$$

Let

$$dV = S \, dx \tag{3-242}$$

where S = constant. Then using Eq. (3-223) gives

$$\frac{d}{dt} (dV) = S \frac{d}{dt} (dx) = (\boldsymbol{\nabla} \cdot \mathbf{v}) S \, dx \tag{3-243}$$

but

$$\boldsymbol{\nabla} \cdot \mathbf{v} = \frac{\partial v_x}{\partial x} \tag{3-244}$$

Therefore

$$\frac{d}{dt} (dx) = \left(dx \frac{\partial}{\partial x} \right) v_x \tag{3-245}$$

which can be written in vector form as

$$\frac{d}{dt} (d\mathbf{r}) = (d\mathbf{r} \cdot \boldsymbol{\nabla})\mathbf{v} \tag{3-246}$$

3-15 KINEMATICS OF A VOLUME INTEGRAL

Suppose that $\rho(\mathbf{r},t)$ represents any per unit volume property of matter, for example, mass per unit volume. The total mass contained within a body whose scalar mass density is $\rho(\mathbf{r},t)$ is

$$m(t) = \int_{V(t)} \rho(\mathbf{r},t) \, dV \tag{3-247}$$

The mass $m(t)$ given by the volume integral (3-247) is a function of time for two reasons: first of all, because the density of material forming the body may itself change with time, and, secondly, because even if the density is independent of time, the volume of the body can change with time.

Consider, for example, a porous spherical shell expanding in air. The density of air within the sphere need not change with time. However, as the sphere expands, air enters its interior through the pores in the surface, thus increasing the total mass of air contained inside. The total time derivative of $m(t)$ is

$$\frac{dm}{dt} = \int_{V(t)} \left\{ \frac{d\rho}{dt} \, dV + \rho \frac{d}{dt} (dV) \right\} \tag{3-248}$$

There are two terms which contribute to Eq. (3-248). The first term arises from the spatial and temporal dependence of the density ρ. The second term has its origin in the time variation of the volume of any infinitesimal portion of the body.

Using Eq. (3-223),

$$\frac{dm}{dt} = \int_{V(t)} \left\{ \frac{d\rho}{dt} + \rho(\boldsymbol{\nabla} \cdot \mathbf{v}) \right\} dV \tag{3-249}$$

and since

$$\frac{d\rho}{dt} = \frac{\partial \rho}{\partial t} + (\mathbf{v} \cdot \mathbf{\nabla})\rho \qquad (3\text{-}250)$$

while

$$\mathbf{\nabla} \cdot (\rho\mathbf{v}) = (\mathbf{v} \cdot \mathbf{\nabla})\rho + \rho(\mathbf{\nabla} \cdot \mathbf{v}) \qquad (3\text{-}251)$$

Eq. (3-249) becomes

$$\frac{dm}{dt} = \int_{V(t)} \left\{ \frac{\partial \rho}{\partial t} + \mathbf{\nabla} \cdot (\rho\mathbf{v}) \right\} dV \qquad (3\text{-}252)$$

Thus

$$\frac{d}{dt} \int_{V(t)} \rho(\mathbf{r},t) \, dV = \int_{V(t)} \left\{ \frac{\partial \rho}{\partial t} + \mathbf{\nabla} \cdot (\rho\mathbf{v}) \right\} dV \qquad (3\text{-}253)$$

gives the total time derivative of a volume integral.

REMARK: If the total mass contained within a body does not change with time, then

$$\frac{dm}{dt} = 0 \qquad (3\text{-}254)$$

However, it does not follow from

$$\int_{V(t)} \left\{ \frac{\partial \rho}{\partial t} + \mathbf{\nabla} \cdot (\rho\mathbf{v}) \right\} dV = 0 \qquad (3\text{-}255)$$

that

$$\frac{\partial \rho}{\partial t} + \mathbf{\nabla} \cdot (\rho\mathbf{v}) = 0 \qquad (3\text{-}256)$$

Equation (3-255) merely implies that for each source of mass of given strength within V there is a sink of mass of equal strength within V. In order for Eq. (3-256) to hold throughout the volume $V(t)$, Eq. (3-255) must be valid not only for $V(t)$ but also for all volumes contained within $V(t)$. If the density of sources and sinks creating or destroying mass per unit time within V is given by $q(\mathbf{r},t)$, then

$$\frac{\partial \rho}{\partial t} + \mathbf{\nabla} \cdot (\rho\mathbf{v}) = q(\mathbf{r},t) \qquad (3\text{-}257)$$

where Eq. (3-257) is known as the "equation on continuity."

   If there are no sources or sinks present within V, then $q(\mathbf{r},t) = 0$ throughout V, and Eq. (3-257) reduces to Eq. (3-256). In this case mass is conserved within $V(t)$.

3-16 KINEMATICS OF A SURFACE INTEGRAL

Consider the flux of the vector field $\mathbf{A} = \mathbf{A}(\mathbf{r},t)$. It is given by the surface integral

$$\Phi(t) = \int_{S(t)} \mathbf{A} \cdot d\mathbf{S} \qquad (3\text{-}258)$$

The flux $\Phi(t)$, which crosses the surface $S(t)$, is a function of time because $\mathbf{A}$ depends explicitly on time. Even if $\mathbf{A}$ is time-independent, Φ still depends on time when the surface S deforms or moves through space as a function of time. The total time derivative of $\Phi(t)$ is given by

$$\frac{d\Phi}{dt} = \int_{S(t)} \left\{ \frac{d\mathbf{A}}{dt} \cdot d\mathbf{S} + \mathbf{A} \cdot \frac{d}{dt}(d\mathbf{S}) \right\} \tag{3-259}$$

The first term in the integrand of Eq. (3-259) arises from the spatial and temporal variation of $\mathbf{A}$. The second term originates in the time-dependent motion of each infinitesimal surface element of $S(t)$. We shall evaluate the surface integral (3-259) for any polyhedral surface, i.e., a surface whose faces are polygons. The result which we shall obtain will apply not only to polyhedral surfaces but to all smooth curved surfaces as well. This follows because a smooth curved surface can be approximated by an inscribed or circumscribed polyhedron. The area of each face of the approximating polyhedron is allowed to approach zero while the number of faces increases without bound. The limiting polyhedral surface converges to the given smooth curved surface.

Using Eq. (3-239),

$$\mathbf{A} \cdot \frac{d}{dt}(d\mathbf{S}) = (\nabla \cdot \mathbf{v})\mathbf{A} \cdot d\mathbf{S} - dS(\mathbf{A} \cdot \nabla)(\mathbf{v} \cdot \mathbf{n}) \tag{3-260}$$

$$(\mathbf{A} \cdot \nabla)(\mathbf{v} \cdot \mathbf{n}) = \mathbf{n} \cdot (\mathbf{A} \cdot \nabla)\mathbf{v} + \mathbf{v} \cdot (\mathbf{A} \cdot \nabla)\mathbf{n} \tag{3-261}$$

The surface $S(t)$ is assumed to be a convex polyhedron. Therefore the outward unit normal $\mathbf{n}$ at any interior point on a face of the polyhedron is a constant vector. This follows because each face is flat. Therefore,

$$(\mathbf{A} \cdot \nabla)\mathbf{n} = 0 \tag{3-262}$$

and

$$\mathbf{A} \cdot \frac{d}{dt}(d\mathbf{S}) = (\nabla \cdot \mathbf{v})\mathbf{A} \cdot d\mathbf{S} - dS \cdot (\mathbf{A} \cdot \nabla)\mathbf{v} \tag{3-263}$$

$$d\mathbf{S} \cdot \frac{d\mathbf{A}}{dt} + \mathbf{A} \cdot \frac{d}{dt}(d\mathbf{S})$$
$$= d\mathbf{S} \cdot \left\{ \frac{\partial \mathbf{A}}{\partial t} + (\mathbf{v} \cdot \nabla)\mathbf{A} + (\nabla \cdot \mathbf{v})\mathbf{A} - (\mathbf{A} \cdot \nabla)\mathbf{v} \right\} \tag{3-264}$$

Notice that

$$(\nabla \cdot \mathbf{A})\mathbf{v} - \nabla \times (\mathbf{v} \times \mathbf{A}) = (\mathbf{v} \cdot \nabla)\mathbf{A} - (\mathbf{A} \cdot \nabla)\mathbf{v} + (\nabla \cdot \mathbf{v})\mathbf{A} \tag{3-265}$$

Hence

$$d\mathbf{S} \cdot \frac{d\mathbf{A}}{dt} + \mathbf{A} \cdot \frac{d}{dt}(d\mathbf{S}) = d\mathbf{S} \cdot \left\{ \frac{\partial \mathbf{A}}{\partial t} - \nabla \times (\mathbf{v} \times \mathbf{A}) + (\nabla \cdot \mathbf{A})\mathbf{v} \right\} \tag{3-266}$$

It follows from Eq. (3-266) that

$$\frac{d}{dt}\int_{S(t)} \mathbf{A} \cdot d\mathbf{S} = \int_{S(t)} d\mathbf{S} \cdot \left\{ \frac{\partial \mathbf{A}}{\partial t} - \nabla \times (\mathbf{v} \times \mathbf{A}) + (\nabla \cdot \mathbf{A})\mathbf{v} \right\} \tag{3-267}$$

Furthermore, Eq. (3-267) applies not only to a polyhedral surface, but to any smooth curved surface $S(t)$ as well.

3-17 KINEMATICS OF A LINE INTEGRAL

Consider the circulation of the vector field $\mathbf{A} = \mathbf{A}(\mathbf{r},t)$. It is given by the line integral

$$\psi(t) = \int_{C(t)} \mathbf{A} \cdot d\mathbf{r} \tag{3-268}$$

The circulation $\psi(t)$ around the curve $C(t)$ is a function of time due to the time dependence of $\mathbf{A}$. Even if $\mathbf{A}$ does not depend on time, ψ is still time-dependent provided that the curve C deforms or moves through space as a function of time.

The total time derivative of $\psi(t)$ is given by

$$\frac{d\psi}{dt} = \int_{C(t)} \left\{ \frac{d\mathbf{A}}{dt} \cdot d\mathbf{r} + \mathbf{A} \cdot \frac{d}{dt}(d\mathbf{r}) \right\} \tag{3-269}$$

The first term in the integrand of Eq. (3-269) arises from the spatial and temporal variation of $\mathbf{A}$. The second term originates in the time-dependent motion of each infinitesimal piece of the curve $C(t)$. We shall evaluate the line integral (3-269) for any polygonal curve $C(t)$, i.e., a curve whose sides are straight lines. The result which we shall obtain will apply not only to polygonal curves but to all smooth curves as well. This follows because a smooth curve can be approximated by an inscribed or circumscribed polygon. The length of each side of the approximating polygon is allowed to approach zero while the number of sides increases without bound. The limiting polygon converges to the given smooth curve.

For a polygonal curve each side is a straight line. Therefore Eq. (3-246) is applicable since it was derived for the differential line element of a straight line. Then Eq. (3-269) becomes

$$\frac{d}{dt} \int_{C(t)} \mathbf{A} \cdot d\mathbf{r} = \int_{C(t)} \left\{ \frac{d\mathbf{A}}{dt} \cdot d\mathbf{r} + \mathbf{A} \cdot (d\mathbf{r} \cdot \boldsymbol{\nabla})\mathbf{v} \right\} \tag{3-270}$$

or

$$\frac{d}{dt} \int_{C(t)} \mathbf{A} \cdot d\mathbf{r} = \int_{C(t)} \left\{ \frac{\partial \mathbf{A}}{\partial t} \cdot d\mathbf{r} + d\mathbf{r} \cdot (\mathbf{v} \cdot \boldsymbol{\nabla})\mathbf{A} + \mathbf{A} \cdot (d\mathbf{r} \cdot \boldsymbol{\nabla})\mathbf{v} \right\} \tag{3-271}$$

Moreover, Eqs. (3-270) and (3-271) apply not only to a polygonal curve but to any smooth curve $C(t)$ as well. Using Eq. (3-271), we can recover Leibniz's rule for evaluating the expression

$$\frac{d}{dt} \int_{a(t)}^{b(t)} A(x,t)\, dx \tag{3-272}$$

Let

$$\mathbf{A} = A(x,t)\mathbf{e}_x \tag{3-273}$$

and

$$\mathbf{r} = x(t)\mathbf{e}_x \tag{3-274}$$

Then

$$\mathbf{v} = \frac{d\mathbf{r}}{dt} = \frac{dx}{dt}\,\mathbf{e}_x = v_x\mathbf{e}_x \tag{3-275}$$

$$\mathbf{A} \cdot d\mathbf{r} = A\,(x,t)\,dx \tag{3-276}$$

$$d\mathbf{r} \cdot (\mathbf{v} \cdot \nabla)\mathbf{A} + \mathbf{A} \cdot (d\mathbf{r} \cdot \nabla)\mathbf{v} = dx\,v_x\frac{\partial A}{\partial x} + dx\,A\,\frac{\partial v_x}{\partial x} \tag{3-277}$$

or

$$d\mathbf{r} \cdot (\mathbf{v} \cdot \nabla)\mathbf{A} + \mathbf{A} \cdot (d\mathbf{r} \cdot \nabla)\mathbf{v} = dx\,\frac{\partial}{\partial x}\,(v_x A) \tag{3-278}$$

Thus,

$$\frac{d}{dt}\int_{a(t)}^{b(t)} A\,(x,t)\,dx = \int_{a(t)}^{b(t)} \frac{\partial A}{\partial t}\,dx + \int_{a(t)}^{b(t)} dx\,\frac{\partial}{\partial x}\,(v_x A) \tag{3-279}$$

and finally,

$$\frac{d}{dt}\int_{a(t)}^{b(t)} A\,(x,t)\,dx = A[b(t),t]b'(t) - A[a(t),t]a'(t)$$
$$+ \int_{a(t)}^{b(t)} \frac{\partial A}{\partial t}\,dx \tag{3-280}$$

3-18 SOLID ANGLE

Consider an element of surface area

$$d\mathbf{S} = \mathbf{n}\,dS \tag{3-281}$$

having a position vector $\mathbf{r}$ with respect to some arbitrary point P. The unit normal to dS is given by $\mathbf{n}$. If we now draw straight lines from P to the boundary points of dS, then these lines will be the generators of an infinitesimal cone with vertex at P and base dS. The solid angular measure $d\Omega$ of this cone is called the solid angle subtended by dS at P (Fig. 3-16), and it is defined by

$$d\Omega = \frac{\mathbf{r} \cdot d\mathbf{S}}{|\mathbf{r}|^3} \tag{3-282}$$

The total solid angle of a surface S is therefore

$$\Omega = \iint_S \frac{\mathbf{r} \cdot d\mathbf{S}}{|\mathbf{r}|^3} \tag{3-283}$$

or

$$\Omega = \iint_S \nabla\left(\frac{-1}{r}\right) \cdot d\mathbf{S} \tag{3-284}$$

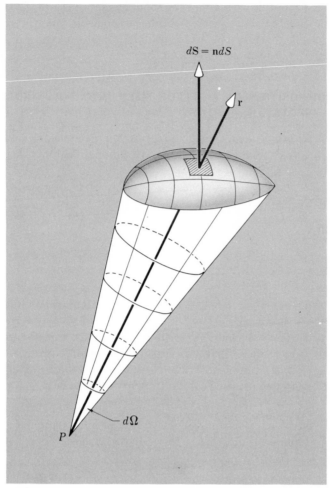

$dS = \mathbf{n}\,dS$

$\mathbf{r}$

$d\Omega$

P

Figure 3-16 Solid angle $d\Omega$ subtended by dS at P.

$3\text{-}16$

EXAMPLE 3-7: Let S be a sphere and P its origin; then

$$\Omega(P) = \iint_S \frac{\mathbf{r}}{|\mathbf{r}|^3} \cdot \left(\frac{\mathbf{r}}{|\mathbf{r}|}\,dS\right)$$

and

$$\Omega(P) = \iint_S \frac{dS}{|\mathbf{r}|^2}$$

For a sphere centered at P,

$$dS = |\mathbf{r}|^2 \sin\theta\,d\theta\,d\phi$$

Thus

$$\Omega(P) = \iint_S \sin\theta\,d\theta\,d\phi = 4\pi \tag{3-285}$$

From this we see that the solid angular measure of a cone is numerically equal to the area which the cone cuts from the surface of a unit sphere when the vertex of the cone is at the center of the sphere and the base of the cone is on the surface.

3-19 DECOMPOSITION OF A VECTOR FIELD INTO SOLENOIDAL AND IRROTATIONAL PARTS

It is often convenient to represent a given vector field $\mathbf{u}$ as a sum of a solenoidal field $\mathbf{u}_S$ and an irrotational field $\mathbf{u}_I$. Then

$$\mathbf{u} = \mathbf{u}_S + \mathbf{u}_I \tag{3-286}$$

where

$$\nabla \cdot \mathbf{u}_S = 0 \tag{3-287}$$

and

$$\nabla \times \mathbf{u}_I = 0 \tag{3-288}$$

Three questions immediately arise:

1. Under what conditions can the decomposition indicated in Eq. (3-286) be performed?
2. How can the unknown fields $\mathbf{u}_S$ and $\mathbf{u}_I$ be computed given the field $\mathbf{u}$?
3. Under what circumstances is the decomposition in Eq. (3-286) unique? Uniqueness here means that for a given $\mathbf{u}$ there is one and only one pair of vectors $(\mathbf{u}_S, \mathbf{u}_I)$ which can satisfy Eq. (3-286).

As is often the case in mathematics, one sidesteps the issues involved by introducing new variables. The original problem is then rephrased in terms of these new variables. Thus a solution of Eq. (3-287) is given by

$$\mathbf{u}_S = \nabla \times \mathbf{A} \tag{3-289}$$

and a solution of Eq. (3-286) is

$$\mathbf{u}_I = \nabla \phi \tag{3-290}$$

assuming that $\nabla \cdot (\nabla \times \mathbf{A}) = 0$ and $\nabla \times (\nabla \phi) = 0$.

It follows from Eqs. (3-286) to (3-288) that

$$\nabla \cdot \mathbf{u}_I = \nabla \cdot \mathbf{u} \tag{3-291}$$

and

$$\nabla \times \mathbf{u}_S = \nabla \times \mathbf{u} \tag{3-292}$$

Hence Eqs. (3-289) and (3-290) become

$$\nabla^2 \phi = \nabla \cdot \mathbf{u} \tag{3-293}$$

$$\nabla \times \nabla \times \mathbf{A} = \nabla \times \mathbf{u} \tag{3-294}$$

The right-hand sides of Eqs. (3-293) and (3-294) are thought of as known quantities because $\mathbf{u}$ is given.

The three components of Eq. (3-294) together with Eq. (3-293) give a set of four partial differential equations in four unknowns.

These unknowns are the three components of $\mathbf{A}$ and the unknown scalar ϕ. When Eqs. (3-293) and (3-294) can be solved for ϕ and $\mathbf{A}$,

$$\mathbf{u} = \nabla\phi + \nabla \times \mathbf{A} \qquad (3\text{-}295)$$

gives the desired decomposition of $\mathbf{u}$. The function ϕ is called the "scalar" potential of $\mathbf{u}$, and $\mathbf{A}$ is known as the "vector" potential of $\mathbf{u}$. Thus we can perform the decomposition indicated in Eq. (3-286), provided that the vector and scalar potentials associated with $\mathbf{u}$ can be found. The fields $\mathbf{u}_s$ and $\mathbf{u}_I$ are then calculated from Eqs. (3-289) and (3-290). The decomposition in Eq. (3-286) is not necessarily unique because it is always possible to choose

$$\phi = \phi_0 + \phi_1 \qquad (3\text{-}296)$$

and

$$\mathbf{A} = \mathbf{A}_0 + \mathbf{A}_1 \qquad (3\text{-}297)$$

where ϕ_0 and $\mathbf{A}_0$ are solutions of Eqs. (3-293) and (3-294) while ϕ_1 and $\mathbf{A}_1$ are arbitrary solutions of

$$\nabla^2\phi_1 = 0 \qquad (3\text{-}298)$$

and

$$\nabla \times \nabla \times \mathbf{A} = 0 \qquad (3\text{-}299)$$

We will show in Chap. 7 that if the curl and divergence of $\mathbf{u}$ are known throughout the interior of a sphere, then the decomposition in Eq. (3-286) is unique when the *normal component* of $\mathbf{u}$ is specified on the boundary of the sphere.

3-20 INTEGRAL THEOREMS FOR DISCONTINUOUS AND UNBOUNDED FUNCTIONS

In Secs. 3-5 through 3-12 several integral theorems were developed for integration over a closed contour. For theorems involving *integration around a closed contour* it is assumed that the *closed contour forms* the *boundary* of an *open surface* such as a cup or a disk. A hollow sphere with two holes punched in its surface is also an open surface. The total boundary curve of this twice-punctured sphere can be constructed by taking a pair of scissors and making a cut in the surface of the sphere running from the first hole to the second. The total boundary contour then consists of the edges of the two holes plus the two edges of the scissor cut. The direction in which the boundary curve is to be traversed is such that a man walking on the outer surface of the sphere and along the boundary curve finds the surface always lying to his left. This convention is consistent with the formulas in Sec. 3-12. If the hollow sphere has n holes punched in its surface, then the total boundary of the punctured surface consists of the edges of the n holes plus $2(n - 1)$ edges associated with $n - 1$ scissor cuts. These cuts are arranged so that the first cut runs from hole 1 to hole 2, the second cut runs from

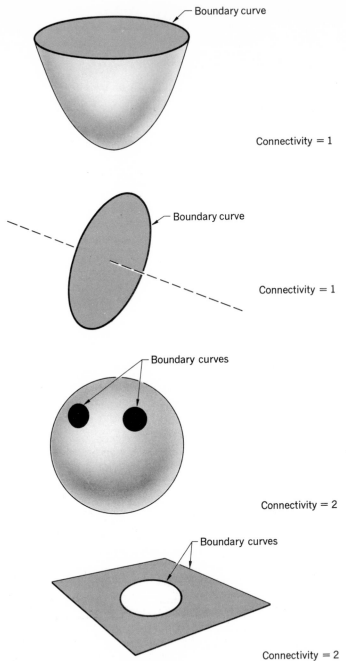

Figure 3-17 Examples of some open surfaces and their boundary curves.

hole 2 to hole 3, and so on. The last cut, which is numbered $n - 1$, connects the $(n - 1)$st hole with the nth hole.

An open surface is called "simply connected" if it has the property that *every* scissor cut starting at one point on a boundary and finishing at another boundary point separates the surface into

VECTOR CALCULUS

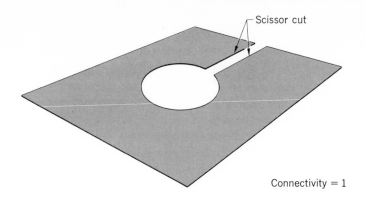

Scissor cut

Connectivity = 1

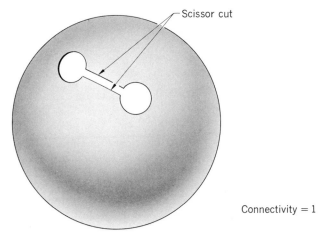

Scissor cut

Connectivity = 1

Figure 3-18 A doubly connected surface is made singly connected by introducing a scissor cut.

unconnected pieces. Thus both a hollow sphere with one hole punched in its surface and the face of a dime are examples of simply connected surfaces. The connectivity of an open surface is 1 plus the number of scissor cuts which can be made *without* separating the surface into two pieces. Thus a spherical surface with n holes and no scissor cuts is of connectivity n. Therefore it is called "multiply connected" if $n \geq 2$. After $n - 1$ scissor cuts are made in the surface, the connectivity is reduced to unity, and the surface is called "simply connected" $(n = 1)$. This is because no further cuts can be made without separating the surface into two pieces.

The same considerations apply to flat surfaces as well. For example, although a disk is simply connected, an annulus is doubly connected $(n = 2)$. This follows because one scissor cut can be made between the two boundary circles of the annulus without separating the annulus into two unconnected parts. These topological considerations are important because all the results of Secs. 3-9 through 3-12 require that the closed curve of integration referred to there be the total boundary of an *open simply connected* surface. Thus scissor cuts must be introduced when necessary to make the open surface simply connected.

In all the integral theorems of Secs. 3-5 through 3-12 it was assumed that the integrand of each integral was an *integrable* function. Roughly speaking, a function is integrable if its behavior is not too irregular, and if the values which it takes are not too large too often. A more precise description of the concept of integrability requires a knowledge of measure theory and is beyond the scope of this book. We shall, however, accept certain elementary results of measure theory. We need these in order to state the conditions under which the integral theorems of Secs. 3-5 through 3-12 are *always* applicable.

The measure of a set of points is a number which often has a natural geometric interpretation. For example, the measure of the set of points represented by a curve is the length of the curve. The measure of the set of points represented by a surface is the area of the surface, and the measure of the point set represented by a solid is the volume of the solid. For our purposes, a set of finite measure means a curve of finite length, a surface of finite area, or a solid of finite volume. The integrands appearing in the integral theorems of Secs. 3-5 to 3-12 are defined throughout volumes, over surfaces, or along curves. These integrands (or their components if they are vectors) are said to satisfy *Dirichlet's conditions* on a set if:

1. They are bounded throughout the set.
2. They have only a finite number of maxima and minima on the set.
3. They have no more than a finite number of (finite) discontinuities over the whole set.

A basic result of measure theory which we shall accept without proof is the following:

If a function satisfies Dirichlet's conditions on a set of finite measure, then it is integrable on that set.

For example, if each component of a vector field satisfies Dirichlet's conditions throughout a sphere of finite volume, then the volume integral of this vector field exists for the given sphere.

To see how an integral theorem is modified when Dirichlet's conditions are not satisfied, we shall consider some particular cases. For example, the three-dimensional divergence theorem

$$\int_V \boldsymbol{\nabla} \cdot \mathbf{A} \, dV = \int_{S(V)} d\mathbf{S} \cdot \mathbf{A} \tag{3-300}$$

for a solid sphere of volume V is valid when $\boldsymbol{\nabla} \cdot \mathbf{A}$ satisfies Dirichlet's conditions throughout V and $\mathbf{A}$ satisfies these conditions everywhere on $\mathbf{S}(\mathbf{V})$. In many applications, $\boldsymbol{\nabla} \cdot \mathbf{A}$ becomes infinite at certain points, or along a certain curve or surface, or even throughout an entire volume, contained within V. When this happens, $\boldsymbol{\nabla} \cdot \mathbf{A}$ is no longer bounded throughout V, and therefore the first Dirichlet condition is violated.

Even in this case Eq. (3-300) will remain valid if the volume and surface integrals in it exist and remain finite. However, the application of Eq. (3-300) then requires detailed information on how rapidly $\nabla \cdot \mathbf{A}$ becomes infinite as each singular point in V is approached. This information is needed in order to determine whether or not the volume integral remains finite. As an alternative procedure, the point or points at which $\nabla \cdot \mathbf{A}$ becomes infinite can be removed from the volume of integration. We remove these points, at which $\nabla \cdot \mathbf{A}$ becomes infinite, from V by enclosing each such point in a small bubble of finite radius. We then remove the entire contents of each bubble from the region V. What remains is a sphere with a number of small cavities in its interior. The volume of the remaining sphere is V' where V' is numerically equal to the volume V of the original sphere minus the total volume of the cavities.

Now $\nabla \cdot \mathbf{A}$ satisfies Dirichlet's conditions throughout the new volume V', and $\mathbf{A}$ satisfies them on $S(V')$; therefore,

$$\int_{V'} \nabla \cdot \mathbf{A} \, dV = \int_{S(V')} d\mathbf{S} \cdot \mathbf{A} \tag{3-301}$$

The volume V' is bounded externally by the original spherical surface $S(V)$ and internally by the walls of the cavities created by removing the bubbles from V. The important point to remember is that on a boundary surface $d\mathbf{S}$ *points out of the region of integration*. Hence, on the external surface of V', $d\mathbf{S}$ always points out of V', while on an internal surface of V', $d\mathbf{S}$ always points *toward the interior of the cavity* enclosed by the internal surface.

Surface discontinuities

If the vector field $\mathbf{A}(\mathbf{r})$ has different values on two sides of a given open surface contained within V, then Eq. (3-146) implies that $\nabla \cdot \mathbf{A}$ becomes infinite along the given surface. Let this surface of discontinuity be labeled $S(d)$. If V is any volume which contains $S(d)$, then $\nabla \cdot \mathbf{A}$ is unbounded in V. Therefore, in order to apply the divergence theorem to $\mathbf{A}$, we shall remove $S(d)$ from V by forming a cavity about $S(d)$. This of course assumes that $S(d)$ is a set of finite measure. The new volume of integration is called V'. It is bounded externally by a convex surface of arbitrary shape and internally by the wall of the cavity containing $S(d)$. If $S(E)$ represents the external boundary surface of V', and $S(I)$ represents the internal boundary surface of V', then Eq. (3-301) gives

$$\int_{V'} \nabla \cdot \mathbf{A} \, dV = \int_{S(E)} d\mathbf{S} \cdot \mathbf{A} + \int_{S(I)} d\mathbf{S} \cdot \mathbf{A} \tag{3-302}$$

The original quantity of physical interest is

$$\int_{V} \nabla \cdot \mathbf{A} \, dV \tag{3-303}$$

which is recovered by shrinking the wall $S(I)$ of the interior cavity

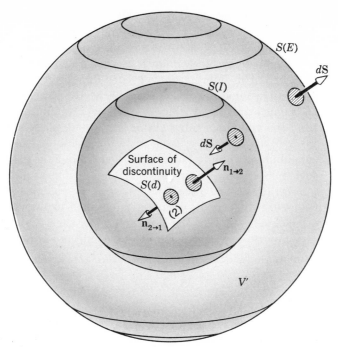

Figure 3-19 Removing a surface of discontinuity by enclosing it in a bubble.

until it coincides with the open surface of discontinuity $S(d)$. Then $V' \rightarrow V$, and we obtain

$$\int_V \boldsymbol{\nabla} \cdot \mathbf{A} \, dV = \int_{S(E)} d\mathbf{S} \cdot \mathbf{A} + \int_{S_1(I)} d\mathbf{S} \cdot \mathbf{A} + \int_{S_2(I)} d\mathbf{S} \cdot \mathbf{A} \qquad (3\text{-}304)$$

where $S(I) = S_1(I) + S_2(I)$. The surface of discontinuity has two sides labeled 1 and 2, respectively. The unit normal at any point on side 2 is labeled $\mathbf{n}_{1\rightarrow 2}$, indicating that this unit normal is directed from side 1 toward side 2. Similarly the unit normal on side 1 is labeled $\mathbf{n}_{2\rightarrow 1}$, and it points from side 2 toward side 1.

On $S(I)$, $d\mathbf{S}$ points *toward the interior of the cavity about* $S(d)$. The piece of $S(I)$ labeled $S_2(I)$ approaches side 2 of $S(d)$ as the cavity vanishes. On $S_2(I)$

$$d\mathbf{S} = -\mathbf{n}_{1\rightarrow 2} \, dS \qquad (3\text{-}305)$$

The piece of $S(I)$ labeled $S_1(I)$ approaches side 1 of $S(d)$ and on $S_1(I)$

$$d\mathbf{S} = -\mathbf{n}_{2\rightarrow 1} \, dS \qquad (3\text{-}306)$$

The minus signs in Eqs. (3-305) and (3-306) are required in order that $d\mathbf{S}$ always points *out* of the *region* of *integration* and *into* the *interior* of the cavity bounded by $S(I)$. Observing that

$$\mathbf{n}_{1\rightarrow 2} = -\mathbf{n}_{2\rightarrow 1} \qquad (3\text{-}307)$$

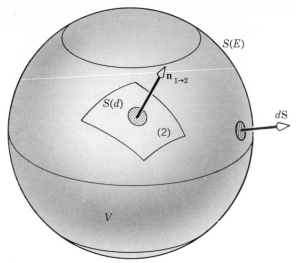

Figure 3-20 The modified domain of integration for a three-dimensional integral theorem involving a surface of discontinuity.

Eq. (3-304) becomes

$$\int_V \nabla \cdot \mathbf{A} \, dV = \int_{S(E)} d\mathbf{S} \cdot \mathbf{A} + \int_{S(d)} dS \, \mathbf{n}_{1 \to 2} \cdot (\mathbf{A}_1 - \mathbf{A}_2) \qquad (3\text{-}308)$$

where $\mathbf{A}_1$ is the value of $\mathbf{A}$ on side 1 of $S(d)$, and $\mathbf{A}_2$ is the value of $\mathbf{A}$ on side 2 of $S(d)$. Equation (3-308) is occasionally written in the form

$$\int_V \nabla \cdot \mathbf{A} \, dV + \int_{S(d)} dS \, \mathbf{n}_{1 \to 2} \cdot (\mathbf{A}_2 - \mathbf{A}_1) = \int_{S(E)} d\mathbf{S} \cdot \mathbf{A} \qquad (3\text{-}309)$$

If $\nabla \cdot \mathbf{A} = 0$ throughout volume V, then the flux which crosses $S(E)$ is generated by the jump in $\mathbf{A}$ across the surface of discontinuity $S(d)$. We think of the jump in the normal component of $\mathbf{A}$ across $S(d)$ as being caused by the presence of surface sources on $S(d)$. In support of this idea we define a *surface divergence* or *flux per unit surface area* by

$$\text{Div } \mathbf{A} = \mathbf{n}_{1 \to 2} \cdot (\mathbf{A}_2 - \mathbf{A}_1) \qquad (3\text{-}310)$$

and, using Eq. (3-310), we rewrite Eq. (3-309) as

$$\int_V \nabla \cdot \mathbf{A} \, dV + \int_{S(d)} \text{Div } \mathbf{A} \, dS = \int_{S(E)} d\mathbf{S} \cdot \mathbf{A} \qquad (3\text{-}311)$$

The capital letter D in Div $\mathbf{A}$ is used to indicate that a surface divergence is meant. A volume divergence, div $\mathbf{A}$ or $\nabla \cdot \mathbf{A}$, measures the volume density of sources of flux. A surface divergence, Div $\mathbf{A}$, measures the surface density of sources of flux.

The jump in $\mathbf{A}$ across $S(d)$ may also cause $\nabla \times \mathbf{A}$ to become infinite on $S(d)$. The preceding argument leads to the following generalized form of the three-dimensional curl theorem:

$$\int_V \nabla \times \mathbf{A} \, dV + \int_{S(d)} \text{Curl } \mathbf{A} \, dS = \int_{S(E)} d\mathbf{S} \times \mathbf{A} \qquad (3\text{-}312)$$

The surface curl is written with a capital C, and it is defined by

$$\text{Curl } \mathbf{A} = \mathbf{n}_{1 \to 2} \times (\mathbf{A}_2 - \mathbf{A}_1) \tag{3-313}$$

Jumps in the *tangential components* of **A** are thought of as being caused by the presence of *surface sources* of *circulation* or *vorticity*. The surface curl measures the surface density of such sources on $S(d)$.

If ϕ is a scalar point function which has different values on two sides of a given open surface $S(d)$ contained within V, then $\nabla \phi$ may become infinite on $S(d)$. The corresponding generalized three-dimensional gradient theorem, obtained by the same arguments as above, is

$$\int_V \nabla \phi \, dV + \int_{S(d)} \text{Grad } \phi \, dS = \int_{S(E)} d\mathbf{S} \, \phi \tag{3-314}$$

The surface gradient is written with a capital G, and it is defined by

$$\text{Grad } \phi = \mathbf{n}_{1 \to 2} (\phi_2 - \phi_1) \tag{3-315}$$

Summary

We have demonstrated how to modify a three-dimensional integral theorem when the volume of integration contains an open surface of discontinuity. The modification requires the introduction of *surface* divergence, curl, and gradient operators defined by

$$\text{Div } \mathbf{A} = \mathbf{n}_{1 \to 2} \cdot (\mathbf{A}_2 - \mathbf{A}_1) \tag{3-316}$$

$$\text{Curl } \mathbf{A} = \mathbf{n}_{1 \to 2} \times (\mathbf{A}_2 - \mathbf{A}_1) \tag{3-317}$$

$$\text{Grad } \phi = \mathbf{n}_{1 \to 2} (\phi_2 - \phi_1) \tag{3-318}$$

The corresponding modified integral theorems are

$$\int_V \nabla \cdot \mathbf{A} \, dV + \int_{S(d)} \text{Div } \mathbf{A} \, dS = \int_{S(E)} d\mathbf{S} \cdot \mathbf{A} \tag{3-319}$$

$$\int_V \nabla \times \mathbf{A} \, dV + \int_{S(d)} \text{Curl } \mathbf{A} \, dS = \int_{S(E)} d\mathbf{S} \times \mathbf{A} \tag{3-320}$$

$$\int_V \nabla \phi \, dV + \int_{S(d)} \text{Grad } \phi \, dS = \int_{S(E)} d\mathbf{S} \, \phi \tag{3-321}$$

Line discontinuities

Formulas corresponding to Eqs. (3-316) to (3-321) can be derived for two-dimensional integral theorems as well. For example, if the vector field $\mathbf{A(r)}$ has different values on two sides of a given open curve which lies upon a simply connected open surface, then $\nabla \cdot \mathbf{A}$ becomes infinite along the given curve. Let this curve of discontinuity be labeled $C(d)$. If S is any surface area which contains $C(d)$, then $\nabla \cdot \mathbf{A}$ is unbounded in S. Therefore, in order to apply the two-dimensional divergence theorem to $\mathbf{A}$, we shall remove $C(d)$ from S. To remove $C(d)$ from S, we cut out a piece of surface from S large enough to contain all of $C(d)$. The curve $C(d)$ is of finite length and is assumed not to cross itself. For example, S could be a disk of radius R, and $C(d)$ can be the arc of a semicircle of radius $r < R$.

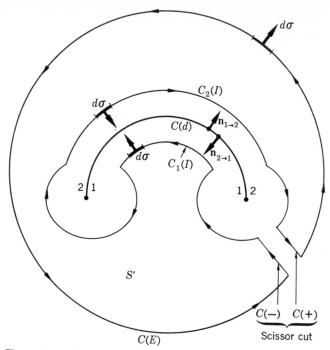

Figure 3-21 Cutting out the curve of discontinuity $C(d)$.

The new surface S' obtained by removing $C(d)$ from S is doubly connected $(n = 2)$. This follows because the process of cutting a hole in a simply connected $(n = 1)$ open surface increases its connectivity by 1. In order to apply a two-dimensional integral theorem to the doubly connected open surface S', it must first be made simply connected. This is accomplished by making a scissor cut from the original edge of S to the new edge created by removing $C(d)$ from S. The direction of traversal on the boundary of S' is chosen so that S' always lies to the left. The open simply connected surface of integration S' is bounded externally by a convex curve of arbitrary shape and internally by the edge of the hole containing $C(d)$. In addition, there are two boundary edges associated with the scissor cut joining the external and internal boundaries of S'. Let $C(E)$ represent the external boundary of S' and $C(I)$ represent the internal boundary of S'. Suppose that the two edges of the scissor cut are represented by $C(+)$ and $C(-)$, respectively. Then the two-dimensional divergence theorem becomes

$$\int_{S'} \boldsymbol{\nabla} \cdot \mathbf{A}\, dS = \int_{C(S')} d\boldsymbol{\sigma} \cdot \mathbf{A} \tag{3-322}$$

where

$$\int_{C(S')} d\boldsymbol{\sigma} \cdot \mathbf{A} = \int_{C(E)} d\boldsymbol{\sigma} \cdot \mathbf{A} + \int_{C(I)} d\boldsymbol{\sigma} \cdot \mathbf{A} + \int_{C(+)} d\boldsymbol{\sigma} \cdot \mathbf{A}$$

$$+ \int_{C(-)} d\boldsymbol{\sigma} \cdot \mathbf{A} \tag{3-323}$$

The direction of traversal along $C(S')$ is such that S' always lies to the left as $C(S')$ is traversed. Notice that

$$\int_{C(+)} d\boldsymbol{\delta} \cdot \mathbf{A} = \int_{C(+)} d\boldsymbol{\delta}_+ \cdot \mathbf{A}_+ \tag{3-324}$$

and

$$\int_{C(-)} d\boldsymbol{\delta} \cdot \mathbf{A} = \int_{C(-)} d\boldsymbol{\delta}_- \cdot \mathbf{A}_- \tag{3-325}$$

where $\mathbf{A}_+$ represents the value of $\mathbf{A}$ on $C(+)$, and $\mathbf{A}_-$ represents the value of $\mathbf{A}$ on $C(-)$. On a boundary, $d\boldsymbol{\delta}$ always *points out of the region of integration*. Therefore, on the external boundary of S', $d\boldsymbol{\delta}$ points out of S'. On the internal boundary of S', $d\boldsymbol{\delta}$ points toward the interior of the enclosed hole. The situation on the scissor cut is clarified by imagining the two edges of the cut to be slightly separated. The normals to the edges $C(+)$ and $C(-)$ must be antiparallel; therefore

$$d\boldsymbol{\delta}_+ = -d\boldsymbol{\delta}_- \tag{3-326}$$

As the *edges of the scissor cut are drawn together,*

$$C(+) = C(-) = C' \tag{3-327}$$

so that

$$\int_{C(+)} d\boldsymbol{\delta} \cdot \mathbf{A} + \int_{C(-)} d\boldsymbol{\delta} \cdot \mathbf{A} = \int_{C'} d\boldsymbol{\delta}_+ \cdot (\mathbf{A}_+ - \mathbf{A}_-) \tag{3-328}$$

as a result of Eqs. (3-324) to (3-327). In Eq. (3-328), $\mathbf{A}_+$ represents the value of $\mathbf{A}$ at any point on C' as that point is approached from the plus side of C'. Similarly, $\mathbf{A}_-$ represents the value of $\mathbf{A}$ at any point on C' as that point is approached from the minus side of C'. Since $\mathbf{A}$ is single-valued and continuous throughout S',

$$\mathbf{A}_+ = \mathbf{A}_- \text{ on } C' \tag{3-329}$$

Hence the right side of Eq. (3-328) vanishes. The contributions from the two edges of the scissor cut cancel each other, leaving

$$\int_{S'} \boldsymbol{\nabla} \cdot \mathbf{A} \, dS = \int_{C(E)} d\boldsymbol{\delta} \cdot \mathbf{A} + \int_{C(I)} d\boldsymbol{\delta} \cdot \mathbf{A} \tag{3-330}$$

The original quantity of physical interest is

$$\int_{S} \boldsymbol{\nabla} \cdot \mathbf{A} \, dS \tag{3-331}$$

We recover expression (3-331) by shrinking the internal curve $C(I)$ enclosing the hole in S. This continues until $C(I)$ coincides with the open curve $C(d)$ across which $\mathbf{A}$ is discontinuous. Then $S' \to S$, and we obtain

$$\int_{S} \boldsymbol{\nabla} \cdot \mathbf{A} \, dS = \int_{C(E)} d\boldsymbol{\delta} \cdot \mathbf{A} + \int_{C_1(I)} d\boldsymbol{\delta} \cdot \mathbf{A} + \int_{C_2(I)} d\boldsymbol{\delta} \cdot \mathbf{A} \tag{3-332}$$

where $C(I) = C_1(I) + C_2(I)$. The curve of discontinuity $C(d)$ has two sides labeled 1 and 2, respectively. The unit normal at any point on side 2 of $C(d)$ is assumed to *lie in the surface S*. This unit normal is labeled $\mathbf{n}_{1 \to 2}$ to indicate that it is directed from side 1 toward side 2 of $C(d)$. Similarly, the unit normal on side 1 is labeled $\mathbf{n}_{2 \to 1}$, and it points from side 2 toward side 1 of $C(d)$. On $C(I)$, $d\boldsymbol{\delta}$ points *toward*

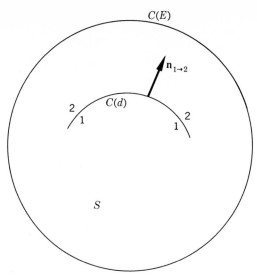

Figure 3-22 The modified domain of integration for a two-dimensional integral theorem involving a curve of discontinuity.

the interior of the hole containing $C(d)$. The piece of $C(I)$ labeled $C_2(I)$ approaches side 2 of $C(d)$ as the hole vanishes. On $C_2(I)$

$$d\mathbf{\sigma} = -\mathbf{n}_{1\to2}\,d\sigma \tag{3-333}$$

The piece of $C(I)$ labeled $C_1(I)$ approaches side 1 of $C(d)$, and on $C_1(I)$

$$d\mathbf{\sigma} = -\mathbf{n}_{2\to1}\,d\sigma \tag{3-334}$$

The minus signs in Eqs. (3-333) and (3-334) are required in order that $d\mathbf{\sigma}$ always points *out* of the *region* of *integration* and *into* the interior of the hole surrounded by $C(I)$. Observing that

$$\mathbf{n}_{1\to2} = -\mathbf{n}_{2\to1} \tag{3-335}$$

Eq. (3-332) becomes

$$\int_S \mathbf{\nabla}\cdot\mathbf{A}\,dS = \int_{C(E)} d\mathbf{\sigma}\cdot\mathbf{A} + \int_{C(d)} d\sigma\,\mathbf{n}_{1\to2}\cdot(\mathbf{A}_1 - \mathbf{A}_2) \tag{3-336}$$

where $\mathbf{A}_1$ is the value of $\mathbf{A}$ on side 1 of $C(d)$, and $\mathbf{A}_2$ is the value of $\mathbf{A}$ on side 2 of $C(d)$. Equation (3-336) is often written in the form

$$\int_S \mathbf{\nabla}\cdot\mathbf{A}\,dS + \int_{C(d)} d\sigma\,\mathbf{n}_{1\to2}\cdot(\mathbf{A}_2 - \mathbf{A}_1) = \int_{C(E)} d\mathbf{\sigma}\cdot\mathbf{A} \tag{3-337}$$

If $\mathbf{\nabla}\cdot\mathbf{A} = 0$ throughout the surface S, then the flux which crosses $C(E)$ is generated by the jump in $\mathbf{A}$ across the curve of discontinuity $C(d)$. We think of the jump in the normal component of $\mathbf{A}$ across $C(d)$ as being caused by the presence of point sources distributed along the curve. In support of this idea we define a *line divergence* or *flux per unit length* of *arc* by

$$\text{Div }\mathbf{A} = \mathbf{n}_{1\to2}\cdot(\mathbf{A}_2 - \mathbf{A}_1) \tag{3-338}$$

and we rewrite Eq. (3-337), using Eq. (3-338), as

$$\int_S \mathbf{\nabla} \cdot \mathbf{A}\, dS + \int_{C(d)} \text{Div } \mathbf{A}\, d\sigma = \int_{C(E)} d\mathbf{\delta} \cdot \mathbf{A} \tag{3-339}$$

The capital letter D in Div $\mathbf{A}$ is now used to indicate that a line divergence is meant. A *volume divergence* div $\mathbf{A}$ or $\mathbf{\nabla} \cdot \mathbf{A}$ measures the *volume density of sources of flux*. A *surface divergence* Div $\mathbf{A}$ measures the *surface density of sources of flux*, and finally a *line divergence* measures the *linear density of sources of flux*.

The jump in $\mathbf{A}$ across $C(d)$ may also cause $\mathbf{\nabla} \times \mathbf{A}$ to become infinite on $C(d)$. The preceding argument leads to the following generalized form of the two-dimensional curl theorem:

$$\int_S \mathbf{\nabla} \times \mathbf{A}\, dS + \int_{C(d)} \text{Curl } \mathbf{A}\, d\sigma = \int_{C(E)} d\mathbf{\delta} \times \mathbf{A} \tag{3-340}$$

The surface curl is written with a capital C, and it is defined by

$$\text{Curl } \mathbf{A} = \mathbf{n}_{1 \to 2} \times (\mathbf{A}_2 - \mathbf{A}_1) \tag{3-341}$$

If $\mathbf{n}$ is a unit vector which is perpendicular to the surface of integration at any point on the surface, then Eq. (3-340) can be written in the form

$$\int_S (\mathbf{\nabla} \times \mathbf{A}) \cdot d\mathbf{S} + \int_{C(d)} \mathbf{n} \cdot \text{Curl } \mathbf{A}\, d\sigma = \int_{C(E)} \mathbf{A} \cdot d\mathbf{r} \tag{3-342}$$

where the directed element of surface area on S is given by

$$d\mathbf{S} = \mathbf{n}\, dS \tag{3-343}$$

The local displacement vector $d\mathbf{r}$ is tangent to $C(E)$ and is directed so that the region S lies to the left of $d\mathbf{r}$ as $C(E)$ is traversed. Notice that Curl $\mathbf{A}$ involves only the components of $\mathbf{A}$ which are *tangential* to the curve $C(d)$. When $\mathbf{\nabla} \times \mathbf{A} = 0$ throughout S, then the circulation of $\mathbf{A}$ around $C(E)$ must be generated by jumps in the components of $\mathbf{A}$ which are tangential to $C(d)$. Such jumps are associated with point sources of *circulation* or *vorticity* which are distributed along $C(d)$. The line curl measures the linear density of such sources on $C(d)$.

If ϕ is a scalar point function which has different values on two sides of a given open curve $C(d)$ contained within S, then $\mathbf{\nabla}\phi$ may become infinite on $C(d)$. The corresponding generalized two-dimensional gradient theorem, obtained by the same arguments as before, is

$$\int_S \mathbf{\nabla}\phi\, dS + \int_{C(d)} \text{Grad } \phi\, d\sigma = \int_{C(E)} d\mathbf{\delta}\, \phi \tag{3-344}$$

The line gradient is written with a capital G and is defined by

$$\text{Grad } \phi = \mathbf{n}_{1 \to 2}(\phi_2 - \phi_1) \tag{3-345}$$

Summary

We have demonstrated how to modify a two-dimensional integral theorem when the open surface of integration contains an open curve of discontinuity. The modification requires the introduction of linear divergence, curl, and gradient operators defined by

$$\text{Div } \mathbf{A} = \mathbf{n}_{1 \to 2} \cdot (\mathbf{A}_2 - \mathbf{A}_1) \tag{3-346}$$

$$\text{Curl } \mathbf{A} = \mathbf{n}_{1 \to 2} \times (\mathbf{A}_2 - \mathbf{A}_1) \tag{3-347}$$

$$\text{Grad } \phi = \mathbf{n}_{1 \to 2}(\phi_2 - \phi_1) \tag{3-348}$$

The corresponding modified integral theorems are

$$\int_S \boldsymbol{\nabla} \cdot \mathbf{A} \, dS + \int_{C(d)} \text{Div } \mathbf{A} \, d\sigma = \int_{C(E)} d\mathbf{\delta} \cdot \mathbf{A} \tag{3-349}$$

$$\int_S \boldsymbol{\nabla} \times \mathbf{A} \, dS + \int_{C(d)} \text{Curl } \mathbf{A} \, d\sigma = \int_{C(E)} d\mathbf{\delta} \times \mathbf{A} \tag{3-350}$$

$$\int_S (\boldsymbol{\nabla} \times \mathbf{A}) \cdot dS + \int_{C(d)} \mathbf{n} \cdot \text{Curl } \mathbf{A} \, d\sigma = \int_{C(E)} \mathbf{A} \cdot d\mathbf{r} \tag{3-351}$$

$$\int_S \boldsymbol{\nabla}\phi \, dS + \int_{C(d)} \text{Grad } \phi \, d\sigma = \int_{C(E)} d\mathbf{\delta} \, \phi \tag{3-352}$$

3-21 PROBLEMS AND APPLICATIONS

1. Show that the differential equation

$$\frac{d^2\mathbf{r}}{dt^2} + 2a\frac{d\mathbf{r}}{dt} + \omega^2\mathbf{r} = 0$$

in which $a = $ constant and $\omega = $ constant is satisfied by

(a) $\mathbf{r} = e^{-at}\{\mathbf{c}_1 e^{\sqrt{a^2 - \omega^2}\,t} + \mathbf{c}_2 e^{-\sqrt{a^2 - \omega^2}\,t}\}$

when $a^2 - \omega^2 > 0$, and $\mathbf{c}_1$ and $\mathbf{c}_2$ are arbitrary constant vectors.

(b) $\mathbf{r} = e^{-at}\{\mathbf{c}_1 \sin\sqrt{\omega^2 - a^2}\,t + \mathbf{c}_2 \cos\sqrt{\omega^2 - a^2}\,t\}$

when $a^2 - \omega^2 < 0$.

(c) $\mathbf{r} = e^{-at}\{\mathbf{c}_1 + \mathbf{c}_2 t\}$

when $a^2 - \omega^2 = 0$.

2. Prove that

(a) $\mathbf{A} = \mathbf{m}_0 \dfrac{e^{i\omega(t - r/c)}}{r} \qquad i = \sqrt{-1}$

is a solution of the equation

$$\nabla^2\mathbf{A} = \frac{1}{c^2}\frac{\partial^2\mathbf{A}}{\partial t^2} \qquad r = |\mathbf{r}| \neq 0$$

where $\mathbf{m}_0$ is an arbitrary constant vector, and ω and c are real constants.

(b) Show that $\mathbf{A}$ satisfies the equation

$$(\nabla^2 + k^2)\mathbf{A} = 0 \qquad r = |\mathbf{r}| \neq 0$$

provided that $\omega = kc$.

Hint: use the Laplacian in spherical coordinates.

3. Prove that

$$(\nabla^2 + k^2)(\mathbf{A} \cdot \mathbf{r}) = 2\nabla \cdot \mathbf{A} + \mathbf{r} \cdot (\nabla\nabla \cdot \mathbf{A} - \nabla \times \nabla \times \mathbf{A} + k^2\mathbf{A})$$

4. Verify that if

$$(\nabla^2 + k^2)\psi = 0 \qquad \text{and} \qquad \nabla \times \mathbf{a} = 0$$

then, given $\mathbf{a} = \mathbf{r}$ or $\mathbf{a} = $ constant, and

$$\mathbf{L} = \nabla\psi$$

$$\mathbf{M} = \nabla \times (\mathbf{a}\psi)$$

$$\mathbf{N} = \frac{1}{k}(\nabla \times \mathbf{M})$$

it follows that

$$(\nabla^2 + k^2)\mathbf{L} = 0 \qquad (\nabla^2 + k^2)\mathbf{M} = 0 \qquad \text{and} \qquad (\nabla^2 + k^2)\mathbf{N} = 0$$

5. Show that if

$$\nabla = \mathbf{e}_x \frac{\partial}{\partial x} + \mathbf{e}_y \frac{\partial}{\partial y} + \mathbf{e}_z \frac{\partial}{\partial z}$$

and

$$\nabla_1 = \mathbf{e}_x \frac{\partial}{\partial x_1} + \mathbf{e}_y \frac{\partial}{\partial y_1} + \mathbf{e}_z \frac{\partial}{\partial z_1}$$

then for

$$F(R) = F(\sqrt{(x - x_1)^2 + (y - y_1)^2 + (z - z_1)^2})$$

$$\nabla F(R) = -\nabla_1 F(R)$$

where $F(R)$ is an arbitrary differentiable function.

6. Consider the expression

$$\mathbf{A} \cdot d\mathbf{r} = A_x \, dx + A_y \, dy$$

If there is a scalar function $\phi(x,y,z)$ such that

$$A_x = \frac{\partial \phi}{\partial x} \qquad A_y = \frac{\partial \phi}{\partial y}$$

then

$$d\phi = \mathbf{A} \cdot d\mathbf{r} = \frac{\partial \phi}{\partial x} \, dx + \frac{\partial \phi}{\partial y} \, dy$$

and we say that $\mathbf{A} \cdot d\mathbf{r}$ is an exact differential. It follows from the two-dimensional curl theorem that if $\nabla \times \mathbf{A} = 0$ *throughout* an open, simply connected two-dimensional surface, then $\mathbf{A} \cdot d\mathbf{r}$ is an exact differential. Therefore ϕ exists, and

$$\frac{\partial^2 \phi}{\partial x \, \partial y} = \frac{\partial^2 \phi}{\partial y \, \partial x}$$

(a) Prove the above statements!

(b) If $\nabla \times \mathbf{A} \neq 0$, then $\mathbf{A} \cdot d\mathbf{r}$ is *not* an exact differential. However, if a scalar function $\mu = \mu(x,y,z)$ exists such that

$$\nabla \times (\mu\mathbf{A}) = 0$$

then $\mu\mathbf{A} \cdot d\mathbf{r}$ *is* an exact differential. Prove that the necessary and sufficient condition for $\mu\mathbf{A} \cdot d\mathbf{r}$ to be an exact differential is that

$$\mathbf{A} \cdot (\nabla \times \mathbf{A}) = 0$$

at each point of an open, simply connected surface. The scalar function $\mu = \mu(x,y,z)$ is called an "integrating factor."

7. Discuss the geometrical interpretation of Eqs. (3-97) and (3-98).

8. Write the reciprocal transformations corresponding to Eqs. (3-97) and (3-98).

9. Let $S(V)$ be the surface of volume V. Prove that

$$\int_{S(V)} \nabla\left(-\frac{1}{r}\right) \cdot d\mathbf{S} = \begin{cases} 0 & \text{if the origin } r = 0 \text{ is outside } V \\ 4\pi & \text{if the origin } r = 0 \text{ is inside } V \end{cases}$$

where $r^2 = x^2 + y^2 + z^2$

Hint: Use the fact that $\nabla^2(1/r) = 0$ for $r \neq 0$, together with the three-dimensional divergence theorem and the definition of the solid angle subtended by $S(V)$.

10. Let $\mathbf{A} = y\mathbf{e}_x + (x + z)^2\mathbf{e}_y + \mathbf{e}_z$, and evaluate

$$I = \int_C \mathbf{A} \cdot d\mathbf{r}$$

along the curve C specified by

$$y = 2x \qquad z = 0$$

from $x = 0$, $y = 0$ to $x = 2$, $y = 4$.

11. Consider the segment of plane surface $2x + 2y + z = 1$ lying in the octant $x \geq 0$, $y \geq 0$, $z \geq 0$. Let it be named S. Given

$$A = y\mathbf{e}_x + z\mathbf{e}_y$$

compute

$$I = \int_S d\mathbf{S} \cdot \mathbf{A}$$

12. Let V be the volume of a sphere of radius $r = a$. Evaluate the volume integral

$$I = \int_V \left(\frac{1}{r}\right) dx\, dy\, dz$$

13. Find the directional derivative of

$$f = x^2yz \qquad \text{at } (3,0,1)$$

in the direction of the vector $\mathbf{e}_x - \mathbf{e}_y - \mathbf{e}_z$. Compute the greatest rate of change of f and the direction of the maximum rate of increase of f.

14. Find the unit normal vector in the direction of the exterior normal to the surface

$$2x^2 + y^2 + 2z^2 = 5 \qquad \text{at } (1,1,1)$$

15. Use the three-dimensional divergence theorem to establish Green's first identity,

$$\int_V (u\, \nabla^2 v + \nabla u \cdot \nabla v)\, dV = \int_{S(V)} u\, \nabla v \cdot d\mathbf{S}$$

and Green's second identity,

$$\int_V (u \nabla^2 v - v \nabla^2 u) \, dV = \int_{S(V)} (u \nabla v - v \nabla u) \cdot d\mathbf{S}$$

16. Compute the integral

$$I = \iint_S \nabla \cdot \mathbf{A} \, dS$$

over the surface S bounded by the ellipses

$$\frac{x^2}{4} + \frac{y^2}{9} = 1 \qquad \text{and} \qquad \frac{x^2}{9} + \frac{y^2}{16} = 1$$

when $\mathbf{A} = x\mathbf{e}_x + y\mathbf{e}_y$.

17. Consider a sphere of radius R, volume V, and surface $S(V)$, centered at point P. Let Q be any other point inside the same sphere. The volume of the sphere is now allowed to shrink to zero in such a manner that Q shrinks toward P. Assuming that $f(Q)$ is continuous throughout V, prove that

$$\lim_{V \to 0} \int_{S(V)} \frac{f(Q)}{R^n} \, dS = \begin{cases} 4\pi f(P) & n = 2 \\ 0 & n < 2 \end{cases}$$

18. Let $f(\mathbf{r})$ be continuous and non-negative in a region V.
(a) If $I = \int f(\mathbf{r}) \, dV = 0$
then prove that $f \equiv 0$ in V.
(b) If $I = \int f(\mathbf{r}) \, dS = 0$
and $f(\mathbf{r})$ is continuous and non-negative on the surface S, then prove that $f \equiv 0$ on S.
(c) If $f(\mathbf{r})$ satisfies Dirichlet's conditions throughout V and if

$$I = \int f(\mathbf{r}) \, dV = 0$$

for each volume $V' \subseteq V$, then prove that $f \equiv 0$ in V.

19. The electric displacement vector due to several point charges q_k is given by

$$\mathbf{D} = \frac{1}{4\pi} \sum_{k=1}^{n} \frac{q_k}{|\mathbf{r}_k|^3} \mathbf{r}_k$$

where $\mathbf{r}_k$ is a radius vector measured away from the kth charge. Verify Gauss' law,

$$\int_{S(V)} \mathbf{D} \cdot d\mathbf{S} = \sum_{k=1}^{n} q_k$$

where $S(V)$ is any smooth convex surface enclosing all the charges.

20. The magnetic intensity vector due to several very long *parallel* conductors which carry currents I_k is given by

$$\mathbf{H} = \frac{1}{2\pi} \sum_{k=1}^{n} \frac{I_k}{r_k} \mathbf{e}_{\theta k}$$

Here r_k is the radial distance away from the kth conductor as measured in the plane perpendicular to the kth conductor. The unit vectors $\mathbf{e}_{rk}$ and $\mathbf{e}_{\theta k}$ form the base vectors of a plane polar coordinate system normal to, and centered on, the kth conductor. Verify that

$$\int_{C(S)} \mathbf{H} \cdot d\mathbf{r} = \sum_{k=1}^{n} I_k$$

where $C(S)$ is the closed boundary curve of any flat disk S which is penetrated by each of the n parallel conductors. The contour $C(S)$ is to be traversed so that the face of the disk from which the positive currents emerge lies to the left.

21. Prove that

$$\frac{d\mathbf{v}}{dt} = \frac{\partial \mathbf{v}}{\partial t} + \frac{1}{2}\, \mathbf{\nabla}(v^2) + (\mathbf{\nabla} \times \mathbf{v}) \times \mathbf{v}$$

22. The three-dimensional divergence theorem for Cartesian tensors is given by

$$\int_V \tau_{ij,j}\, dV = \int_{S(V)} \tau_{ij} n_j\, dS$$

where $d\mathbf{S} = n_j\, dS$ is the element of surface area on $S(V)$. The symbol $\tau_{ij,j}$ stands for the divergence of the tensor τ_{ij}. Using the summation convention with $i,j = 1,2,3$, we obtain

$$\mathrm{div}\,(\tau_{ij}) = \tau_{ij,j} = \tau_{i1,1} + \tau_{i2,2} + \tau_{i3,3}$$

For Cartesian tensors this reduces to

$$\mathrm{div}\,(\tau_{ij}) = \tau_{ij,j} = \frac{\partial \tau_{ij}}{\partial x_j} = \frac{\partial \tau_{i1}}{\partial x_1} + \frac{\partial \tau_{i2}}{\partial x_2} + \frac{\partial \tau_{i3}}{\partial x_3} \qquad i = 1,2,3$$

Prove the three-dimensional divergence theorem for Cartesian tensors.

Hint: Apply the ordinary three-dimensional divergence theorem to each component of the vector div (τ_{ij}).

23. Consider a solid of volume V bounded by a closed surface $S(V)$. Let the local unit normal at any point on $S(V)$ be represented by n_i, $i = 1,2,3$. At any point on $S(V)$ the force per unit area acting on the surface is a vector quantity whose direction differs in general from the direction of the normal. This force per unit area or stress vector S_i is related to the normal n_i by the equation

$$S_i = \tau_{ij} n_j \qquad i,j = 1,2,3$$

The tensor τ_{ij} acts as an operator which rotates the unit normal vector n_i into the direction of the local stress vector S_i. The magnitude of S_i equals the force per unit area at any point on $S(V)$. The tensor τ_{ij} is called the "stress tensor," and S_i is the "stress vector" or traction on the surface $S(V)$. Suppose that a solid experiences a deformation due to the action of a body force per unit volume F_i and a surface force per unit area S_i. Let ρ be the density of the body and v_i the velocity vector of any point in the body. Newton's second law gives

$$\int_{V(t)} F_i\, dV + \int_{S(V)} S_i\, dS = \frac{d}{dt} \int_{V(t)} \rho v_i\, dV$$

Using the result of Prob. 22, show that the integral form of Newton's second law yields the partial differential equation

$$\text{div } (\tau_{ij}) + \mathbf{F} = \frac{d}{dt} (\rho \mathbf{v}) + \rho \mathbf{v} (\mathbf{\nabla} \cdot \mathbf{v})$$

The mass contained within V is given by

$$m(t) = \int_{V(t)} \rho(\mathbf{r},t) \, dV$$

If the volume $V(t)$ is free of mass sinks and sources, and if conservation of mass holds, show that

$$\text{div } (\tau_{ij}) + \mathbf{F} = \rho \left[\frac{\partial \mathbf{v}}{\partial t} + \frac{1}{2} \mathbf{\nabla}(v^2) + (\mathbf{\nabla} \times \mathbf{v}) \times \mathbf{v} \right]$$

24. Consider a small sphere immersed in a fluid. Let n_i be the outward normal to the surface of this sphere. If the stress acting on the surface of the sphere is always directed inward along $-n_i$, *regardless* of the state of *motion* of the sphere, then the fluid is called ideal or nonviscous. The stress acting on the surface of a sphere in an ideal fluid is therefore

$$S_i = -pn_i$$

where $|S_i| = p = \text{pressure} = \text{force/area}$. Then $\tau_{ij} = -p\delta_{ij}$ is the corresponding stress tensor, since

$$S_i = \tau_{ij}n_j = -p\delta_{ij}n_j = -pn_i$$

Show that for an ideal fluid deforming in such a way that mass is conserved,

$$\mathbf{F} - \mathbf{\nabla}p = \rho \frac{d\mathbf{v}}{dt}$$

and

$$\frac{\partial \rho}{\partial t} + \mathbf{\nabla} \cdot (\rho \mathbf{v}) = 0$$

If the fluid is incompressible, show that

$$\mathbf{\nabla} \cdot \mathbf{v} = 0$$

25. Consider an ideal compressible gas for which the body force is $\mathbf{F} = 0$. Let the adiabatic equation of state of the gas be given by

$$p = p(\rho)$$

where p is the pressure, and ρ is the density. The adiabatic speed of sound in such a gas is defined by

$$c^2 = \frac{dp}{d\rho}$$

Show that the equation which governs *small-amplitude* pressure fluctuations in the gas is

$$\mathbf{\nabla}^2 p = \frac{1}{c^2} \frac{\partial^2 p}{\partial t^2}$$

Hint: For small-amplitude disturbances the nonlinear terms such as $\mathbf{v} \cdot (\nabla p)$ and $\frac{1}{2}\nabla(v^2) + (\nabla \times \mathbf{v}) \times \mathbf{v}$ can be neglected. In addition, both the density ρ and the adiabatic sound speed c can be regarded as approximately constant.

26. Let the vector u_i represent the displacement of a point in a homogeneous isotropic body from its position of stable equilibrium. The relation between the stress τ_{ij} and the displacement u_i is expressed by Hooke's law as

$$\tau_{ij} = \lambda u_{k,k}\delta_{ij} + \mu(u_{i,j} + u_{j,i})$$

where λ and μ are called "Lamé's constants," and $u_{k,k} = \nabla \cdot \mathbf{u}$; $u_{i,j} = \partial u_i/\partial x_j$. Show that small-amplitude elastic vibrations in a solid are governed by the equation

$$(\lambda + 2\mu)\nabla\nabla \cdot \mathbf{u} - \mu\nabla \times \nabla \times \mathbf{u} + \mathbf{F} = \rho\frac{\partial^2 \mathbf{u}}{\partial t^2}$$

27. Since heat flows from higher to lower temperatures in a solid, the heat current due to a temperature field T is given by

$$\mathbf{q} = -k\,\nabla T \qquad k = \text{cal/cm-sec } °\text{C}$$

where k is called the thermal conductivity of the solid. If H represents the heat per unit volume in the solid, then thermodynamics gives

$$dH = \rho c\, dT$$

where ρ is the density in grams per cubic centimeter, and c is the specific heat of the solid in *calories* per gram per degree centigrade. This equation means that a change in temperature dT is produced by the addition of an amount of heat $dH/\rho c$ to the solid. Thus

$$\frac{dH}{dt} = \rho c\,\frac{dT}{dt}$$

If the solid remains rigid, then $\mathbf{v} = 0$, and we have

$$\frac{\partial H}{\partial t} = \rho c\,\frac{\partial T}{\partial t}$$

The total decrease in heat in the region V per unit time is given by

$$-\int_V \frac{\partial H}{\partial t}\,dV$$

and if heat is conserved, then

$$-\int_V \frac{\partial H}{\partial t}\,dV = \int_{S(V)} d\mathbf{S} \cdot \mathbf{q}$$

which states that the rate of decrease of heat in region V is equal to the flux of heat current emerging from the boundary of V. Derive the equation of heat diffusion,

$$\nabla \cdot (k\,\nabla T) = \rho c\,\frac{\partial T}{\partial t}$$

which governs the temperature distribution in the solid. When the thermal conductivity is constant, this becomes

$$\nabla^2 T = \frac{1}{\alpha} \frac{\partial T}{\partial t}$$

where $\alpha = k/\rho c$ is called the "diffusivity" of the solid.

28. Consider a closed loop of wire which can rotate, translate, and deform as a function of time. Let the area of the loop be $S(t)$, and its boundary curve be $C(t)$. Suppose that there is an electric field $\mathbf{E}$ inside the wire and a magnetic field $\mathbf{B}$ throughout the space in which the wire is embedded. The electric field $\mathbf{E}$ in the wire can be produced by connecting the loop to a battery. The magnetic field $\mathbf{B}$ is due to an external source, the earth for example. The current flowing in the loop generates a magnetic field *in addition* to the external field $\mathbf{B}$ already present. The total magnetic flux crossing $S(t)$ is thus generated by two sources:

(a) The current flowing in the loop due to the electric field $\mathbf{E}$ and
(b) The external magnetic field, a portion of which crosses the area of the loop

There are two effects which cause the magnetic flux across $S(t)$ to change with time. First of all, the electric field $\mathbf{E}$ accelerates the charges in the loop. This increases the current flowing in the loop, and therefore the magnetic flux due to this current is increased. Secondly, the mechanical motion of the loop in the external magnetic field produces a change in the magnetic flux crossing the loop. These ideas are summarized in Faraday's law,

$$\frac{d\Phi}{dt} = - \int_{C(t)} (\mathbf{E} + \mathbf{v} \times \mathbf{B}) \cdot d\mathbf{r}$$

where $\mathbf{v}$ represents the velocity of any point on the loop $C(t)$, and

$$\Phi = \int_{S(t)} \mathbf{B} \cdot d\mathbf{S}$$

Deduce that

$$\nabla \times \mathbf{E} + \frac{\partial \mathbf{B}}{\partial t} = -\mathbf{v}(\nabla \cdot \mathbf{B})$$

and

$$\nabla \cdot \mathbf{B} = (\nabla \cdot \mathbf{B})_{t=0} \exp - \int_0^t \nabla \cdot \mathbf{v} \, dt$$

If it is assumed that

$$(\nabla \cdot \mathbf{B})_{t=0} = 0$$

then Faraday's law yields two of Maxwell's equations, i.e.:

$$\nabla \times \mathbf{E} + \frac{\partial \mathbf{B}}{\partial t} = 0 \qquad \nabla \cdot \mathbf{B} = 0$$

29. Consider the same closed loop of wire as in Prob. 28. Suppose that there is an electric field inside the wire. This electric field can be produced by connecting the loop to a battery as before. Suppose also that there is an external electric displacement field $\mathbf{D}$ throughout

the space in which the loop is embedded. This electric displacement field **D** is thought of as being generated by remote electric charges which are *initially at rest* with respect to the loop. The battery causes a current I to flow in the loop, and as a result lines of magnetic field link the loop. Suppose we now permit the loop to undergo mechanical motion. There is then relative motion between the remote charges generating the **D** field and the loop itself. The motion of the loop consists in general of a translation, a rotation, and a deformation. The deformation changes the shape of the loop. By choosing a rigid coordinate frame attached to the loop, the effects of rotation and translation can be eliminated. However, in this new frame the distant charges are no longer at rest. An observer in the rigid frame attached to the loop would interpret the distant charges to be in motion, thus generating an electric current. This distant current produces a *magnetic field in addition* to the one already generated by the current flowing in the loop.

Imagine now a very large hollow sphere, large enough to contain both the loop and the remote charges which generate the **D** field. For this sphere Gauss' law gives

$$\int_{S(V)} \mathbf{D} \cdot d\mathbf{S} = q$$

where q is the total charge contained inside the volume V. Prove that inside V

$$\mathbf{\nabla} \cdot \mathbf{D} = \rho$$

where

$$\int_V \rho \, dV = q$$

Let us now puncture a hole in the surface of this sphere. Let the boundary curve of this hole be labeled $P(t)$ and the surface of the punctured sphere be labeled $S(t)$. We now adjust the wire loop so that it is linked by the curve $P(t)$ which forms the border of $S(t)$. This has the effect of permitting the current I flowing in the loop to intersect $S(t)$ at one and only one point. Ampère's law states that

$$I + \frac{d}{dt} \int_{S(t)} \mathbf{D} \cdot d\mathbf{S} = \int_{P(t)} [\mathbf{H} - (\mathbf{v} \times \mathbf{D})] \cdot d\mathbf{r}$$

In this equation I is the total battery-produced current flowing in the loop, and **v** is the velocity of any point on the curve $P(t)$ which must always link the moving loop. Ampère's law considers the total circulation of two separate magnetic fields around a path which encircles a moving, current-carrying wire loop. The first magnetic field, **H**, is produced by the battery current I flowing in the loop. The second magnetic field, **v × D**, is due to the relative motion between the distant charges and the path $P(t)$. Ampère's law states that the total circulation is equal to the total current which crosses the surface $S(t)$. This total current is made up of two parts. They are the current I being conducted in the loop and the current

$$\frac{d}{dt} \int_{S(t)} \mathbf{D} \cdot d\mathbf{S}$$

generated by the relative motion between the surface $S(t)$ and the electric charges. If the loop and the remote charges are at rest with respect to each other, then Ampère's law reduces to

$$I = \int_p \mathbf{H} \cdot d\mathbf{r}$$

It is customary to define the *conduction current* density vector $\mathbf{J}$ so that

$$\int_{S(t)} \mathbf{J} \cdot d\mathbf{S} = I$$

where I is the current being conducted in the loop of wire, and $S(t)$ is the surface which is penetrated by I. Using Gauss' law and Ampère's law, show that

$$\nabla \times \mathbf{H} - \frac{\partial \mathbf{D}}{\partial t} = \mathbf{J}_T$$

where $\mathbf{J}_T = \mathbf{J} + \rho \mathbf{v}$. Here $\nabla \cdot \mathbf{D} = \rho$ is the electric charge density. The term $\rho \mathbf{v}$ is called the "convection current density," and the total current density $\mathbf{J}_T$ consists of the sum of the conduction and convection current densities. Next deduce that

$$\nabla \cdot \mathbf{J}_T + \frac{\partial \rho}{\partial t} = 0$$

which is the equation of charge conservation.

30. The complete set of Maxwell's equations is

$$\nabla \cdot \mathbf{D} = \rho \qquad\qquad \nabla \cdot \mathbf{B} = 0$$

$$\nabla \times \mathbf{H} = \mathbf{J} + \frac{\partial \mathbf{D}}{\partial t} \qquad \nabla \times \mathbf{E} + \frac{\partial \mathbf{B}}{\partial t} = 0$$

Let $\mathbf{J} = 0$ and $\rho = 0$ and assume

$$\mathbf{B} = \mu_0 \mathbf{H} \qquad \mathbf{D} = \epsilon_0 \mathbf{E}$$

Prove that

$$\nabla^2 \mathbf{E} = \frac{1}{c^2} \frac{\partial^2 \mathbf{E}}{\partial t^2}$$

and

$$\nabla^2 \mathbf{H} = \frac{1}{c^2} \frac{\partial^2 \mathbf{H}}{\partial t^2}$$

where

$$c^2 = \frac{1}{\mu_0 \epsilon_0}$$

31. Show that across a surface of discontinuity in an electromagnetic field the boundary conditions consistent with Maxwell's equations are

$$\text{Div } \mathbf{B} = 0$$
$$\text{Div } \mathbf{D} = \omega$$
$$\text{Curl } \mathbf{H} = \mathbf{K}$$
$$\text{Curl } \mathbf{E} = 0$$
$$\text{Div } \mathbf{J} = -\frac{\partial \omega}{\partial t}$$

Here ω represents the surface charge density on the surface of discontinuity, and $\mathbf{K}$ represents the surface current density there. The operators Div and Curl represent the surface divergence and the surface curl, respectively.

Hint: See Sec. 3-20.

32. If $\nabla \times \mathbf{A} = 0$ *throughout* an open, simply connected two-dimensional surface, then it follows from Prob. 6 that $\mathbf{A} \cdot d\mathbf{r}$ is an exact differential. Prove that

$$I = \int_{P_0}^{P_1} \mathbf{A} \cdot d\mathbf{r}$$

is independent of the path connecting the points P_0 and P_1.

33. If it is known that $\mathbf{A} \cdot d\mathbf{r}$ is an exact differential, is it always true that

$$I = \int_{P_0}^{P_1} \mathbf{A} \cdot d\mathbf{r}$$

is independent of the path connecting P_0 with P_1? Why?

34. Consider the volume integral of a function $f(\mathbf{r})$ which is continuous in the region of space bounded by the surfaces

$$g(\mathbf{r}) = ct_0 \qquad \text{and} \qquad g(\mathbf{r}) = ct$$

We assume that c and t_0 are fixed constants while t is permitted to vary. Prove that

$$\frac{1}{c} \frac{d}{dt} \int_{ct_0 \leq g(\mathbf{r}) \leq ct} f(\mathbf{r}) \, dV = \int_{g(\mathbf{r}) = ct} \frac{f(\mathbf{r})}{|\nabla g|} \, dS$$

functions of a complex variable

4-1 INTRODUCTION

A knowledge of complex analysis, even if only a limited one, is of the first importance in the study of ordinary and partial differential equations, integral transforms, and the special functions of mathematical physics.

This brief introduction to complex analysis is intended to acquaint the student with at least the rudiments of this important subject.

4-2 DEFINITIONS

Modern complex analysis represents the final union and maturity of three originally separate and distinct approaches to the subject. The basic ideas were initiated and separately developed by Weierstrass, Cauchy, and Riemann. Weierstrass began by considering functions of a real variable which could be expanded in a convergent, infinite Taylor series for some range of the independent variable; for example,

$$w = e^x = \sum_{k=0}^{\infty} \frac{x^k}{k!} \qquad |x| < \infty \qquad (4\text{-}1)$$

$$w = \frac{1}{1-x} = \sum_{k=0}^{\infty} x^k \qquad |x| < 1 \qquad (4\text{-}2)$$

$$w = \sin x = \sum_{k=0}^{\infty} \frac{(-1)^k x^{2k+1}}{(2k+1)!} \qquad 0 \le x \le \frac{\pi}{2} \qquad (4\text{-}3)$$

$$w = \cos x = \sum_{k=0}^{\infty} \frac{(-1)^k x^{2k}}{(2k)!} \qquad 0 \le x \le \frac{\pi}{2} \qquad (4\text{-}4)$$

(note $0! = 1$)

or

$$w = f(x) = \sum_{k=0}^{\infty} a_k x^k \qquad |x| \le R \qquad (4\text{-}5)$$

To obtain a function of a complex variable, Weierstrass introduced an operation called "analytic continuation." To perform this operation, one replaces the real variable x by a complex variable $z = x + iy$, where $i = \sqrt{-1}$, in each of the formulas (4-1) to (4-5). These formulas then become

$$w = e^z = \sum_{k=0}^{\infty} \frac{z^k}{k!} \tag{4-6}$$

$$w = \frac{1}{1-z} = \sum_{k=0}^{\infty} z^k \tag{4-7}$$

$$w = \sin z = \sum_{k=0}^{\infty} \frac{(-1)^k z^{2k+1}}{(2k+1)!} \tag{4-8}$$

$$w = \cos z = \sum_{k=0}^{\infty} \frac{(-1)^k z^{2k}}{(2k)!} \tag{4-9}$$

$$w = f(z) = \sum_{k=0}^{\infty} a_k z^k \tag{4-10}$$

The function $f(z)$ is referred to as the analytic continuation of the function $f(x)$ into the complex z plane (Fig. 4-1). The reason for speaking of a "complex z plane" is that the equation

$$z = x + iy \tag{4-11}$$

assigns a complex number z to every ordered pair of real numbers (x,y). Therefore, every point in the real x, y plane has a distinct complex number assigned to it. Conversely, each complex number represents a distinct point in the x, y plane. We call x the real part of z, and y the imaginary part of z, and we indicate this by writing

$$x = \text{Re } (z) \tag{4-12}$$

$$y = \text{Im } (z) \tag{4-13}$$

Thus

$$z = \text{Re } (z) + i \text{ Im } (z) \tag{4-14}$$

In polar form,

$$x = r \cos \theta \tag{4-15}$$

$$y = r \sin \theta \tag{4-16}$$

which yields

$$z = x + iy = r(\cos \theta + i \sin \theta) \tag{4-17}$$

We define the modulus or absolute value of z by

$$|z| = + \sqrt{x^2 + y^2} = r \tag{4-18}$$

The argument of z is defined by

$$\theta = \arg (z) = \tan^{-1} \frac{y}{x} = \tan^{-1} \frac{\text{Im } (z)}{\text{Re } (z)} \tag{4-19}$$

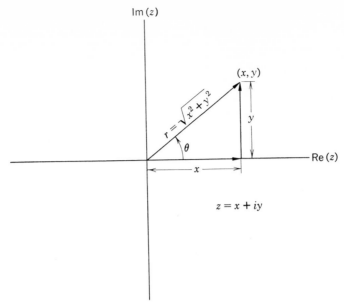

Figure 4.1 The complex z plane.

The student should recall Euler's equation,

$$e^{i\theta} = \cos\theta + i\sin\theta \qquad (4\text{-}20)$$

from elementary studies. With the use of Euler's equation we can write

$$z = x + iy = re^{i\theta} \qquad (4\text{-}21)$$

where $z = re^{i\theta}$ is referred to as the polar form of the complex number z.

4-3 COMPLEX ALGEBRA

In order to give meaning to Eqs. (4-6) to (4-10) it is necessary to know the rules of complex algebra, which are quite simple. For example, if

$$z_1 = x_1 + iy_1 \qquad (4\text{-}22)$$

and

$$z_2 = x_2 + iy_2 \qquad (4\text{-}23)$$

then

$$z_1 + z_2 = (x_1 + x_2) + i(y_1 + y_2) \qquad (4\text{-}24)$$

$$z_1 - z_2 = (x_1 - x_2) + i(y_1 - y_2) \qquad (4\text{-}25)$$

$$z_1 z_2 = (x_1 x_2 - y_1 y_2) + i(x_1 y_2 + x_2 y_1) \qquad (4\text{-}26)$$

Notice that in multiplication we use the fact that $i = \sqrt{-1}$ to obtain $i^2 = -1$. The complex number $z = 0$ is defined by

$$z = 0 + i0 = 0 \qquad (4\text{-}27)$$

Thus the complex number 0 has an indeterminate argument and zero absolute value. The statement

$$z_1 = z_2 \tag{4-28}$$

implies that

$$z_1 - z_2 = 0 \tag{4-29}$$

Hence $z_1 = z_2$ if and only if

$$x_1 = x_2 \tag{4-30}$$

$$y_1 = y_2 \tag{4-31}$$

The complex conjugate of $z_1 = x_1 + iy_1$ is obtained by substituting $-i$ for i in z_1; thus,

$$\bar{z}_1 = x_1 - iy_1 \tag{4-32}$$

and, similarly,

$$\bar{z}_2 = x_2 - iy_2 \tag{4-33}$$

Notice that

$$z_1\bar{z}_1 = \bar{z}_1 z_1 = x_1{}^2 + y_1{}^2 = |z_1|^2 \tag{4-34}$$

The division of complex numbers is defined by

$$\frac{z_1}{z_2} = \frac{z_1}{z_2}\frac{\bar{z}_2}{\bar{z}_2} = \frac{z_1\bar{z}_2}{|z_2|^2} \tag{4-35}$$

or

$$\frac{z_1}{z_2} = \frac{(x_1x_2 + y_1y_2) + i(y_1x_2 - x_1y_2)}{(x_2{}^2 + y_2{}^2)} \tag{4-36}$$

where $|z_2| \neq 0$.

In polar form,

$$z_1 = r_1e^{i\theta_1} \qquad \bar{z}_1 = r_1e^{-i\theta_1} \tag{4-37}$$

$$z_2 = r_2e^{i\theta_2} \qquad \bar{z}_2 = r_2e^{-i\theta_2} \tag{4-38}$$

yields

$$z_1z_2 = r_1r_2e^{i(\theta_1+\theta_2)} \tag{4-39}$$

$$\frac{z_1}{z_2} = \frac{r_1}{r_2}e^{i(\theta_1-\theta_2)} \tag{4-40}$$

The student should examine the geometric interpretation of complex algebraic operations for himself.

4-4 DOMAIN OF CONVERGENCE

In elementary calculus one learns that if

$$\sum_{k=0}^{\infty} a_k x^k \tag{4-41}$$

converges for a particular value $x = x_0$, then the series converges absolutely whenever $|x| < |x_0|$, and uniformly in the interval

$|x| \leq |x_1|$ for each fixed x_1 such that $|x_1| < |x_0|$. If the series diverges for $x = x_0$, then it diverges for all x such that $|x| > |x_0|$. If we now consider the analytic continuation of expression (4-41),

$$\sum_{k=0}^{\infty} a_k z^k \tag{4-42}$$

it can be shown that if expression (4-42) converges for $z = z_0$, then it converges absolutely [i.e., with z replaced by $|z|$ in (4-42)] for all z such that $|z| < |z_0|$, and uniformly for all z such that $|z| \leq |z_1| < |z_0|$.

This shows us that absolute convergence of (4-41) in the interval

$$|x| < R \tag{4-43}$$

as a function of a real variable implies absolute convergence of the analytic continuation (4-42) of (4-41) inside the circle:

$$|z| < R \tag{4-44}$$

This circle is known as the circle or domain of convergence, and its radius R is known as the radius of convergence.

Notice that R is not necessarily the maximum radius of convergence. For example, the fact that Eq. (4-2) converges for $x = \frac{1}{2}$ guarantees that Eq. (4-7) converges for $|z| < \frac{1}{2}$. However, Eq. (4-2) also converges for $x = \frac{3}{4}$, which guarantees that Eq. (4-7) converges for $|z| < \frac{3}{4}$, etc. For a power series such as (4-42) the largest region of convergence is always some circle of finite or even infinite radius centered at $z = 0$. When the maximum radius of convergence of the series

$$\sum_{n=0}^{\infty} a_n z^n \tag{4-45}$$

is finite and

$$f(z) = \sum_{n=0}^{\infty} a_n z^n \tag{4-46}$$

then $f(z)$ has at least one singularity on the largest circle of convergence. One can say that the largest circle of convergence of the power series representing $f(z)$ passes through the singularity of $f(z)$ nearest to the origin $z = 0$.

The real power series (4-5) may be differentiated or integrated *term* by *term* in any interval *interior* to its interval of convergence. The resulting series has the same interval of convergence as the original series and represents the derivative (or integral) of the function to which the original series converges. This remark also applies to complex power series.

4-5 ANALYTIC FUNCTIONS

If a function is single-valued and differentiable at every point of a domain D, save possibly for a finite number of singular points, it is called "analytic" in D. If no point of D is a singular point of the analytic function, then one says that the analytic function is "regular" or "holomorphic" in D. It follows from this that if a power series has a nonzero radius of convergence, its sum is an analytic function *regular* (*holomorphic*) within its circle of convergence. Suppose that the circle of convergence of

$$f(z) = \sum_{k=0}^{\infty} a_k z^k \tag{4-47}$$

has a finite radius $|z_0| = R$. The domain of convergence can sometimes be enlarged by repeated applications of the method of analytic continuation. For example, choose any point a inside the original circle of convergence,

$$|a| < |z_0| = R \tag{4-48}$$

and compute $f(a)$, $f'(a)$, $f''(a)$, . . . , $f^n(a)$, . . . , etc. This can be done by repeated differentiation of Eq. (4-47). We can then form the Taylor-series expansion of $f(z)$ about the point $z = a$. It will be a power series of the form

$$f(z) = \sum_{k=0}^{\infty} b_k (z - a)^k \tag{4-49}$$

The series given by Eq. (4-49) will certainly converge in any circle of center a lying inside the original circle $|z_0| = R$. It may also converge in a larger circle, and so provide an analytic continuation of the function into a domain *larger* than the original circle. The new domain of convergence consists of the union of the two circles of convergence, one centered on $z = 0$, the other on $z = a$. The repeated application of this principle will result in defining the function $f(z)$ for all values of z, or everywhere except at singular points; or only in some restricted region of the z plane beyond which we are unable to pass. Such a region is called the "region of existence" of the function, and its boundary is called the "natural boundary" of the function. According to Weierstrass, a *complete* analytic function is the set of *all power series* obtainable from an initial power series by analytic continuation.

Each *individual power series* is called an *element* of the *complete* analytic function. The result of analytic continuation can be shown to be unique in the following sense. If two complete analytic functions have an element in common, then they are identical. We can restate this uniqueness principle in several equivalent and useful ways. For example, it follows that any function analytic in a region A is completely determined in the whole of that region if it is known in a region, however small, surrounding any point a in the interior of A, or even if it is known at all points of an arc of a curve, however short, ending at the point a. In other words, the values of an analytic function cannot be arbitrarily altered if any one of its elements is prescribed in advance. This is in marked contrast to the behavior of a function of a real variable whose values can be specified on any interval and then arbitrarily specified outside this interval as well.

4-6 CAUCHY'S APPROACH

Cauchy starts with a function which is regular and analytic in a domain. Such a function has a derivative at each point of the domain in question. It is then shown that a regular analytic function can be represented by a certain integral. This integral representation can then be expanded in a Taylor series which converges in a sufficiently small circle about any point in the domain of regularity of the function. Thus the connection with the theory of Weierstrass is established.

The Cauchy-Riemann equations

Let

$$w = f(z) \tag{4-50}$$

be an analytic function of z at each point of a domain D. Then by definition, $f(z)$ has a derivative at each point of D. For example, at $z = z_0$ inside D the derivative of $f(z)$ is defined by

$$f'(z_0) = \lim_{\Delta z \to 0} \frac{\Delta w}{\Delta z} = \lim_{\Delta z \to 0} \frac{f(z_0 + \Delta z) - f(z_0)}{\Delta z} \tag{4-51}$$

In Eq. (4-51), $z = z_0 + \Delta z$ can be any point in a small circular disk centered on z_0, and Δz *can approach zero along any one of infinitely many paths joining z with z_0.* Hence, if the derivative $f'(z_0)$ is to have a unique value, *we must require that the limit* in Eq. (4-51) be *independent of the way in which Δz is made to approach zero.*

The Cauchy-Riemann equations provide a set of necessary conditions on the real and imaginary parts of

$$w = f(z) \equiv u(x,y) + iv(x,y) \tag{4-52}$$

which must be satisfied if $f(z)$ is to have a unique derivative at a given point $z = x + iy$. Since

$$\Delta w = \Delta u + i \, \Delta v \tag{4-53}$$

and

$$\Delta z = \Delta x + \Delta y$$

$$f'(z) = \lim_{\Delta z \to 0} \frac{\Delta u + i \, \Delta v}{\Delta x + i \, \Delta y} \tag{4-54}$$

Now, if we let $\Delta z \to 0$ by first putting $\Delta y = 0$ and allowing $\Delta x \to 0$ and then putting $\Delta x = 0$ and allowing $\Delta y \to 0$, we obtain

$$f'(z) = \lim_{\substack{\Delta x \to 0 \\ \Delta y = 0}} \frac{\Delta u + i \, \Delta v}{\Delta x} = \frac{\partial u}{\partial x} + i \frac{\partial v}{\partial x} \tag{4-55}$$

and

$$f'(z) = \lim_{\substack{\Delta v \to 0 \\ \Delta x = 0}} \frac{\Delta u + i\,\Delta v}{i\,\Delta y} = \frac{\partial v}{\partial y} - i\,\frac{\partial u}{\partial y} \tag{4-56}$$

and on equating Eqs. (4-55) and (4-56) we find

$$\frac{\partial u}{\partial x} = \frac{\partial v}{\partial y} \tag{4-57}$$

$$\frac{\partial u}{\partial y} = -\frac{\partial v}{\partial x} \tag{4-58}$$

which are the Cauchy-Riemann equations.

Equations (4-57) and (4-58) constitute *necessary* conditions for the existence of a unique derivative of $f(z) = u(x,y) + iv(x,y)$ at $z = x + iy$. It can be shown that these equations are also *sufficient* *if one* further *assumes* the *continuity* of the *partial derivatives* in Eqs. (4-57) and (4-58) at the point (x,y).

4-7 CAUCHY'S INTEGRAL THEOREM

In preparation for the development of Cauchy's integral representation of an analytic function we shall prove a simple form of Cauchy's integral theorem.

THEOREM: If $f(z)$ is an analytic function whose derivative $f'(z)$ exists and is continuous at each point within and on the closed contour C, then

$$\oint_C f(z)\,dz = 0 \tag{4-59}$$

REMARK: Although the proof below assumes the continuity of $f'(z)$, the theorem can actually be established, assuming only that $f'(z)$ exists at each point of the region. One can then deduce the continuity of $f'(z)$ from Cauchy's theorem. In fact, Cauchy's integral theorem implies existence and continuity of derivatives of all orders (see Titchmarsh, "The Theory of Functions," pp. 75–83).

proof: Let S be the closed domain consisting of all points within and on C. If we write $z = x + iy$, $f(z) = u + iv$, where x, y, u, and v are real, then

$$\oint_{C(S)} f(z)\,dz = \oint_{C(S)} (u + iv)(dx + i\,dy)$$

$$= \oint_{C(S)} (u\,dx - v\,dy) + i \oint_{C(S)} (v\,dx + u\,dy) \tag{4-60}$$

To evaluate the two line integrals in Eq. (4-60) we shall employ the two-dimensional curl theorem (3-201) written in the form

$$\oint_{C(S)} (A_x\,dx + A_y\,dy) = \int_S \left(\frac{\partial A_y}{\partial x} - \frac{\partial A_x}{\partial y} \right) dx\,dy \tag{4-61}$$

When

$$v = A_x \tag{4-62}$$

$$u = A_y \tag{4-63}$$

then

$$\oint_{C(S)} (v\,dx + u\,dy) = \int_S \left(\frac{\partial u}{\partial x} - \frac{\partial v}{\partial y}\right) dx\,dy \qquad (4\text{-}64)$$

and when

$$u = A_x \qquad (4\text{-}65)$$

$$v = -A_y \qquad (4\text{-}66)$$

we have

$$\oint_{C(S)} (u\,dx - v\,dy) = -\int_S \left(\frac{\partial v}{\partial x} + \frac{\partial u}{\partial y}\right) dx\,dy \qquad (4\text{-}67)$$

Thus

$$\oint_{C(S)} f(z)\,dz = -\int_S \left(\frac{\partial u}{\partial y} + \frac{\partial v}{\partial x}\right) dx\,dy + i \int_S \left(\frac{\partial u}{\partial x} - \frac{\partial v}{\partial y}\right) dx\,dy$$
$$= 0 \qquad (4\text{-}68)$$

by virtue of the Cauchy-Riemann equations (4-57) and (4-58) which hold throughout S.

REMARK: The closed curve $C(S)$ forms the boundary of a simply connected two-dimensional surface. The boundary is to be traversed so that the region S always lies to the left. This is indicated by the counter-clockwise arrow on the integral in Eq. (4-60). If the region S is not initially simply connected, then we make it so by introducing scissor cuts, as discussed in Sec. 3-20. It should be remembered that $C(S)$ is always the *total* boundary of the open, simply connected surface S. For example, consider an annulus bounded by an outer circle C_2 and an inner circle C_1. Let $f(z)$ be holomorphic in the annulus. We make the annulus simply connected by introducing a scissor cut running from C_1 to C_2. Let the two edges of the scissor cut be $C(+)$ and $C(-)$. Then Cauchy's integral theorem becomes

$$\oint_{C(S)} f(z)\,dz = \oint_{C_2} f(z)\,dz + \oint_{C_1} f(z)\,dz$$
$$+ \int_{C(+)} f(z)\,dz + \int_{C(-)} f(z)\,dz = 0 \qquad (4\text{-}69)$$

If both $C(+)$ and $C(-)$ have the end points a on C_1 and b on C_2, then

$$\int_{C(+)} f(z)\,dz = \int_a^b f(z)\,dz \qquad (4\text{-}70)$$

while

$$\int_{C(-)} f(z)\,dz = \int_b^a f(z)\,dz \qquad (4\text{-}71)$$

However

$$\int_a^b f(z)\,dz = -\int_b^a f(z)\,dz \qquad (4\text{-}72)$$

therefore the contributions from $C(+)$ and $C(-)$ cancel each other, leaving

$$\oint_{C(S)} f(z)\,dz = \oint_{C_2} f(z)\,dz + \oint_{C_1} f(z)\,dz = 0 \qquad (4\text{-}73)$$

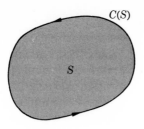

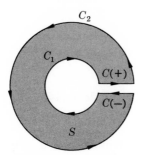

Figure 4-2 The domain of integration for Cauchy's integral theorem is the total boundary of an open, simply connected surface S.

Notice that the outer circle C_2 is traversed in the counterclockwise direction while the inner circle C_1 is traversed in the clockwise direction. This is necessary so that the interior of the annulus always lies to the left as $C(S)$ is traversed.

4-8 CAUCHY'S INTEGRAL REPRESENTATION OF AN ANALYTIC FUNCTION THEOREM:

Let $f(z)$ be an analytic function, regular within a closed contour C_E and continuous within and on C_E. If a is any point within C_E, then

$$f(a) = \frac{1}{2\pi i} \oint_{C_E} \frac{f(z)}{z - a} \, dz \tag{4-74}$$

If a is any point outside C_E, then

$$0 = \frac{1}{2\pi i} \oint_{C_E} \frac{f(z)}{z - a} \, dz \tag{4-75}$$

proof: Regularity of $f(z)$ inside C_E means that $f(z)$ is single-valued and differentiable at $z = a$. This together with the assumed continuity of $f(z)$ at $z = a$ implies that

$$f(z) = f(a) + f'(a)(z - a) + g(z)(z - a) \tag{4-76}$$

where $g(z)$ is a regular analytic function within C_E such that

$$\lim_{z \to a} g(z) = 0 \tag{4-77}$$

As a consequence of Eq. (4-77), given any positive number ϵ, there exists a neighborhood $|z - a| < \delta$ such that

$$|g(z)| < \epsilon \qquad \text{for} \qquad |z - a| < \delta \qquad (4\text{-}78)$$

Consider a circle C_I of radius r centered on $z = a$. Choose $r < \delta$ and small enough so that C_I lies entirely inside C_E. We observe that

$$\frac{f(z)}{z - a} = \frac{f(a)}{z - a} + f'(a) + g(z) \qquad (4\text{-}79)$$

is holomorphic within the annular surface S bounded externally by C_E and internally by C_I. Using Eq. (4-73) and integrating over the *total* boundary $C(S)$ of the *annulus* gives

$$\frac{1}{2\pi i} \oint_{C(S)} \frac{f(z)}{z - a}\, dz = \frac{1}{2\pi i} \oint_{C_E} \frac{f(z)}{z - a}\, dz$$
$$+ \frac{1}{2\pi i} \oint_{C_I} \frac{f(z)}{z - a}\, dz = 0 \qquad (4\text{-}80)$$

Reversing the direction of traversal on C_I then reduces Eq. (4-80) to

$$\frac{1}{2\pi i} \oint_{C_E} \frac{f(z)}{z - a}\, dz = \frac{1}{2\pi i} \oint_{C_I} \frac{f(z)}{z - a}\, dz \qquad (4\text{-}81)$$

Inserting Eq. (4-79) into Eq. (4-81) gives

$$\frac{1}{2\pi i} \oint_{C_E} \frac{f(z)}{z - a}\, dz = \frac{f(a)}{2\pi i} \oint_{C_I} \frac{dz}{z - a}$$
$$+ \frac{f'(a)}{2\pi i} \oint_{C_I} dz + \frac{1}{2\pi i} \oint_{C_I} g(z)\, dz \qquad (4\text{-}82)$$

On C_I, $r = $ constant; thus

$$z - a = re^{i\theta} \qquad (4\text{-}83)$$

$$dz = rie^{i\theta}\, d\theta \qquad (4\text{-}84)$$

$$\frac{dz}{z - a} = i\, d\theta \qquad (4\text{-}85)$$

so that

$$\frac{1}{2\pi i} \oint_{C_I} \frac{dz}{z - a} = \frac{1}{2\pi} \int_0^{2\pi} d\theta = 1 \qquad (4\text{-}86)$$

Furthermore,

$$\oint_{C_I} dz = ir \oint_{C_I} e^{i\theta}\, d\theta = ir \int_0^{2\pi} (\cos\theta + \sin\theta)\, d\theta = 0 \qquad (4\text{-}87)$$

yields, together with Eqs. (4-82) and (4-86),

$$\left| \oint_{C_E} \frac{f(z)}{z - a}\, dz - 2\pi i f(a) \right| = \left| \oint_{C_I} g(z)\, dz \right| \qquad (4\text{-}88)$$

Notice from Eq. (4-84) that

$$\left| \oint_{C_I} dz \right| \leq \oint_{C_I} |dz| = r \int_0^{2\pi} d\theta = 2\pi r \qquad (4\text{-}89)$$

Since $r < \delta$, it follows that

$$|g(z)| < \epsilon \text{ on } C_I \qquad (4\text{-}90)$$

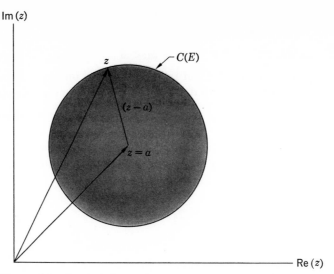

Figure 4-3 Cauchy's integral representation of an analytic function.

and

$$\left| \oint_{C_I} g(z) \, dz \right| \le \oint_{C_I} |g(z)| \, |dz| < \epsilon \oint_{C_I} |dz| = 2\pi r \epsilon \tag{4-91}$$

It follows from Eq. (4-91) that

$$\lim_{r \to 0} \oint_{C_I} g(z) \, dz = 0 \tag{4-92}$$

On the other hand, the left-hand side of Eq. (4-88) is *independent* of r and so must be identically zero. Thus,

$$f(a) = \frac{1}{2\pi i} \oint_{C_E} \frac{f(z)}{z - a} \, dz \tag{4-93}$$

expresses the value of an analytic function at a point $z = a$ within a closed contour in terms of its values on the contour. When $z = a$ is located outside C_E, then $f(z)/(z - a)$ is holomorphic in the simply connected region bounded by C_E. Thus Eq. (4-60) implies that

$$\frac{1}{2\pi i} \oint_{C_E} \frac{f(z)}{z - a} \, dz = 0 \tag{4-94}$$

This completes the proof of Cauchy's integral representation theorem.

Let the variable of integration in Cauchy's formula be denoted by ζ so that

$$f(z) = \frac{1}{2\pi i} \oint_C \frac{f(\zeta)}{\zeta - z} \, d\zeta \tag{4-95}$$

where z is any point interior to C.

It follows from a consideration of

$$\lim_{h \to 0} \frac{f(z + h) - f(z)}{h} \tag{4-96}$$

using Eq. (4-95) that

$$f'(z) = \frac{1}{2\pi i} \oint_C \frac{f(\zeta)}{(\zeta - z)^2} \, d\zeta \qquad (4\text{-}97)$$

This is formally equivalent to differentiating Eq. (4-95) under the integral sign. As mentioned at the beginning of Sec. 4-7, it is a consequence of Cauchy's integral theorem that if $f(\zeta)$ is an analytic function, regular (i.e., single-valued and differentiable) within the closed contour C, and continuous within and on C, then it possesses derivatives of *all orders* which are regular within C. The nth derivative is given by

$$f^{(n)}(z) = \frac{n!}{2\pi i} \oint_C \frac{f(\zeta)}{(\zeta - z)^{n+1}} \, d\zeta \qquad (4\text{-}98)$$

4-9 TAYLOR'S SERIES

We are now able to establish the connection between the definition of an analytic function as a power series and the integral representation of an analytic function.

THEOREM: Let $f(z)$ be analytic on and inside a simple closed contour C, and let a be a point inside C. Then

$$f(z) = f(a) + f'(a)(z - a) + \cdots + \frac{f^{(n)}(a)}{n!} (z - a)^n + \cdots \qquad (4\text{-}99)$$

the series being convergent for $|z - a| < \delta$, where δ is the distance from a to the nearest point of C.

proof: Let

$$f(z) = \frac{1}{2\pi i} \oint_C \frac{f(\zeta)}{\zeta - z} \, d\zeta \qquad (4\text{-}100)$$

where C is a circle centered at a and of radius $r < \delta$. Equation (4-100) holds if z lies inside C, i.e., when

$$|z - a| < r \qquad (4\text{-}101)$$

Suppose that

$$k = \frac{z - a}{\zeta - a} \qquad (4\text{-}102)$$

Then

$$1 - k = \frac{\zeta - z}{\zeta - a} \qquad (4\text{-}103)$$

and

$$\frac{1}{1 - k} = \frac{\zeta - a}{\zeta - z} = \sum_{k=0}^{\infty} k^n \qquad |k| < 1 \qquad (4\text{-}104)$$

Hence dividing Eq. (4-104) by $\zeta - a$ gives

$$\frac{1}{\zeta - z} = \frac{1}{\zeta - a} + \frac{z - a}{(\zeta - a)^2} + \cdots + \frac{(z - a)^n}{(\zeta - a)^{n+1}} + \cdots$$

$$(4\text{-}105)$$

which converges uniformly for $|k| \le |k_1| < 1$. On the circle C,

$$|k| = \left| \frac{z - a}{\zeta - a} \right| = \frac{r}{\delta} < 1$$

$$(4\text{-}106)$$

so that Eq. (4-105) converges uniformly on C. Therefore Eq. (4-105) may be multiplied by $f(\zeta)/2\pi i$ and integrated term by term around C. The result is

$$f(z) = \frac{1}{2\pi i} \oint_C \frac{f(\zeta)}{\zeta - a} \, d\zeta + \frac{z - a}{2\pi i} \oint_C \frac{f(\zeta)}{(\zeta - a)^2} \, d\zeta$$
$$+ \cdots + \frac{(z - a)^n}{2\pi i} \oint_C \frac{f(\zeta)}{(\zeta - a)^{n+1}} \, d\zeta + \cdots \qquad (4\text{-}107)$$

and Eq. (4-99) follows from an application of Eqs. (4-97) to (4-107).

4-10 CAUCHY'S INEQUALITIES

The fact that a function is regular in some region places severe constraints upon its behavior. For example, if $f(\zeta)$ is an analytic function, regular within a circle C of center z and radius R, it follows that the inequality $|f(\zeta)| \le M$ on C implies that

$$|f^{(n)}(z)| \le \frac{n!}{R^n} M$$

$$(4\text{-}108)$$

To prove inequality (4-108) consider Eq. (4-97). On C

$$\left| \frac{f(\zeta)}{(\zeta - z)^{n+1}} \right| \le \frac{M}{R^{n+1}}$$

$$(4\text{-}109)$$

and

$$|f^{(n)}(z)| \le \frac{n!}{2\pi} \left| \oint_C \frac{f(\zeta)}{(\zeta - z)^{n+1}} \, d\zeta \right|$$
$$\le \frac{n!}{2\pi} \oint_C \left| \frac{f(\zeta)}{(\zeta - z)^{n+1}} \right| |d\zeta| \le \frac{n!}{2\pi} \frac{M}{R^{n+1}} \oint_C |d\zeta|$$
$$= \frac{n!}{2\pi} \frac{M}{R^{n+1}} (2\pi R) = \frac{n!}{R^n} M \qquad (4\text{-}110)$$

which was to be demonstrated.

4-11 ENTIRE FUNCTIONS

An analytic function which is regular in *every finite* region of the z plane is called an "entire function" or sometimes an "integral function." Many of the elementary functions of interest in physics are entire. For example, polynomials in z, $\sin z$, $\cos z$, e^z, $\sinh z$, and $\cosh z$ are all entire functions.

The class of entire functions has an interesting property which is summarized in Liouville's theorem:

"The only *bounded* analytic function which can be *regular everywhere* is a constant."

The proof follows from (4-108). If a is any point of the z plane, then $f(z)$ is regular when $|z - a| < R$, no matter how large we choose R to be. Since $f(z)$ is bounded, we have

$$|f(z)| \leq M \tag{4-111}$$

and from inequality (4-108),

$$|f'(a)| \leq \frac{M}{R} \tag{4-112}$$

Making $R \to \infty$, we obtain

$$f'(a) = 0 \tag{4-113}$$

and since a is arbitrary, we conclude that $f'(z) = 0$ for all z; hence $f(z)$ must be a constant.

4-12 RIEMANN'S THEORY OF FUNCTIONS OF A COMPLEX VARIABLE

Riemann's approach to functions of a complex variable was remarkably different from the analytic attacks of Weierstrass and Cauchy. Riemann thought of a single-valued analytic function of a complex variable as providing a certain one-to-one mapping or correspondence between the points of two *different* two-dimensional surfaces. A characteristic property of this mapping is that the angle of intersection of a pair of curves on one surface is the same as the angle of intersection of their images on a second surface. A mapping which preserves angles in this sense is called a "conformal" mapping.

According to the famous *Riemann mapping theorem*, a single-valued analytic function can be geometrically characterized by the fact that it maps an infinitesimal circle on one surface onto an infinitesimal ellipse on a second surface. It does this in such a way that the interiors of the two curves correspond, with the center of the circle going into the center of the ellipse. Thus a pair of straight lines which intersect at right angles at the center of the circle are mapped onto a pair of straight lines intersecting at right angles at the center of the ellipse. The mapping is thus conformal. However, the circumference of the ellipse is not in general equal to the circumference of the circle, and so we say that a conformal mapping is not generally isometric, i.e., length-preserving.

The essence of Riemann's method is to take a two-dimensional surface and imagine a family of curves to be drawn upon it. One then classifies single-valued analytic functions geometrically, according to how such functions map the first surface with its family of curves onto a second surface with a corresponding family of curves. The *geometric characterization* of the *mapping* then *dictates* the *analytic form* which the *mapping* must assume. Thus an analytic function can be represented by an integral, can be expanded in a power series, and provides a conformal mapping of one surface onto another.

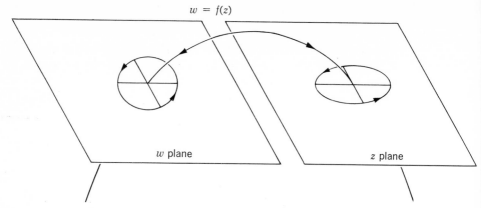

Figure 4-4 Geometric content of the Riemann mapping theorem.

4-13 PHYSICAL INTERPRETATION

The geometric function theory of Riemann admits a simple and important physical interpretation. Consider an incompressible fluid flowing in a steady state over the x, y plane. Let $\mathbf{v}$ be the velocity vector of the fluid at any point in the x, y plane. Since the fluid is incompressible, and we assume that there are no sources or sinks of fluid in any region A of the x, y plane, it follows that

$$\iint_A \boldsymbol{\nabla} \cdot \mathbf{v} \, dx \, dy = 0 \tag{4-114}$$

over *any* region A. Hence

$$\boldsymbol{\nabla} \cdot \mathbf{v} = \frac{\partial v_x}{\partial x} + \frac{\partial v_y}{\partial y} = 0 \tag{4-115}$$

Thus the velocity field of the fluid is solenoidal. The circulation of a fluid around a closed curve C is by definition

$$\oint_C \mathbf{v} \cdot d\mathbf{r} = \oint_C v_x \, dx + v_y \, dy \tag{4-116}$$

The fluid flow defined by v is irrotational if its circulation around *any* closed curve is zero. In that case

$$v_x \, dx + v_y \, dy \tag{4-117}$$

is an exact differential, and there is a function $u(x,y)$ such that

$$v_x = \frac{\partial u}{\partial x} \tag{4-118}$$

$$v_y = \frac{\partial u}{\partial y} \tag{4-119}$$

Inserting Eqs. (4-118) and (4-119) into Eq. (4-115) gives

$$\nabla^2 u = \frac{\partial^2 u}{\partial x^2} + \frac{\partial^2 u}{\partial y^2} = 0 \tag{4-120}$$

which is Laplace's equation. Any solution of Laplace's equation is called a *harmonic function*, and the particular solution u which generates the velocity vector $\mathbf{v}$ from Eqs. (4-118) and (4-119) is known as the velocity potential of the flow. The curves $u(x,y) = $ constant are called "level curves" or "equipotential lines." To find the angle that the tangent to an equipotential line makes with the x axis notice that on $u(x,y) = $ constant

$$du = \frac{\partial u}{\partial x}\,dx + \frac{\partial u}{\partial y}\,dy = \nabla u \cdot d\mathbf{r} = 0 \tag{4-121}$$

Thus

$$\frac{dy}{dx} = \tan\alpha = -\frac{\partial u/\partial x}{\partial u/\partial y} \tag{4-122}$$

follows from Eq. (4-121) provided that

$$(\nabla u)^2 = \left(\frac{\partial u}{\partial x}\right)^2 + \left(\frac{\partial u}{\partial y}\right)^2 = v_x{}^2 + v_y{}^2 = |\mathbf{v}|^2 \neq 0 \tag{4-123}$$

The velocity vector

$$\mathbf{v} = (v_x, v_y) = \left(\frac{\partial u}{\partial x}, \frac{\partial u}{\partial y}\right) = \nabla u \tag{4-124}$$

makes an angle β with the x axis, given by

$$\tan\beta = \frac{v_y}{v_x} = \frac{\partial u/\partial y}{\partial u/\partial x} \tag{4-125}$$

Comparison of Eqs. (4-122) and (4-125) shows that

$$\tan\alpha \tan\beta = -1 \tag{4-126}$$

from which it is seen that α and β differ by 90 degrees and that the flow is perpendicular to the equipotential lines in the direction of increasing u. Given the harmonic function u, we can *define* a *conjugate harmonic function* v by means of the Cauchy-Riemann equations (4-57) and (4-58). Then

$$w = u(x,y) + iv(x,y) = f(z) \tag{4-127}$$

is an *analytic* function of z, and is called the *complex potential* of the flow. The tangent to the curve $v(x,y) = $ constant makes an angle γ with the x axis, given by

$$\frac{dy}{dx} = \tan\gamma = -\frac{\partial v/\partial x}{\partial v/\partial y} \tag{4-128}$$

Using the Cauchy-Riemann equations again yields

$$\tan\gamma = -\frac{\partial v/\partial x}{\partial v/\partial y} = \frac{\partial u/\partial y}{\partial u/\partial x} = \tan\beta \tag{4-129}$$

or $\tan\gamma = \tan\beta$. Since β is the angle which the velocity vector $\mathbf{v}$ makes with the x axis, we conclude that the fluid flows in the direction of the curves $v(x,y) = $ constant which are therefore called

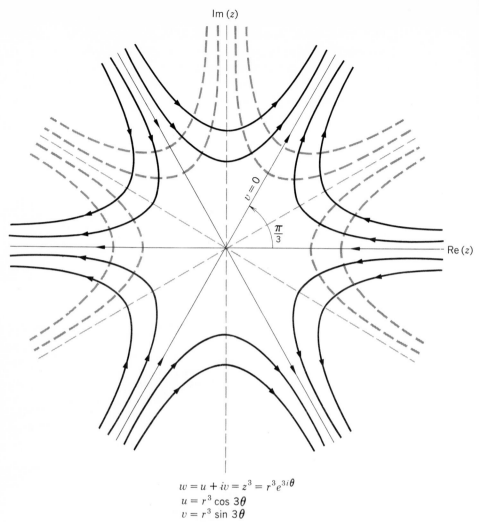

$$w = u + iv = z^3 = r^3 e^{3i\theta}$$
$$u = r^3 \cos 3\theta$$
$$v = r^3 \sin 3\theta$$

Figure 4-5 Solid streamlines v = constant and dashed equipotentials u = constant for $w = z^3$. Arrows on the streamlines v = constant point toward decreasing values of u, and $z = 0$ is a second-order saddle point.

"streamlines." Notice that Eqs. (4-55) and (4-57) yield

$$f'(z) = \frac{\partial u}{\partial x} + i \frac{\partial v}{\partial x} = \frac{\partial u}{\partial x} - i \frac{\partial u}{\partial y} \tag{4-130}$$

Thus the assumption that

$$|\mathbf{v}| = \sqrt{v_x{}^2 + v_y{}^2} = \sqrt{\left(\frac{\partial u}{\partial x}\right)^2 + \left(\frac{\partial u}{\partial y}\right)^2} \neq 0 \tag{4-131}$$

is equivalent to the condition

$$|f'(z)| \neq 0 \tag{4-132}$$

This means that the streamlines are orthogonal to the equipotential lines, except at points where

$$f'(z) = 0 \tag{4-133}$$

Notice that if $u + iv$ is analytic, then the Cauchy-Riemann equations

$$\frac{\partial u}{\partial x} = \frac{\partial v}{\partial y} \qquad \frac{\partial u}{\partial y} = -\frac{\partial v}{\partial x}$$

can also be written as

$$\frac{\partial v}{\partial x} = \frac{\partial}{\partial y}(-u) \qquad \frac{\partial v}{\partial y} = -\frac{\partial}{\partial x}(-u)$$

which means that $v - iu$ is analytic as well. Thus the curves $v = $ constant can be equipotential lines, and the curves $u = $ constant can be streamlines. The flow given by $v - iu$ is called the "conjugate" flow to $u + iv$. If the analytic function $w = f(z)$ is finite and differentiable at z_0, but $f'(z_0) = 0$, then $z = z_0$ is called a "saddle point" or "stationary point" of $f(z)$. The curves $u = $ constant and $v = $ constant do not intersect orthogonally at saddle points. For example, let

$$f(z) = a_0 + a_k(z - z_0)^k + a_{k+1}(z - z_0)^{k+1} + \cdots \tag{4-134}$$

where $a_k \neq 0$; then there are k equipotentials and k streamlines going through z_0. The angle between equipotentials is π/k, and the angle between streamlines is also π/k. The streamlines and the equipotentials bisect one another so that the lines $u = $ constant and $v = $ constant intersect at an angle of $\pi/2k$ at z_0. The point z_0 in (Eq. 4-134) is called a saddle point of order $k - 1$ of $f(z)$. The student can verify these statements by substituting

$$z - z_0 = re^{i\theta} \tag{4-135}$$

into Eq. (4-134) and examining the behavior of Re $f(z)$ and Im $f(z)$ as $z \to z_0$.

4-14 FUNCTIONS DEFINED ON CURVED SURFACES

We have seen how a one-to-one correspondence between points (x,y) in a flat plane and complex numbers can be established, using the equation $z = x + iy$. The complex function $w = f(z)$ then assigns a complex number w to every point z of the x, y plane. We have just seen that the curves Re $f(z) = u(x,y) = $ constant and Im $f(z) = v(x,y) = $ constant, as drawn upon the x, y plane, can be physically interpreted as the equipotentials and streamlines of a fluid flowing in the x, y plane, in a pattern dictated by the choice of $f(z)$.

However, a fluid can flow on a curved surface in space such as a sphere or a torus just as on a flat plane. Moreover, a fluid flow on a closed curved surface in space has associated with it a complex potential function $f(z)$ whose real part gives the equipotential curves on the surface and whose imaginary part gives the streamlines.

It was Riemann's discovery that there is an intimate relationship between the nature of the flows which are possible on a given surface and whether the surface is simply connected or not.

In the case of a closed surface in space, we say that the surface is simply connected if *every* closed curve drawn on the surface separates it into two disconnected pieces. For example, a sphere is a simply connected closed surface while a torus or a sphere with several handles on it is not.

Riemann's approach was to systematically examine closed surfaces in space such as spheres with zero, one, two, three, . . . , n handles attached to them (Fig. 4-6). He then determined which functions on a given surface corresponded to analytic functions in the z plane. From this class of functions he then singled out those which were single-valued on the surface. In this way, he arrived at a classification of analytic functions according to their "Riemann surfaces." Riemann was able to show that on a sphere S with $g < m$ handles there is at least one single-valued complex potential function w whose real and imaginary parts provide the equipotentials and streamlines for a hydrodynamic flow on S. He showed that if the flow has a total number of sinks and sources equal to m, arranged so that their strengths balance in order to conserve mass, then the single-valued complex potential function w assumes any given complex value, say $2 + 3i$, exactly m times on S, one at each of m different places on S.

Now consider m complex planes stacked one above the other. In order to make a connected surface of these m separate sheets, we shall select r points at which two or more of the m sheets are to be welded together. We do this in such a way that every one of the m separate sheets is welded at least once to at least one of the other $m - 1$ sheets. We shall call the resulting welded surface S^* and the points at which the welds are made the branch points of S^*.

Riemann showed that the number of branch points on S^* was related to the total number of sinks and sources on S and to the total number of handles on S according to the formula

$$r = 2m + 2g - 2 \tag{4-136}$$

Moreover, he showed that the single-valued complex potential w on S establishes a one-to-one conformal correspondence between the points on S and the points on S^*. Each saddle point of w on S corresponds to some one of the r branch points on S^*. This correspondence is such that a saddle point of w of order $k - 1$ on S goes into a branch point on S^* at which k of the m sheets are welded together. Obviously $k < m$. There is a reason for welding together k of the m sheets of S^* at a branch point of order $k - 1$. It is that corresponding to the branch point of order $k - 1$ on S^* there is a saddle point of order $k - 1$ on S, and at this saddle point the single-valued function w assumes the single value w_0 exactly k times. This can be seen from Eq. (4-134).

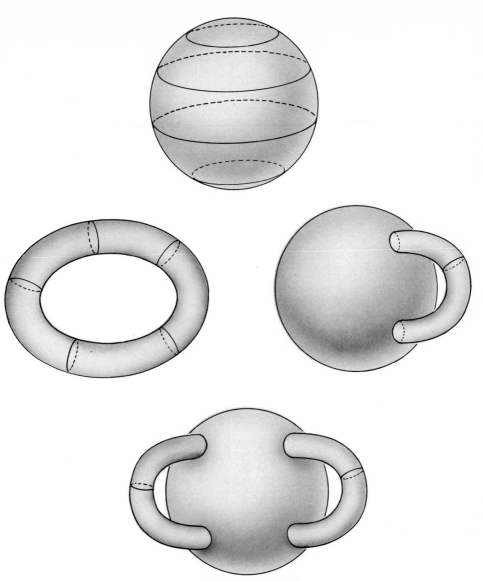

Figure 4-6 Spheres with 0, 1, and 2 handles.

The original Riemann surface S which is a sphere with g handles attached to it is thus conformally equivalent to an m-sheeted Riemann surface S^* composed of flat sheets joined together at $r = 2m + 2g - 2$ branch points.

Very frequently in theoretical physics, it is necessary to examine the behavior of a function of a complex variable *defined on a Riemann surface*. We can use either S^* *or* S as the Riemann surface. By a single-valued function defined on a Riemann surface, we have in mind the assignment of a definite power series to every point P of S.

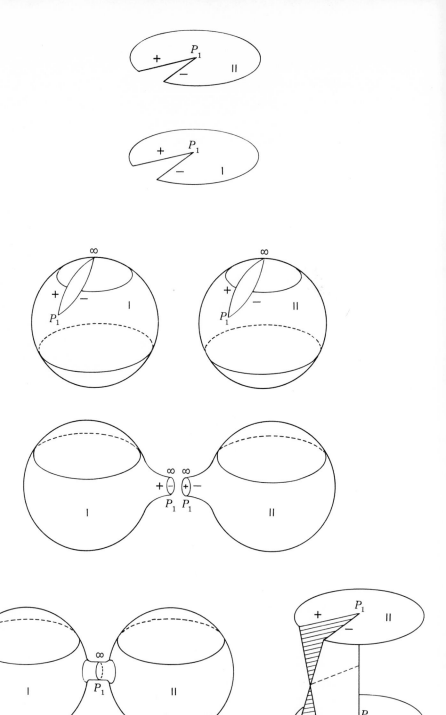

Figure 4-7 Two sheets welded together at the branch points P_1 and ∞ and interconnected along the edges of the cuts terminating at P_1 and ∞ form a Riemann surface topologically equivalent to a sphere with zero handles.

This single-valued function then consists of the totality of power series obtained by assigning one series to each point P of S. Let the resulting function be denoted by

$$z = z(P) \qquad P \in S \tag{4-137}$$

There are now two single-valued functions defined on the Riemann surface S. The first of these is

$$w = w(P) \tag{4-138}$$

which is the complex potential that maps S one to one and conformally onto S^*, where S^* is the m-sheeted Riemann surface which is joined together at branch points. The existence of w on S is guaranteed to us by Riemann. The second single-valued function $z = z(P)$ we have just constructed by assigning a power series to each point P of S. How are z and w related to each other? To answer this question, let us select a point P_1 on S which is not a saddle point of w, and thus corresponds to a point of S^* which is not a branch point. Let the value of w at P_1 be denoted by w_0. The value w_0 will also be assumed by w at $m - 1$ other points on S, say $P_2, P_3, \ldots, P_m$. By analogy the function $\sin x$ assumes the value 0 at $x_1 = 0$ and also at $m - 1$ other points, namely $x_2 = \pi$, $x_3 = 2\pi$, $x_m = (m - 1)\pi$ on the x axis, which in this case plays the role of S. Since $z = z(P)$ is also a single-valued function on S, then z will have m values $z(P_1), z(P_2), \ldots, z(P_m)$ corresponding to *one* value of w, namely w_0.

For this reason we say that z is an m-valued function of w, and we indicate this by writing m separate power series for z, using w as the independent variable. Thus,

$$z = \sum_{k=0}^{\infty} a_{kq} w^k \qquad q = 1, 2, \ldots, m \tag{4-139}$$

represents z as an *m-valued function of w*. However, z is single-valued on S in the sense that to any point P on S, there is only one value of z, namely $z = z(P)$. Since w maps S one to one and conformally onto the m-sheeted Riemann surface S^*, it follows that z is also single-valued on S^*. We are thus led to the conclusion that the complex function z, although m-valued when considered as a function of w, is single-valued on the m-sheeted Riemann surface S. The discovery by Riemann that an m-valued function could be made single-valued on a multisheeted surface or on a sphere with handles was one of the great advances in mathematics.

Suppose that both z and w are complex potential functions giving hydrodynamic flows on the sphere with g handles denoted by S. Let the total number of sinks and sources associated with w be given by m, and the same quantity for z be given by n. It can then be shown that z and w satisfy an *algebraic* equation of degree m in z and of degree n in w having the form

$$f(z,w) = a_0(w)z^m + a_1(w)a^{m-1} + \cdots + a_{m-1}(w)z$$
$$+ a_m(w) = 0 \tag{4-140}$$

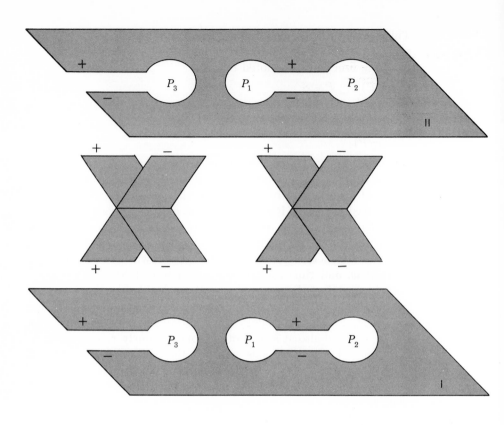

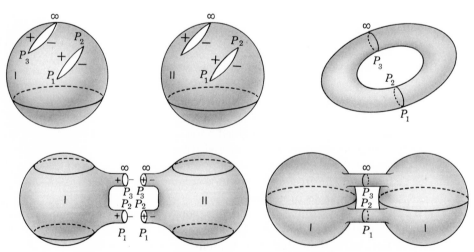

Figure 4-8 Two sheets welded together at the four branch points P_1, P_2, P_3, and ∞ form a Riemann surface which is topologically equivalent to a sphere with one handle, i.e., a torus.

To each point on S^* or S corresponds one pair of values (z,w) which satisfies the equation $f(z,w) = 0$, and, conversely, to each (z,w) corresponds in general *one* point on the surface S or S^*. Thus S or S^* is the Riemann surface of the algebraic function $f(z,w) = 0$. We say that

$$w = w(z) \tag{4-141}$$

is an algebraic function of z and that

$$z = z(w) \tag{4-142}$$

is an algebraic function of w. Both z and w are single-valued functions on the Riemann surface S or S^* associated with $f(z,w) = 0$.

Given the complex potential $w = w(P)$ on S together with its total of m sinks and sources, there still remains considerable latitude in our choice of the second single-valued function $z = z(P)$ defined on S. It can be shown that if $z = z(P)$ is any other complex potential function on S, then z satisfies an algebraic equation of degree m in z of the form

$$f(z,w) = z^m + r_1(w)z^{m-1} + \cdots + r_{m-1}(w)z \\ + r_m(w) = 0 \tag{4-143}$$

where $r_k(w)$, $k = 1,2, \ldots ,m$, are rational functions of w. Furthermore, if $w = w(P)$ is a given complex potential function on S taking on each value m times, there is a second complex potential function $z = z(P)$ such that the mth-degree algebraic equation satisfied by z in terms of w is *irreducible*. To be irreducible means that $f(z,w)$ *cannot* be *factored* into the product of two other algebraic functions of positive degree in z, both of which have coefficients which are *rational* functions of w. In other words, we *cannot* find a pair of algebraic functions $f_1(z,w)$ and $f_2(z,w)$ such that

$$f(z,w) = f_1(z,w)f_2(z,w) \tag{4-144}$$

If there is a total of n sinks and sources associated with $z = z(P)$, then $f(z,w)$ is of degree n in w, and Eq. (4-143) may also be written as

$$f(z,w) = w^n + R_1(z)w^{n-1} + \cdots + R_{n-1}(z)w \\ + R_n(z) = 0 \tag{4-145}$$

where the $R_k(z)$, $k = 1,2, \ldots ,n$, are rational functions of z.

Each one of the m power series in Eq. (4-139) is called a "distinct branch" of the m-valued algebraic function $z = z(w)$. These power series represent the m solutions of Eq. (4-143) in the sense that

$$f(z(w),w) \equiv 0 \tag{4-146}$$

Because of the total of n sinks and sources assumed to be associated with $z = z(P)$, we may assume that $z = z(P)$ takes on the value $z = \infty$ exactly n times on S. Consequently, it assumes every value $z = a$ exactly n times. It follows that $z = z(P)$ gives a one-to-one conformal mapping of S onto the n-sheeted branched Riemann surface S^*. The n points on S^* at which $z(P) = a$ need not be distinct.

If at a point P_0 on S^*, $z(P)$ assumes the value of a r times, in terms of a local parameter t about P_0, we have

$$z(t) - a = C_r t^r + C_{r+1} t^{r+1} + \cdots \tag{4-147}$$

The parameter t is called the "local uniformizer" at P_0 on S^*.

In general, $w(P)$ is single-valued and analytic on the Riemann surface S^*. This means that it is an analytic function of the local uniformizer t at any point on S^*. For example, at the point P_0, w assumes the value b once, and we have

$$w(t) - b = g_1 t + g_2 t^2 + \cdots + g_n t^n + \cdots \tag{4-148}$$

Notice that $\sqrt[r]{z - a}$ can be taken as a local parameter about P_0. The point P_0 is an $(r - 1)$st-order branch point of S^*. This means that in the vicinity of the branch point P_0 of S^* where z assumes the value of a r times, $w - b$ is expressed as a power series not in $z - a$ but instead in terms of the rth root $(z - a)^{1/r}$. Thus

$$w - b = d_1(z - a)^{1/r} + d_2(z - a)^{2/r} + \cdots$$
$$+ d_n(z - a)^{n/r} + \cdots \tag{4-149}$$

where we have assumed that w takes on the value b once at P_0. If w takes on the value of b k times at P_0, then Eq. (4-149) becomes

$$w - b = d_k(z - a)^{k/r} + d_{k+1}(z - a)^{k+1/r} + \cdots \tag{4-150}$$

If the value $z = \infty$ is assumed s times at the point P_0, then

$$z(t) = c_{-s} t^{-s} + c_{-s+1} t^{-s+1} + \cdots \tag{4-151}$$

We may also take as the local uniformizing parameter $\sqrt[s]{1/z}$. Notice that $z = \infty$ is a branch point of order $s - 1$ of S^*.

It is a remarkable fact that given the Riemann surface S or S^* associated with the algebraic function $f(z,w) = 0$, we can always find a local uniformizing parameter t about any point on S, such that

$$f(z(t),w(t)) \equiv 0 \tag{4-152}$$

and such that $z(t)$ and $w(t)$ are power series in t.

4-15 LAURENT'S SERIES

If $f(z)$ is single-valued and analytic throughout the closed annulus bounded by the outer circle C_2 and the inner concentric circle C_1, then $f(z)$ can be expanded in a series of positive and negative powers of $z - a$. This series converges at all points of the annulus.

proof: Let z be a point of the annulus, and consider

$$\frac{1}{2\pi i} \oint_C \frac{f(\zeta)}{\zeta - z}\, d\zeta \tag{4-153}$$

where C represents the *total* boundary of the annulus traversed so that the interior of the annulus always lies to the left. Expression (4-153) becomes

$$\frac{1}{2\pi i} \oint_C \frac{f(\zeta)}{\zeta - z}\, d\zeta = \frac{1}{2\pi i} \oint_{C_2} \frac{f(\zeta)}{\zeta - z}\, d\zeta - \oint_{C_1} \frac{f(\zeta)}{\zeta - z}\, d\zeta \tag{4-154}$$

where the minus sign in the second term of Eq. (4-154) arises because

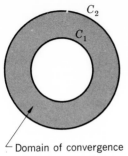

Domain of convergence

Figure 4-9 Domain of convergence for Laurent's series.

the inner circle must be traversed in a clockwise direction in order
to keep the interior of the annulus on the left. Since z is inside the
annulus, Cauchy's integral theorem (4-74) gives

$$f(z) = \frac{1}{2\pi i} \oint_{C_2} \frac{f(\zeta)}{\zeta - z} d\zeta - \oint_{C_1} \frac{f(\zeta)}{\zeta - z} d\zeta \qquad (4\text{-}155)$$

It follows from Sec. 4-9 that

$$\frac{1}{2\pi i} \oint_{C_2} \frac{f(\zeta)}{\zeta - z} d\zeta = \sum_{n=0}^{\infty} a_n (z - a)^n \qquad (4\text{-}156)$$

where a is the common center of C_1 and C_2. And

$$a_n = \frac{1}{2\pi i} \oint_{C_2} \frac{f(\zeta)}{(\zeta - a)^{n+1}} d\zeta \qquad (4\text{-}157)$$

Notice that a_n is not in general equal to $f^{(n)}(a)/n!$ since $f(z)$ is not
necessarily analytic *throughout* the *interior* of C_2.

It follows from Eq. (4-105) that

$$\frac{1}{z - \zeta} = \frac{1}{z - a} + \frac{\zeta - a}{(z - a)^2}$$
$$+ \cdots + \frac{(\zeta - a)^n}{(z - a)^{n+1}} + \cdots \qquad (4\text{-}158)$$

on interchanging z and ζ. The series (4-158) converges uniformly on
C_1; hence

$$-\frac{1}{2\pi i} \oint_{C_1} \frac{f(\zeta)}{\zeta - z} d\zeta = \frac{1}{2\pi i} \frac{1}{z - a} \oint_{C_1} f(\zeta) d\zeta + \cdots$$
$$+ \frac{1}{2\pi i} \frac{1}{(z - a)^{n+1}} \oint_{C_1} (\zeta - a)^n f(\zeta) d\zeta + \cdots \qquad (4\text{-}159)$$

which gives

$$-\frac{1}{2\pi i} \oint_{C_1} \frac{f(\zeta)}{\zeta - z} d\zeta = \sum_{n=1}^{\infty} \frac{b_n}{(z - a)^n} \qquad (4\text{-}160)$$

Here

$$b_n = \frac{1}{2\pi i} \oint_{C_1} (\zeta - a)^{n-1} f(\zeta) d\zeta \qquad (4\text{-}161)$$

Combining Eqs. (4-155), (4-156), and (4-160), we obtain Laurent's series for $f(z)$,

$$f(z) = \sum_{n=-\infty}^{\infty} a_n(z-a)^n \tag{4-162}$$

where

$$a_n = \frac{1}{2\pi i} \oint_C \frac{f(\zeta)}{(\zeta-a)^{n+1}} d\zeta \tag{4-163}$$

for all values of n. The contour C in Eq. (4-163) is any simple closed contour which passes around the annulus and lies between C_1 and C_2. (Proof?)

Notice that when $f(z)$ is analytic throughout the interior of the inner circle C_1, all the terms with negative n in Eq. (4-162) are absent by virtue of Cauchy's theorem. The series of positive powers of $z - a$ converges, not merely in the annulus but everywhere inside circle C_2. Similarly the series of negative powers converges everywhere outside C_1. Their common domain of convergence is the interior of the annulus.

4-16 SINGULARITIES OF AN ANALYTIC FUNCTION

Isolated singularities

If $f(z)$ is analytic throughout the neighborhood of a point a, say for $|z-a| < R$, but is not analytic at a itself, then the point a is an isolated singularity of $f(z)$.

Classification of isolated singularities

The main tool for classifying isolated singularities of single-valued analytic functions is the Laurent series.

Given an isolated singular point a of $f(z)$, we can always expand $f(z)$ in a Laurent series about $z = a$, and we can choose the inner circle C_1 to be arbitrarily small since the singular point a is isolated. Three possible cases arise.

1. If each a_n for which $n < 0$ vanishes in Eq. (4-162), then $f(z)$ is analytic for $|z-a| < R$, except at the point a. This kind of singular point is called a "removable" singular point. The singularity can be removed by defining $f(z)$ at $z = a$ in such a way that $f(z)$ becomes analytic there. For example, if $f(z) = z$ for $0 < |z| < 1$ and $f(0) = 1$, then $f(z)$ has a removable singularity at $z = 0$. To remove it, we define $f(z) = z$ for $0 \le |z| < 1$. Now $f(z)$ is analytic at $z = 0$.

2. If Eq. (4-162) contains only a finite number of terms having negative powers of $z - a$, then $f(z)$ is said to have a pole at the point $z = a$. For example, if

$$f(z) = \sum_{n=-k}^{\infty} a_n(z-a)^n \tag{4-164}$$

then $f(z)$ has a pole of order k at $z = a$.

3. If Eq. (4-162) contains an infinite number of terms having negative powers of $z - a$, then $f(z)$ is said to have an essential singularity at $z = a$. For example, $e^{1/z}$ has an isolated essential singularity at $z = 0$.

The behavior of $f(z)$ in the vicinity of an essential singularity is very complicated. It can be shown that in the neighborhood of an essential singularity, $f(z)$ takes on every complex number, with at most one exception, an infinity of times. For example, $e^{1/z}$ takes on every value except 0 an infinity of times in an arbitrarily small disk centered on $z = 0$.

4-17   MULTIVALUED FUNCTIONS

The simplest type of multivalued functions arises when one solves an algebraic equation of the form

$$f(z,w) = 0 \tag{4-165}$$

For example, take the equation

$$w^2 - (z - a) = 0 \tag{4-166}$$

For any value of z different from $z = a$ there are two distinct values of w, say $w_1(z)$ and $w_2(z)$. These two functions, $w_1(z)$ and $w_2(z)$, each satisfy Eq. (4-166) and are known as the *single-valued branches* of the *double*-valued algebraic function

$$w(z) = \sqrt{z - a} \tag{4-167}$$

It is $w(z)$ which gives the *formal* solution of Eq. (4-166). It helps in understanding the significance of $w_1(z)$ and $w_2(z)$ if we first imagine w, z, and a to be strictly real, and then look upon Eq. (4-167) as a geometric curve drawn on a plane in which w is the ordinate and z is the abscissa. Obviously Eq. (4-167) is a parabola intersecting the z axis at $z = a$ and opening toward the positive z axis. The upper branch of the parabola corresponds to $w_1(z)$, while the lower branch of the parabola corresponds to $w_2(z)$. This labeling, of course, is arbitrary and can just as well be reversed. The full significance of $w_1(z)$ and $w_2(z)$ is now obtained by performing an analytic continuation on each of these real functions. This is done by allowing z to become complex. Now we can no longer look at pictures in the real z, w plane since both z and w have become complex variables. Nevertheless, except at $z = a$, we still have two distinct single-valued functions $w_1(z)$ and $w_2(z)$. These are what one means by the single-valued branches of $w(z) = \sqrt{z - a}$. For complex z we can write

$$z - a = re^{i\theta} \tag{4-168}$$

and

$$w_1(z) = |\sqrt{r}|\, e^{i\theta/2} \tag{4-169}$$

$$w_2(z) = |\sqrt{r}|\, e^{i(\theta/2+\pi)} \tag{4-170}$$

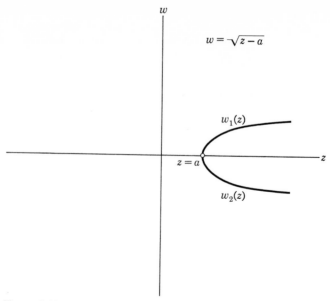

Figure 4-10 Graph of $w = \sqrt{z-a}$ for real values of w and z.

At $z = a$, $r = 0$, forcing $w_1(z)$ and $w_2(z)$ to coalesce to $w_1(a) = 0$ and $w_2(a) = 0$.

The point $z = a$ at which these two branches w_1 and w_2 become equal is a *singular* point of the *algebraic function* $w(z)$ given by Eq. (4-167). This type of singular point of $w(z)$ is called a *branch point*. In Eq. (4-167) the branch point $z = a$ is the point at which the upper and lower branches of parabola, described by the equation, for real z, coalesce.

To study the behavior of Eq. (4-167) in the neighborhood of the branch point $z = a$, let

$$w = \rho e^{i\phi} \tag{4-171}$$

and let z circumscribe the point a along a simple closed curve. Then as $\theta = \arg(z - a)$ increases from an initial value θ_0 to $\theta_0 + 2\pi$, $\phi = \arg(w)$ increases from an initial value $\phi_0 = \theta_0/2$ to $\theta_0/2 + \pi$.

Thus, starting from the value of one branch, say w_1, we arrive at the value of the other branch w_2 when we make one complete closed circuit in the z plane about the branch point. In order to regain the initial value w_1, we must permit θ_0 to change from θ_0 to $\theta_0 + 4\pi$, as we can see from Eq. (4-169). Thus two complete circuits of the branch point $z = a$ are required to cause w_1 to come back to its original value. In other words, a double circuit in the z plane about $z = a$ corresponds to a single circuit in the w plane about $w = 0$.

The Riemann surface for Eq. (4-167) provides a new domain for z to vary upon. On the Riemann surface, $w(z)$ becomes a single-valued function of z instead of a doubled-valued function of z. The

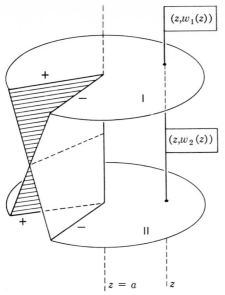

Figure 4-11   The Riemann surface for $w = \sqrt{z - a}$ near $z = a$.

Riemann surface for Eq. (4-167) consists of two identical complex z planes stacked one above the other so that the values of z coincide. These two sheets are "welded" together at the branch point $z = a$ to form a single surface. We name the top sheet I and associate with each point z on it a definite value $w_1(z)$. Similarly, we name the bottom sheet II and associate with each point z on it a definite value $w_2(z)$. In order to justify the fact that the initial values of w are obtained only after a double circuit about the branch point $z = a$, we proceed as follows: We make a scissor cut on each sheet from $z = a$ to ∞. We label the two edges of the cut on each sheet the plus and minus edges, respectively. We do this in such a way that the plus and minus edges of sheet I lie directly above the plus and minus edges of sheet II. These two cuts are called *branch cuts*. We now complete the Riemann surface by connecting the top plus edge to the bottom minus edge and the top minus edge to the bottom plus edge. To any point on this Riemann surface there now corresponds one and only one value of $w(z)$. Suppose we now start a circuit of branch point $z = a$ beginning at some point $z = z_0$ on the top sheet. After one complete circuit about the point $z = a$ we find ourselves back at $z = z_0$, but now we are on the bottom sheet instead of the top sheet. This happens because the top and bottom sheets are interconnected along the edges of the branch cuts on sheets I and II. If we now make a second circuit of the branch point $z = a$ beginning at $z = z_0$ on the lower sheet, we will return to $z = z_0$ on the upper sheet, having once again transferred sheets at the cut.

As a second example, consider

$$w(z) = \sqrt[m]{z - a} \tag{4-172}$$

For $z \neq a$, $w(z)$ is an m-valued function of z. At $z = a$, the m branches of $w(z)$ coalesce to zero, and $w(z)$ has a branch point of mth order at $z = a$. The corresponding Riemann surface consists of m distinct sheets, the first being connected with the mth along the branch cut starting from $z = a$.

For our last example we shall consider a multivalued function which is not algebraic.

$$w(z) = \log z = \log |z| + i \left[\arg (z) + 2\pi k \right] \tag{4-173}$$

where $k = 0, \pm 1, \pm 2, \ldots$. This function is infinitely many-valued; $z = 0$ is a branch point of infinitely high order. The corresponding Riemann surface consists of an infinite number of sheets connected together at $z = 0$. A branch point is a genuine singular point at which a function fails to be analytic. For example, if $w = \sqrt{z - a}$, then

$$\frac{dw}{dz} = \frac{1}{2}(z - a)^{-\frac{1}{2}}$$

shows that w is not analytic at $z = a$.

4-18 RESIDUES

Let $f(z)$ be single-valued and analytic throughout a simply connected domain D, *except* at one isolated singular point $z = a$ inside D. Let the boundary of D be a simple closed curve C. Consider the integral of $f(z)$ taken around C in the positive sense:

$$I = \oint_C f(z)\, dz \tag{4-174}$$

The student can easily prove that the value of I is the same for all curves C enclosing only the singular point $z = a$.

It is this common value of I which is defined as proportional to the residue of $f(z)$ at $z = a$. It is customary to include a normalizing factor of $1/2\pi i$ in the definition, so that

$$\text{Res}\left[f(z),\, z = a \right] = \frac{1}{2\pi i} \oint f(z)\, dz \tag{4-175}$$

The evaluation of the residue of a function at an isolated singularity becomes especially easy if we know its Laurent-series expansion about the singularity. For example, if $f(z)$ has a pole of kth order at $z = a$, then

$$f(z) = \sum_{n=-k}^{\infty} a_n (z - a)^n \tag{4-176}$$

$$\oint_C f(z)\, dz = \sum_{n=-k}^{\infty} a_n \oint_C (z - a)^n\, dz \tag{4-177}$$

Choose C to be a circle of radius r centered on $z = a$, and consider

$$\oint_C (z - a)^n \, dz \tag{4-178}$$

with

$$z - a = re^{i\theta} \tag{4-179}$$

$$dz = ire^{i\theta} \, d\theta \tag{4-180}$$

Then

$$\oint_C (z - a)^n \, dz = ir^{n+1} \int_0^{2\pi} e^{i(n+1)\theta} \, d\theta \tag{4-181}$$

but

$$\int_0^{2\pi} e^{i(n+1)\theta} \, d\theta = \begin{cases} 2\pi & n = -1 \\ 0 & n \neq -1 \end{cases} \tag{4-182}$$

Therefore

$$\frac{1}{2\pi i} \oint_C f(z) \, dz = a_{-1} \tag{4-183}$$

giving

$$\text{Res} \, [f(z), z = a] = a_{-1} \tag{4-184}$$

Notice that the only term in Eq. (4-176) which contributes to the residue of $f(z)$ is $a_{-1}/(z - a)$. If $a_{-1} = 0$, then $f(z)$ has a zero residue at $z = a$. Nevertheless, $f(z)$ is still singular at $z = a$, provided $k \geq 2$.

EXAMPLE 4-1:

$$\text{Res} \left[\frac{1}{z^3(1 - z)}, z = 0 \right] = 1$$

since

$$\frac{1}{z^3(1 - z)} = \frac{1}{z^3} + \frac{1}{z^2} + \frac{1}{z} + 1 + z + \cdots + z^{n-3}$$
$$+ \cdots \qquad 0 < |z| < 1$$

$$\text{Res} \left[\frac{1}{z^2(1 - z^2)}, z = 0 \right] = 0$$

since

$$\frac{1}{z^2(1 - z^2)} = \frac{1}{z^2} + 1 + z^2 + \cdots + z^{2n-2} + \cdots$$
$$0 < |z| < 1$$

If C is any circle centered on $z = 0$ and of radius less than unity, then

$$\oint_C \frac{dz}{z^3(1 - z)} = 2\pi i \tag{4-185}$$

and

$$\oint_C \frac{dz}{z^2(1 - z^2)} = 0 \tag{4-186}$$

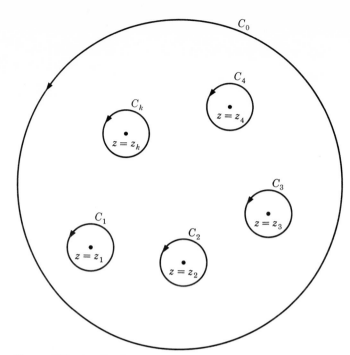

Figure 4-12 Application of the residue theorem.

Equation (4-183) is generalized in one of the most useful theorems of complex analysis:

Cauchy's residue theorem

Let $f(z)$ be single-valued and analytic except at a finite number of isolated singular points z_1, z_2, . . . , z_n lying within a domain D. Let the boundary of D be the simple closed curve C_0; then

$$\oint_{C_0} f(z)\, dz = 2\pi i \sum_{k=1}^{n} \text{Res}\,[f(z),\, z = z_k] \tag{4-187}$$

proof: To prove this theorem we construct a new domain D' such that $f(z)$ is everywhere analytic in D'. This is accomplished by removing all the singular points z_k from D by surrounding each z_k with a small circle C_k whose interior is then removed from D. The region D' has the appearance of a piece of Swiss cheese having n holes and an outer circumference C_0.

Now $f(z)$ is everywhere analytic in D'; however, D' is not simply connected. We apply Cauchy's integral theorem (4-60) to $f(z)$, being careful to integrate around the *total* boundary of D', i.e., around C_0 and around each of the n circles C_k. The integration must be done so that the interior of D' always lies to the left as the boundary is traversed. We obtain

$$\oint_C f(z) \, dz = 0 \tag{4-188}$$

where

$$C = \sum_{k=0}^{n} C_k \tag{4-189}$$

It follows that

$$\oint_{C_0} f(z) \, dz = \sum_{k=1}^{n} \oint_{C_k} f(z) \, dz \tag{4-190}$$

which on application of Eq. (4-175) becomes

$$\oint_{C_0} f(z) \, dz = 2\pi i \sum_{k=1}^{n} \text{Res} \, [f(z), z = z_k] \tag{4-191}$$

The residue theorem permits rapid evaluation of integrals on closed paths. Here are some useful rules for computing residues:

1. If $z = a$ is a first-order pole of $f(z)$, then

$$\text{Res} \, [f(z), z = a] = \lim_{z \to a} (z - a)f(z) \tag{4-192}$$

2. If $z = a$ is a pole of order n of $f(z)$, then

$$\text{Res} \, [f(z), z = a] = \lim_{z \to a} \frac{1}{(n-1)!} \frac{d^{n-1}}{dz^{n-1}} h(z) \tag{4-193}$$

where

$$h(z) = (z - a)^n f(z)$$

3. If $A(z)$ and $B(z)$ are analytic in a neighborhood of $z = a$, $A(a) \neq 0$, and $B(z)$ goes to zero as a constant times $(z - a)$ at $z = a$, then

$$f(z) = \frac{A(z)}{B(z)} \tag{4-194}$$

has a pole of first order at $z = a$, and

$$\text{Res} \, [f(z), z = a] = \lim_{z \to a} \frac{A(z)}{B'(z)} \tag{4-195}$$

These rules can be established by obtaining the coefficient a_{-1} of the appropriate Laurent series in each case.

4-19 RESIDUE AT INFINITY

DEFINITION: Let $f(z)$ be single-valued and analytic for $|z| > R$ with the exception of the point $z = \infty$ at which $f(z)$ is assumed to have an isolated singularity. Let C be any simple closed contour in the domain of analyticity of $f(z)$. Then

$$\text{Res} \, [f(z), z = \infty] = \frac{1}{2\pi i} \oint_C f(z) \, dz \tag{4-196}$$

defines the residue of $f(z)$ at ∞. Notice that the contour C is now traversed in the clockwise (negative) direction. The reason is that the domain of analyticity of $f(z)$ (in this case $|z| > R$) must always lie to the left as any portion of a boundary curve is traversed.

If the Laurent series of $f(z)$ is given by

$$f(z) = \sum_{n=-k}^{\infty} a_n z^n \tag{4-197}$$

then an argument like that in Sec. 4-18 yields

$$\text{Res}\,[f(z), z = \infty] = -a_{-1} \tag{4-198}$$

Notice that the presence of a residue at $z = \infty$ is not related to the presence of a pole or essential singularity at $z = \infty$. A pole at infinity causes

$$\lim_{z \to \infty} f(z) = \infty \tag{4-199}$$

and this is due to $a_n z^n$ terms in Eq. (4-197) having $n > 0$, whereas the residue comes from a_{-1}/z. Similarly, $e^{1/z}$ is analytic at $z = \infty$; however, since

$$e^{1/z} = \sum_{n=0}^{\infty} \frac{1}{n!z^n} \tag{4-200}$$

it follows that

$$\text{Res}\,[e^{1/z}, z = \infty] = -1 \tag{4-201}$$

In summary, if a function has a residue at infinity, this does not mean that it has a pole or essential singularity there, nor does this necessarily prevent the function from being analytic at infinity.

4-20 GENERALIZED RESIDUE THEOREM OF CAUCHY

Let $f(z)$ be a single-valued function analytic except at a finite number of isolated singular points $z_1, z_2, \ldots, z_n$ lying in the complex z plane. Let C_0 be any simple closed curve lying in the z plane and such that none of the isolated singularities falls exactly on C_0. Let the interior of C_0 be called D and the exterior D'. The point $z = \infty$ belongs to D'. Some of the n isolated singularities, say r of them, will lie in D while the remaining $n - r$ singularities will lie in D'. Then

$$\oint_{C_0} f(z)\,dz = \begin{cases} 2\pi i \sum_{k=1}^{r} \text{Res}\,[f(z), z = z_k] \\[2mm] -2\pi i \left\{ \sum_{k=r+1}^{n} \text{Res}\,[f(z), z = z_k] \right. \\[2mm] \left. + \text{Res}\,[f(z), z = \infty] \right\} \end{cases} \tag{4-202}$$

gives two alternative means of evaluating a contour integral taken around the closed curve C_0 surrounding D. One can take the value of the integral (4-202) as either $2\pi i$ times the sum of the residues

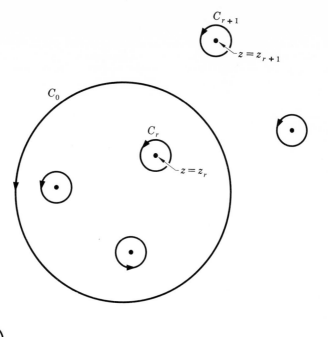

Figure 4-13 An integral can be evaluated by residues in two ways. Either the poles inside C_0 or outside C_0 can be used.

enclosed by C_0 or as $-2\pi i$ times the sum of the residues lying outside C_0, *including* the residue at infinity (Fig. 4-13). An integral can be evaluated in both ways and the results checked against each other. Frequently one method of evaluation is computationally easier than the other.

The proof of this theorem is essentially the same as that of (Eq. 4-187). The evaluation of residues at infinity is often facilitated by use of the following rules:

1. If $\lim_{z \to \infty} f(z)$ approaches zero like constant/z, then

$$\text{Res}\,[f(z),\, z = \infty] = - \lim_{z \to \infty} zf(z) \tag{4-203}$$

2. If $\lim_{z \to \infty} f(z)$ approaches zero like constant/z^n with $n \geq 2$, then

$$\text{Res}\,[f(z),\, z = \infty] = 0 \tag{4-204}$$

3. $\text{Res}\,[f(z),\, z = \infty] = - \text{Res}\left[\dfrac{1}{z^2} f\left(\dfrac{1}{z}\right),\, z = 0\right] \tag{4-205}$

EXAMPLE 4-2:

$$I = \oint_{|z|=4} \frac{z\,dz}{1 - z^3}$$

Let us first evaluate I by use of the isolated singularities of the integrand lying inside the circle $|z| = 4$. We have

$$1 - z^3 = 0$$

for $z = 1$, $z = e^{2\pi i/3}$, and $z = e^{4\pi i/3}$. These three values of z are each first-order poles of $z/(1 - z^3)$. Rule (4-195) gives

$$\frac{A(z)}{B'(z)} = -\frac{z}{3z^2}$$

for the residue at any of the three poles of the integrand. At each of these poles $z^3 = 1$; hence

$$\text{Res}\,[f(z),z] = -\frac{z}{3z^2} = -\frac{z^2}{3}$$

Therefore

$$I = 2\pi i\,\{\text{Res}\,[f(z),\, z = 1] + \text{Res}\,[f(z),\, z = e^{2\pi i/3}] \\ + \text{Res}\,[f(z),\, z = e^{4\pi i/3}]\}$$

yields

$$I = -\frac{2\pi i}{3}\,(1 + e^{4\pi i/3} + e^{8\pi i/3})$$

which can be written

$$I = -\frac{2\pi i}{3}\,(1 - e^{\pi i/3} + e^{2\pi i/3})$$

Notice that

$$e^{i\pi/3} + e^{-i\pi/3} = 1$$

Hence

$$e^{2\pi i/3} + 1 = e^{i\pi/3}$$

Therefore

$$I = 0 \tag{4-206}$$

We shall now evaluate I, using the singularities lying outside $|z| = 4$. The only singularity outside $|z| = 4$ is at infinity. We have

$$\lim_{z \to \infty} \frac{z}{1 - z^3} \to -\frac{1}{z^2}$$

Hence rule (4-204) yields

$$I = 0$$

again.

EXAMPLE 4-3:

$$I = \oint_{|z|=2} \frac{dz}{(z - 1)^5(z^2 - 16)(z + 5)} \tag{4-207}$$

In this case there is a fifth-order pole at $z = 1$ inside the contour $|z| = 2$, and first-order poles at $z = \pm 4$ and $z = -5$ outside the contour. The residue at infinity is zero. The evaluation of a residue at a fifth-order pole involves considerably more calculation than at a first-order pole. Hence we evaluate I using the singularities outside $|z| = 2$, obtaining

$$I = -2\pi i \left[\frac{1}{3^5 \cdot 8 \cdot 9} + \frac{1}{(-5)^5 \cdot (-8)} + \frac{1}{(-6)^5 \cdot 9} \right] \qquad (4\text{-}208)$$

EXAMPLE 4-4: A real integral of the form

$$I = \int_{-\infty}^{+\infty} f(x)\, dx \qquad (4\text{-}209)$$

converges when $f(x)$ is a ratio of polynomials in x if and only if the degree of the denominator is at least two units higher than the degree of the numerator, and provided that no pole lies on the x axis. If we now analytically continue $f(x)$ into the complex z plane, replacing x by $z = x + iy$, we must consider

$$I = \int_{-\infty}^{+\infty} f(z)\, dz \qquad (4\text{-}210)$$

integrated on the path

$$-\infty \le x \le +\infty \qquad (4\text{-}211)$$

$$y = 0 \qquad (4\text{-}212)$$

In order to use the residue theorem to evaluate Eq. (4-210), we shall integrate over a closed curve consisting of a line segment $(-r, r)$ and the semicircle from r to $-r$ in the upper half plane. If r is large enough, this curve encloses all poles in the upper half plane, and the corresponding integral is equal to $2\pi i$ times the sum of the residues in the upper half plane. It can be shown that the contribution to the integral arising from integration around the semicircle tends to zero as the radius r becomes infinite. Therefore

$$\int_{-\infty}^{+\infty} f(z)\, dz = 2\pi i \sum_{\text{Im } (z) > 0} \text{Res } f(z) \qquad (4\text{-}213)$$

EXAMPLE 4-5: The same method can be applied to evaluate an integral of the form

$$I = \int_{-\infty}^{+\infty} f(x) e^{ix}\, dx \qquad (4\text{-}214)$$

Once again we make an analytic continuation of the integrand of Eq. (4-214) into the complex z plane, obtaining

$$I = \int_{-\infty}^{+\infty} f(z) e^{iz}\, dz \qquad (4\text{-}215)$$

which is to be evaluated on the path (4-211) and (4-212). Since

$$|e^{iz}| = e^{-y} \qquad (4\text{-}216)$$

is bounded in the upper half plane, we can again conclude that the integral over the upper semicircle tends to zero, provided that the rational function $f(z)$ goes to zero at $z = \infty$ like constant$/z^n$ for $n \ge 2$. We get

$$\int_{-\infty}^{+\infty} f(z) e^{iz}\, dz = 2\pi i \sum_{\text{Im } (z) > 0} \text{Res } [f(z) e^{iz}] \qquad (4\text{-}217)$$

In fact, a theorem (Jordan's lemma) which is proved in many text-books on complex variables guarantees that Eq. (4-217) holds even when $f(z)$ goes to zero like constant$/z$ as z approaches infinity. Notice that (4-217) is valid only if there are no poles of $f(z)$ on the real z axis.

EXAMPLE 4-6: An identical procedure can be used to evaluate the integral

$$I(t) = \int_{-\infty}^{+\infty} f(x)e^{-ixt}\,dx \tag{4-218}$$

where $f(x)$ is a rational function of x. Here t is a real-valued parameter. Again we continue the integrand of Eq. (4-218) analytically into the complex z plane, replacing x by $z = x + iy$. Thus

$$I(t) = \int_{-\infty}^{+\infty} f(z)e^{-izt}\,dz \tag{4-219}$$

must be evaluated on the path (4-211) and (4-212). Notice that

$$|e^{-izt}| = e^{yt} \tag{4-220}$$

Hence, for $t < 0$, e^{yt} is bounded in the upper half plane. We therefore choose a semicircle lying in the upper half plane when $t < 0$ in order to close the contour of integration. Provided that

$$\lim_{z \to \infty} f(z) = \frac{\text{const}}{z} \tag{4-221}$$

we obtain

$$I(t) = \int_{-\infty}^{+\infty} f(z)e^{-izt}\,dz = 2\pi i \sum_{\substack{\text{Im } (y) > 0 \\ t < 0}} \text{Res}\,[f(z)e^{-izt}] \tag{4-222}$$

On the other hand, Eq. (4-220) shows that e^{yt} is bounded in the lower half plane $y < 0$ when $t > 0$. Hence, for $t > 0$ we close the contour of integration with a semicircle in the lower half plane. Notice that the singularities in the lower half plane are encircled in the clockwise (negative) direction as the path of integration is traversed. Therefore, when $t > 0$, we find

$$I(t) = \int_{-\infty}^{+\infty} f(z)e^{-izt}\,dz = -2\pi i \sum_{\substack{\text{Im } (y) < 0 \\ t > 0}} \text{Res}\,[f(z)e^{-izt}] \tag{4-223}$$

Summarizing,

$$I(t) = \int_{-\infty}^{+\infty} f(z)e^{-izt}\,dz = \begin{cases} 2\pi i \sum\limits_{\text{Im } (y) > 0} \text{Res}\,[f(z)e^{-izt}] & t < 0 \\ -2\pi i \sum\limits_{\text{Im } (y) < 0} \text{Res}\,[f(z)e^{-izt}] & t > 0 \end{cases} \tag{4-224}$$

provided

$$\lim_{z \to \infty} f(z) = \frac{\text{const}}{z} \tag{4-225}$$

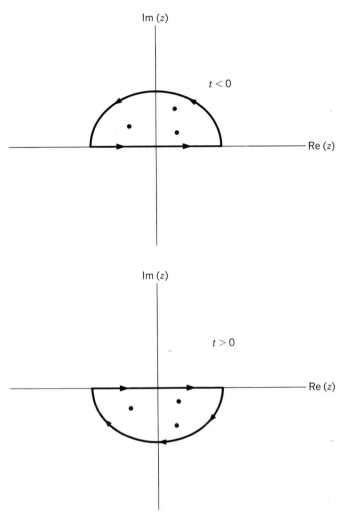

Figure 4-14 If $I(t) = 0$ for $t \leq 0$, then $f(z)$ must be analytic at every point of the upper half plane Im $(z) \geq 0$.

4-21 PROBLEMS AND APPLICATIONS

1. Given $z = x + iy$ show that:

$$\sin z = \sin x \cosh y + i \cos x \sinh y$$
$$\cos z = \cos x \cosh y - i \sin x \sinh y$$
$$\sinh iz = i \sin z$$
$$\cosh iz = \cos z$$
$$e^{iz} = \cos z + i \sin z$$
$$\sin iz = i \sinh z$$
$$\cos iz = \cosh z$$

2. Prove that

$$\sqrt{x + iy} = \pm \left\{ \left[\frac{x + (x^2 + y^2)^{\frac{1}{2}}}{2} \right]^{\frac{1}{2}} + (sgn\ y)i \left[\frac{-x + (x^2 + y^2)^{\frac{1}{2}}}{2} \right]^{\frac{1}{2}} \right\}$$

where

$$sgn\ y = \begin{cases} +1 & y > 0 \\ 0 & y = 0 \\ -1 & y < 0 \end{cases}$$

3. Prove that the complex roots of an algebraic equation with real coefficients occur in complex conjugate pairs.

4. Show that

$$\ln (1 + z) = \sum_{n=1}^{\infty} (-)^{n-1} \frac{z^n}{n}$$

and determine the region of analyticity of the series.

5. Show that $u + iv = (x + iy)^n$ gives a solution of the Cauchy-Riemann equations.

6. Derive the Cauchy-Riemann equations in polar coordinates (r,θ),

$$\frac{\partial u}{\partial r} = \frac{1}{r} \frac{\partial v}{\partial \theta} \qquad \frac{1}{r} \frac{\partial u}{\partial \theta} = -\frac{\partial v}{\partial r}$$

for $r \neq 0$.

7. Let t be a real-valued parameter such that $a \leq t \leq b$. As t varies, the function $z(t)$ traces out the curve C in the complex z plane, beginning at $z_0 = z(a)$ and ending at $z_1 = z(b)$. Prove that

$$\int_C f(z)\ dz = \int_a^b f[z(t)] \frac{dz}{dt}\ dt$$

8. Let C be the path

$$z(t) = e^{it} \qquad 0 \leq t \leq 2\pi$$

and let $f(z) = 1/z$. Use the result of Prob. 7 to show that

$$\int_C f(z)\ dz = 2\pi i$$

9. Let C be a circle centered on the origin of the z plane. Suppose that $f(z)$ is a function which is analytic in the upper semicircle and real-valued on any portion of the real axis inside the circle. Show that

$$f(z^*) = f^*(z)$$

10. Let t be a real-valued parameter such that $a \leq t \leq b$. As t varies, the function $z(t)$ traces out the curve C in the complex z plane, beginning at $z_0 = z(a)$ and ending $z_1 = z(b)$. Suppose that C is a simple curve which lies entirely in the upper half plane Im $(z) > 0$. Let the mirror image of C be called C^*. Thus C^* is obtained by reflecting C in the real axis. Show that if $f(z)$ is such that

$$f(z^*) = f^*(z)$$

168

FUNCTIONS OF A COMPLEX VARIABLE

then

$$\int_{C-C*} f(z)\, dz = 2i \, \mathrm{Im} \int_a^b f[z(t)] \frac{dz}{dt}\, dt$$

11. Graph the streamlines and equipotentials in the complex z plane for the function

$$w = z^3$$

What is the order of the saddle point at $z = 0$?

12. Graph the streamlines and equipotentials in the complex z plane for the functions

$$w = \log z \quad \text{and} \quad w = \frac{A}{z}$$

13. Show that if

$$u + iv = f(x + iy)$$

is an analytic function, then

$$\nabla^2 u = 0 \quad \text{and} \quad \nabla^2 v = 0$$

14. Expand the following functions in a Taylor series about $z = 0$:

(a) e^z
(b) $\sinh z$
(c) $\cosh z$
(d) $\sin z$
(e) $\cos z$
(f) $\log (1 + z)$
(g) $1/(1 - z^2)$

and state the radius of convergence in each case.

15. Obtain the Laurent series expansion about $z = 0$ for

(a) e^z/z^2
(b) $e^{1/z}$
(c) $(1 - \sin z)/z^2$
(d) $1/\sin z$

Give the domain of convergence for each series.

16. Expand

$$f(z) = \frac{z}{(2 - z)(4 - z)}$$

in a Laurent series about

(a) $z = 2$
(b) $z = 4$

and determine the domain of convergence in each case.

17. Discuss the singular points of the functions

$$w = \sqrt{(z - 1)(z + 1)}$$

and
$$w = \sqrt{(z - 1)(z + 1)(z + 2)}$$
with respect to type and order.

Construct the Riemann surfaces for these functions, showing the branch points, branch cuts, and the interconnection of the sheets.

18. Evaluate by residues

(a) $\displaystyle\oint_{|z|=5} \frac{ze^z}{1 - z^2}\, dz$

(b) $\displaystyle\oint_{|z|=4} \frac{e^z\, dz}{z(1 - z)^2}$

(c) $\displaystyle\oint_{|z|=1} \frac{(z + 2)}{z(4 - z)}\, dz$

(d) $\displaystyle\oint_{|z|=1} \frac{\sin z}{z^4}\, dz$

(e) $\displaystyle\oint_{|z|=1} \frac{e^z}{z^2}\, dz$

19. Evaluate the following real integrals by using the substitutions
$$z = e^{i\theta}$$
$$\cos\theta = \frac{e^{i\theta} + e^{-i\theta}}{2} = \frac{1}{2}\left(\frac{z^2 + 1}{z}\right)$$
$$\sin\theta = \frac{e^{i\theta} - e^{-i\theta}}{2} = \frac{1}{2i}\left(\frac{z^2 - 1}{z}\right)$$
and then applying the method of residues:

(a) $\displaystyle\int_0^{2\pi} \frac{d\theta}{2 + \cos\theta}$

(b) $\displaystyle\int_{-\pi}^{\pi} \frac{d\theta}{a + b\cos\theta + c\sin\theta}$

20. Prove that if $R(\sin\theta, \cos\theta)$ is a rational function of its two arguments, then
$$\int_0^{2\pi} R(\sin\theta, \cos\theta)\, d\theta = \oint_{|z|=1} R\left(\frac{z^2 - 1}{2iz}, \frac{z^2 + 1}{2z}\right) \frac{dz}{iz}$$

21. Evaluate by residues

(a) $\displaystyle\int_{-\infty}^{+\infty} \frac{dx}{1 + x^4}$

(b) $\displaystyle\int_{-\infty}^{+\infty} \frac{x\cos x}{x^2 + a^2}\, dx$

(c) $\displaystyle\int_{-\infty}^{+\infty} \frac{x\sin x}{x^2 + z^2}\, dx$

(d) $\displaystyle\int_0^{\infty} \frac{\cos kx}{(x^2 + a^2)^2}\, dx$

22. Let $f(z)$ be analytic inside a circle C except at the isolated singular point $z = z_k$ at which $f(z)$ has a pole of kth order. Let C have a radius $r > |z_k|$, and show that

$$I(t) = \oint_{|z|=r} f(z)e^{-izt}\,dz = 2\pi \exp\left[\frac{i(3k - 2)\pi}{2}\right]\frac{t^{k-1}}{(k-1)!}e^{-iz_k t}$$

$$f(z) = 1/(z - z_k)^k \qquad k \geq 1$$

Notice that the *order of the pole* determines the power of t and that the *location of the pole* determines the type of exponential. Thus, since

$$|e^{-iz_k t}| = e^{y_k t}$$

we can construct the following table:

Location of Pole	Order of Pole	Nature of $I(t)$
Origin: $z_k = 0$	$k = 1$	Const
Origin: $z_k = 0$	$k > 1$	Const $\cdot t^{k-1}$
Lower half plane: Im $(z_k) = y_k < 0$	$k = 1$	Exponentially decaying oscillation for $t > 0$. Exponentially growing oscillation for $t < 0$.
Lower half plane: Im $(z_k) = y_k < 0$	$k > 1$	Const $\cdot t^{k-1} \cdot$ exponentially decaying oscillation for $t > 0$. Const $\cdot t^{k-1} \cdot$ exponentially growing oscillation for $t < 0$.
Upper half plane: Im $(z_k) = y_k > 0$	$k = 1$	Exponentially growing oscillation for $t > 0$. Exponentially decaying oscillation for $t < 0$.
Upper half plane: Im $(z_k) = y_k > 0$	$k > 1$	Const $\cdot t^{k-1} \cdot$ exponentially growing oscillation for $t > 0$. Const $\cdot t^{k-1} \cdot$ exponentially decaying oscillation for $t < 0$.

integral transforms

5-1   INTRODUCTION

The problem of representing an arbitrary function $A(x)$ in a given interval $a \leq x \leq b$ as a linear combination of members of some infinite set of functions, say $\{e_1(x), e_2(x), \ldots, e_n(x), \ldots\}$, bears a strong formal resemblance to the problem of expressing a vector in n-dimensional space as a linear combination of n linearly independent vectors.

Thus in the case where $\mathbf{A}$ is a vector, we represent $\mathbf{A}$ in the form

$$\mathbf{A} = \sum_{k=1}^{n} a_k \mathbf{e}_k \tag{5-1}$$

When A is a scalar function of x, the desired representation is

$$A(x) = \sum_{k=1}^{\infty} a_k e_k(x) \tag{5-2}$$

In each case the problem is to calculate the expansion coefficients a_k. In the vector case (5-1) we have seen that the problem can be solved, when $\{\mathbf{e}_k\}$ is an orthonormal basis, by taking the scalar product of $\mathbf{A}$ with each $\mathbf{e}_k$ in succession. The results are summarized by Eqs. (1-42) and (1-43).

When $A(x)$ is infinitely differentiable in the interval $a \leq x \leq b$, one solution of case (5-2) is provided by choosing

$$e_k(x) = x^{k-1} \tag{5-3}$$

so that

$$\{e_1(x), e_2(x), \ldots, e_n(x), \ldots\} = \{1, x, x^2, \ldots, x^n, \ldots\} \tag{5-4}$$

Then

$$A(x) = \sum_{k=0}^{\infty} a_k x^k \tag{5-5}$$

represents $A(x)$ as a power series in x. The coefficients a_k are then obtained from the familiar Taylor formula:

$$a_k = \frac{1}{k!} \frac{d^k}{dx^k} A(x) \Big|_{x=0} \tag{5-6}$$

One must still prove, however, that the series on the right-hand side of Eq. (5-5) converges to the function on the left-hand side for each x in the interval $a \leq x \leq b$.

Frequently, the power-series expansion fails because $A(x)$ or some of its derivatives has a finite discontinuity at a finite number of points in the interval $a \leq x \leq b$. In such a case it is often possible to divide up the interval $a \leq x \leq b$ into subintervals such that in each subinterval $A(x)$ is continuous. Such an $A(x)$ is called piecewise-continuous, and if in addition $A(x)$ has a piecewise-continuous first derivative, then $A(x)$ is called piecewise-smooth. We can obtain a representation of a piecewise-continuous function of the form (5-2) by employing the properties of an orthogonal set of functions.

5-2 ORTHOGONAL FUNCTIONS

Suppose that $A(x)$ is a piecewise-continuous function in the interval $a \leq x \leq b$. We then postulate a development of the form

$$A(x) = \sum_{k=1}^{\infty} a_k e_k(x) \tag{5-7}$$

where each $e_k(x)$ is in general a complex-valued function of the real variable x. Next, we multiply both sides of Eq. (5-7) by $e_j^*(x)$ and form the integral with respect to x, obtaining

$$\int_a^b e_j^*(x) A(x)\, dx = \sum_{k=1}^{\infty} a_k \int_a^b e_j^*(x) e_k(x)\, dx \tag{5-8}$$

Here $e_j^*(x)$ is the complex conjugate of $e_j(x)$. We shall put off for the time being the justification of interchanging the order of integration and summation in going from Eq. (5-7) to Eq. (5-8). We can solve Eq. (5-8) for a_j if

$$\int_a^b e_j^*(x) e_k(x)\, dx = \lambda_k \delta_{jk} \tag{5-9}$$

for then

$$\int_a^b e_j^*(x) A(x)\, dx = \sum_{k=1}^{\infty} a_k \lambda_k \delta_{jk} = a_j \lambda_j \tag{5-10}$$

so that

$$a_j = \frac{1}{\lambda_j} \int_a^b e_j^*(x) A(x)\, dx \tag{5-11}$$

It is customary to alter the definitions and notation slightly when discussing integral transforms. Thus one writes

$$\mathbf{A}(j) = \int_a^b e_j^*(x) A(x)\, dx \tag{5-12}$$

and refers to Eq. (5-12) as the finite integral transform of $A(x)$. The postulated expansion (5-7) is called the "inversion theorem" corresponding to the finite integral transform (5-12). Since

$$a_j = \frac{\mathbf{A}(j)}{\lambda_j} \tag{5-13}$$

the inversion theorem for Eq. (5-12) becomes

$$A(x) = \sum_{k=1}^{\infty} \frac{\mathbf{A}(k)}{\lambda_k} e_k(x) \tag{5-14}$$

Two complex-valued functions such as $e_j(x)$ and $e_k(x)$ are said to be orthogonal over the interval $a \le x \le b$ if the relations

$$\int_a^b e_j^*(x)e_k(x)\,dx = \int_a^b e_j(x)e_k^*(x)\,dx = 0 \tag{5-15}$$

hold for $j \ne k$. Thus Eq. (5-9) specifies that $e_j(x)$ is orthogonal to $e_k(x)$ for $j \ne k$. Since j and k are arbitrary indices, it follows that $\{e_k(x); k = 1,2, \ldots\}$ is an orthogonal set of functions. If it should also be true that $\lambda_j = 1$ for $j = 1,2, \ldots$, then $\{e_k(x); k = 1,2, \ldots\}$ is called an "orthonormal" set of functions.

EXAMPLE 5-1: Interval $[-a,a]$:

$$\int_{-a}^{+a} \sin \frac{n\pi x}{a} \sin \frac{m\pi x}{a}\,dx = a\delta_{nm} \tag{5-16}$$

$$\int_{-a}^{+a} \cos \frac{n\pi x}{a} \cos \frac{m\pi x}{a}\,dx = a\delta_{nm} \tag{5-17}$$

$$\int_{-a}^{+a} \sin \frac{n\pi x}{a} \cos \frac{m\pi x}{a}\,dx = 0 \tag{5-18}$$

$$\int_{-a}^{+a} e^{i(n-m)\pi x/a}\,dx = 2a\delta_{nm} \tag{5-19}$$

Interval $[0,a]$:

$$\int_0^{+a} \sin \frac{n\pi x}{a} \sin \frac{m\pi x}{a}\,dx = \frac{a}{2}\delta_{nm} \tag{5-20}$$

$$\int_0^a \cos \frac{n\pi x}{a} \cos \frac{m\pi x}{a}\,dx = \frac{a}{2}\delta_{nm} \tag{5-21}$$

$$\int_0^a \sin \frac{n\pi x}{a} \cos \frac{m\pi x}{a}\,dx = \frac{an}{\pi(n^2 - m^2)}[1 - (-1)^{n-m}] \tag{5-22}$$

5-3   DIRAC'S NOTATION

A notation invented by Dirac and very popular with physicists makes the analogy between the expansion of a function in terms of an orthogonal set of functions and the expansion of a vector in terms of an orthogonal set of vectors particularly evident. We write

$$e_k(x) \equiv e_k(x)\rangle \tag{5-23}$$

and we call the symbol $e_k(x)\rangle$ a "ket vector." The complex conjugate $e_k^*(x)$ is written as

$$e_k^*(x) \equiv \langle e_k(x) \tag{5-24}$$

The symbol $\langle e_k(x)$ is called a "bra vector." The expression

$$\int_a^b e_j^*(x)e_k(x)\,dx \tag{5-25}$$

is called the "inner product" of the bra vector $\langle e_j(x)$ with the ket vector $e_k(x)\rangle$, or simply a "bracket." In Dirac's notation, expression (5-25) becomes

$$\langle e_j(x)|e_k(x)\rangle \equiv \int_a^b e_j^*(x)e_k(x)\,dx \tag{5-26}$$

The vertical line in the left member of expression (5-26) indicates the operation of forming an inner product. Frequently, the dummy variable of integration is omitted since it is integrated out anyway. Then (5-26) becomes simply

$$\langle e_j | e_k \rangle \equiv \int_a^b e_j^*(x) e_k(x) \, dx \tag{5-27}$$

Using Dirac's notation, Eq. (5-7) is written as

$$A(x)\rangle = \sum_{k=1}^{\infty} a_k e_k(x)\rangle \tag{5-28}$$

and Eq. (5-8) becomes

$$\langle e_j | A \rangle = \sum_{k=1}^{\infty} a_k \langle e_j | e_k \rangle \tag{5-29}$$

The orthogonality property (5-9) takes the form

$$\langle e_j | e_k \rangle = \lambda_k \delta_{jk} \tag{5-30}$$

and the definition of orthogonality (5-15) requires that

$$\langle e_j | e_k \rangle = \langle e_k | e_j \rangle = 0 \tag{5-31}$$

for $j \neq k$. Thus,

$$\langle e_j | A \rangle = \sum_{k=1}^{\infty} a_k \lambda_k \delta_{jk} = a_j \lambda_j \tag{5-32}$$

yields

$$a_j = \frac{1}{\lambda_j} \langle e_j | A \rangle \tag{5-33}$$

as the expression of the expansion coefficient. The finite integral transform (5-12) becomes

$$\mathbf{A}(j) = \langle e_j | A \rangle \tag{5-34}$$

and the inversion theorem (5-14) is written as

$$A(x)\rangle = \sum_{k=1}^{\infty} \frac{\langle e_k | A \rangle}{\lambda_k} e_k(x)\rangle \tag{5-35}$$

Notice that

$$\frac{\langle e_k | A \rangle}{\lambda_k} e_k(x)\rangle = e_k(x)\rangle \frac{\langle e_k | A \rangle}{\lambda_k} \tag{5-36}$$

Hence Eq. (5-35) can also be written in the form

$$A(x)\rangle = \sum_{k=1}^{\infty} \frac{1}{\lambda_k} e_k(x)\rangle\langle e_k | A \rangle \tag{5-37}$$

Observe that the formal algebraic expression

$$1 = \sum_{k=1}^{\infty} \frac{1}{\lambda_k} e_k(x)\rangle\langle e_k(x) \tag{5-38}$$

has the property that it reproduces Eq. (5-37) when Eq. (5-38) is multiplied *from the right* by $A\rangle$. In the multiplication, an inner product is understood, and use is made of the following definition:

$$1A\rangle = A\rangle \tag{5-39}$$

It follows from Eq. (5-39) that

$$\langle A1 = \langle A \tag{5-40}$$

as well.

EXAMPLE 5-2:

$$A(x) = \frac{a_0}{2} + \sum_{n=1}^{\infty} \left(a_n \cos \frac{n\pi x}{a} + b_n \sin \frac{n\pi x}{a} \right) \tag{5-41}$$

$$a_n = \frac{1}{a} \int_{-a}^{+a} A(x) \cos \frac{n\pi x}{a} \, dx \tag{5-42}$$

$$b_n = \frac{1}{a} \int_{-a}^{+a} A(x) \sin \frac{n\pi x}{a} \, dx \tag{5-43}$$

$$A(x) = \sum_{n=-\infty}^{+\infty} C_n e^{in\pi x/a} \tag{5-44}$$

$$C_n = \frac{1}{2a} \int_{-a}^{+a} A(x) e^{-in\pi x/a} \, dx \tag{5-45}$$

$$A(x) = \frac{a_0}{2} + \sum_{n=1}^{\infty} a_n \cos \frac{n\pi x}{a} \tag{5-46}$$

$$a_n = \frac{2}{a} \int_{0}^{a} A(x) \cos \frac{n\pi x}{a} \, dx \tag{5-47}$$

$$A(x) = \sum_{n=1}^{\infty} b_n \sin \frac{n\pi x}{a} \tag{5-48}$$

$$b_n = \frac{2}{a} \int_{0}^{a} A(x) \sin \frac{n\pi x}{a} \, dx \tag{5-49}$$

5-4 ANALOGY BETWEEN EXPANSION IN ORTHOGONAL FUNCTIONS AND EXPANSION IN ORTHOGONAL VECTORS

Let $\{e_k(x); k = 1,2, \ldots , \infty \}$ be a countably infinite set of orthonormal functions for the interval $a \leq x \leq b$. Therefore

$$\langle e_j | e_k \rangle = \delta_{jk} \tag{5-50}$$

Similarly, let $\{\mathbf{e}_k; k = 1,2, \ldots ,n\}$ be a set of n orthogonal unit vectors in a finite-dimensional space. Then

$$\mathbf{e}_j \cdot \mathbf{e}_k = \delta_{jk} \tag{5-51}$$

An arbitrary n-dimensional vector $\mathbf{A}$ can be expanded in terms of the vectors $\{\mathbf{e}_k; k = 1,2, \ldots ,n\}$ in the form

$$\mathbf{A} = \sum_{k=1}^{n} a_k\mathbf{e}_k \tag{5-52}$$

and the expansion coefficients a_k can be calculated by taking the *scalar* product of $\mathbf{A}$ with each $\mathbf{e}_k$ in succession, thus:

$$a_k = \mathbf{e}_k \cdot \mathbf{A} \tag{5-53}$$

A function $A(x)$ which is piecewise-continuous in the interval $a \le x \le b$ can be expanded in terms of the infinite set of functions $\{e_k(x); k = 1,2, \ldots ,\infty \}$ in the form

$$A(x)\rangle = \sum_{k=1}^{\infty} a_k e_k(x)\rangle \tag{5-54}$$

and the expansion coefficients a_k can be calculated by taking the *inner* product of $A(x)\rangle$ with each $\langle e_k$ in succession, obtaining

$$a_k = \langle e_k|A\rangle \tag{5-55}$$

The coefficients a_k appearing in (Eq. 5-54) can be considered the components of a vector. Since the functions $e_k(x)\rangle$ form a countably infinite set of orthonormal functions for the interval $a \le x \le b$, the components a_k may be thought of as an infinite-dimensional row vector $(a_1,a_2, \ldots ,a_k, \ldots)$ representing $A(x)$. This is analogous to the representation of an arbitrary n-dimensional vector $\mathbf{A}$ in terms of its components.

Then assuming

$$A(x)\rangle = \sum_{k=1}^{\infty} a_k e_k(x)\rangle \tag{5-56}$$

and

$$B(x)\rangle = \sum_{n=1}^{\infty} b_n e_n(x)\rangle \tag{5-57}$$

we have

$$
\begin{aligned}
\langle A|B\rangle &= \int_a^b A^*(x)B(x)\, dx \\
&= \sum_{k=1}^{\infty} \sum_{n=1}^{\infty} \int_a^b a_k^* b_n e_k^*(x) e_n(x)\, dx \\
&= \sum_{k=1}^{\infty} \sum_{n=1}^{\infty} a_k^* b_n \delta_{kn} = \sum_{k=1}^{\infty} a_k^* b_k
\end{aligned}
\tag{5-58}
$$

We ignore, for the present, questions of interchanging orders of summation and integration. Thus the expression $\langle A|B\rangle$ is a natural generalization of the scalar product in n dimensions:

$$\mathbf{A} \cdot \mathbf{B} = \sum_{k=1}^{n} a_k b_k \tag{5-59}$$

The form

$$\langle A|B \rangle = \sum_{k=1}^{\infty} a_k^* b_k \qquad (5\text{-}60)$$

is a slight generalization to allow us to deal with complex as well as real functions in such a way that

$$\langle A|A \rangle \geq 0 \qquad (5\text{-}61)$$

5-5 LINEAR INDEPENDENCE OF FUNCTIONS

We say that r functions $f_1(x)$, $f_2(x)$, $\ldots$, $f_r(x)$ are linearly independent if and only if the equation

$$c_1 f_1 + c_2 f_2 + \cdots + c_r f_r = 0 \qquad (5\text{-}62)$$

has no solution other than

$$c_1 = 0, \, c_2 = 0, \, \ldots , \, c_r = 0 \qquad (5\text{-}63)$$

for all x.

Consider the orthonormal system $\{e_k(x); \, k = 1,2, \, \ldots , \infty \}$. It is easy to see that any finite number of distinct $e_k(x)$ always form a linearly independent set of functions. For if an identity

$$\sum_{k=1}^{n} c_k e_k(x) \rangle = 0 \qquad (5\text{-}64)$$

holds, then

$$\sum_{k=1}^{n} c_k \langle e_j|e_k \rangle = 0 \qquad (5\text{-}65)$$

but

$$\langle e_j|e_k \rangle = \delta_{jk} \qquad (5\text{-}66)$$

Hence

$$c_k = 0 \qquad (5\text{-}67)$$

for $k = 1,2, \, \ldots ,n$. The important thing to observe is that given a system of infinitely many functions $i_1(x)$, $i_2(x)$, $\ldots$, any r of which are linearly independent for arbitrary r, an orthonormal system $e_1(x)$, $e_2(x)$, $\ldots$ may be constructed by means of the Schmidt orthogonalization process discussed for vectors in Chap. 1.

For example, we can choose

$$e_1(x) \rangle = \frac{i_1(x) \rangle}{|\langle i_1|i_1 \rangle|^{1/2}} \qquad (5\text{-}68)$$

and

$$e_2'(x) \rangle = i_2(x) \rangle - e_1(x) \rangle \langle e_1|i_2 \rangle \qquad (5\text{-}69)$$

Then

$$\langle e_1|e_2' \rangle = \langle e_1|i_2 \rangle - \langle e_1|e_1 \rangle \langle e_1|i_2 \rangle \qquad (5\text{-}70)$$

However

$$\langle e_1 | e_1 \rangle = 1 \tag{5-71}$$

Therefore

$$\langle e_1 | e_2' \rangle = 0 \tag{5-72}$$

In order to normalize $e_2(x)\rangle$ to unity, let

$$e_2(x)\rangle = \frac{e_2'(x)\rangle}{|\langle e_2' | e_2' \rangle|^{1/2}} \tag{5-73}$$

Continuing the Schmidt process, we obtain the analogue of Eq. (1-49),

$$e_m'(x)\rangle = i_m(x)\rangle - \sum_{k=1}^{m-1} e_k(x)\rangle\langle e_k | i_m\rangle \tag{5-74}$$

where

$$e_m(x)\rangle = \frac{e_m'(x)\rangle}{|\langle e_m'(x) | e_m'(x)\rangle|^{1/2}} \tag{5-75}$$

Thus, formulas (5-74) and (5-75) show how to construct a set of orthonormal functions $\{e_k(x); k = 1,2, \ldots ,r\}$ from a given set of r linearly independent functions $\{i_k(x); k = 1,2, \ldots ,r\}$.

REMARK: Notice that it follows from (5-23) and (5-24) that

$$(e_k(x)\rangle)^* = \langle e_k(x) \tag{5-76}$$

and

$$(\langle e_k(x))^* = e_k(x)\rangle \tag{5-77}$$

Similarly expression (5-26) shows that

$$(\langle e_j | e_k \rangle)^* = \langle e_k | e_j \rangle \tag{5-78}$$

5-6   MEAN-SQUARE CONVERGENCE OF AN EXPANSION IN ORTHOGONAL FUNCTIONS

Let us look more closely into the meaning of the equality sign in the expansion

$$A(x)\rangle = \sum_{k=1}^{\infty} a_k e_k(x)\rangle \tag{5-79}$$

introduced in Sec. 5-2. We shall begin by defining

$$S_n(x)\rangle = \sum_{k=1}^{n} a_k e_k(x)\rangle \tag{5-80}$$

so that Eq. (5-79) becomes

$$A(x)\rangle = \lim_{n \to \infty} S_n(x)\rangle \tag{5-81}$$

One can then consider $S_n(x)\rangle$ as an approximation to $A(x)\rangle$ which grows better and better as n increases indefinitely. A useful measure of the deviation of $S_n(x)\rangle$ from $A(x)\rangle$ which applies simultaneously to the whole interval $a \leq x \leq b$ is given by the following inner product:

$$E_n = \langle \{A(x) - S_n(x)\} | \{A(x) - S_n(x)\} \rangle \qquad (5\text{-}82)$$

Notice that for an arbitrary function $f(x)$ defined on $a \leq x \leq b$,

$$\langle f|f \rangle = \int_a^b f^*f \, dx = \int_a^b |f|^2 \, dx \qquad (5\text{-}83)$$

and

$$\text{Av}(\langle f|f \rangle) = \frac{1}{b-a} \langle f|f \rangle = \text{Av}(|f|^2) \qquad (5\text{-}84)$$

Hence we see that $E_n/(b-a)$ represents the mean of the square of the error $\{A(x) - S_n(x)\}$ integrated over the interval $[a,b]$. It is customary to call E_n simply the "mean-square error" of the approximation of $A(x)\rangle$ by $S_n(x)\rangle$.

If

$$\lim_{n \to \infty} E_n = 0 \qquad (5\text{-}85)$$

then we say that $S_n(x)\rangle$ *converges in the mean* to $A(x)\rangle$. This type of convergence is called "mean-square convergence," and one writes

$$A(x)\rangle = \underset{n \to \infty}{\text{l.i.m.}} S_n(x)\rangle \qquad (5\text{-}86)$$

which is read "$A(x)\rangle$ equals the *limit in the mean* of the sequence $S_n(x)\rangle$ as n approaches infinity."

Let us suppose that n functions $e_1(x)\rangle, e_2(x)\rangle, \ldots, e_n(x)\rangle$ form an orthonormal set, and let us examine Eq. (5-82). This becomes

$$E_n = \left\langle \left\{ A(x) - \sum_{k=1}^n a_k e_k(x) \right\} \middle| \left\{ A(x) - \sum_{k=1}^n a_k e_k(x) \right\} \right\rangle \qquad (5\text{-}87)$$

which upon expansion yields

$$E_n = \langle A|A \rangle - \left\{ \left\langle \sum_{k=1}^n a_k e_k \middle| A \right\rangle + \left\langle A \middle| \sum_{k=1}^n a_k e_k \right\rangle \right\}$$
$$+ \left\langle \sum_{k=1}^n a_k e_k \middle| \sum_{k=1}^n a_k e_k \right\rangle \qquad (5\text{-}88)$$

Let

$$c_k = \langle e_k | A \rangle \qquad (5\text{-}89)$$

and

$$c_k^* = \langle A | e_k \rangle \qquad (5\text{-}90)$$

Then Eq. (5-88) becomes

$$E_n = \langle A|A \rangle - \sum_{k=1}^n (a_k^* c_k + a_k c_k^*) + \sum_{k=1}^n a_k^* a_k \qquad (5\text{-}91)$$

where we have made use of the fact that

$$\langle e_j | e_k \rangle = \langle e_k | e_j \rangle = \delta_{jk} \qquad (5\text{-}92)$$

Notice that

$$(a_k - c_k)^*(a_k - c_k) = a_k^* a_k - (a_k^* c_k + a_k c_k^*) + c_k^* c_k \qquad (5\text{-}93)$$

Therefore

$$E_n = \langle A | A \rangle - \sum_{k=1}^{n} c_k^* c_k + \sum_{k=1}^{n} (a_k - c_k)^*(a_k - c_k) \qquad (5\text{-}94)$$

We see that

$$(a_k - c_k)^*(a_k - c_k) \geq 0 \qquad (5\text{-}95)$$

Hence the mean-square error in the approximation of $A(x)\rangle$ by $S_n(x)\rangle$ as given by Eq. (5-80) is minimized by choosing

$$a_k = c_k \qquad (5\text{-}96)$$

or

$$a_k = \langle e_k | A \rangle \qquad (5\text{-}97)$$

Thus choosing the expansion coefficient a_k in Eq. (5-80) to be the finite integral transform of $A(x)$ exactly minimizes the mean-square error in the approximation of $A(x)$ by $S_n(x)$. We have

$$\min (E_n) = \langle A | A \rangle - \sum_{k=1}^{n} c_k^* c_k \qquad (5\text{-}98)$$

Returning to Eq. (5-82), we can write it as

$$E_n = \int_a^b |\{A(x) - S_n(x)\}|^2 \, dx \qquad (5\text{-}99)$$

so that $E_n \geq 0$ for $b \geq a$, and therefore

$$\min (E_n) \geq 0 \qquad b \geq a \qquad (5\text{-}100)$$

as well. Thus

$$\sum_{k=1}^{n} c_k^* c_k \leq \langle A | A \rangle \qquad (5\text{-}101)$$

or

$$\sum_{k=1}^{n} \langle A | e_k \rangle \langle e_k | A \rangle \leq \langle A | A \rangle \qquad (5\text{-}102)$$

Since $c_k^* c_k \geq 0$, the sequence

$$\sum_{k=1}^{n} c_k^* c_k \qquad (5\text{-}103)$$

is nondecreasing. Then, provided that there is some constant $M < \infty$ such that

$$0 < \langle A | A \rangle = \int_a^b |A(x)|^2 \, dx < M \qquad (5\text{-}104)$$

expression (5-101) gives

$$\sum_{k=1}^{n} |c_k|^2 < M \qquad (5\text{-}105)$$

independent of n. Therefore

$$\lim_{n \to \infty} \sum_{k=1}^{n} |c_k|^2 \qquad (5\text{-}106)$$

must exist, and we have

$$\sum_{k=1}^{\infty} |c_k|^2 \leq \int_a^b |A(x)|^2 \, dx \qquad (5\text{-}107)$$

where

$$c_k = \int_a^b e_k^*(x) A(x) \, dx \qquad (5\text{-}108)$$

Expression (5-107) is known as "Bessel's inequality." Since the series $\sum_{k=1}^{\infty} |c_k|^2$ converges, it follows that

$$\lim_{k \to \infty} c_k = \lim_{k \to \infty} \langle e_k | A \rangle = 0 \qquad (5\text{-}109)$$

Next we shall derive a necessary and sufficient condition for the mean-square error (5-82) to approach zero as $n \to \infty$. Since both the error E_n and the minimum error $\min(E_n)$ are non-negative, we have

$$0 \leq \min(E_n) \leq E_n \qquad (5\text{-}110)$$

Therefore,

$$\lim_{n \to \infty} E_n = 0 \qquad (5\text{-}111)$$

only if

$$\lim_{n \to \infty} \min(E_n) = 0 \qquad (5\text{-}112)$$

and Eq. (5-112) with the use of Eq. (5-98) gives

$$\sum_{k=1}^{\infty} |c_k|^2 = \int_a^b |A(x)|^2 \, dx \qquad (5\text{-}113)$$

which is called "Parseval's equality." In Dirac's notation Parseval's equality becomes

$$\sum_{k=1}^{\infty} \langle A | e_k \rangle \langle e_k | A \rangle = \langle A | A \rangle \qquad (5\text{-}114)$$

or

$$\sum_{k=1}^{\infty} |\langle e_k | A \rangle|^2 = \langle A | A \rangle \qquad (5\text{-}115)$$

Parseval's equality provides a necessary and sufficient condition for the series

$$\sum_{k=1}^{\infty} e_k(x) \rangle \langle e_k | A \rangle \qquad (5\text{-}116)$$

to converge to $A(x)\rangle$ in the *mean-square sense*. It is this idea which makes precise the meaning of the equality in the equation

$$A(x)\rangle = \sum_{k=1}^{\infty} e_k(x)\rangle\langle e_k|A\rangle \tag{5-117}$$

If any arbitrary piecewise-continuous function $A(x)$ can be represented in the mean-square sense by a series expansion such as Eq. (5-117), then the orthonormal set of functions

$$\{e_k(x); k = 1,2, \ldots , \infty \}$$

is said to be closed. This set is also said to be complete if there is no nontrivial function $B(x)$ which is orthogonal to each $e_k(x)$. In other words,

$$\{e_k(x); k = 1,2, \ldots , \infty \}$$

is a complete set of functions if

$$\langle e_k|B\rangle = 0 \tag{5-118}$$

for

$k = 1,2, \ldots , \infty$ implies that

$$\langle B|B\rangle = 0 \tag{5-119}$$

where Eq. (5-119) defines what we mean by saying that $B(x)$ is a trivial function. It follows from Parseval's equality (5-115) that a closed orthonormal set is also complete. The converse is also true: Every complete set is closed. However, we shall not prove this here. In term of vectors, the notions of closure and completeness are readily seen to be equivalent. Thus the set of vectors $\{e_1,e_2,e_3\}$ is closed if every vector $\mathbf{A}$ can be written in the form

$$\mathbf{A} = a_1\mathbf{e}_1 + a_2\mathbf{e}_2 + a_3\mathbf{e}_3 \tag{5-120}$$

for some set of numbers a_1, a_2, and a_3. The set of vectors $\{e_1,e_2,e_3\}$ is called "complete" if there is no nontrivial vector orthogonal to all of them. In other words, $\{e_1,e_2,e_3\}$ is complete if

$$\mathbf{e}_k \cdot \mathbf{A} = 0 \tag{5-121}$$

for $k = 1,2,3$ implies

$$\mathbf{A} \cdot \mathbf{A} = 0 \tag{5-122}$$

Thus, in the case of a finite-dimensional vector space, both closure and completeness state that the vectors $\{e_1,e_2,e_3\}$ are noncoplanar and, therefore, that they are linearly independent.

REMARK: Notice that a crucial point in the entire discussion above is that

$$0 < \int_a^b |A(x)|^2 \, dx < M \tag{5-123}$$

Functions $A(x)$ satisfying inequality (5-123) are called "square or quadratically integrable." Such functions play an important role in physical problems. The reason is that in many physical systems the square of a function can be identified with the energy of the system.

In such cases quadratic integrability means that the total energy in the system must remain finite.

5-7 INTEGRATION AND DIFFERENTIATION OF ORTHOGONAL EXPANSIONS

We are now able to justify the interchange of summation and integration in Eq. (5-8) with the use of Parseval's equality (5-115). Consider the orthogonal expansion of $A(x)\rangle$ in the *complete* set of functions $\{e_k(x); \ k = 1,2, \ \ldots, \infty\}$,

$$A(x)\rangle = \sum_{k=1}^{\infty} a_k e_k(x)\rangle \tag{5-124}$$

and form

$$\left\langle A \ \Big| \ \sum_{k=1}^{\infty} a_k e_k(x)\right\rangle - \sum_{k=1}^{\infty} a_k\langle A | e_k\rangle = \langle A | A\rangle - \sum_{k=1}^{\infty} a_k\langle A | e_k\rangle$$

$$= \langle A | A\rangle - \sum_{k=1}^{\infty} a_k a_k^* = 0 \tag{5-125}$$

Equation (5-125) is Parseval's equality (5-115) which applies because of the assumed completeness of the set of functions $\{e_k(x);\ k = 1,2, \ \ldots, \infty\}$.

In general, the orthogonal expansion of a piecewise-continuous function $A(x)$ in a complete set of functions $\{e_k(x)\}$ can always be integrated term by term. The integrated series will converge in the mean-square sense to the integral of $A(x)$.

Term-by-term differentiation, however, is a much more precarious matter. In general, term-by-term differentiation of a convergent orthogonal expansion is permissible when it can be shown that differentiated expansion *converges uniformly* in the interval considered.

5-8 POINTWISE CONVERGENCE OF AN ORTHOGONAL EXPANSION

Instead of considering the mean-square error as in Eq. (5-82), we can examine instead the actual error,

$$E_n(x)\rangle = \{A(x) - S_n(x)\}\rangle \tag{5-126}$$

in approximating $A(x)\rangle$ by Eq. (5-80). Notice that $E_n(x)$ depends upon the particular value of x in the interval $a \le x \le b$. If we could show that

$$\lim_{n \to \infty} E_n(x) = 0 \tag{5-127}$$

for each $a \le x \le b$, then we could say that $S_n(x)\rangle$ converges pointwise to $A(x)\rangle$ in the interval $[a,b]$. The exact mathematical conditions under which an expansion in an arbitrary complete set of orthogonal functions is pointwise-convergent lie outside the scope of our discussion. We shall content ourselves with some general remarks and reserve more detailed comments for special examples later on.

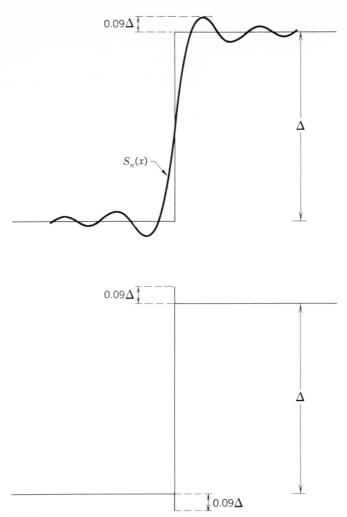

Figure 5-1 Gibbs's phenomenon.

5-9 GIBBS'S PHENOMENON

We have established that the orthogonal expansion of a square integrable piecewise-continuous function converges in the mean-square sense. Nevertheless, a piecewise-continuous function $A(x)$ can have a finite number of finite discontinuities in the interval $a \leq x \leq b$. Near such finite discontinuities the approximating function

$$S_n(x)\rangle = \sum_{k=1}^{n} a_k e_k(x)\rangle \tag{5-128}$$

fails to match the jump in $A(x)\rangle$. This situation is illustrated in Fig. 5-1 and is known as "Gibbs's phenomenon." This behavior can be qualitatively understood on the following basis: At a point x_0 at which $A(x)$ becomes discontinuous, the slope of $A(x)$, i.e., $A'(x)$, becomes infinite. However $S_n(x)$ consists of the sum of a finite number of *smoothly varying functions* forming the first n terms of a convergent series. Therefore $S_n'(x)$ must be a smoothly varying bounded function for $a \leq x \leq b$. Hence S_n' cannot match the infinite slope $A'(x)$ of $A(x)$ at a point of discontinuity $x = x_0$ in $[a,b]$. The *finite* series $S_n(x)$ tries to achieve the infinite slope of $A(x)$ at $x = x_0$ and thereby *overshoots* the discontinuity by a certain amount. Even in the limit $n \to \infty$ the overshooting persists, and the complete infinite series for $A(x)$ has spikes of zero thickness on the ends of the discontinuity. Since these additional spikes have zero thickness, they do not effect the mean-square convergence of the infinite series for $A(x)$, but they do indicate the limitations of the process of representing $A(x)$ by an orthogonal expansion. The amount by which $\lim_{n \to \infty} S_n(x)$ overshoots $A(x)$ at the discontinuity $x = x_0$ depends on the precise forms of both $A(x)$ and the functions $e_k(x)$. In general it is of the order of 9 percent of the jump in $A(x)$ at $x = x_0$.

5-10   THE FINITE SINE TRANSFORM

We shall now consider some special examples of orthogonal expansions. Let us examine the integral

$$\int_0^a \sin rx \sin sx \, dx$$

$$= \frac{1}{2} \int_0^a [\cos (r - s)x - \cos (r + s)x] \, dx \qquad (5\text{-}129)$$

Simple integration gives

$$\int_0^a \sin rx \sin sx \, dx = \frac{1}{2} \left[\frac{\sin (r - s)a}{r - s} - \frac{\sin (r + s)a}{r + s} \right] \qquad (5\text{-}130)$$

If we now expand the right-hand side of Eq. (5-130), using the well-known trigonometric identities for $\sin (r - s)a$ and $\sin (r + s)a$, we obtain

$$\int_0^a \sin rx \sin sx \, dx = \frac{\sin ra \sin sa}{r^2 - s^2} (s \cot sa - r \cot ra) \qquad (5\text{-}131)$$

Then the functions $\sin rx$, for different values of r, will form an orthogonal set if *either*

1. $r = n\pi/a$, where n is an integer, or
2. $r = p_n$, where $p_1, p_2, \ldots, p_n, \ldots$ are positive roots of the transcendental equation

$$p \cot pa + h = 0 \qquad h = \text{const} \qquad (5\text{-}132)$$

The validity of Eq. (5-132) can readily be checked. For example, let p_1 and p_2 be different positive roots of (5-132). Then

$$p_1 \cot p_1 a + h = 0 \qquad (5\text{-}133)$$

and

$$p_2 \cot p_2 a + h = 0 \qquad (5\text{-}134)$$

Subtracting Eq. (5-133) from Eq. (5-134) gives

$$p_2 \cot p_2 a - p_1 \cot p_1 a = 0 \tag{5-135}$$

Now let $r = p_1$ and $s = p_2$, so that Eq. (5-131) becomes

$$\int_0^a \sin p_1 x \sin p_2 x \, dx = 0 \tag{5-136}$$

Normalization

The normalization constants are computed, using Eq. (5-9), which in this case reduces to

$$\int_0^a \sin^2 rx \, dx = \lambda_r \tag{5-137}$$

To evaluate λ_r notice that

$$\sin^2 rx = \frac{1 - \cos 2rx}{2} \tag{5-138}$$

Hence

$$\int_0^a \sin^2 rx \, dx = \frac{a}{2}\left(1 - \frac{\sin 2ra}{2ra}\right) \tag{5-139}$$

For $r = n\pi/a$, we find

$$\lambda_n = \frac{a}{2} \tag{5-140}$$

When $r = p_n$,

$$\lambda_n = \frac{a}{2}\left(1 - \frac{\sin 2p_n a}{2p_n a}\right) \tag{5-141}$$

In order to simplify Eq. (5-141) we make use of Eq. (5-132), which gives

$$\cot p_n a = -\frac{h}{p_n} \tag{5-142}$$

from which we conclude that

$$\sin p_n a = \frac{p_n}{\sqrt{p_n{}^2 + h^2}} \tag{5-143}$$

and

$$\cos p_n a = \frac{-h}{\sqrt{p_n{}^2 + h^2}} \tag{5-144}$$

However,

$$\sin 2p_n a = 2 \sin p_n a \cos p_n a \tag{5-145}$$

Therefore

$$\sin 2p_n a = \frac{-2hp_n}{p_n{}^2 + h^2} \tag{5-146}$$

and

$$\lambda_n = \frac{a}{2}\left(1 - \frac{\sin 2p_n a}{2p_n a}\right) \tag{5-147}$$

becomes

$$\lambda_n = \frac{a}{2}\left[1 + \frac{h}{a(p_n{}^2 + h)}\right] \tag{5-148}$$

or

$$\lambda_n = \frac{a(h^2 + p_n{}^2) + h}{2(h^2 + p_n{}^2)} \tag{5-149}$$

Hence, if we define a finite sine transform by

$$\bar{A}_s(n) = \int_0^a A(x) \sin \frac{n\pi x}{a}\, dx \tag{5-150}$$

the corresponding inversion theorem (5-14) gives an orthogonal expansion of the form

$$A(x) = \frac{2}{a} \sum_{n=1}^{\infty} \bar{A}_s(n) \sin \frac{n\pi x}{a} \tag{5-151}$$

The orthogonal expansion (5-151) is called a "Fourier sine series," and it converges to $A(x)$ in the mean-square sense for $0 \le x \le a$.

We can even make a precise statement regarding the pointwise convergence of Eq. (5-151).

The function $A(x)$ is said to satisfy Dirichlet's conditions on $0 \le x \le a$ provided:

1. $A(x)$ is continuous almost everywhere on $[0,a]$.
2. $A(x)$ has only a finite number of finite discontinuities on $[0,a]$ (and no infinite discontinuities).
3. $A(x)$ has only a finite number of maxima and minima on $[0,a]$.

If $A(x)$ satisfies Dirichlet's conditions on $[0,a]$, then

$$\frac{2}{a} \sum_{n=0}^{\infty} \bar{A}_s(n) \sin \frac{n\pi x}{a} \tag{5-152}$$

converges at every point x in $[0,a]$ to

$$\tfrac{1}{2}\{A(x + 0) + A(x - 0)\} \tag{5-153}$$

The notation $A(x \pm 0)$ means

$$\lim_{\epsilon \to 0} A(x \pm \epsilon) \tag{5-154}$$

In a similar fashion we can define the so-called finite radiation sine transform by

$$\bar{A}_{sr}(n) = \int_0^a A(x) \sin (p_n x)\, dx \tag{5-155}$$

where p_n is a positive root of the transcendental equation

$$p \cot pa + h = 0 \tag{5-156}$$

for $h = $ constant. The corresponding inversion theorem (5-14) gives, using Eq. (5-149),

$$A(x) = 2 \sum_{n=1}^{\infty} \frac{h^2 + p_n{}^2}{a(h^2 + p_n{}^2) + h} \bar{A}_{sr}(n) \sin p_n x \tag{5-157}$$

5-11 THE FINITE COSINE TRANSFORM

Arguments similar to those used to obtain Eq. (5-131) yield

$$\int_0^a \cos rx \cos sx \, dx = \frac{\cos ra \cos sa}{r^2 - s^2} (r \tan ra - s \tan sa) \tag{5-158}$$

Therefore the functions $\cos rx$ will form an orthogonal set if either

1. $r = n\pi/a$ for n integer

or

2. $r = q_n$

where q_n is a positive root of the transcendental equation

$$q \tan qa = h \tag{5-159}$$

$$h = \text{const} \tag{5-160}$$

The normalization integral becomes

$$\int_0^a \cos^2 rx \, dx = \frac{a}{2} \left(1 + \frac{\sin 2ra}{2ra} \right) \tag{5-161}$$

so that, for $r = n\pi/a$,

$$\lambda_n = \frac{a}{2} \tag{5-162}$$

or, for $r = q_n$,

$$\lambda_n = \frac{a(h^2 + q_n{}^2) + h}{2(h^2 + q_n{}^2)} \tag{5-163}$$

We define the finite cosine transform by

$$\bar{A}_c(n) = \int_0^a A(x) \cos \frac{n\pi x}{a} \, dx \tag{5-164}$$

and the corresponding inversion formula by

$$A(x) = \frac{1}{a} \bar{A}_c(0) + \frac{2}{a} \sum_{n=1}^{\infty} \bar{A}_c(n) \cos \frac{n\pi x}{a} \tag{5-165}$$

The finite radiation cosine transform is defined by

$$\bar{A}_{cr}(n) = \int_0^a A(x) \cos q_n x \, dx \tag{5-166}$$

where q_n is a positive root of

$$q \tan qa = h$$

with $h = \text{constant}$. The corresponding inversion formula is

$$A(x) = 2 \sum_{n=1}^{\infty} \frac{h^2 + q_n{}^2}{a(h^2 + q_n{}^2) + h} \bar{A}_{cr}(n) \cos q_n x \tag{5-167}$$

Observe that in Eqs. (5-157) and (5-167) the sums are to be taken over *all* positive roots p_n and q_n, respectively.

Consider

$$\bar{A}_s(n) = \int_0^a A(x) \sin \frac{n\pi x}{a} \, dx \tag{5-168}$$

and

$$\bar{A}_c(n) = \int_0^a A(x) \cos \frac{n\pi x}{a} \, dx \tag{5-169}$$

We can write Eqs. (5-168) and (5-169) in symbolic form as

$$\bar{A}_s(n) = T_s\{A(x)\} \tag{5-170}$$

and

$$\bar{A}_c(n) = T_c\{A(x)\} \tag{5-171}$$

respectively. Using this notation, many properties of finite Fourier sine and cosine transforms can be exhibited in compact form. For example, if we integrate

$$\int_0^a \frac{\partial A}{\partial x} \sin \frac{n\pi x}{a} \, dx \tag{5-172}$$

by parts, we obtain

$$A(x) \sin \frac{n\pi x}{a} \Big|_{x=0}^{x=a} - \frac{n\pi}{a} \int_0^a A(x) \cos \frac{n\pi x}{a} \, dx \tag{5-173}$$

The first term in expression (5-173) vanishes at the limits of integration $x = 0$ and $x = a$. Thus (5-172) and (5-173) give us

$$T_s\left\{\frac{\partial A}{\partial x}\right\} = -\frac{n\pi}{a} T_c\{A\} \tag{5-174}$$

and, by a similar argument,

$$T_c\left\{\frac{\partial A}{\partial x}\right\} = (-1)^n A(a) - A(0) + \frac{n\pi}{a} T_s\{A\} \tag{5-175}$$

Further application of integration by parts gives

$$T_s\left\{\frac{\partial^2 A}{\partial x^2}\right\} = \frac{n\pi}{a}[(-1)^{n+1}A(a) + A(0)] - \left(\frac{n\pi}{a}\right)^2 T_s\{A\} \tag{5-176}$$

and

$$T_c\left\{\frac{\partial^2 A}{\partial x^2}\right\} = (-1)^n A'(a) - A'(0) - \left(\frac{n\pi}{a}\right)^2 T_c\{A\} \tag{5-177}$$

The radiation transforms give similar formulas. Thus

$$\bar{A}_{sr}(n) = T_{sr}\{A(x)\} \tag{5-178}$$

and

$$\bar{A}_{cr}(n) = T_{cr}\{A(x)\} \tag{5-179}$$

together with integration by parts, permit us to write

$$T_{sr}\left\{\frac{\partial^2 A}{\partial x^2}\right\} = p_n A(0) + \left(\frac{\partial A}{\partial x} + hA\right)_{x=a} \sin p_n a$$
$$- p_n^2 T_{sr}\{A\} \tag{5-180}$$

and

$$T_{cr}\left\{\frac{\partial^2 A}{\partial x^2}\right\} = -A'(0) + \left(\frac{\partial A}{\partial x} + hA\right)_{x=a} \cos q_n a$$
$$- q_n{}^2 T_{cr}\{A\} \qquad (5\text{-}181)$$

5-13 CONNECTION WITH CLASSICAL THEORY OF FOURIER SERIES

The classical theory of Fourier series begins by considering a function $A(x)$ defined for $0 \leq x \leq 2\pi$. One seeks to expand $A(x)$ in a Fourier series which is of the form

$$A(x) = \frac{a_0}{2} + \sum_{n=1}^{\infty} (a_n \cos nx + b_n \sin nx) \qquad (5\text{-}182)$$

The coefficient a_n is found by multiplying Eq. (5-182) by $\cos nx$ and integrating from $x = 0$ to $x = 2\pi$. A similar procedure using $\sin nx$ suffices to give b_n. Thus

$$a_n = \frac{1}{\pi} \int_0^{2\pi} A(x) \cos nx \, dx \qquad (5\text{-}183)$$

$$b_n = \frac{1}{\pi} \int_0^{2\pi} A(x) \sin nx \, dx \qquad (5\text{-}184)$$

The Fourier series (5-182) converges to $\frac{1}{2}\{A(x+0) + A(x-0)\}$, provided $A(x)$ satisfies Dirichlet's conditions for $0 \leq x \leq 2\pi$. Notice that the Fourier series (5-182) is periodic so that $A(x)$ is repeated for $2\pi \leq x \leq 4\pi$, $-2\pi \leq x \leq 0$, and so on.

Certain types of functions have especially simple Fourier series. For example, if $A(x) = A(-x)$, then $A(x)$ is an even function, and only the cosine terms appear in Eq. (5-182); i.e.,

$$b_n = 0 \qquad (5\text{-}185)$$

If $A(x) = -A(-x)$, then $A(x)$ is an odd function of x, and only the sine terms appear in Eq. (5-182); thus

$$a_n = 0 \qquad (5\text{-}186)$$

Notice that any function $A(x)$ can be written as the sum of an even and an odd part. In other words,

$$A(x) = A_e(x) + A_o(x) \qquad (5\text{-}187)$$

where

$$A_e(x) = \frac{A(x) + A(-x)}{2} \qquad (5\text{-}188)$$

and

$$A_o(x) = \frac{A(x) - A(-x)}{2} \qquad (5\text{-}189)$$

Obviously,

$$A_e(x) = A_e(-x) \tag{5-190}$$

and

$$A_o(x) = -A_o(-x) \tag{5-191}$$

If we are initially given a function $A(x)$ *defined only for* $0 \leq x \leq 2\pi$, then we possess no information on how $A(x)$ behaves outside the interval $[0,2\pi]$. It is possible to define infinitely many functions which coincide exactly with $A(x)$ for $0 \leq x \leq 2\pi$ and have arbitrary shapes outside $[0,2\pi]$. For example,

$$A(x) = A(x + 2\pi) \tag{5-192}$$

defines the periodic extension or continuation of $A(x)$. Similarly,

$$A(x) = A(-x) \tag{5-193}$$

and

$$A(x) = -A(-x) \tag{5-194}$$

define the even and odd extensions of $A(x)$, respectively. Formulas (5-192) to (5-194) permit us to calculate values of $A(x)$ for points x which lie outside the original interval $[0,2\pi]$ for which $A(x)$ was defined. For this reason we say that Eqs. (5-192) to (5-194) provide us with extensions of $A(x)$. Thus, given an arbitrary function $A(x)$ originally defined for $0 \leq x \leq 2\pi$, we can represent it as:

1. A Fourier sine series: in which case the series coincides with $A(x)$ for $0 \leq x \leq 2\pi$ and coincides with the odd extension of $A(x)$ for $-2\pi \leq x \leq 0$.
2. A Fourier cosine series: in which case the series coincides with $A(x)$ for $0 \leq x \leq 2\pi$ and coincides with the even extension of $A(x)$ for $-2\pi \leq x \leq 0$.
3. A classical Fourier series (5-182): in which case the series coincides with $A(x)$ for $0 \leq x \leq 2\pi$ and coincides with the periodic extension of $A(x)$ for values of x lying outside the interval $0 \leq x \leq 2\pi$.

Complex form of classical Fourier series

The Fourier series (5-182) to (5-184) can be written in complex form by use of Euler's formula,

$$e^{ix} = \cos x + i \sin x \tag{5-195}$$

with the result that

$$A(x) = \sum_{n=-\infty}^{+\infty} C_n e^{inx} \tag{5-196}$$

and

$$C_n = \frac{1}{2\pi} \int_0^{2\pi} A(x) e^{-inx}\, dx \tag{5-197}$$

Comparison of Eqs. (5-196) and (5-197) with (5-182) to (5-184) gives

$$C_0 = \frac{a_0}{2} \tag{5-198}$$

$$C_n = \tfrac{1}{2}(a_n - ib_n) \qquad n > 0 \tag{5-199}$$

$$C_{-n} = \tfrac{1}{2}(a_n + ib_n) \qquad n > 0 \tag{5-200}$$

For an arbitrary interval $0 \leq x \leq a$, formulas (5-196) and (5-197) are replaced by

$$A(x) = \sum_{n = -\infty}^{+\infty} C_n e^{in\pi x/a} \tag{5-201}$$

$$C_n = \frac{1}{2a} \int_0^{2a} A(x) e^{-in\pi x/a}\, dx \tag{5-202}$$

5-14 APPLICATIONS OF FINITE FOURIER TRANSFORMS

There are two general tasks for which the finite Fourier transform is well suited. The first is the representation of a given function $A(x)$ on some definite interval such as $0 \leq x \leq a$, and the second is the solution of certain differential equations subject to boundary conditions applied at the end points of a finite interval like $0 \leq x \leq a$. We shall illustrate both these usages with some specific examples.

Representation of arbitrary functions

EXAMPLE 5-3: Let

$$A(x) = |x| \qquad |x| \leq a \tag{5-203}$$

The fundamental interval is $0 \leq x \leq a$ so that

$$A(x) = x \qquad 0 \leq x \leq a \tag{5-204}$$

Notice that Eq. (5-203) satisfies

$$A(x) = A(-x) \tag{5-205}$$

Therefore we employ the finite cosine transform,

$$\bar{A}_c(n) = \int_0^a x \cos \frac{n\pi x}{a}\, dx \tag{5-206}$$

which gives

$$\bar{A}_c(n) = \frac{ax}{n\pi} \sin \frac{n\pi x}{a} \Big|_0^a - \frac{a}{n\pi} \int_0^a \sin \frac{n\pi x}{a}\, dx \tag{5-207}$$

The integrated term vanishes so that

$$\bar{A}_c(n) = \left(\frac{a}{n\pi}\right)^2 \cos \frac{n\pi x}{a} \Big|_0^a \tag{5-208}$$

$$\bar{A}_c(n) = \left(\frac{a}{n\pi}\right)^2 [(-1)^n - 1] \qquad n > 0 \tag{5-209}$$

For $n = 0$, Eq. (5-206) gives

$$\bar{A}_c(0) = \frac{a^2}{2} \tag{5-210}$$

Thus Eqs. (5-209) and (5-210), together with the inversion theorem (5-165), yield

$$A(x) = x = \frac{a}{2} + \frac{2a}{\pi^2} \sum_{n=1}^{\infty} \frac{(-1)^n - 1}{n^2} \cos \frac{n\pi x}{a} \tag{5-211}$$

for $0 \leq x \leq a$. However, since the right side of Eq. (5-211) is even in x, we see that (5-211) actually represents $|x|$ for $|x| \leq a$.

EXAMPLE 5-4: Suppose that

$$A(x) = x \qquad -a \leq x \leq a \tag{5-212}$$

Again we take as the fundamental interval $0 \leq x \leq a$, so that

$$A(x) = x \qquad 0 \leq x \leq a \tag{5-213}$$

Now, however, we see from Eq. (5-212) that

$$A(x) = -A(-x) \tag{5-214}$$

Hence we employ the finite sine transform to represent $A(x)$ for $0 \leq x \leq a$.

$$\bar{A}_s(n) = \int_0^a x \sin \frac{n\pi x}{a} \, dx \tag{5-215}$$

$$\bar{A}_s(n) = -\frac{ax}{n\pi} \cos \frac{n\pi x}{a} \Big|_0^a + \frac{a}{n\pi} \int_0^a \cos \frac{n\pi x}{a} \, dx \tag{5-216}$$

Then the integral on the right side of Eq. (5-216) vanishes, so that

$$\bar{A}_s(n) = \frac{a^2}{n\pi} (-1)^{n+1} \tag{5-217}$$

It follows from Eqs. (5-217) and (5-151) that

$$A(x) = x = \frac{2a}{\pi} \sum_{n=1}^{\infty} \frac{(-1)^{n+1}}{n} \sin \frac{n\pi x}{a} \tag{5-218}$$

for $0 \leq x \leq a$. However, since the right side of Eq. (5-218) is odd in x, we see that (5-218) represents $A(x) = x$ for the entire interval $-a \leq x \leq a$.

EXAMPLE 5-5: Let

$$A(x) = x \qquad 0 \leq x \leq a \tag{5-219}$$

and

$$A(x) = -b \qquad -a \leq x \leq 0 \tag{5-220}$$

In this case the function $A(x)$ is neither even nor odd. Two choices are open to us. We can either decompose $A(x)$ into even and odd parts and then generate the corresponding Fourier cosine and sine series separately, or we can use a modified version of Eq. (5-182) directly. We shall choose the last alternative. Let

$$A(x) = \frac{a_0}{2} + \sum_{n=1}^{\infty} \left(a_n \cos \frac{n\pi x}{a} + b_n \sin \frac{n\pi x}{a} \right) \tag{5-221}$$

It can be shown by direct integration that

$$a_n = \frac{1}{a} \int_{-a}^{+a} A(x) \cos \frac{n\pi x}{a} \, dx \tag{5-222}$$

and that

$$b_n = \frac{1}{a} \int_{-a}^{+a} A(x) \sin \frac{n\pi x}{a} \, dx \tag{5-223}$$

Therefore

$$a_n = \frac{1}{a} \left(\int_{-a}^{0} -b \cos \frac{n\pi x}{a} \, dx + \int_{0}^{a} x \cos \frac{n\pi x}{a} \, dx \right) \tag{5-224}$$

giving

$$a_0 = \frac{a - 2b}{2} \tag{5-225}$$

$$a_n = \frac{a}{\pi^2} \frac{(-1)^n - 1}{n^2} \tag{5-226}$$

Similarly,

$$b_n = \frac{1}{a} \left(\int_{-a}^{0} -b \sin \frac{n\pi x}{a} \, dx + \int_{0}^{a} x \sin \frac{n\pi x}{a} \, dx \right) \tag{5-227}$$

giving

$$b_n = \frac{b}{n\pi} - \frac{a + b}{n\pi} (-1)^n \tag{5-228}$$

Thus we write

$$A(x) = \frac{a - 2b}{4} + \sum_{n=1}^{\infty} \left\{ \frac{a}{\pi^2} \frac{(-1)^n - 1}{n^2} \cos \frac{n\pi x}{a} \right.$$
$$\left. + \left[\frac{b}{n\pi} - \frac{a + b}{n\pi} (-1)^n \right] \sin \frac{n\pi x}{a} \right\} \tag{5-229}$$

for the Fourier-series representation of Eqs. (5-219) and (5-220).

REMARK: Consider the Fourier series (5-221). In complex form Eqs. (5-221) to (5-223) become

$$A(x) = \sum_{n=-\infty}^{+\infty} C_n e^{i(n\pi x/a)} \tag{5-230}$$

$$C_n = \frac{1}{2a} \int_{-a}^{+a} A(x) e^{-i(n\pi x/a)} \, dx \tag{5-231}$$

Equation (5-231) is the same as Eq. (5-202), as can be seen by substituting $y = x + a$ into (5-231). With this substitution Eq. (5-231) becomes

$$C_n = \frac{1}{2a} \int_{0}^{2a} A(y - a) e^{-i(n\pi/a)(y-a)} \, d(y - a) \tag{5-232}$$

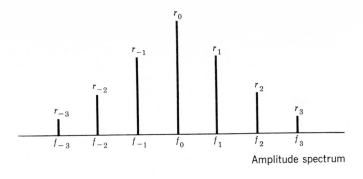

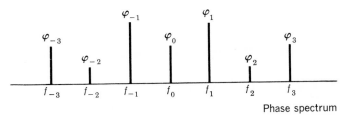

Figure 5-2 Discrete amplitude and phase spectra for a function of finite duration.

which, on noting that $y - a$ is a dummy variable of integration, is seen to be identical to Eq. (5-202).

Notice that if we write

$$\omega_n = 2\pi f_n = \frac{n\pi}{a} \tag{5-233}$$

then Eq. (5-230) becomes

$$A(x) = \sum_{n=-\infty}^{+\infty} C_n e^{i\omega_n x} \tag{5-234}$$

From the physical standpoint Eq. (5-234) states that $A(x)$ is a superposition of harmonic oscillations of frequencies $f_n = n/2a$, where n takes on the values $n = 0, \pm1, \pm2, \ldots$, etc. Since C_n is complex, we can write

$$C_n = r_n e^{-i(n\pi\phi_n)/a} \tag{5-235}$$

for some amplitude r_n and some phase angle ϕ_n. Then Eq. (5-234) becomes

$$A(x) = \sum_{n=-\infty}^{+\infty} r_n e^{i\omega_n(x-\phi_n)} \tag{5-236}$$

from which we see that $A(x)$ is a superposition of terms of which the general term has amplitude r_n, angular frequency ω_n, and phase angle ϕ_n.

If we plot a graph with the amplitude r_n as ordinate and the frequency f_n as abscissa, then the resulting curve is called the "amplitude spectrum" of $A(x)$. Since the frequencies f_0, f_1, f_2, . . . form an infinite sequence of discrete numbers, the amplitude spectrum of $A(x)$ will appear as an infinite number of horizontally spaced vertical lines, the nth one of which is of height r_n. For this reason, the amplitude spectrum of $A(x)$ is said to be "discrete."

A similar plot of ϕ_n versus f_n yields what is called the "phase spectrum" of $A(x)$. The phase spectrum is also discrete. A complete knowledge of the amplitude and phase spectra of a function determines the function completely through Eq. (5-236). The process of determining the amplitude and phase spectra of a function is called "Fourier analysis," and the process of reconstructing the function through Eq. (5-236) is known as "Fourier synthesis."

Solution of an ordinary differential equation with boundary conditions

EXAMPLE 5-6: Consider the quantum-mechanical problem of a particle trapped inside of an infinite potential well specified by

$$V(x) = 0 \qquad 0 < x < a \tag{5-237}$$

$$V(x) = +\infty \qquad x = 0,\, x = a \tag{5-238}$$

This corresponds to a particle trapped between two perfectly rigid impenetrable walls at the points $x = 0$ and $x = a$. In general, an abrupt increase in potential energy at the boundaries of a region forces a particle toward the interior of the region. The force $F_x = -dV/dx$ associated with the potential [Eqs. (5-237) and (5-238)] is zero except at the boundaries $x = 0$ and $x = a$ where $-dV/dx$ becomes infinite. Let us plot Eqs. (5-237) and (5-238) with V as ordinate and x as abscissa. We can imagine the resulting rectangular well as the limiting form of a parabola opening toward the positive V axis. We proceed to flatten the bottom of the parabola until it coincides with Eq. (5-237), while at the same time we straighten the arms of the parabola until they match Eq. (5-238). With this picture it becomes apparent that

$$F_x = -\frac{dV}{dx} = -\infty \qquad x = a \tag{5-239}$$

$$F_x = -\frac{dV}{dx} = +\infty \qquad x = 0 \tag{5-240}$$

Hence the force acting on the particle is directed toward the left at $x = a$ and toward the right at $x = 0$. The effect is to keep the particle inside the well. The Schrödinger equation satisfied by the wave function of our particle is shown in quantum mechanics to be

$$\frac{d^2\psi}{dx^2} + \frac{2mE}{\hbar^2}\,\psi = 0 \tag{5-241}$$

where m is the mass and E is the total energy of the particle. The symbol $\hbar$ is known as Planck's constant($\hbar = 1.054 \times 10^{-27}$ erg-sec). The infinite repulsion experienced by the particle at the walls $x = 0$ and $x = a$ means that the probability of finding the particle at $x = 0$ or $x = a$ is zero; hence $\psi(x)$ must be such that

$$\psi(0) = 0 \tag{5-242}$$

and

$$\psi(a) = 0 \tag{5-243}$$

Conditions (5-242) and (5-243) are the boundary conditions which the solution $\psi(x)$ of (5-241) must satisfy.

We now examine Sec. 5-12 and observe that Eq. (5-176) is suitable for use with Eq. (5-241) because

$$(-1)^{n-1}\psi(a) + \psi(0) = 0 \tag{5-244}$$

as a result of Eqs. (5-242) and (5-243). Now taking the finite sine transform of Eq. (5-241), we obtain

$$T_s\left\{\frac{d^2\psi}{dx^2}\right\} + \frac{2mE}{\hbar^2} T_s\{\psi\} = 0 \tag{5-245}$$

and from Eq. (5-176)

$$T_s\left\{\frac{d^2\psi}{dx^2}\right\} = -\left(\frac{n\pi}{a}\right)^2 T_s\{\psi\} \tag{5-246}$$

Hence Eq. (5-245) becomes

$$\left[\frac{2mE}{\hbar^2} - \left(\frac{n\pi}{a}\right)^2\right] T_s\{\psi\} = 0 \tag{5-247}$$

where

$$T_s\{\psi\} = \bar{\psi}_s(n) \tag{5-248}$$

Equation (5-247) provides us with an infinite number of equations, each taking the form

$$\left[\frac{2mE}{\hbar^2} - \left(\frac{k\pi}{a}\right)^2\right] \bar{\psi}_s(k) = 0 \tag{5-249}$$

as k runs through the values $k = 1, 2, \ldots, \infty$. There are now two possibilities. Either one or more values of k exist for which $\bar{\psi}_s(k) \neq 0$ or $\bar{\psi}_s(k) = 0$ for all values of $k = 1, 2, \ldots, \infty$. Let us first assume that $\bar{\psi}_s(k) = 0$ for all values of k. As a result,

$$\bar{\psi}_s(k) = \int_0^a \psi(x) \sin \frac{k\pi x}{a} \, dx = 0 \qquad k = 1, 2, \ldots, \infty \tag{5-250}$$

One solution of Eq. (5-250) is $\psi(x) = 0$ for $0 \leq x \leq a$. This solution also satisfies Eqs. (5-241) to (5-243). However, we must reject it on physical grounds. The statement that the particle is located inside the infinite potential well means that the probability of finding it in the interval $0 \leq x \leq a$ is unity; therefore

$$\int_0^a |\psi|^2 \, dx = 1 \tag{5-251}$$

This excludes the solution $\psi(x) = 0$. Is it possible that there is some other function $\psi(x)$ which is not identically zero on $[0,a]$ and yet satisfies Eq. (5-250)? The answer to this question revolves around the concept of completeness of an infinite set of orthogonal functions, a notion which we first introduced at the end of Sec. 5-6. If we can show that the infinite set of orthogonal functions $\{\sin k\pi x/a;$ $k = 1,2, \ldots ,\infty \}$ is *complete on the interval* $0 \leq x \leq a$, then as a consequence there can be no nontrivial function $\psi(x)$ which is orthogonal to all of them. It then follows that $\psi(x) \equiv 0$ for $0 \leq x \leq a$ is the *only* solution of Eq. (5-250), and since this solution is excluded by Eq. (5-251), we conclude that $\bar{\psi}_s(k) \neq 0$ for at least one integer k.

It follows from an application of Parseval's theorem (5-133) to (5-221) that the set of orthogonal functions $\{\cos k\pi x/a, \sin k\pi x/a;$ $k = 1,2, \ldots ,\infty \}$ is *complete on the interval* $-a \leq x \leq a$. From this we can prove the following:

THEOREM: The set of orthogonal functions $\{\sin k\pi x/a; \ k = 1,2, \ldots ,\infty \}$ is *complete on the interval* $0 \leq x \leq a$.

proof: Let us assume that there exists a square integrable function $A(x)$ defined for $0 \leq x \leq a$ and such that

$$\int_0^a |A|^2 \, dx = 1 \tag{5-252}$$

and

$$\int_0^a A(x) \sin \frac{k\pi x}{a} \, dx = 0 \tag{5-253}$$

for $k = 1,2, \ldots ,\infty$. If we extend $A(x)$ from $0 \leq x \leq a$ to $-a \leq x \leq 0$ by means of the equation

$$A(-x) = -A(x) \tag{5-254}$$

we shall obtain

$$\int_{-a}^{+a} |A|^2 \, dx = 2 \tag{5-255}$$

$$\int_{-a}^{a} A(x) \sin \frac{k\pi x}{a} \, dx = 0 \tag{5-256}$$

$$\int_{-a}^{+a} A(x) \cos \frac{k\pi x}{a} \, dx = 0 \tag{5-257}$$

for $k = 1,2, \ldots ,\infty$. Now the completeness of

$$\left\{ \cos \frac{k\pi x}{a}, \sin \frac{k\pi x}{a}; \quad k = 1,2, \ldots ,\infty \right\}$$

on $-a \leq x \leq a$ together with Eqs. (5-256) and (5-257) implies that

$$\int_{-a}^{+a} |A|^2 \, dx = 0 \tag{5-258}$$

which contradicts Eq. (5-255). Therefore our original assumption that a nontrivial square integrable function $A(x)$ satisfying Eqs. (5-252) and (5-253) exists must be false, and our theorem follows.

REMARK: Notice that completeness of a set of functions is intimately related to the interval on which they are defined. Thus, while the set of functions $\{\sin k\pi x/a; k = 1,2, \ldots ,\infty\}$ is complete for $0 \le x \le a$, it is not complete for $-a \le x \le a$.

Now we may return to Eq. (5-249), safe in the knowledge that for at least one value of k, say $k = n$, $\Psi_s(k) \ne 0$. Consequently Eq. (5-249) gives

$$E = n^2 \frac{\hbar^2 \pi^2}{2ma^2} \tag{5-259}$$

which is an energy eigenvalue of the particle in the infinite potential well. The inversion theorem (5-151) for the finite sine transform yields the wave function of the particle,

$$\psi(x) = \frac{2}{a} \sum_{n=1}^{\infty} \Psi_s(n) \sin \frac{n\pi x}{a} \tag{5-260}$$

The normalization condition

$$\int_0^a |\psi|^2 \, dx = 1 \tag{5-261}$$

using

$$\int_0^a \sin \frac{n\pi x}{a} \sin \frac{m\pi x}{a} \, dx = \frac{a}{2} \delta_{nm} \tag{5-262}$$

yields

$$\int_0^a |\psi|^2 \, dx = \sum_{n=1}^{\infty} |\Psi_s(n)|^2 = 1 \tag{5-263}$$

which is nothing more than Parseval's equation (5-113). The physical interpretation of Eq. (5-263) is interesting. According to quantum mechanics, the probability $P(E_n)$ that the particle has energy

$$E_n = n^2 \frac{\hbar^2 \pi^2}{2ma^2} \tag{5-264}$$

is given by

$$P(E_n) = |\Psi_s(n)|^2 \tag{5-265}$$

Equation (5-263) then states that the probability that the particle has one of the infinite number of energy eigenvalues $E_1, E_2, \ldots ,E_\infty$ is equal to the probability that the particle is trapped in the interval $0 \le x \le a$. Therefore both probabilities must equal unity.

EXAMPLE 5-7: As an example of the application of the finite sine radiation transform we shall consider the problem of a particle trapped in a semi-infinite potential well specified by

$$V(x) = 0 \qquad 0 < x < a \tag{5-266}$$

$$V(x) = +\infty \qquad x = 0 \tag{5-267}$$

$$V(x) = V_0 \qquad x \ge a \tag{5-268}$$

The Schrödinger equation satisfied by the wave function ψ of the particle is

$$\frac{d^2\psi}{dx^2} + \frac{2mE}{\hbar^2}\psi = 0 \tag{5-269}$$

for $0 < x < a$, and

$$\frac{d^2\psi}{dx^2} - \left[\frac{2m}{\hbar^2}(V_0 - E)\right]\psi = 0 \tag{5-270}$$

for $a \leq x \leq \infty$. The boundary conditions to be satisfied by ψ are

$$\psi(0) = 0 \tag{5-271}$$

and

$$\frac{1}{\psi^-}\frac{\partial\psi^-}{\partial x} = \frac{1}{\psi^+}\frac{\partial\psi^+}{\partial x} \tag{5-272}$$

at $x = a$. In Eq. (5-272),

$$\psi^+ = \psi(x) \qquad x \geq a \tag{5-273}$$

$$\psi^- = \psi(x) \qquad x \leq a \tag{5-274}$$

We shall be interested in studying a particle whose total energy E is less than the finite potential energy barrier V_0.

$$E < V_0 \tag{5-275}$$

In a classical problem, a particle satisfying inequality (5-275) would have insufficient energy to escape the barrier. For the quantum-mechanical case it is known that there is a finite positive probability that the particle will escape from the barrier, even though (5-275) holds.

We shall choose a solution of Eq. (5-270) which permits the particle to be found in the region $a < x < +\infty$ but which yields zero probability that the particle is at $x = +\infty$. In other words, we choose a solution of Eq. (5-270) which satisfies the boundary condition,

$$\lim_{x \to \infty} \psi(x) = 0 \tag{5-276}$$

at infinity. This solution is

$$\psi^+(x) = Ce^{-\beta x} \tag{5-277}$$

where C is a constant and

$$\beta = +\left[\frac{2m}{\hbar^2}(V_0 - E)\right]^{1/2} \tag{5-278}$$

The solution (5-277) can be verified by substitution into Eq. (5-270). Notice that

$$\frac{1}{\psi^+}\frac{\partial\psi^+}{\partial x} = -\beta \tag{5-279}$$

Hence Eq. (5-270) becomes

$$\frac{\partial\psi^-}{\partial x} + \beta\psi^- = 0 \tag{5-280}$$

at $x = a$. We must now solve

$$\frac{d^2\psi}{dx^2} + \frac{2mE}{\hbar^2}\psi^- = 0 \qquad (5\text{-}281)$$

for $0 < x < a$ subject to the boundary conditions $\psi^-(0) = 0$ and $\partial\psi^-/\partial x + \beta\psi^- = 0$ at $x = a$. We again examine Sec. 5-12 and we find that Eq. (5-180) is suitable for use with Eq. (5-281) because

$$p_n\psi(0) + \left(\frac{\partial\psi}{\partial x} + \beta\psi\right)_{x=a} \sin p_n a = 0 \qquad (5\text{-}282)$$

provided that p_n is a positive root of

$$p \cot pa + \beta = 0 \qquad (5\text{-}283)$$

and given Eqs. (5-271) and (5-280). Application of the finite sine radiation transform to Eq. (5-281) gives

$$T_{sr}\left\{\frac{d^2\psi}{dx^2}\right\} + \frac{2mE}{\hbar^2} T_{sr}\{\psi\} = 0 \qquad (5\text{-}284)$$

and, from Eq. (5-180),

$$T_{sr}\left\{\frac{d^2\psi}{dx^2}\right\} = -p_n^2 T_{sr}\{\psi\} \qquad (5\text{-}285)$$

Hence Eq. (5-284) becomes

$$\left(\frac{2mE}{\hbar^2} - p_n^2\right) T_{sr}\{\psi\} = 0 \qquad (5\text{-}286)$$

where

$$T_{sr}\{\psi\} = \bar{\psi}_{sr}(n) \qquad (5\text{-}287)$$

Equation (5-286) provides us with an infinite number of equations each of the form

$$\left(\frac{2mE}{\hbar^2} - p_k^2\right) \bar{\psi}_{sr}(k) = 0 \qquad (5\text{-}288)$$

as k runs through the values $k = 1, 2, \ldots, \infty$. If $\bar{\psi}_{sr}(k) = 0$ for all values of $k = 1, 2, \ldots, \infty$; then

$$\bar{\psi}_{sr}(k) = \int_0^a \psi(x) \sin p_k x \, dx = 0 \qquad k = 1, 2, \ldots, \infty \qquad (5\text{-}289)$$

Because of the completeness of the orthogonal set of functions $\{\cos p_k x, \sin p_k x; k = 1, 2, \ldots, \infty\}$ on the interval $-a \le x \le +a$, it follows that the orthogonal set of functions $\{\sin p_k x; k = 1, 2, \ldots, \infty\}$ is complete on the interval $0 \le x \le a$. Therefore, the only solution of Eq. (5-289) is $\psi(x) = 0$ for $0 \le x \le a$. This solution must be excluded on physical grounds because it implies that the particle has zero probability of being inside the semi-infinite well. Thus we conclude that there is at least one value of k, say $k = n$, for which $\bar{\psi}_{sr}(n) \ne 0$. Consequently Eq. (5-288) gives

$$E = \frac{\hbar^2}{2m} p_n^2 \qquad (5\text{-}290)$$

for the energy eigenvalues of a particle in a semi-infinite potential well. In Eq. (5-290), p_n is one of the positive roots of Eq. (5-283). The inversion theorem (5-147) gives

$$\psi^-(x) = 2 \sum_{n=1}^{\infty} \frac{\beta^2 + p_n{}^2}{a(\beta^2 + p_n{}^2) + \beta} \psi_{sr}(n) \sin p_n x \qquad (5\text{-}291)$$

The normalization condition becomes

$$\int_0^{\infty} |\psi|^2 \, dx = \int_0^a |\psi^-|^2 \, dx + \int_a^{\infty} |\psi^+|^2 \, dx = 1 \qquad (5\text{-}292)$$

and using

$$\int_0^a \sin p_n x \sin p_m x = \lambda_n \delta_{nm} \qquad (5\text{-}293)$$

where

$$\lambda_n = \frac{a(\beta^2 + p_n{}^2) + \beta}{2(\beta^2 + p_n{}^2)} \qquad (5\text{-}294)$$

we obtain, with the aid of Eqs. (5-277) and (5-291),

$$\int_0^{\infty} |\psi|^2 \, dx = \sum_{n=1}^{\infty} |\psi_{sr}(n)|^2 = \frac{C^2}{2\beta} e^{-2\beta a} = 1 \qquad (5\text{-}295)$$

REMARK: It is worthwhile to observe that there is a smallest positive root p of Eq. (5-283). Consequently, there is a minimum positive-energy eigenvalue (5-290) for a given particle and a given semi-infinite potential well.

EXAMPLE 5-8: The finite Fourier transform can be used to solve certain inhomogeneous boundary-value problems also. For example, solve

$$\frac{d^2 A}{dx^2} + k^2 A = f(x) \qquad (5\text{-}296)$$

in the interval $0 \leq x \leq a$ subject to the boundary conditions

$$A'(0) = 0 \qquad (5\text{-}297)$$

and

$$A'(a) = 0 \qquad (5\text{-}298)$$

In this case we use the finite cosine transform, and we obtain

$$T_c \left\{ \frac{d^2 A}{dx^2} \right\} + k^2 T_c\{A\} = T_c\{f\} \qquad (5\text{-}299)$$

Then Eq. (5-177), together with Eqs. (5-297) and (5-298), gives

$$\left[k^2 - \left(\frac{n\pi}{a} \right)^2 \right] T_c\{A\} = T_c\{f\} \qquad (5\text{-}300)$$

Let

$$T_c\{A\} = \bar{A}_c(n) = \int_0^a A(x) \cos \frac{n\pi x}{a} \, dx \qquad (5\text{-}301)$$

and

$$T_c\{f\} = \tilde{f}_c(n) = \int_0^a f(x) \cos \frac{n\pi x}{a}\, dx \tag{5-302}$$

If we assume that $f(x)$ is not identically zero for $0 \leq x \leq a$, then completeness of the orthogonal set $\{\cos n\pi x/a;\ n = 1,2,\ldots,\infty\}$ on $0 \leq x \leq a$ guarantees that $\tilde{f}_c(n)$ does not vanish identically. Thus solving Eq. (5-300), we find

$$\bar{A}_c(n) = \frac{\tilde{f}_c(n)}{k^2 - (n\pi/a)^2} \tag{5-303}$$

and applying the inversion theorem (5-165) gives

$$A(x) = \frac{\tilde{f}_c(0)}{ak^2} + \frac{2}{a} \sum_{n=1}^{\infty} \frac{\tilde{f}_c(n)}{k^2 - (n\pi/a)^2} \cos \frac{n\pi x}{a} \tag{5-304}$$

If $k^2 = (n\pi/a)^2$ for some value of n, then the sum in Eq. (5-304) becomes infinite. We interpret this physically as follows. Consider a weightless spring, one end of which is attached to a rigid wall and the other end of which supports a freely suspended mass m. Let the spring constant be K. According to Hooke's law, the displacement A of the mass m from equilibrium is opposed by the restoring force of the spring $F = -KA$. Then Newton's second law gives the equation of motion of the mass as

$$m \frac{d^2 A}{dt^2} + KA = 0 \tag{5-305}$$

If the mass is now *forced* to vibrate by some *external force* $g(t)$, then Eq. (5-305) becomes

$$m \frac{d^2 A}{dt^2} + KA = g(t) \tag{5-306}$$

Letting

$$k^2 = \frac{K}{m} \tag{5-307}$$

and

$$f(t) = \frac{1}{m} g(t) \tag{5-308}$$

Eq. (5-306) becomes

$$\frac{d^2 A}{dt^2} + k^2 A = f(t) \tag{5-309}$$

which is identical to Eq. (5-296) if we interpret x as time. We see from Eqs. (5-305) to (5-307) that k is the natural resonant (angular) frequency of the simple harmonic oscillator represented by the spring and mass system. In other words, the solution of Eq. (5-309) when $f(t) = 0$ is simply

$$A = c_1 \cos kt + c_2 \sin kt \tag{5-310}$$

Now if $f(t) \neq 0$ and $k^2 = (n\pi/a)^2$ for some value of n, then that particular frequency component of $f(t)$ "resonates" with the natural frequency of the spring-mass system. The result is that energy is transferred from the mechanism generating the forcing function $f(t)$ into the motion of the mass m. Since the system is conservative, the maximum amplitude of oscillation grows without limit as more and more energy is transferred into the spring-mass system. Thus the infinity in Eq. (5-304) for $k^2 = (n\pi/a)^2$ implies that the forcing function f has a frequency component which is in resonance with the natural frequency of the system. The boundary conditions (5-297) and (5-298) tell us that the velocity of the mass m must be zero at times $t = 0$ and $t = a$. These times correspond therefore to the instants at which the vibrating mass m reverses its direction, provided of course that there is no resonance. If resonance were to occur in an actual physical system, either inherent friction, neglected here, would absorb the excess energy, or the system would vibrate itself to pieces.

5-15 INFINITE-RANGE FOURIER TRANSFORMS

Let us return to the complex form of Fourier's series (5-230) and (5-231). For convenience we shall repeat these formulas here:

$$A(x) = \sum_{n=-\infty}^{+\infty} C_n e^{i(n\pi x/a)} \tag{5-311}$$

$$C_n = \frac{1}{2a} \int_{-a}^{+a} A(x) e^{-i(n\pi x/a)} \, dx \tag{5-312}$$

If we are concerned with obtaining the Fourier decomposition of a function $A(x)$ defined on the *entire real axis* $-\infty \leq x \leq +\infty$, instead of merely on the finite interval $-a \leq x \leq +a$, then we must allow $a \to \infty$ in Eqs. (5-311) and (5-312). Consider the following substitutions:

$$k = \frac{n\pi}{a} = n \, \Delta k \tag{5-313}$$

$$\Delta k = \frac{\pi}{a} \tag{5-314}$$

$$\frac{\Delta k}{2\pi} = \frac{1}{2a} \tag{5-315}$$

$$2a C_n = \bar{A}(k) = \bar{A}(n \, \Delta k) \tag{5-316}$$

$$C_n = \frac{1}{2\pi} \bar{A}(k) \, \Delta k = \frac{1}{2\pi} \bar{A}(n \, \Delta k) \, \Delta k \tag{5-317}$$

As $a \to \infty$, Eq. (5-312) becomes

$$\bar{A}(k) = \int_{-\infty}^{+\infty} A(x) e^{-ikx} \, dx \tag{5-318}$$

Let us rewrite Eq. (5-311) as

$$A(x) = \frac{1}{2\pi} \sum_{n=-\infty}^{+\infty} \bar{A}(n\,\Delta k) e^{in\Delta kx}\,\Delta k \tag{5-319}$$

which suggests that for $a \to \infty$

$$A(x) = \frac{1}{2\pi} \int_{-\infty}^{+\infty} \bar{A}(k) e^{ikx}\,dk \tag{5-320}$$

We cannot emphasize too strongly that the arguments leading to Eqs. (5-318) and (5-320) which have just been presented do not constitute a proof in any sense of the word. The rigorous analysis of the conditions under which Eqs. (5-318) and (5-320) hold is beyond the scope of our work. We shall content ourselves with merely stating without proof some conditions, not necessarily the most general ones, for which Eqs. (5-318) and (5-320) do hold.

The functions $\bar{A}(k)$ and $A(x)$ are called Fourier transforms of each other. It is customary to call $\bar{A}(k)$ as given by Eq. (5-318) the Fourier transform of $A(x)$, and to refer to Eq. (5-320) as the inversion theorem for $A(x)$. This terminology is quite analogous to that introduced in Eqs. (5-12) and (5-14). Sometimes the Fourier transform and its inversion theorem are written in symmetric form as

$$\bar{A}(k) = \frac{1}{\sqrt{2\pi}} \int_{-\infty}^{+\infty} A(x) e^{-ikx}\,dx \tag{5-321}$$

$$A(x) = \frac{1}{\sqrt{2\pi}} \int_{-\infty}^{+\infty} \bar{A}(k) e^{ikx}\,dk \tag{5-322}$$

or as

$$\bar{A}(f) = \int_{-\infty}^{+\infty} A(t) e^{-2\pi ift}\,dt \tag{5-323}$$

$$A(t) = \int_{-\infty}^{+\infty} \bar{A}(f) e^{2\pi ift}\,df \tag{5-324}$$

The formulas (5-321) and (5-322) can be obtained by changing Eq. (5-316) to

$$2aC_n = \sqrt{2\pi}\,\bar{A}(k) \tag{5-325}$$

and Eqs. (5-323) and (5-324) come from inserting

$$x = \sqrt{2\pi}\,t \tag{5-326}$$

$$k = \sqrt{2\pi}\,f \tag{5-327}$$

into Eqs. (5-321) and (5-322).

Suppose we now combine Eqs. (5-318) and (5-320). Then we obtain

$$A(x) = \frac{1}{2\pi} \int_{-\infty}^{+\infty} e^{ikx}\,dk \int_{-\infty}^{+\infty} A(y) e^{-iky}\,dy \tag{5-328}$$

where we have changed the dummy variable of integration in Eq. (5-318) from x to y, i.e.,

$$\bar{A}(k) = \int_{-\infty}^{+\infty} A(y) e^{-iky}\,dy \tag{5-329}$$

Let us assume that we can interchange the order of integration in Eq. (5-328) so that it becomes

$$A(x) = \int_{-\infty}^{+\infty} A(y)\, dy \, \frac{1}{2\pi} \int_{-\infty}^{+\infty} e^{ik(x-y)}\, dk \qquad (5\text{-}330)$$

Consider the "definition" of a new kind of "function" obtained by setting

$$\delta(x - y) = \frac{1}{2\pi} \int_{-\infty}^{+\infty} e^{ik(x-y)}\, dk \qquad (5\text{-}331)$$

Using Eq. (5-331), we can write Eq. (5-330) as

$$A(x) = \int_{-\infty}^{+\infty} A(y)\, \delta(x - y)\, dy \qquad (5\text{-}332)$$

What are the properties of $\delta(x - y)$? We can investigate this question by considering

$$\delta(x - y) = \lim_{a \to \infty} \frac{1}{2\pi} \int_{-a}^{+a} e^{ik(x-y)}\, dk \qquad (5\text{-}333)$$

Direct integration of Eq. (5-333) yields

$$\delta(x - y) = \lim_{a \to \infty} \frac{\sin a(x - y)}{\pi(x - y)} \qquad (5\text{-}334)$$

Let us plot the function

$$\frac{\sin a(x - y)}{\pi(x - y)} \qquad (5\text{-}335)$$

versus x, considering a and y to be fixed positive numbers. Equation (5-335) has a sharp peak at the point $x = y$, and the amplitude of this peak is given by L'Hospital's rule as a/π. The width of this main peak is $2\pi/a$. Thus the larger a becomes, the higher and narrower the peak is. In the limit $a = \infty$ the peak would be infinitely high and of zero width.

Consider the area contained under the main peak of Eq. (5-335) in the limit $a \to \infty$. The main peak can be approximated by an isosceles triangle of altitude a/π and base $2\pi/a$. This approximation improves as a gets larger. The area of the triangle is

$$\text{Area} = \tfrac{1}{2} \text{ altitude} \times \text{base} = \frac{1}{2}\frac{a}{\pi}\frac{2\pi}{a} = 1$$

independent of a. Let us now examine the secondary peaks of Eq. (5-335). These combine with the area under the main peak in such a way that the area under the entire curve (5-335) is exactly unity. In fact,

$$\lim_{s \to 0} \int_{-\infty}^{+\infty} e^{-s|x|} \frac{\sin ax}{\pi x}\, dx = \lim_{s \to 0} \frac{2}{\pi} \tan^{-1}\frac{a}{s} = 1 \qquad (5\text{-}336)$$

for any fixed finite $a > 0$. Notice that the farther a peak is from $x = y$, the less its amplitude can be, since these amplitudes must drop off as $1/(x - y)$. On the other hand, the distance to the kth

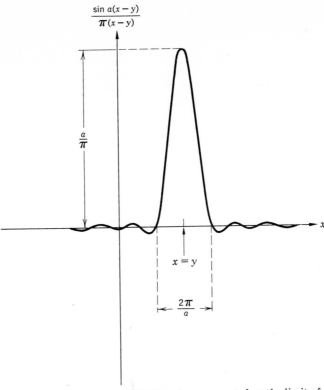

Figure 5-3 The delta function can be represented as the limit of $\sin a(x - y)/\pi(x - y)$ as $a \to \infty$.

secondary peak is

$$x - y = \frac{(2k - 1)\pi}{2a} \tag{5-337}$$

Therefore as a becomes larger, the kth peak moves toward the point $x = y$. In the limit $a = \infty$ the entire curve (5-335) is squeezed together at $x = y$. The result is that

$$\delta(x - y) = \begin{cases} 0 & x \neq y \\ \infty & x = y \end{cases} \tag{5-338}$$

and, because of Eq. (5-336),

$$\int_{y-\epsilon}^{y+\epsilon} \delta(x - y) \, dy = 1 \tag{5-339}$$

for every $\epsilon > 0$. Obviously Eq. (5-339) also includes the case

$$\int_{-\infty}^{+\infty} \delta(x - y) \, dy = 1 \tag{5-340}$$

Furthermore, since

$$\frac{\sin a(x - y)}{\pi(x - y)} = \frac{\sin a(y - x)}{\pi(y - x)} \tag{5-341}$$

we conclude that

$$\delta(x - y) = \delta(y - x) \tag{5-342}$$

The even function defined in Eq. (5-331) is known as the Dirac delta function. It is not actually a function at all; however, it shares many of the formal manipulative properties enjoyed by true functions.

The most important and, in fact, the true defining property of the delta function is its behavior under an integral sign. It picks out a single value of the integrand. For example, Eq. (5-332) becomes

$$A(x) = \int_{-\infty}^{+\infty} A(y)\, \delta(x - y)\, dy = A(x) \int_{-\infty}^{+\infty} \delta(x - y)\, dy = A(x) \tag{5-343}$$

on application of Eqs. (5-338) and (5-339).

5-16 CONDITIONS FOR THE APPLICABILITY OF THE FOURIER TRANSFORMATION

Sufficient conditions for the existence of the Fourier transform of $A(x)$ can be stated as follows: If $A(x)$ satisfies Dirichlet's conditions (see Sec. 5-10) on the interval $-\infty \leq x \leq +\infty$, and if in addition

$$0 \leq \int_{-\infty}^{+\infty} |A(x)|\, dx \leq M < \infty \tag{5-344}$$

then

$$\bar{A}(k) = \int_{-\infty}^{+\infty} A(x) e^{-ikx}\, dx \tag{5-345}$$

exists for every real k. Furthermore, $\bar{A}(k)$ is bounded since

$$|\bar{A}(k)| \leq \left| \int_{-\infty}^{+\infty} A(x) e^{-ikx}\, dx \right| \leq \int_{-\infty}^{+\infty} |A(x)|\, dx \leq M < \infty \tag{5-346}$$

and one can show that $\bar{A}(k)$ is a uniformly continuous function of k for $-\infty < k < +\infty$. It can also be demonstrated that

$$\lim_{k \to \infty} \bar{A}(k) = 0 \tag{5-347}$$

which is known as the "Riemann-Lesbesgue lemma." The precise inversion theorem for Eq. (5-345) is given by

$$\frac{1}{2\pi} \int_{-\infty}^{+\infty} \bar{A}(k) e^{ikx}\, dk = \begin{cases} A(x) & \text{if } A(x) \text{ is continuous at } x \\ \frac{1}{2}\{A(x + 0) + A(x - 0)\} \\ & \text{if } A(x) \text{ has a finite discontinuity at } x \end{cases} \tag{5-348}$$

Since $A(x)$ has at most a finite number of points of discontinuity (by hypothesis), we see that

$$\frac{1}{2\pi} \int_{-\infty}^{+\infty} \bar{A}(k) e^{ikx}\, dk \tag{5-349}$$

is equal to $A(x)$ everywhere except at a finite number of points.

Parseval's theorem

If

$$\bar{A}(k) = \int_{-\infty}^{+\infty} A(x)e^{-ikx}\,dx \tag{5-350}$$

and

$$A(x) = \frac{1}{2\pi} \int_{-\infty}^{+\infty} \bar{A}(k)e^{ikx}\,dk \tag{5-351}$$

then

$$\int_{-\infty}^{+\infty} |A(x)|^2\,dx = \frac{1}{2\pi} \int_{-\infty}^{+\infty} |\bar{A}(k)|^2\,dk \tag{5-352}$$

Equation (5-352) can be made plausible as follows:

$$
\begin{aligned}
\int_{-\infty}^{+\infty} |A(x)|^2\,dx &= \int_{-\infty}^{+\infty} A^*(x)A(x)\,dx \\
&= \int_{-\infty}^{+\infty} dx\,\frac{1}{2\pi} \int_{-\infty}^{+\infty} \bar{A}^*(n)e^{-inx}\,dn\,\frac{1}{2\pi} \int_{-\infty}^{+\infty} \bar{A}(k)e^{ikx}\,dk \\
&= \frac{1}{2\pi} \int_{-\infty}^{+\infty} \int_{-\infty}^{+\infty} \bar{A}^*(n)\bar{A}(k)\,\delta(k-n)\,dk\,dn \\
&= \frac{1}{2\pi} \int_{-\infty}^{+\infty} |\bar{A}(k)|^2\,dk
\end{aligned}
\tag{5-353}
$$

5-17 FOURIER SINE AND COSINE TRANSFORMS

We define the Fourier sine transform of a function $A(x)$ as

$$\bar{A}_s(k) = \sqrt{\frac{2}{\pi}} \int_0^\infty \bar{A}(x) \sin kx\,dx \tag{5-354}$$

and its corresponding inversion theorem by

$$A(x) = \sqrt{\frac{2}{\pi}} \int_0^\infty \bar{A}_s(k) \sin kx\,dk \tag{5-355}$$

Similarly, the Fourier cosine transform of a function $A(x)$ is given by

$$\bar{A}_c(k) = \sqrt{\frac{2}{\pi}} \int_0^\infty A(x) \cos kx\,dx \tag{5-356}$$

and its inversion theorem is

$$A(x) = \sqrt{\frac{2}{\pi}} \int_0^\infty \bar{A}_c(k) \cos kx\,dk \tag{5-357}$$

Notice the complete symmetry of these formulas and the fact that Eqs. (5-354) and (5-356) *involve only the behavior of* $A(x)$ *for* $0 \le x \le +\infty$. If $A(x)$ is originally given only for $0 \le x \le +\infty$, then we can extend $A(x)$ to $-\infty \le x \le 0$, as either an even or an odd function of x. Thus we may write

$$A(x) = A(-x) \tag{5-358}$$

or

$$A(x) = -A(-x) \tag{5-359}$$

and so obtain $A(x)$ on the entire real axis $-\infty \le x \le +\infty$. Now consider

$$\bar{A}(k) = \frac{1}{\sqrt{2\pi}} \int_{-\infty}^{+\infty} A(x)e^{-ikx}\, dx \tag{5-360}$$

which can be written

$$\bar{A}(k) = \frac{1}{\sqrt{2\pi}} \int_{-\infty}^{+\infty} A(x)(\cos kx - i \sin kx)\, dx \tag{5-361}$$

If Eq. (5-358) holds, then

$$\frac{1}{\sqrt{2\pi}} \int_{-\infty}^{+\infty} A(x) \sin kx\, dx = 0 \tag{5-362}$$

since the integral of an odd function over a symmetric interval is zero. Also

$$\bar{A}(k) = \frac{1}{\sqrt{2\pi}} \int_{-\infty}^{+\infty} A(x) \cos kx\, dx$$
$$= \sqrt{\frac{2}{\pi}} \int_{0}^{\infty} A(x) \cos kx\, dx \tag{5-363}$$

because the integral of an even function over a symmetric interval is twice the integral taken over one-half the interval. This shows that if $A(x)$ is an even function of x, then its complex Fourier transform is purely real and equal to its Fourier cosine transform,

$$\bar{A}(k) = \bar{A}_c(k) \qquad A(x) = A(-x) \tag{5-364}$$

Similarly, if $A(x)$ is an odd function of x so that Eq. (5-359) holds, then

$$\bar{A}(k) = \frac{-i}{\sqrt{2\pi}} \int_{-\infty}^{+\infty} A(x) \sin kx\, dx$$
$$= -i \sqrt{\frac{2}{\pi}} \int_{0}^{\infty} A(x) \sin kx\, dx \tag{5-365}$$

because the integrand in Eq. (5-365) is again even; i.e., it is the product of two odd functions of x. Hence if $A(x)$ is an odd function of x,

$$\bar{A}(k) = -i\bar{A}_s(k) \qquad A(x) = -A(-x) \tag{5-366}$$

states that the complex Fourier transform of $A(x)$ is $-i$ times the Fourier sine transform of $A(x)$.

Given an arbitrary function $A(x)$, we have two alternatives at our disposal. We can either take the complex Fourier transform of $A(x)$ directly, or we can first decompose $A(x)$ into its even and odd parts, and then take the Fourier cosine and sine transforms of each of these parts.

That is, given $A(x)$, we can immediately compute $\bar{A}(k)$, or we can first write

$$A(x) = E(x) + O(x) \qquad (5\text{-}367)$$

where

$$E(x) = \tfrac{1}{2}\{A(x) + A(-x)\} \qquad (5\text{-}368)$$

$$O(x) = \tfrac{1}{2}\{A(x) - A(-x)\} \qquad (5\text{-}369)$$

and then

$$\bar{A}(k) = \bar{E}_c(k) - i\bar{O}_s(k) \qquad (5\text{-}370)$$

Parseval's theorem (5-352) becomes

$$\int_{-\infty}^{+\infty} |A(x)|^2\, dx = \frac{1}{\pi} \int_0^\infty [\bar{E}_c{}^2(k) + \bar{O}_s{}^2(k)]\, dk \qquad (5\text{-}371)$$

5-18 FOURIER TRANSFORMS IN n DIMENSIONS

The Fourier transform can be readily generalized to n dimensions. For example,

$$\bar{A}(k_1, k_2, \ldots, k_n) = \int_{-\infty}^{+\infty} dx_1 \int_{-\infty}^{+\infty} dx_2 \cdots$$
$$\int_{-\infty}^{+\infty} dx_n A(x_1, x_2, \ldots, x_n) e^{-i(k_1 x_1 + \cdots + k_n x_n)} \qquad (5\text{-}372)$$

and the inversion theorem which corresponds to Eq. (5-372) is

$$A(x_1, x_2, \ldots, x_n) = \frac{1}{(2\pi)^n} \int_{-\infty}^{+\infty} dx_1 \cdots$$
$$\int_{-\infty}^{+\infty} dx_n \bar{A}(k_1, \ldots, k_n) e^{i(k_1 x_1 + \cdots + k_n x_n)} \qquad (5\text{-}373)$$

In a shorter notation Eqs. (5-372) and (5-373) are often written as

$$\bar{A}(\mathbf{k}) = \int A(\mathbf{x}) e^{-i\mathbf{k}\cdot\mathbf{x}}\, dV_x \qquad (5\text{-}374)$$

and

$$A(\mathbf{x}) = \frac{1}{(2\pi)^n} \int \bar{A}(\mathbf{k}) e^{i\mathbf{k}\cdot\mathbf{x}}\, dV_k \qquad (5\text{-}375)$$

It can be shown that the n-dimensional Dirac delta function is given by

$$\delta(\mathbf{x} - \mathbf{y}) = \frac{1}{(2\pi)^n} \int e^{i\mathbf{k}\cdot(\mathbf{x}-\mathbf{y})}\, dV_k \qquad (5\text{-}376)$$

where

$$\delta(\mathbf{x} - \mathbf{y}) = \begin{cases} 0 & \mathbf{x} \neq \mathbf{y} \\ \infty & \mathbf{x} = \mathbf{y} \end{cases} \qquad (5\text{-}377)$$

and

$$\int \delta(\mathbf{x} - \mathbf{y})\, dV_y = 1 \qquad (5\text{-}378)$$

with the understanding that

$$\int \delta(\mathbf{x} - \mathbf{y})\, dV_y = \int_{-\infty}^{+\infty} dy_1 \cdots \int_{-\infty}^{+\infty} dy_n\, \delta(\mathbf{x} - \mathbf{y}) \qquad (5\text{-}379)$$

The n-dimensional Dirac delta function has the property of Eq. (5-343), i.e.,

$$\int A(\mathbf{y}) \, \delta(\mathbf{x} - \mathbf{y}) \, dV_y = A(\mathbf{x}) \tag{5-380}$$

5-19   PROPERTIES OF FOURIER TRANSFORMS

We shall list some of the more important properties of the Fourier transform in this section.

Convolution theorem

The convolution of a pair of functions $A(x)$ and $B(x)$ is given by the following convolution integral:

$$C(x) = \int_{-\infty}^{+\infty} A(x - y)B(y) \, dy \tag{5-381}$$

If we let

$$z = x - y \tag{5-382}$$

$$dz = -dy \tag{5-383}$$

then

$$C(x) = \int_{-\infty}^{+\infty} A(z)B(x - z) \, dz \tag{5-384}$$

as well. Let

$$\bar{C}(k) = \int_{-\infty}^{+\infty} C(x)e^{-ikx} \, dx \tag{5-385}$$

$$\bar{A}(k) = \int_{-\infty}^{+\infty} A(x)e^{-ikx} \, dx \tag{5-386}$$

$$\bar{B}(k) = \int_{-\infty}^{+\infty} B(x)e^{-ikx} \, dx \tag{5-387}$$

be the Fourier transforms of $C(x)$, $A(x)$, and $B(x)$, respectively. The convolution theorem says that if

$$C(x) = \int_{-\infty}^{+\infty} A(x - y)B(y) \, dy \tag{5-388}$$

then

$$\bar{C}(k) = \bar{A}(k)\bar{B}(k) \tag{5-389}$$

We can make Eq. (5-389) plausible as follows:

$$\bar{C}(k) = \int_{-\infty}^{+\infty} e^{-ikx} \, dx \int_{-\infty}^{+\infty} A(x - y)B(y) \, dy \tag{5-390}$$

Now let

$$z = x - y \tag{5-391}$$

and

$$dz = dx \tag{5-392}$$

Then Eq. (5-390) becomes

$$\bar{C}(k) = \int_{-\infty}^{+\infty} e^{-ik(y+z)} \, dz \int_{-\infty}^{+\infty} A(z)B(y) \, dy \tag{5-393}$$

and, provided the order of integration can be inverted, Eq. (5-393) gives

$$\bar{C}(k) = \int_{-\infty}^{+\infty} A(z)e^{-ikz}\,dz \int_{-\infty}^{+\infty} B(y)e^{-iky}\,dy \tag{5-394}$$

Then using Eqs. (5-386) and (5-387), we find

$$\bar{C}(k) = \bar{A}(k)\bar{B}(k) \tag{5-395}$$

The convolution theorem converts integration in x space into multiplication in k space.

Fourier transforms of derivatives

Let the following abbreviation be introduced for the Fourier transform of $A(x)$:

$$F\{A(x)\} = \bar{A}(k) = \int_{-\infty}^{+\infty} A(x)e^{-ikx}\,dx \tag{5-396}$$

By using this notation many properties of Fourier transforms can be exhibited in compact form. For example, if we integrate

$$\int_{-\infty}^{+\infty} \frac{\partial A}{\partial x}\, e^{-ikx}\,dx \tag{5-397}$$

by parts, we obtain

$$\int_{-\infty}^{+\infty} \frac{\partial A}{\partial x}\, e^{-ikx}\,dx = A(x)e^{-ikx}\Big|_{x=-\infty}^{x=+\infty} + ik \int_{-\infty}^{+\infty} A(x)e^{-ikx}\,dx \tag{5-398}$$

and if

$$\lim_{|x|\to\infty} A(x) = 0 \tag{5-399}$$

then

$$F\left\{\frac{\partial A}{\partial x}\right\} = ikF\{A(x)\} \tag{5-400}$$

Similarly,

$$\int_{-\infty}^{+\infty} \frac{\partial^2 A}{\partial x^2}\, e^{-ikx}\,dx = \frac{\partial A}{\partial x}\, e^{-ikx}\Big|_{x=-\infty}^{x=+\infty} + ik \int_{-\infty}^{+\infty} \frac{\partial A}{\partial x}\, e^{-ikx}\,dx \tag{5-401}$$

which can be written with the aid of Eq. (5-398) as

$$\int_{-\infty}^{+\infty} \frac{\partial^2 A}{\partial x^2}\, e^{-ikx}\,dx = \left(\frac{\partial A}{\partial x} + ikA\right) e^{-ikx}\Big|_{x=-\infty}^{x=+\infty}$$
$$+ (ik)^2 \int_{-\infty}^{+\infty} A(x)e^{-ikx}\,dx \tag{5-402}$$

and if

$$\lim_{|x|\to\infty} \left[\frac{\partial A}{\partial x} + ikA(x)\right] = 0 \tag{5-403}$$

then

$$F\left\{\frac{\partial^n A}{\partial x^2}\right\} = (ik)^2 F\{A(x)\} \tag{5-404}$$

In general, integration by parts gives

$$F\left\{\frac{\partial^n A}{\partial x^n}\right\} = \left[\frac{\partial^{n-1} A}{\partial x^{n-1}} + ik\frac{\partial^{n-2} A}{\partial x^{n-2}} + (ik)^2\frac{\partial^{n-3} A}{\partial x^{n-3}} + \cdots\right.$$
$$\left. + (ik)^{n-1}A\right]e^{-ikx}\bigg|_{x=-\infty}^{x=+\infty} + (ik)^n F\{A\} \qquad (5\text{-}405)$$

so that if A and its first $n-1$ derivatives vanish at $x = \pm\infty$,

$$F\left\{\frac{\partial^n A}{\partial x^n}\right\} = (ik)^n F\{A(x)\} \qquad (5\text{-}406)$$

Notice that differentiation in x space is converted into multiplication by an appropriate power of k in k space.

Fourier transform of an indefinite integral

Consider the indefinite integral

$$\int^x A(s)\,ds \qquad (5\text{-}407)$$

We have

$$\frac{d}{dx}\int^x A(s)\,ds = A(x) \qquad (5\text{-}408)$$

Therefore,

$$F\left\{\frac{d}{dx}\int^x A(s)\,ds\right\} = ikF\left\{\int^x A(s)\,ds\right\} = F\{A(x)\} \qquad (5\text{-}409)$$

which gives

$$F\left\{\int^x A(s)\,ds\right\} = \frac{1}{ik}F\{A(x)\} \qquad (5\text{-}410)$$

provided $k \neq 0$ and

$$\int_{-\infty}^{+\infty}|A(s)|\,ds < \infty \qquad (5\text{-}411)$$

From Eq. (5-410) it is seen that integration in x space is converted into division by ik in k space.

5-20 PHYSICAL INTERPRETATION OF THE FOURIER TRANSFORM

Consider the Fourier transform

$$\bar{A}(\omega) = \int_{-\infty}^{+\infty} A(t)e^{-i\omega t}\,dt \qquad (5\text{-}412)$$

and its inversion theorem

$$A(t) = \frac{1}{2\pi}\int_{-\infty}^{+\infty} \bar{A}(\omega)e^{i\omega t}\,d\omega \qquad (5\text{-}413)$$

In general, $\bar{A}(\omega)$ is a complex-valued function of ω and can therefore be written in polar form as

$$\bar{A}(\omega) = r(\omega)e^{-i\phi(\omega)} \qquad (5\text{-}414)$$

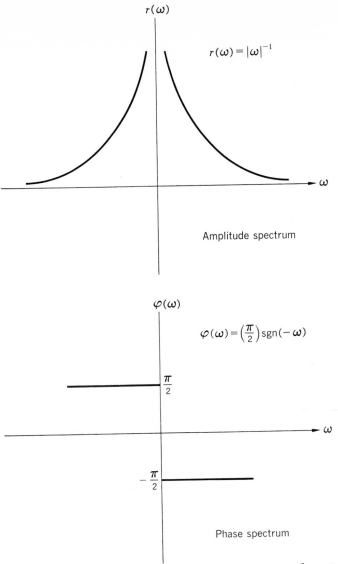

Figure 5-4 The phase and amplitude spectra of $H(x) = \begin{cases} 1 & x > 0 \\ 0 & x < 0 \end{cases}$

In Eq. (5-414)

$$r(\omega) = |\bar{A}(\omega)| \qquad (5\text{-}415)$$

and

$$\varphi(\omega) = -\arg[\bar{A}(\omega)] \qquad (5\text{-}416)$$

are real-valued functions of ω.

Suppose that t represents time and ω represents an angular frequency $\omega = 2\pi f$. If we plot a graph with the amplitude $r(\omega)$ as ordinate and the angular frequency ω as abscissa, then the resulting curve is called the "amplitude spectrum" of $A(t)$. In general, $r(\omega)$ is a continuous function of ω, and therefore the amplitude spectrum of a function defined over an infinite interval $-\infty \leq t \leq +\infty$ is called a "continuous spectrum." A similar plot of $\varphi(\omega)$ versus ω is called the "phase spectrum" of $A(t)$. It is also a continuous spectrum. These results differ from those discussed in connection with Eq. (5-236). There we saw that a function defined on a finite interval $[0,a]$ has discrete amplitude and phase spectra.

The inversion theorem (5-413) can be written as

$$A(t) = \frac{1}{2\pi} \int_{-\infty}^{+\infty} r(\omega) e^{i[\omega t - \varphi(\omega)]} \, d\omega \qquad (5\text{-}417)$$

which shows that $A(t)$ is a superposition of simple harmonic oscillations of continuously varying amplitude $r(\omega)$, phase $\varphi(\omega)$, and angular frequency ω.

Suppose that the total energy in a signal $A(t)$ is equal to

$$\int_{-\infty}^{+\infty} |A(t)|^2 \, dt \qquad (5\text{-}418)$$

From Parseval's theorem (5-353) we have

$$\int_{-\infty}^{+\infty} |A(t)|^2 \, dt = \frac{1}{2\pi} \int_{-\infty}^{+\infty} r^2(\omega) \, d\omega \qquad (5\text{-}419)$$

Equation (5-417) represents $A(t)$ as a superposition of a continuum of harmonic oscillations, while Eq. (5-419) states that a harmonic oscillator of angular frequency ω and amplitude $r(\omega)$ contributes an amount of energy $r^2(\omega) \, d\omega$ to the total energy in the signal $A(t)$.

5-21 APPLICATIONS OF THE INFINITE-RANGE FOURIER TRANSFORM

The Fourier transform is one of the most powerful tools in applied mathematics, essentially because it reduces the operations of differentiation and integration to multiplication and division, respectively. In the present section we shall only touch upon a few of the many problems in which the Fourier transform may be applied. Further applications will be found in Chaps. 6 and 7.

EXAMPLE 5-9: *Series-resonant Electric Circuit.* Consider a current I flowing in a series-resonant electric circuit composed of an inductance L, a resistance R, and a capacitance C, all in series with a generator whose voltage is $V(t)$. The current $I(t)$ satisfies the following ordinary differential equation:

$$L \frac{d^2 I}{dt^2} + R \frac{dI}{dt} + \frac{I}{C} = \frac{dV}{dt} \qquad (5\text{-}420)$$

The general solution of Eq. (5-420) consists of a sum of two terms:

$$I(t) = I_c(t) + I_{ss}(t) \qquad (5\text{-}421)$$

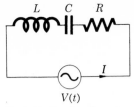

Figure 5-5 A series-resonant a-c circuit.

The first term $I_c(t)$ satisfies

$$L \frac{d^2 I_c}{dt^2} + R \frac{dI_c}{dt} + \frac{I_c}{C} = 0 \tag{5-422}$$

and the second term $I_{ss}(t)$ satisfies Eq. (5-420). The sum $I(t)$ satisfies (5-420) because (5-420) is a *linear* differential equation. In other words, if we define an operator A by

$$A = L \frac{d^2}{dt^2} + R \frac{d}{dt} + \frac{1}{C} \qquad L, R, C = \text{const} \tag{5-423}$$

then Eq. (5-420) becomes

$$A\{I\} = \frac{dV}{dt} \tag{5-424}$$

and

$$A\{I\} = A\{I_c + I_{ss}\} = A\{I_c\} + A\{I_{ss}\} = \frac{dV}{dt} \tag{5-425}$$

but

$$A\{I_c\} = 0 \tag{5-426}$$

so that

$$A\{I\} = A\{I_{ss}\} = \frac{dV}{dt} \tag{5-427}$$

The term $I_c(t)$ satisfying the homogeneous equation (5-422) is called the "complementary function." It represents the transient current which flows in the circuit after the opening or closing of a switch. The term $I_{ss}(t)$ is called a particular integral of Eq. (5-420). It represents the steady-state current flowing in the circuit, i.e., the current flowing at a time long after the circuit has been turned on.

The current $I_{ss}(t)$ is driven around the circuit by the action of the generator. We shall solve for $I_{ss}(t)$, using the Fourier transform method. The complementary function $I_c(t)$ is more readily found by other means, and we shall not treat it here.

Let us multiply Eq. (5-420) by $e^{-i\omega t}$ and integrate by parts with respect to time from $t = -\infty$ to $t = +\infty$. Referring to Eq. (5-402), we see that we must examine

$$\left(\frac{\partial I}{\partial t} + i\omega I \right) e^{-i\omega t} \tag{5-428}$$

and

$$I(t)e^{-i\omega t} \tag{5-429}$$

at $t \to \pm \infty$.

It is important to notice that expressions (5-428) and (5-429) *do not vanish* as $t \to \pm \infty$ when ω is purely real. The steady-state current and its time derivatives do not approach zero as $t \to \pm \infty$, so long as the generator continues to operate from the beginning of time to the end of time.

One way out of this dilemma is to assume that the circuit was switched on at some time far in the past, say $t = -T$, and that it will be switched off again at some time far in the future, say $t = +T$. In that case all the transient current will be damped out for $t \gg T$, and no current will be present for $t \ll -T$. This follows because the switch remains open until $t = -T$. As a result, (5-428) and (5-429) will vanish as $t \to \pm \infty$. The result is that Eq. (5-420) becomes

$$\left[L(i\omega)^2 + (i\omega)R + \frac{1}{C} \right] \bar{I}(\omega) = i\omega \bar{V}(\omega) \tag{5-430}$$

where

$$\bar{I}(\omega) = \int_{-\infty}^{+\infty} I(t)e^{-i\omega t}\, dt \tag{5-431}$$

and

$$\bar{V}(\omega) = \int_{-\infty}^{+\infty} V(t)e^{-i\omega t}\, dt \tag{5-432}$$

Solving for $\bar{I}(\omega)$, we find

$$\bar{I}(\omega) = \frac{\bar{V}(\omega)}{R + i(\omega L - 1/\omega C)} \tag{5-433}$$

Let

$$X_L = \omega L \qquad X_C = \frac{1}{\omega C} \tag{5-434}$$

Then in polar form,

$$R + i(X_L - X_C) = \sqrt{R^2 + (X_L - X_C)^2}\; e^{i\,\tan^{-1}(X_L - X_C)/R} \tag{5-435}$$

so that Eq. (5-433) becomes

$$\bar{I}(\omega) = \frac{\bar{V}(\omega)}{\bar{Z}(\omega)}\, e^{-i\phi(\omega)} \tag{5-436}$$

where

$$\bar{Z}(\omega) = \sqrt{R^2 + (X_L - X_C)^2} \tag{5-437}$$

$$\varphi(\omega) = \tan^{-1}\frac{X_L - X_C}{R} \tag{5-438}$$

The student will recognize that $\bar{Z}(\omega)$ is the impedance of a series circuit and that X_L and X_C are the inductive and capacitative reactances, respectively. The phase shift in the circuit is given by $\varphi(\omega)$. The steady-state response in the time domain is obtained by applying the inversion theorem (5-413) to Eq. (5-436). The result is

$$I_{ss}(t) = \frac{1}{2\pi} \int_{-\infty}^{+\infty} \frac{\bar{V}(\omega)}{\bar{Z}(\omega)} e^{i[\omega t - \varphi(\omega)]} \, d\omega \tag{5-439}$$

We see from Eq. (5-439) how the generator spectrum $\bar{V}(\omega)$ combines with the impedance and phase shift of the circuit to yield the steady-state current $I_{ss}(t)$.

EXAMPLE 5-10: *Spectrum of a Rectangular Pulse.* Let $A(t)$ be a rectangular pulse of duration T defined by

$$A(t) = \begin{cases} 1 & |t| \le T/2 \\ 0 & |t| > T/2 \end{cases} \tag{5-440}$$

The spectrum of $A(t)$ is given by

$$\bar{A}(\omega) = \int_{-T/2}^{T/2} e^{-i\omega t} \, dt = T \frac{\sin \omega T/2}{\omega T/2} \tag{5-441}$$

If we plot $\bar{A}(\omega)$ as a function of ω, we see that $\bar{A}(\omega)$ has a peak value T centered on $\omega = 0$. This central peak crosses the ω axis at $\omega = \pm 2\pi/T$.

As T increases without limit, the pulse grows increasingly broad in time. Consequently, the central peak in the pulse-amplitude spectrum grows increasingly high and narrow. Most of the energy in the pulse lies in this central peak. Therefore the longer the duration of a pulse is, the more narrow a spectral bandwidth its energy is concentrated into (Fig. 5-6). If we choose the bandwidth $\Delta\omega$ of the pulse to be the angular frequency interval separating the central maximum at $\omega = 0$ from the first zero at $\omega = 2\pi/T$, then

$$\Delta\omega = \frac{2\pi}{T} \tag{5-442}$$

However, T represents the duration of the pulse in time, and therefore we write $\Delta\tau = T$ in Eq. (5-442), obtaining

$$\Delta\omega \, \Delta\tau = 2\pi \tag{5-443}$$

or

$$\Delta f \, \Delta\tau = 1 \tag{5-444}$$

Equations (5-443) and (5-444) provide a relation between the time duration of the pulse and its frequency bandwidth.

Such relations between pulse duration and frequency bandwidth express in a general way the fact that the shape of a pulse in time

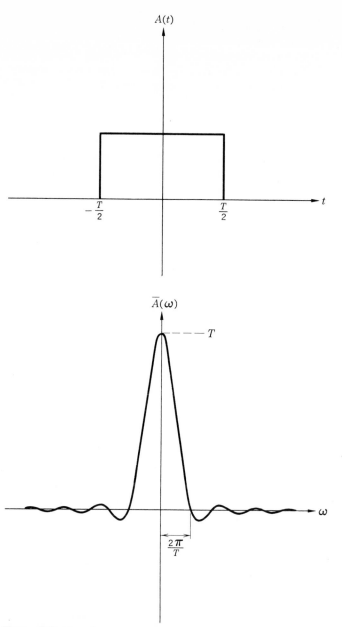

Figure 5-6 The time duration of a pulse and the bandwidth of its Fourier spectrum are inversely related.

and the shape of its amplitude spectrum are not independent. In quantum mechanics, relations such as Eq. (5-444) form the basis of the so-called uncertainty principles. The magnitude of the constant on the right side of Eq. (5-444) depends on the precise details of how the bandwidth of a pulse is defined.

Let us consider the Fourier transform

$$\bar{A}(\omega) = \int_{-\infty}^{+\infty} A(t)e^{-i\omega t}\,dt \tag{5-445}$$

and its inversion theorem

$$A(t) = \frac{1}{2\pi}\int_{-\infty}^{+\infty} \bar{A}(\omega)e^{i\omega t}\,d\omega \tag{5-446}$$

The Fourier transform (5-445) exists only for functions $A(t)$ which satisfy the condition

$$0 < \int_{-\infty}^{+\infty} |A(t)|\,dt \leq M < \infty \tag{5-447}$$

We have already noted this in Sec. 5-16. Even in the most simple common cases, $A(t) = 1$ or $A(t) = e^{i\omega t}$, the integral (5-447) fails to converge. Thus, for these functions, we cannot use inequality (5-346) to establish the convergence of Eq. (5-445). Consequently these simple functions do not have Fourier transforms in the classical sense. Of course, we could say that

$$2\pi\,\delta(\omega) = \int_{-\infty}^{+\infty} e^{i\omega t}\,dt \tag{5-448}$$

is the Fourier transform of $A(t) = 1$. However, a formal result such as Eq. (5-448) must receive a great deal more mathematical attention before it becomes rigorously meaningful. We shall accept the idea that *classical* Fourier transforms are defined only when the integral (5-445) converges, and thereby we may dispose of any contradiction associated with Eq. (5-448).

The problem of what to do about $A(t) = 1$ and $A(t) = e^{i\omega t}$ can be resolved in the following way. As a first step, we can observe that most physical processes begin at some definite time, which we can define to be $t = 0$. Thus the time interval in question becomes $0 \leq t \leq \infty$ rather than $-\infty \leq t \leq +\infty$. The function $A(t)$ is now defined *only* for the interval $0 \leq t \leq +\infty$. We would like to compute the Fourier transform (5-445) of $A(t)$, but we cannot do so until we know what $A(t)$ is for negative values of time. Since $A(t)$ represents a physical phenomenon beginning at $t = 0$, we can extend $A(t)$ to negative values of time by *defining* $A(t)$ to be zero for $t < 0$. Thus

$$A(t) = \begin{cases} A(t) & 0 \leq t \leq \infty \\ 0 & t < 0 \end{cases} \tag{5-449}$$

Then Eq. (5-445) becomes

$$\bar{A}(\omega) = \int_{0}^{\infty} A(t)e^{-i\omega t}\,dt \tag{5-450}$$

but Eq. (5-450) also fails to converge for

$$A(t) = \begin{cases} 1 & 0 \leq t \leq \infty \\ 0 & t < 0 \end{cases} \tag{5-451}$$

and

$$A(t) = \begin{cases} e^{i\omega t} & 0 \leq t \leq \infty \\ 0 & t < 0 \end{cases} \tag{5-452}$$

Here we employ an artifice. Instead of considering $A(t)$, we consider an entire family of functions of the form

$$F(t) = \begin{cases} e^{-\sigma t}A(t) & 0 \leq t \leq \infty \\ 0 & t < 0 \end{cases} \tag{5-453}$$

where the real parameter σ runs through values $\sigma \geq \sigma_0 > 0$. The Fourier transform of Eq. (5-453) becomes

$$\bar{A}_\sigma(\omega) = \int_0^\infty e^{-i\omega t}[e^{-\sigma t}A(t)] \, dt \tag{5-454}$$

In Eq. (5-454) the subscript σ in $\bar{A}_\sigma(\omega)$ indicates that this Fourier transform depends on σ as well as ω. Now Eq. (5-454) converges for both Eqs. (5-451) and (5-452). For the case of (5-451) we find

$$\bar{A}_\sigma(\omega) = \int_0^\infty e^{-(\sigma+i\omega)t} \, dt = \frac{-e^{-(\sigma+i\omega)t}}{\sigma + i\omega} \Big|_{t=0}^{t=\infty} \tag{5-455}$$

giving

$$\bar{A}_\sigma(\omega) = \frac{1}{\sigma + i\omega} \tag{5-456}$$

while Eq. (5-452) gives

$$\bar{A}_\sigma(\omega) = \int_0^\infty e^{-\sigma t} \, dt = \frac{-1}{\sigma} e^{-\sigma t} \Big|_{t=0}^{t=\infty} = \frac{1}{\sigma} \tag{5-457}$$

More generally, Eq. (5-454) will converge for any function of time $A(t)$ which does not grow more rapidly in time than e^{at}, $a > 0$, as $t \to \infty$, provided of course that

$$\sigma \geq \sigma_0 > a > 0 \tag{5-458}$$

That this is actually the case can be seen as follows: Suppose that $A(t)$ is piecewise-continuous on every finite interval and that

$$|A(t)| \leq Me^{at} \tag{5-459}$$

for some choice of the constants M and a. Then,

$$\left| \int_0^T e^{-i\omega t} [e^{-\sigma t}A(t)] \, dt \right| \leq \int_0^T e^{-\sigma t}|A(t)| \, dt$$
$$\leq \int_0^T Me^{-(\sigma-a)t} \, dt \leq \int_0^\infty Me^{-(\sigma-a)t} \, dt = \frac{M}{\sigma - a} \tag{5-460}$$

provided

$$\sigma - a > 0 \tag{5-461}$$

Since Eq. (5-460) holds for any $T > 0$ and

$$\int_0^\infty e^{-i\omega t}[e^{-\sigma t}A(t)] \, dt \leq \left| \int_0^\infty e^{-i\omega t}[e^{-\sigma t}A(t)] \, dt \right| \tag{5-462}$$

we conclude that Eq. (5-454) converges and in fact that it converges absolutely. It can be shown that the convergence of Eq. (5-454) is uniform for any fixed σ_0 such that

$$\sigma \geq \sigma_0 > a \tag{5-463}$$

Using Eqs. (5-454) and (5-460) gives

$$\lim_{\sigma \to \infty} \bar{A}_\sigma(\omega) = 0 \tag{5-464}$$

which always holds whenever Eq. (5-454) converges for any finite $\sigma = \sigma_0$, even if inequality (5-459) does not apply.

Remembering that $A(t) = 0$ for $t < 0$ and

$$\bar{A}_\sigma(\omega) = \int_0^\infty e^{-i\omega t}[e^{-\sigma t}A(t)]\,dt \tag{5-465}$$

use of the inversion theorem (5-348) for Fourier transforms yields

$$\frac{1}{2\pi}\int_{-\infty}^{+\infty}\bar{A}_\sigma(\omega)e^{i\omega t}\,d\omega = \begin{cases} 0 & t < 0 \\ e^{-\sigma t}A(t) & \text{if } A(t) \text{ is continuous} \\ & \text{at } t \\ \tfrac{1}{2}e^{-\sigma t}\{A(t+0) + A(t-0)\} \\ & \text{if } A(t) \text{ has a finite discon-} \\ & \text{tinuity at } t \end{cases} \tag{5-466}$$

We can also write Eqs. (5-465) and (5-466) in a slightly different form as follows:

$$\bar{A}_\sigma(\omega) = \int_0^\infty e^{-(\sigma+i\omega)t}A(t)\,dt \tag{5-467}$$

$$\frac{1}{2\pi}\int_{-\infty}^{+\infty}\bar{A}_\sigma(\omega)e^{(\sigma+i\omega)t}\,d\omega = \begin{cases} 0 & t < 0 \\ A(t) & \text{if } A(t) \text{ is continu-} \\ & \text{ous at } t \\ \tfrac{1}{2}\{A(t+0) + A(t-0)\} \\ & \text{if } A(t) \text{ has a finite dis-} \\ & \text{continuity at } t \end{cases} \tag{5-468}$$

The quantity $\sigma + i\omega$ appears in both Eqs. (5-467) and (5-468). In particular, it is apparent that $\bar{A}_\sigma(\omega)$ does not depend on σ and ω in an arbitrary manner but only in the aggregate

$$s = \sigma + i\omega \tag{5-469}$$

This means that the sequence of spectral amplitudes $\bar{A}_\sigma(\omega)$ corresponding to different values of σ coalesce in such a way that they can be represented as a function of one complex variable. Thus one writes

$$\bar{A}_\sigma(\omega) = \bar{A}(\sigma + i\omega) = \bar{A}(s) \tag{5-470}$$

It follows from inequality (5-463) that we can set $\sigma = \sigma_0 = \text{constant}$ in discussing Eqs. (5-467) to (5-469); then

$$ds = i\,d\omega \tag{5-471}$$

while the limits of integration $\omega = -\infty$ and $\omega = +\infty$ correspond to $s = \sigma_0 - i\infty$ and $s = \sigma_0 + i\infty$, respectively. In terms of the variable s, Eqs. (5-467) and (5-468) take the forms

$$\bar{A}(s) = \int_0^\infty e^{-st}A(t)\,dt \tag{5-472}$$

and

$$F(t) = \frac{1}{2\pi i} \int_{\sigma_0 - i\infty}^{\sigma_0 + i\infty} \bar{A}(s) e^{st} \, ds \tag{5-473}$$

where

$$F(t) = 0 \quad t < 0 \tag{5-474}$$

$$F(t) = A(t) \tag{5-475}$$

when $A(t)$ is continuous at t, and

$$F(t) = \tfrac{1}{2}\{A(t+0) + A(t-0)\} \tag{5-476}$$

when $A(t)$ has a finite discontinuity at t. The path of integration for Eq. (5-473) in the complex s plane is a vertical line with abscissa $\sigma = \sigma_0$. The integral (5-472) is called the *Laplace transform* of $A(t)$, and Eq. (5-473) is its corresponding inversion theorem.

In physical terms, the Laplace transform

$$\bar{A}(s) = \bar{A}_\sigma(\omega) = \bar{A}(\sigma + i\omega)$$

is the spectral amplitude, at frequency ω, of a damped signal $e^{-\sigma t} A(t)$ which begins at time $t = 0$ and decays to $1/e$ of its initial value in a time $t = 1/\sigma$. The inversion theorem (5-466) represents this damped signal as a superposition of harmonic oscillations of frequency ω and amplitude $\bar{A}_\sigma(\omega)$. On the other hand, the inversion theorem (5-473) represents only the function $A(t)$ as a superposition of harmonic oscillations of different frequencies. The amplitude of each of these harmonic oscillations grows exponentially in time. The rate of growth is such that each amplitude is multiplied by a factor of e after a time interval $t = 1/\sigma$.

5-23 PROPERTIES OF LAPLACE TRANSFORMS

Convolution theorem

Let $A(t)$ and $B(t)$ be functions which vanish identically for $t < 0$. The convolution integral (5-381) becomes

$$C(t) = \int_0^t A(t - \tau) B(\tau) \, d\tau \tag{5-477}$$

and Eq. (5-384) gives

$$C(t) = \int_0^t A(\tau) B(t - \tau) \, d\tau \tag{5-478}$$

as well. Let

$$\bar{C}(s) = \int_0^\infty C(t) e^{-st} \, dt \tag{5-479}$$

$$\bar{A}(s) = \int_0^\infty A(t) e^{-st} \, dt \tag{5-480}$$

$$\bar{B}(s) = \int_0^\infty B(t) e^{-st} \, dt \tag{5-481}$$

be the Laplace transforms of $C(t)$, $A(t)$, and $B(t)$, respectively. The convolution theorem for Laplace transforms states that if

$$C(t) = \int_0^t A(t - \tau) B(\tau) \, d\tau \tag{5-482}$$

then

$$\bar{C}(s) = \bar{A}(s) \bar{B}(s) \tag{5-483}$$

The result (5-483) can be made plausible by the same type of argument used to establish Eq. (5-389). Therefore we shall not justify Eq. (5-483) here.

Laplace transforms of derivatives

Let the following abbreviation be introduced for the Laplace transform of $A(t)$:

$$L\{A(t)\} = \bar{A}(s) = \int_0^\infty A(t) e^{-st} \, dt \tag{5-484}$$

Using this notation, many properties of Laplace transforms take on a simple form. For example, if we integrate

$$\int_0^\infty \frac{\partial A}{\partial t} e^{-st} \, dt \tag{5-485}$$

by parts, we obtain

$$\int_0^\infty \frac{\partial A}{\partial t} e^{-st} \, dt = A(t) e^{-st} \Big|_{t=0}^{t=\infty} + s \int_0^\infty A(t) e^{-st} \, dt \tag{5-486}$$

and if

$$\lim_{t \to \infty} A(t) e^{-st} = 0 \tag{5-487}$$

then

$$L\left\{\frac{\partial A}{\partial t}\right\} = sL\{A\} - A(0) \tag{5-488}$$

Similarly,

$$\int_0^\infty \frac{\partial^2 A}{\partial t^2} e^{-st} \, dt = \frac{\partial A}{\partial t} e^{-st} \Big|_{t=0}^{t=\infty} + s \int_0^\infty \frac{\partial A}{\partial t} e^{-st} \, dt \tag{5-489}$$

which, using Eq. (5-486), becomes

$$\int_0^\infty \frac{\partial^2 A}{\partial t^2} e^{-st} \, dt = \left[\frac{\partial A}{\partial t} + sA(t)\right] e^{-st} \Big|_{t=0}^{t=\infty}$$
$$+ s^2 \int_0^\infty A(t) e^{-st} \, dt \tag{5-490}$$

and if

$$\lim_{t \to \infty} \left[\frac{\partial A}{\partial t} + sA(t)\right] e^{-st} = 0 \tag{5-491}$$

then

$$L\left\{\frac{\partial^2 A}{\partial t^2}\right\} = s^2 L\{A\} - sA(0) - \left(\frac{\partial A}{\partial t}\right)_{t=0} \tag{5-492}$$

In general, integration by parts gives

$$L\left\{\frac{\partial^n A}{\partial t^n}\right\} = \left[\frac{\partial^{n-1}A}{\partial t^{n-1}} + s\frac{\partial^{n-2}A}{\partial t^{n-2}} + s^2\frac{\partial^{n-3}A}{\partial t^{n-3}} + \cdots \right.$$

$$\left. + s^{n-1}A(t)\right] e^{-st}\bigg|_{t=0}^{t=\infty} + s^n L\{A\} \qquad (5\text{-}493)$$

so that if

$$\lim_{t\to\infty}\left[\frac{\partial^{n-1}A}{\partial t^{n-1}} + s\frac{\partial^{n-2}A}{\partial t^{n-2}} + s^2\frac{\partial^{n-3}A}{\partial t^{n-3}} + \cdots \right.$$

$$\left. + s^{n-1}A(t)\right] e^{-st} = 0 \qquad (5\text{-}494)$$

then

$$L\left\{\frac{\partial^n A}{\partial t^n}\right\} = s^n L\{A\} - s^{n-1}A(0) - s^{n-2}\left(\frac{\partial A}{\partial t}\right)_0 - s^{n-3}\left(\frac{\partial^2 A}{\partial t^2}\right)_0$$

$$- \cdots - s^{(n-1)-k}\left(\frac{\partial^k A}{\partial t^k}\right)_0 - \cdots - \left(\frac{\partial^{n-1}A}{\partial t^{n-1}}\right)_0 \qquad (5\text{-}495)$$

We see that differentiation in t space is converted into multiplication by an appropriate power of s in s space.

Laplace transform of an integral

Consider

$$\frac{d}{dt}\int_0^t A(\tau)\,d\tau = A(t) \qquad (5\text{-}496)$$

Then

$$L\left\{\frac{d}{dt}\int_0^t A(\tau)\,d\tau\right\} = sL\left\{\int_0^t A(\tau)\,d\tau\right\} \qquad (5\text{-}497)$$

provided

$$\lim_{t\to\infty} e^{-st}\int_0^t A(\tau)\,d\tau = 0 \qquad (5\text{-}498)$$

However

$$L\left\{\frac{d}{dt}\int_0^t A(\tau)\,d\tau\right\} = L\{A\} \qquad (5\text{-}499)$$

directly from Eq. (5-496). Therefore,

$$L\left\{\int_0^t A(\tau)\,d\tau\right\} = \frac{1}{s}L\{A\} \qquad (5\text{-}500)$$

provided $s \neq 0$. Thus integration in t space is converted into division by s in s space.

5-24 APPLICATION OF THE LAPLACE TRANSFORM

The Laplace transform shares with the Fourier transform the property of reducing differentiation and integration to multiplication and division in transform space. Moreover, the Laplace transform

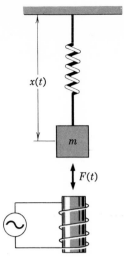

Figure 5-7 Forced oscillations of a spring driven by an electromagnet.

is particularly well suited for application to a function which vanishes for $t < 0$ and which, together with its time derivatives, must satisfy some initial conditions at $t = 0$.

EXAMPLE 5-11: *Forced Oscillations of Springs.* Consider a spring whose initial displacement from a stable equilibrium is

$$x = x(0) \tag{5-501}$$

at $t = 0$, and whose initial velocity is given by

$$\left(\frac{dx}{dt}\right)_{t=0} = x'(0) \tag{5-502}$$

When a forcing function $F(t)$ acts upon a unit mass attached to the spring, the equation of motion becomes

$$\frac{d^2x}{dt^2} + \omega^2 x = F(t) \tag{5-503}$$

Let us multiply Eq. (5-503) by e^{-st} and integrate by parts with respect to time from $t = 0$ to $t = \infty$. We see from Eq. (5-490) that we must examine

$$\lim_{t \to \infty} \left[\frac{dx}{dt} + sx(t)\right] e^{-st} \tag{5-504}$$

If we *assume* that

$$|x(t)| < Me^{at} \tag{5-505}$$

for some choice of constants M and a, then expression (5-504) will vanish, and the Laplace transform

$$L\{x(t)\} = \bar{x}(s) = \int_0^\infty x(t)e^{-st}\, dt \tag{5-506}$$

will converge, provided

$$\text{Re } (s) > a \tag{5-507}$$

In that case we can use Eq. (5-492) to transform Eq. (5-503) into an algebraic equation,

$$s^2 \bar{x}(s) - s x(0) - x'(0) + \omega^2 \bar{x}(s) = \bar{F}(s) \tag{5-508}$$

provided that

$$\bar{F}(s) = \int_0^\infty F(t) e^{-st} \, dt \tag{5-509}$$

converges. Solving for $\bar{x}(s)$, we obtain

$$\bar{x}(s) = \frac{s x(0) + x'(0)}{s^2 + \omega^2} + \frac{\bar{F}(s)}{s^2 + \omega^2} \tag{5-510}$$

The inversion theorem (5-473) permits us to compute $x(t)$ from our knowledge of $\bar{x}(s)$. Thus

$$x(t) = \frac{1}{2\pi i} \int_{\sigma_0 - i\infty}^{\sigma_0 + i\infty} \frac{s x(0) + x'(0) + \bar{F}(s)}{s^2 + \omega^2} e^{st} \, ds \tag{5-511}$$

where σ_0 is any real number such that

$$\text{Re } (s) \geq \sigma_0 > a \tag{5-512}$$

It is customary to write Eq. (5-511) as the sum of a complementary function $x_c(t)$ which satisfies Eq. (5-503) when $F(t) \equiv 0$ and involves the initial conditions (5-501) and (5-502) and a particular integral (steady-state solution) $x_{ss}(t)$ which represents the effects of the forcing function $F(t)$ alone. Thus one writes

$$x(t) = x_c(t) + x_{ss}(t) \tag{5-513}$$

where

$$x_c(t) = \frac{1}{2\pi i} \int_{\sigma_0 - i\infty}^{\sigma_0 + i\infty} \frac{s x(0) + x'(0)}{s^2 + \omega^2} e^{st} \, ds \tag{5-514}$$

and

$$x_{ss}(t) = \frac{1}{2\pi i} \int_{\sigma_0 - i\infty}^{\sigma_0 + i\infty} \frac{\bar{F}(s)}{s^2 + \omega^2} e^{st} \, ds \tag{5-515}$$

The integrals (5-514) and (5-515) can be evaluated directly by the method of residues discussed in Chap. 4. Since Laplace transforms are of such great use, many tables of transforms and their inversions have been published. Frequently, this makes it unnecessary to actually compute inversion integrals. For example, in the case of Eq. (5-514) one goes to the tables and looks to find a function whose Laplace transform is

$$\frac{s}{s^2 + \omega^2} \tag{5-516}$$

and one whose Laplace transform is

$$\frac{1}{s^2 + \omega^2} \tag{5-517}$$

It happens that

$$\int_0^\infty e^{-st} \frac{\sin \omega t}{\omega} \, dt = \frac{1}{s^2 + \omega^2} \tag{5-518}$$

and

$$\int_0^\infty e^{-st} \cos \omega t \, dt = \frac{s}{s^2 + \omega^2} \tag{5-519}$$

Therefore

$$x_c(t) = x(0) \cos \omega t + x'(0) \frac{\sin \omega t}{\omega} \tag{5-520}$$

In the case of Eq. (5-515) we are confronted with a slightly more involved problem because we have a general $\bar{F}(s)$ to deal with. We can circumvent this difficulty by using the convolution theorem (5-482) and (5-483). We observe that the integrand in Eq. (5-515) is the product of two Laplace transforms, $\bar{F}(s)$ and $1/(s^2 + \omega^2)$. Therefore, by the convolution theorem, the function whose Laplace transform is $\bar{F}(s)/(s^2 + \omega^2)$ is

$$x_{ss}(t) = \int_0^t F(\tau) \frac{\sin \omega(t - \tau)}{\omega} \, d\tau \tag{5-521}$$

Thus the general solution of Eqs. (5-501) to (5-503) is given by

$$x(t) = x(0) \cos \omega t + x'(0) \frac{\sin \omega t}{\omega} + \frac{1}{\omega} \int_0^t F(\tau) \sin \omega(t - \tau) \, d\tau \tag{5-522}$$

EXAMPLE 5-12: *Computation of Laplace Transforms.* Consider

$$\int_0^\infty e^{-st} \cos \omega t \, dt \tag{5-523}$$

This can be written as

$$\frac{1}{2} \int_0^\infty e^{-st} (e^{i\omega t} + e^{-i\omega t}) \, dt \tag{5-524}$$

or

$$\frac{1}{2} \int_0^\infty (e^{-(s-i\omega)t} + e^{-(s+i\omega)t}) \, dt \tag{5-525}$$

which upon integration gives

$$\int_0^\infty e^{-st} \cos \omega t \, dt = \frac{1}{2} \left(\frac{1}{s - i\omega} + \frac{1}{s + i\omega} \right) \tag{5-526}$$

Combining the two terms in Eq. (5-526) gives

$$L\{\cos \omega t\} = \frac{s}{s^2 + \omega^2} \tag{5-527}$$

and we can conclude therefore that

$$\cos \omega t = \frac{1}{2\pi i} \int_{\sigma_0 - i\infty}^{\sigma_0 + i\infty} \frac{se^{st}}{s^2 + \omega^2} \, ds \tag{5-528}$$

for $t > 0$. Similarly,

$$\int_0^\infty e^{-st} \sin \omega t \, dt = \frac{1}{2i} \int_0^\infty (e^{-(s-i\omega)t} - e^{-(s+i\omega)t}) \, dt \tag{5-529}$$

yields

$$\int_0^\infty e^{-st} \sin \omega t \, dt = \frac{1}{2i} \left(\frac{1}{s - i\omega} - \frac{1}{s + i\omega} \right) \tag{5-530}$$

or

$$L\{\sin \omega t\} = \frac{\omega}{s^2 + \omega^2} \tag{5-531}$$

from which we obtain

$$\sin \omega t = \frac{1}{2\pi i} \int_{\sigma_0 + i\infty}^{\sigma_0 - i\infty} \frac{\omega e^{st}}{s^2 + \omega^2} \, ds \tag{5-532}$$

for $t > 0$.

5-25 PROBLEMS AND APPLICATIONS

1. Let $A(x) = -1$ for $-\pi \le x \le 0$ and $A(x) = +1$ for $0 \le x \le \pi$.
Show that

$$A(x) = \frac{4}{\pi} \sum_{n=1}^\infty \frac{\sin (2n - 1)x}{2n - 1}$$

2. Let $A(x) = \pi/2 + x$ for $-\pi \le x \le 0$ and $A(x) = \pi/2 - x$ for $0 \le x \le \pi$. Show that

$$A(x) = \frac{4}{\pi} \sum_{n=1}^\infty \frac{\cos (2n - 1)x}{(2n - 1)^2}$$

Graph the sum of the first three terms for both Probs. 1 and 2.
3. Solve the differential equation

$$\frac{d^2 A}{dx^2} + k^2 A = -\delta(x - x_1)$$

in the interval $0 \le x \le a$ subject to the boundary conditions

$$A(0) = 0 \qquad A(a) = 0$$

Let $\delta(x - x_1)$ be the Dirac delta function and let $0 \le x_1 \le a$.
Hint: Use a finite sine transform.
4. Solve the differential equation

$$\frac{d^2 A}{dx^2} + k^2 A = -\delta(x - x_1)$$

in the interval $0 \le x \le a$ subject to the boundary conditions

$$A'(0) = 0 \qquad A'(a) = 0$$

by use of the finite cosine transform
5. Solve the differential equation

$$\frac{d^2 A}{dx^2} + k^2 A = -\delta(x - x_1)$$

in the interval $0 \le x \le a$ subject to the boundary conditions

(a) $A(0) = 0$

$$\frac{\partial A}{\partial x} + hA = 0 \qquad x = a$$

by use of the finite sine radiation transform, and subject to the boundary conditions

(b) $A'(0) = 0$

$$\frac{\partial A}{\partial x} + hA = 0 \qquad x = a$$

by use of the finite cosine radiation transform.

6. Consider the problem of solving the differential equation

$$\frac{d^2 A}{dx^2} + k^2 A = -F(x)$$

in the interval $0 \leq x \leq a$ subject to the boundary conditions

$$A(0) = 0 \qquad A(a) = 0$$

(a) Solve the problem directly using the finite sine transform.

(b) Let $G(x|x_1)$ be the solution of

$$\frac{d^2 G}{dx^2} + k^2 G = -\delta(x - x_1)$$

subject to the boundary conditions

$$G(0) = 0 \qquad G(a) = 0$$

Prove that

$$A(x) = \int_0^a F(x_1)G(x|x_1) \, dx_1$$

Hint: Use the identity

$$G\left(\frac{d^2 A}{dx^2} + k^2 A\right) - A\left(\frac{d^2 G}{dx^2} + k^2 G\right) = \frac{d}{dx}\left(G\frac{dA}{dx} - A\frac{dG}{dx}\right)$$

The function $G(x|x_1)$ is called the "Green's function" of the problem.

7. Solve the differential equation

$$\frac{d^2 A}{dt^2} + \omega_0^2 A = -f(t)$$

for $\omega_0 = $ constant, subject to the boundary conditions

$$\frac{dA}{dt} + i\omega A = 0 \qquad t = \pm \infty$$

by use of an infinite-range Fourier transform.

8. Suppose that

$$g(t) = \frac{1}{2\pi} \int_{-\infty}^{+\infty} \frac{e^{i\omega t}}{\omega^2 - \omega_0^2} \, d\omega$$

Show that the solution of Prob. 7 can be written as

$$A(t) = \int_{-\infty}^{+\infty} f(\tau)g(t - \tau) \, d\tau$$

PROBLEMS AND APPLICATIONS

9. Let $g(t|\tau)$ be the solution of

$$\frac{d^2g}{dt^2} + \omega_0{}^2 g = -\delta(t - \tau)$$

subject to the boundary conditions

$$\frac{dg}{dt} + i\omega g = 0 \qquad t \pm \infty$$

Prove that the solution of

$$\frac{d^2A}{dt^2} + \omega_0{}^2 A = -f(t)$$

subject to the boundary conditions

$$\frac{dA}{dt} + i\omega A = 0 \qquad t \pm \infty$$

is

$$A(t) = \int_{-\infty}^{+\infty} f(\tau) g(t|\tau) \, d\tau$$

by using the identity

$$g\left(\frac{d^2A}{dt^2} + \omega_0{}^2 A\right) - A\left(\frac{d^2g}{dt^2} + \omega_0{}^2 g\right) = \frac{d}{dt}\left(g\,\frac{dA}{dt} - A\,\frac{dg}{dt}\right)$$

Notice that a comparison with Prob. 8 gives

$$g(t|\tau) = g(t - \tau)$$

10. Let

$$\mathbf{F}\{\mathbf{A}(\mathbf{x})\} = \int_{-\infty}^{+\infty}\int_{-\infty}^{+\infty}\int_{-\infty}^{+\infty} \mathbf{A}(\mathbf{x}) e^{-i\mathbf{k}\cdot\mathbf{x}} \, dx_1 \, dx_2 \, dx_3$$

where

$$\mathbf{k}\cdot\mathbf{x} = k_1 x_1 + k_2 x_2 + k_3 x_3$$

Prove that

$$F\{\nabla\cdot\mathbf{A}\} = i\mathbf{k}\cdot F\{\mathbf{A}(\mathbf{x})\}$$

provided

$$\lim_{|\mathbf{x}|\to\infty} \mathbf{A}(\mathbf{x})e^{-i\mathbf{k}\cdot\mathbf{x}} = 0$$

and that

$$F\{\nabla\times\mathbf{A}\} = i\mathbf{k}\times F\{\mathbf{A}(\mathbf{x})\}$$

under the same condition. If $g = g(\mathbf{x})$ is a scalar function of $\mathbf{x}$ prove that

$$F\{\nabla g\} = i\mathbf{k}F\{g(\mathbf{x})\}$$

provided that the condition

$$\lim_{|\mathbf{x}|\to\infty} g(\mathbf{x})e^{-i\mathbf{k}\cdot\mathbf{x}} = 0$$

holds.

11. Consider the Helmholtz equation

$$(\nabla^2 + k_0{}^2)A(\mathbf{x}) = -f(\mathbf{x})$$

in a rectangular, three-dimensional Cartesian coordinate system (x_1, x_2, x_3). Let the Fourier transform of $A(\mathbf{x})$ be represented by

$$\bar{A}(\mathbf{k}) = F\{A(\mathbf{x})\}$$

and the Fourier transform of $f(\mathbf{x})$ by

$$\bar{f}(\mathbf{k}) = F\{f(\mathbf{x})\}$$

(a) Show that

$$F\{\nabla^2 A(\mathbf{x})\} = -k^2 F\{A(\mathbf{x})\}$$

provided

$$\lim_{|x_1| \to \infty} \left(\frac{\partial A}{\partial x_1} + ik_1 A\right) = 0$$

$$\lim_{|x_2| \to \infty} \left(\frac{\partial A}{\partial x_2} + ik_2 A\right) = 0$$

and

$$\lim_{|x_3| \to \infty} \left(\frac{\partial A}{\partial x_3} + ik_3 A\right) = 0$$

where $\mathbf{k} = (k_1, k_2, k_3)$ and $\mathbf{x} = (x_1, x_2, x_3)$.

(b) Show that a solution of Helmholtz's equation satisfying the boundary conditions of part (a) is given by

$$A(\mathbf{x}) = \left(\frac{1}{2\pi}\right)^3 \int \frac{\bar{f}(\mathbf{k})e^{i\mathbf{k}\cdot\mathbf{x}}}{k^2 - k_0{}^2}\, dV_k$$

with $k^2 = \mathbf{k} \cdot \mathbf{k}$ and where the volume integral is understood to be taken over the entire volume of $\mathbf{k}$ space.

12. Consider once again the problem of solving

$$(\nabla^2 + k_0{}^2)A = -f(\mathbf{x})$$

subject to the boundary conditions at infinity given in Prob. 11. Suppose that $G(\mathbf{x}|\mathbf{y})$ is a function which satisfies

$$(\nabla^2 + k_0{}^2)G = -\delta(\mathbf{x} - \mathbf{y})$$

together with the boundary conditions

$$\lim_{|x_1| \to \infty} \left(\frac{\partial G}{\partial x_1} + ik_1 G\right) = 0$$

$$\lim_{|x_2| \to \infty} \left(\frac{\partial G}{\partial x_2} + ik_2 G\right) = 0$$

$$\lim_{|x_3| \to \infty} \left(\frac{\partial G}{\partial x_3} + ik_3 G\right) = 0$$

at infinity where $\mathbf{x} = (x_1, x_2, x_3)$, $\mathbf{k} = (k_1, k_2, k_3)$, and $\mathbf{y} = (y_1, y_2, y_3)$. Show that

$$A(\mathbf{x}) = \int f(\mathbf{y})G(\mathbf{x}|\mathbf{y})\, dV_y$$

where the volume integral is understood to be taken over the entire volume of **y** space.

Hint: Use the identity

$$G(\nabla^2 + k_0{}^2)A - A(\nabla^2 + k_0{}^2)G = \nabla \cdot (G\,\nabla A - A\,\nabla G)$$

together with the three-dimensional divergence theorem to transform the volume integral into a surface integral. Then eliminate the surface-integral terms by properly using the boundary conditions at infinity. Notice that the boundary conditions at infinity can be written

$$\lim_{|x| \to \infty} (\nabla A + ikA) = 0$$

and

$$\lim_{|x| \to \infty} (\nabla G + ikG) = 0$$

where $\mathbf{k} = k_1\mathbf{e}_1 + k_2\mathbf{e}_2 + k_3\mathbf{e}_3$ and $\nabla = \mathbf{e}_1\partial/\partial x_1 + \mathbf{e}_2\partial/\partial x_2 + \mathbf{e}_3\partial/\partial x_3$. The function $G(\mathbf{x}|\mathbf{y})$ is called the "Green's function" for the Helmholtz equation.

13. Use the Fourier transform to show directly that the solution of

$$(\nabla^2 + k_0{}^2)G = -\delta(\mathbf{x})$$

is

$$G(\mathbf{x}) = \left(\frac{1}{2\pi}\right)^3 \int \frac{e^{i\mathbf{k}\cdot\mathbf{x}}}{k^2 - k_0{}^2}\,dV_k$$

Now use the convolution theorem for Fourier transforms to show that the answer to Prob. 11 can be written as

$$A(\mathbf{x}) = \int f(\mathbf{y})G(\mathbf{x}|\mathbf{y})\,dV_y$$

and prove that

$$G(\mathbf{x}|\mathbf{y}) = G(\mathbf{y}|\mathbf{x})$$

14. Let $\quad \bar{A}(s) = \displaystyle\int_0^\infty A(t)e^{-st}\,dt$

Prove that for

$$A(t) = \cosh at$$

$$\bar{A}(s) = \frac{s}{s^2 - a^2}$$

and for

$$A(t) = \sinh at$$

$$\bar{A}(s) = \frac{a}{s^2 - a^2}$$

15. Solve the differential equation

$$\frac{d^2A}{dt^2} - a^2 A = f(t)$$

for α = constant, subject to the initial conditions

$$A = A(0) \qquad t = 0$$

$$\frac{dA}{dt} = A'(0) \qquad t = 0$$

and under the assumption that

$$\lim_{t \to \infty} \left[\frac{dA}{dt} + sA(t) \right] e^{-st} = 0$$

by use of the Laplace transform.

16. Suppose that

$$g(t) = \frac{1}{2\pi i} \int_{\sigma_0 - i\infty}^{\sigma_0 + i\infty} \frac{e^{st}}{s^2 - \alpha^2} \, ds$$

Show that the particular integral contribution to Prob. 15 can be written in the form

$$\int_0^t f(\tau) g(t - \tau) \, d\tau$$

17. Use the Laplace transform to solve the differential equation

$$\frac{d^2 I}{dt^2} + \frac{R}{L} \frac{dI}{dt} + \frac{1}{LC} I = \frac{dV}{dt}$$

subject to the initial conditions

$$I = I(0) \qquad t = 0$$

$$\frac{dI}{dt} = I'(0) \qquad t = 0$$

Evaluate the inversion integrals for all possible relations between R, L, and C.

Hint: Use the convolution theorem and a table of Laplace transforms.

18. Consider the scalar wave equation

$$\nabla^2 A = \frac{1}{v^2} \frac{\partial^2 A}{\partial t^2}$$

and let

$$\bar{A}(\mathbf{r}, s) = \int_0^\infty A(\mathbf{r}, t) e^{-st} \, dt$$

Show that if

$$A(\mathbf{r}, 0) = 0 \qquad t = 0$$

$$\frac{\partial A}{\partial t}(\mathbf{r}, 0) = 0 \qquad t = 0$$

and

$$\lim_{t \to \infty} \left(\frac{\partial A}{\partial t} + sA \right) e^{-st} = 0$$

then $\bar{A}(\mathbf{r}, s)$ satisfies

$$(\nabla^2 - k^2) \bar{A}(\mathbf{r}, s) = 0$$

where

$$k^2 = \frac{s^2}{v^2}$$

19. The Heaviside unit step function is defined as

$$H(t) = \begin{cases} 1 & t \geq 0 \\ 0 & t < 0 \end{cases}$$

Calculate its Laplace transform, and use the inversion theorem for the Laplace transform to obtain integral representations for both $H(t)$ and the Dirac delta function $\delta(t)$.
Hint:

$$\delta(t) = \frac{d}{dt} H(t)$$

20. Consider the scalar wave equation

$$\nabla^2 A = \frac{1}{v^2} \frac{\partial^2 A}{\partial t^2}$$

in spherical coordinates (R,θ,Φ). Suppose that A depends only on R and t so that $A = A(R,t)$; then show:
(a) That the wave equation can be written as

$$\frac{\partial^2}{\partial R^2} (RA) = \frac{1}{v^2} \frac{\partial^2}{\partial t^2} (RA)$$

(Notice that R is an independent variable.)
(b) That if

$$A(R,0) = 0 \qquad t = 0,\, R \neq 0$$

$$\frac{\partial A}{\partial t} (R,0) = 0 \qquad t = 0,\, R \neq 0$$

then

$$\left(\frac{d^2}{dR^2} - k^2 \right) R\bar{A}(R,s) = 0$$

where $\bar{A}(R,s)$ is the time Laplace transform of $A(R,t)$, and $k^2 = s^2/v^2$.
(c) That in general

$$R\bar{A}(R,s) = F(s)e^{-kR} + G(s)e^{+kR}$$

satisfies

$$\left(\frac{d^2}{dR^2} - k^2 \right) R\bar{A} = 0$$

where $F(s)$ and $G(s)$ are arbitrary functions of s *alone*.
(d) That $F(s)e^{-sR/v}$ is the Laplace transform of $f(t - R/v)$ if $F(s)$ is the Laplace transform of $f(t)$, and that $G(s)e^{sR/v}$ is the Laplace transform of $g(t + R/v)$ if $G(s)$ is the Laplace transform of $g(t)$.
(e) That

$$A(R,t) = \frac{f(t - R/v)}{R}$$

satisfies the equation of part (a) *and the initial conditions* of part (b), provided $f(t) = 0$ for $t < 0$.

linear differential equations

6.1 INTRODUCTION

An algebraic equation in two variables is an expression of the form

$$\Omega(y,x) = y^n + R_1(x)y^{n-1} + \cdots + R_{n-1}(x)y + R_n(x) = 0 \qquad (6\text{-}1)$$

where $R_1(x)$, $R_2(x)$, . . . , $R_n(x)$ are each rational functions of x, i.e., the ratios of polynomials in x. Suppose that we now interpret the symbol y^n to mean the nth derivative of y with respect to x instead of the nth power of y. Then

$$y^n = \frac{d^n y}{dx^n} \qquad y = \frac{d^0 y}{dx^0} \qquad (6\text{-}2)$$

and Eq. (6-1) reduces to the form

$$\frac{d^n y}{dx^n} + R_1(x)\frac{d^{n-1}y}{dx^{n-1}} + \cdots + R_n(x)y = 0 \qquad (6\text{-}3)$$

This expression is called an nth-order, ordinary, linear, *homogeneous* differential equation with variable coefficients. The equation

$$\frac{d^n y}{dx^n} + R_1(x)\frac{dy^{n-1}}{dx^{n-1}} + \cdots + R_n(x)y = f(x) \qquad (6\text{-}4)$$

in which $f(x)$ is an arbitrary function of x is an nth-order, ordinary, linear, *inhomogeneous* differential equation with variable coefficients. If all the coefficients $R_1(x)$, . . . ,$R_n(x)$ are constants independent of x, then Eq. (6-3) becomes a homogeneous, and Eq. (6-4) an inhomogeneous, linear differential equation with constant coefficients. Equations (6-3) and (6-4) are called "linear" differential equations because they do not involve any powers of y, dy/dx, d^2y/dx^2, . . . , d^ny/dx^n higher than the first, nor do they involve any cross products such as

$$y\frac{d^n y}{dx^n} \qquad \text{or} \qquad \frac{d^{n-k}y}{dx^{n-k}}\frac{dy^n}{dx^n} \qquad \text{etc.}$$

For example,

$$y^2\frac{dy}{dx} + R_1(x) = 0$$

and

$$\left(\frac{d^2y}{dx^2}\right)^2 + Ry\frac{dy}{dx} + \omega^2 y = 0$$

are nonlinear ordinary differential equations.

Linear differential equations such as Eq. (6-3) have a very important feature. If $y_C(x)$ is the general solution of the homogeneous equation (6-3), and $y_P(x)$ is a particular solution of the inhomogeneous equation (6-4), then

$$y(x) = y_C(x) + y_P(x) \tag{6-5}$$

is a general solution of Eq. (6-4). The function $y_C(x)$ is called the "complementary function," and $y_P(x)$ is called the "particular integral," associated with Eq. (6-4).

We shall confine ourselves here to the treatment of ordinary linear differential equations with either constant or variable coefficients, and we shall examine both the homogeneous and inhomogeneous forms for each case. Such differential equations constitute the bulk of those whose solutions should be familiar to the student of physics, and our emphasis is accordingly placed on the methods of solution in each case.

6.2 LINEAR DIFFERENTIAL EQUATIONS WITH CONSTANT COEFFICIENTS

We have already seen in Chap. 5 how the powerful Laplace and Fourier transform techniques can be used to obtain solutions to linear differential equations with constant coefficients. The methods which we are about to review here are considerably more elementary and are the ones which a student usually learns first in elementary studies on differential equations.

Consider Eq. (6-3) when each coefficient $R_1, R_2, \ldots, R_n$ is a constant. Let the operator D be defined by

$$D = \frac{d}{dx} \tag{6-6}$$

so that Eq. (6-3) becomes

$$L(D)y = (D^n + R_1 D^{n-1} + \cdots + R_n)y = 0 \tag{6-7}$$

where $L(D)$ is a polynomial operator in D. The polynomial operator $L(D)$ can be factorized thus,

$$L(D) = (D - k_1)(D - k_2) \cdots (D - k_n) \tag{6-8}$$

where $k_1, k_2, \ldots, k_n$ are the n roots of the nth-order algebraic equation

$$k^n + R_1 k^{n-1} + \cdots + R_n = 0 \tag{6-9}$$

Equation (6-9) is called the "characteristic equation" of the differential equation (6-7). The roots k_n of Eq. (6-9) are constants, and therefore the operators

$$(D - k_1), (D - k_2), \ldots, (D - k_n) \tag{6-10}$$

can be permuted.

We can rewrite Eq. (6-7) in the form

$$L(D)y = (D - k_1)(D - k_2) \cdots (D - k_n)y = 0 \tag{6-11}$$

and since the operators (6-10) are permutable, it follows that the given homogeneous equation is satisfied by the solution of each of the n equations of first order:

$$(D - k_1)y = 0, (D - k_2)y = 0, \ldots, (D - k_n)y = 0 \tag{6-12}$$

Solution of the homogeneous equation

CASE I: *The n characteristic roots $k_1, k_2, \ldots, k_n$ are all different.* Let y_r be the general solution of

$$(D - k_r)y = 0 \tag{6-13}$$

Then

$$y_r = C_r e^{k_r x} \tag{6-14}$$

and therefore the general solution of Eq. (6-7) becomes

$$y = \sum_{r=1}^{n} C_r e^{k_r x} \tag{6-15}$$

where $C_1, C_2, \ldots, C_n$ are a set of n arbitrary constants. Notice that the general solution of a homogeneous nth-order linear differential equation with constant coefficients involves n arbitrary constants.

If the coefficients $R_1, \ldots, R_n$ in Eq. (6-9) are real numbers, then the complex roots of Eq. (6-9) must occur in conjugate pairs. For example, let

$$k_r = \alpha_r + i\beta_r \quad \text{and} \quad k_s = \alpha_r - i\beta_r \tag{6-16}$$

be a pair of complex conjugate roots of Eq. (6-9). Then Eq. (6-15) involves pairs of terms like

$$y_r = C_r e^{(\alpha_r + i\beta_r)x} + C_s e^{(\alpha_r - i\beta_r)x} \tag{6-17}$$

which may be written as

$$y_r = e^{\alpha_r x}\{C_r e^{i\beta_r x} + C_s e^{-i\beta_r x}\} \tag{6-18}$$

or

$$y_r = e^{\alpha_r x}\{(C_r + C_s)\cos \beta_r x + i(C_r - C_s)\sin \beta_r x\} \tag{6-19}$$

If we now put

$$A_r = C_r + C_s \tag{6-20}$$

and

$$B_r = i(C_r - C_s) \tag{6-21}$$

then the terms in Eq. (6-15) containing k_r and k_s combine to form the term

$$y_r = e^{\alpha_r x}\{A_r \cos \beta_r x + B_r \sin \beta_r x\} \tag{6-22}$$

The general solution (6-15) becomes

$$y = \sum_{r=1}^{n} e^{\alpha_r x}\{A_r \cos \beta_r x + B_r \sin \beta_r x\} \tag{6-23}$$

Notice that although it appears that Eq. (6-23) contains $2n$ arbitrary constants, that is not the case. Given the n original arbitrary constants $\{C_1, C_2, \ldots, C_n\}$, Eqs. (6-20) and (6-21) completely determine *both* $\{A_1, A_2, \ldots, A_n\}$ and $\{B_1, B_2, \ldots, B_n\}$. Therefore Eq. (6-23) involves only n arbitrary constants.

CASE II: *The n characteristic roots $k_1, k_2, \ldots, k_n$ are not all different.* Suppose that p of the characteristic roots, say $k_1, \ldots, k_p$, are all equal so that

$$k_1 = k_2 = \cdots = k_p = k \tag{6-24}$$

The factorized form (6-8) of $L(D)$ then becomes

$$L(D) = (D - k)^p(D - k_{p+1})(D - k_{p+2}) \cdots (D - k_n) \tag{6-25}$$

The general solution of

$$(D - k)^p y = 0 \tag{6-26}$$

must be included in the general solution of $L(D)y = 0$. To solve Eq. (6-26) let

$$y = v e^{kx} \tag{6-27}$$

where v is a function to be determined. Consider

$$(D - k)^p v e^{kx} \tag{6-28}$$

We write this as

$$(D - k)^{p-1}(D - k)v e^{kx} \tag{6-29}$$

However

$$(D - k)v e^{kx} = e^{kx} Dv \tag{6-30}$$

so that

$$(D - k)^p v e^{kx} = (D - k)^{p-1} e^{kx} Dv \tag{6-31}$$

By successive repetition of this procedure we find

$$(D - k)^p v e^{kx} = (D - k)^{p-1} e^{kx} Dv = (D - k)^{p-2} e^{kx} D^2 v$$
$$= (D - k)^{p-3} e^{kx} D^3 v = \cdots = e^{kx} D^p v \tag{6-32}$$

Consequently,

$$y = v e^{kx} \tag{6-33}$$

satisfies

$$(D - k)^p y = 0 \tag{6-34}$$

provided that v is a solution of

$$D^p v = 0 \tag{6-35}$$

and therefore v is an arbitrary polynomial in x of degree $p - 1$. Thus

$$y = \{C_1 + C_2x + \cdots + C_px^{p-1}\}e^{kx} \tag{6-36}$$

is the general solution of Eq. (6-34) and contains p arbitrary constants as it should. Notice that if a complex conjugate pair of roots such as Eqs. (6-16) occurs, each in a factor repeated p times, then $L(D)$ becomes

$$L(D) = (D - k_r)^p(D - k_s)^p(D - k_{2p+1})(D - k_{2p+2}) \cdots (D - k_n) \tag{6-37}$$

where

$$k_r = \alpha_r + i\beta_r \tag{6-38}$$

and

$$k_s = \alpha_r - i\beta_r \tag{6-39}$$

The general solution of $L(D)y = 0$ will then contain the general solutions of

$$(D - k_r)^p y = 0 \tag{6-40}$$

and

$$(D - k_s)^p y = 0 \tag{6-41}$$

These solutions, when combined, give a term of the form

$$y_r = e^{\alpha_r x}\{(A_1 + A_2x + \cdots + A_px^{p-1}) \cos \beta_r x$$
$$+ (B_1 + B_2x + \cdots + B_px^{p-1}) \sin \beta_r x\} \tag{6-42}$$

In Eq. (6-42) the constants $\{A_1, A_2, \ldots, A_p\}$ and $\{B_1, B_2, \ldots, B_p\}$ are derived from solving *two* pth-order differential equations. Therefore, they provide $2p$ of the n independent constants required in the general solution of $L(D)y = 0$.

Particular integral of an inhomogeneous equation

There are several methods of constructing the particular integral of the inhomogeneous equation

$$L(D)y = f(x) \tag{6-43}$$

The simplest method is to just "guess" the particular integral, and for simple equations this actually works. For example,

$$(D^2 + D + 1)y = x + 2 \tag{6-44}$$

is obviously satisfied by choosing

$$y_p(x) = x + 1 \tag{6-45}$$

If

$$(D^2 + D + 1)y = Be^{ikx} \tag{6-46}$$

then we can try

$$y_p(x) = Ae^{ikx} \tag{6-47}$$

as a particular integral of Eq. (6-46). It will be a particular integral of Eq. (6-46) provided that we choose

$$A = \frac{B}{1 - k^2 + ik} \tag{6-48}$$

In general,

$$L(D)y = Be^{ikx} \tag{6-49}$$

has

$$y_p(x) = \frac{B}{L(ik)} e^{ikx} \tag{6-50}$$

as its particular integral. The result (6-50) is closely related to the Fourier transform technique of obtaining particular integrals, as was discussed in Chap. 5. Formulas such as Eqs. (6-48) and (6-50) require, of course, that the denominators be nonzero.

The method of reduction to quadratures

Consider the simple first-order inhomogeneous equation

$$(D - k)y = f(x) \tag{6-51}$$

where k is assumed to be a constant. We observe that

$$D(ye^{-kx}) = e^{-kx}(D - k)y = f(x)e^{-kx} \tag{6-52}$$

and therefore

$$\int_0^x D(ye^{-kx}) \, dx = \int_0^x f(z)e^{-kz} \, dz \tag{6-53}$$

where we have substituted the dummy variable of integration z for x in the right-hand side of Eq. (6-53). Thus

$$y(x)e^{-kx} - y(0) = \int_0^x f(z)e^{-kz} \, dz \tag{6-54}$$

and

$$y(x) = y(0)e^{kx} + \int_0^x f(z)e^{-k(z-x)} \, dz \tag{6-55}$$

gives the solution (6-51) which reduces to $y(0)$ at $x = 0$. Since the complementary function of Eq. (6-51) is $y(x) = Ae^{kx}$, it follows from a comparison with Eq. (6-55) that

$$y_p(x) = \int_0^x f(z)e^{-k(z-x)} \, dz \tag{6-56}$$

is the particular integral of Eq. (6-51). Formula (6-56) reduces the problem of obtaining the particular integral of Eq. (6-51) to the problem of evaluating an integral, or in other words, to the problem of performing a quadrature.

Generalization

The method of reduction to quadratures can be easily generalized to higher-order equations with constant coefficients. For example, consider

$$(D^2 - k^2)y = f(x) \tag{6-57}$$

We first factor the operator $D^2 - k^2$, obtaining

$$(D - k)(D + k)y = f(x) \tag{6-58}$$

Let

$$(D + k)y = w \tag{6-59}$$

Then

$$(D - k)w = f(x) \tag{6-60}$$

Hence

$$w(x) = w(0)e^{kx} + \int_0^x f(z)e^{-k(z-x)} \, dz \tag{6-61}$$

We now solve

$$(D + k)y = w(x) \tag{6-62}$$

obtaining

$$y(x) = y(0)e^{-kx} + \int_0^x w(u)e^{k(u-x)} \, du \tag{6-63}$$

Since we are interested in only the particular integral of Eq. (6-57), we can set

$$y(0) = 0 \tag{6-64}$$

and

$$w(0) = 0 \tag{6-65}$$

in order to eliminate the terms associated with the complementary function of Eq. (6-57). Then Eqs. (6-61) and (6-63) give

$$y_p(x) = \int_0^x e^{k(u-x)} \, du \int_0^u f(z)e^{-k(z-u)} \, dz \tag{6-66}$$

for the particular integral of Eq. (6-57).

A successive repetition of the method of reduction to quadrature, when applied to the nth-order differential equation with constant coefficients,

$$(D - k_1)(D - k_2) \cdots (D - k_n)y = f(x) \tag{6-67}$$

yields a particular integral of the form

$$y_p(x) = \int_0^x e^{-k_n(z_n-x)} \, dz_n \int_0^{z_n} e^{-k_{n-1}(z_{n-1}-z_n)} \, dz_{n-1} \\ \cdots \int_0^{z_2} e^{-k_1(z_1-z_2)} f(z_1) \, dz_1 \tag{6-68}$$

For example,

$$(D - k_1)(D - k_2)y = f(x) \tag{6-69}$$

has the particular integral

$$y_p(x) = \int_0^x e^{-k_2(z_2-x)} \, dz_2 \int_0^{z_2} e^{-k_1(z_1-z_2)} f(z_1) \, dz_1 \tag{6-70}$$

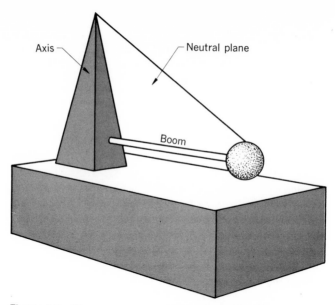

Figure 6-1 The components of a seismograph for measuring horizontal earth movements.

and if we set

$$k_2 = -k \qquad k_1 = +k$$
$$z_2 = u \qquad z_1 = z \tag{6-71}$$

then Eq. (6-70) reduces to

$$y_p(x) = \int_0^x e^{k(u-x)} \, du \int_0^u e^{-k(z-u)} f(z) \, dz \tag{6-72}$$

which is the result obtained in Eq. (6-66).

6.3 THE THEORY OF THE SEISMOGRAPH

A seismograph is an instrument designed to measure the ground movements arising from earthquakes or underground explosions (Fig. 6-1). Its theory affords an excellent practical application of a linear differential equation with constant coefficients.

In its simplest form, the seismograph consists of a damped pendulum whose axis is rigidly attached to the ground and which will oscillate in response to some particular component, $u(t)$ say, of the local ground translatory motion. In practice, $u(t)$ is taken to be the motion of a point on the earth's surface as measured in the north-south, east-west, or vertical (z) direction. The equilibrium plane formed by the boom supporting the pendulum mass and the axis which is anchored to the ground is arranged so that it is perpendicular to the direction in which $u(t)$ is measured.

Values of a parameter $\theta(t)$, proportional to the angular displacement of the boom, are recorded on a seismogram, which consists of a trace on photographic paper placed on a drum which is made to revolve at a uniform rate. In an ideal seismograph the angular acceleration $\ddot{\theta}$ of the pendulum would be exactly proportional to the angular acceleration $\ddot{u}$ of the ground so that

$$\ddot{\theta} = -K\ddot{u} \tag{6-73}$$

where K is an instrumental constant. However, in a practical instrument there must be a spring to return the pendulum to its equilibrium position after the disturbance has ceased, as well as to limit the amplitude of the pendulum swing. In addition, there are frictional forces which are present in any mechanical system. To a first approximation, these frictional forces can be regarded as proportional to the angular velocity $\dot{\theta}$ of the pendulum. Thus the angular acceleration of a simple seismograph is given by

$$\ddot{\theta} = -2\lambda\dot{\theta} - \omega_0^2\theta - K\ddot{u} \tag{6-74}$$

or

$$\frac{d^2\theta}{dt^2} + 2\lambda\frac{d\theta}{dt} + \omega_0^2\theta = -K\frac{d^2u}{dt^2} \tag{6-75}$$

where λ is the damping coefficient, $2\pi/\omega_0$ is the natural period, and K is the static magnification of the instrument.

The general solution of Eq. (6-75) consists of a complementary function containing two arbitrary constants, plus a particular integral. To find the complementary function we use the method of Sec. 6-2. The characteristic equation (6-9) becomes

$$k^2 + 2\lambda k + \omega_0^2 = 0 \tag{6-76}$$

giving roots

$$k_1 = -\lambda + \sqrt{\lambda^2 - \omega_0^2} \tag{6-77}$$

$$k_2 = -\lambda - \sqrt{\lambda^2 - \omega_0^2} \tag{6-78}$$

We must distinguish three cases, $\lambda^2 < \omega_0^2$, $\lambda^2 > \omega_0^2$, and $\lambda^2 = \omega_0^2$.

CASE I: $\lambda^2 < \omega_0^2$. In this case k_1 and k_2 become complex conjugate roots

$$k_1 = -\lambda + i\sqrt{\omega_0^2 - \lambda^2} \tag{6-79}$$

$$k_2 = -\lambda - i\sqrt{\omega_0^2 - \lambda^2} \tag{6-80}$$

yielding

$$\theta_c(t) = e^{-\lambda t}(c_1 e^{i\sqrt{\omega_0^2 - \lambda^2}\,t} + c_2 e^{-i\sqrt{\omega_0^2 - \lambda^2}\,t}) \tag{6-81}$$

which contains two arbitrary constants as it should.

We can rewrite Eq. (6-81) in the form

$$\theta_c(t) = Ae^{-\lambda t}\cos(\omega t - \beta) \tag{6-82}$$

where A and β are two other arbitrary constants and

$$\omega = \sqrt{\omega_0^2 - \lambda^2} \tag{6-83}$$

Equation (6-82) represents the free oscillations of the seismograph.

On account of the exponential factor, the amplitude decreases with time, falling to a value of $1/e$ of its initial value after a time interval of duration $t = 1/\lambda$. The natural frequency of oscillation is seen from Eq. (6-83) to be less than the natural frequency ω_0 of the spring because of the presence of mechanical damping λ. The maximum angular deflection of the pendulum will occur at those times for which

$$\frac{d\theta_c}{dt} = -Ae^{-\lambda t}[\lambda \cos(\omega t - \beta) + \omega \sin(\omega t - \beta)] = 0 \tag{6-84}$$

giving

$$\tan(\omega t - \beta) = -\frac{\lambda}{\omega} \tag{6-85}$$

Let t_1 be the smallest positive value of time which satisfies Eq. (6-85) Then

$$t = t_1 + \frac{n\pi}{\omega} \qquad n = 1, 2, \ldots \tag{6-86}$$

also satisfies Eq. (6-85).

The stationary values of $\theta_c(t)$ occurring for values of t given by Eq. (6-86) are alternate maxima and minima. The time interval T between a pair of successive maxima (or minima) is the natural period $T = 2\pi/\omega$ of the seismograph. The cosine factor in Eq. (6-82) has the same value at all maxima. Hence, if $\theta_c(t)$ and $\theta_c(t + T)$ represent *two successive maxima* in angular deflection, then

$$\frac{\theta_c(t)}{\theta_c(t + T)} = e^{-\lambda t}/e^{-\lambda(t+T)} \tag{6-87}$$

or

$$\frac{\theta_c(t)}{\theta_c(t + T)} = e^{\lambda T} \tag{6-88}$$

The quantity δ defined by

$$\delta \equiv \log \frac{\theta_c(t)}{\theta_c(t + T)} = \lambda T = \frac{2\pi\lambda}{\sqrt{\omega_0{}^2 - \lambda^2}} \tag{6-89}$$

is known as the "logarithmic decrement." It is a measure of the effect of friction on the instrument. If δ and the period T are measured, then the damping constant λ can be computed from formula (6-89).

CASE II: $\lambda^2 > \omega_0{}^2$. In this case

$$k_1 = -\lambda + \sqrt{\lambda^2 - \omega_0{}^2} \tag{6-90}$$

$$k_2 = -\lambda - \sqrt{\lambda^2 - \omega_0{}^2} \tag{6-91}$$

are real numbers so that

$$\theta_c(t) = c_1 e^{-(\lambda + \sqrt{\lambda^2 - \omega_0{}^2})\,t} + c_2 e^{-(\lambda - \sqrt{\lambda^2 - \omega_0{}^2})\,t} \tag{6-92}$$

where c_1 and c_2 are arbitrary constants. The exponential terms in Eq. (6-92) are always positive; hence the response of the pendulum to a sudden short impulse is aperiodic. This means that if the pendulum is deflected from equilibrium by a sudden earth shock, then because of the large amount of damping, it comes to rest without ever swinging through the equilibrium point $\theta_c = 0$. The response of the pendulum in this case is said to be "overdamped" while for $\lambda^2 < \omega_0^2$, as in case I, it is called "underdamped." An underdamped pendulum goes through many oscillations before finally coming to rest.

CASE III: $\lambda^2 = \omega_0^2$. In this case, the pendulum is said to be critically damped. The two roots k_1 and k_2 coalesce to give

$$k_1 = k_2 = -\lambda \tag{6-93}$$

Using Eq. (6-36), we find

$$\theta_c(t) = (c_1 + c_2 t)e^{-\lambda t} \tag{6-94}$$

for the deflection of a critically damped pendulum.

The constants c_1 and c_2 in Eqs. (6-81), (6-92), and (6-94) are determined by the initial conditions on $\theta(t)$ and $d\theta/dt$ at some initial instant, say $t = t_0$. The important practical point is that the transient responses (6-81), (6-92), and (6-94) are unrelated to ground movements taking place after $t = t_0$. The general solution of Eq. (6-75) consists of one of the three complementary functions (6-81), (6-92), or (6-94), plus a particular integral $\theta_p(t)$:

$$\theta(t) = \theta_c(t) + \theta_p(t) \tag{6-95}$$

It is desirable that $\theta_c(t)$, being unrelated to ground movements taking place after $t = t_0$, should interfere as little as possible with the term $\theta_p(t)$ which is the response to these later movements.

If the damping is made too large, then the instrument will not respond to weak signals, but if it is made too small, $\theta_c(t)$ will interfere with the desired signal $\theta_p(t)$. In practice, one adjusts the seismograph so that

$$\lambda = \alpha\omega_0 = \frac{2\pi\alpha}{T_0} \tag{6-96}$$

where

$$0.7 \leq \alpha \leq 1 \tag{6-97}$$

and T_0 is the free period of the pendulum. Using Eq. (6-96), the factor $e^{-\lambda t}$ appearing in Eq. (6-82) becomes $e^{-2\pi\alpha(t/T_0)}$. Thus in a time interval $t = T_0$ equal to one free period of the pendulum, the amplitude of $\theta_c(t)$ as given by Eq. (6-82) is reduced to $e^{-2\pi\alpha}$ of its initial value. For the range of α given in inequality (6-97) this means that the amplitude of the transient pendulum swing decreases by between two and three orders of magnitude in a time interval equal to one free period of the pendulum. Also, the largest exponential factor in Eq. (6-92) decreases as $\alpha \to 1$.

The point on the surface of the earth directly above the origin

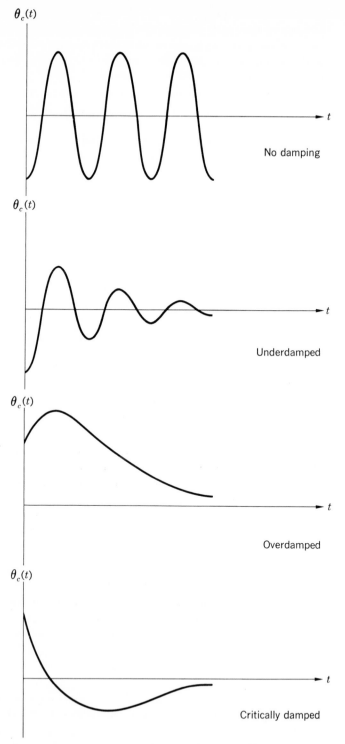

Figure 6-2 The natural modes of a damped simple-harmonic oscillator.

or focal point of an earthquake is called the "epicenter." The ground motion at large epicentral distances from the focus of an earthquake is quite complicated. In general, it consists of a superposition of waves some of which have traveled through the interior of the earth while others have traveled over the earth's surface. An earthquake arriving from a distant epicenter displays a ground motion which consists of a number of weak sudden changes or jerks in ground displacement and ground velocity. These are associated with energy arriving at the seismograph via the earth's interior. The last ground motion to arrive consists of a large-amplitude, slow-rolling or sinusoidal motion of very long duration. The energy in this last ground movement reaches the seismograph by means of waves which have traveled over the surface of the earth. The duration of the surface wave signal is long in comparison to the duration of the original ground movement at the focus. The explanation for this is dispersion, which means that waves of different frequencies travel at different speeds. One basic unit of time is the duration of the original ground movement at the focus. Frequently, this time interval is very short so that the original ground movement approximates a delta function in time. The Fourier spectrum of the original ground movement must therefore contain all frequencies. It is a property of the millions of tons of rock through which the seismic energy must travel in order to reach the observer that different frequencies are propagated at different speeds, i.e., rocks are dispersive materials.

Consider a point on the earth's surface. Let it be far enough removed from the epicenter of a given earthquake so that the time it takes seismic surface energy of any frequency to reach the point is long compared to the duration of the ground movement at the focus. If a pulse of seismic energy is generated at the focus in the form of a sudden ground movement, and if seismic surface energy of any frequency travels at one and the same speed, then neglecting frictional losses in the earth, all the surface-wave energy associated with the given pulse will arrive at the point of observation at exactly the same instant of time. This arrival time corresponds to the travel time of energy from the epicenter to the point of observation. However, because the earth is dispersive, the higher-frequency waves travel more slowly. Surface wave energy is received from the epicenter for a time interval beginning at the time of arrival of the fastest, i.e., lowest-frequency, wave and ending at the arrival time of the slowest, i.e., highest-frequency, wave. If T_s is the duration of arrival of surface-wave energy, and v_L and v_H represent the speeds with which the lowest and highest frequencies travel, then for an epicentral distance Δ,

$$T_s = \frac{\Delta}{v_L - v_H} \tag{6-98}$$

Thus we see that the farther the seismograph is from the epicenter, the longer the time interval T_s becomes.

Because of the roughly sinuosoidal ground motion accompanying the surface wave, it becomes interesting to consider the response of a seismograph to ground movements of the special form

$$u(t) = a \cos (pt - \Phi) \tag{6-99}$$

in which case Eq. (6-75) becomes

$$\frac{d^2\theta}{dt^2} + 2\lambda \frac{d\theta}{dt} + \omega_0^2\theta = aKp^2 \cos (pt - \Phi) \tag{6-100}$$

where a, p, K, and Φ are constants. The method of Eqs. (6-49) and (6-50) yields

$$\theta_p(t) = Ma \cos (pt - \beta) \tag{6-101}$$

for the particular integral of Eq. (6-100). In Eq. (6-101),

$$M = Kp^2[(p^2 - \omega_0^2)^2 + 4\lambda^2p^2]^{-\frac{1}{2}} \tag{6-102}$$

and

$$\beta = \Phi + \tan^{-1} \frac{2\lambda p}{\omega_0^2 - p^2} \tag{6-103}$$

The factor M, unlike K, depends on the period $2\pi/p$ of the ground motion, as well as on the instrumental constants. Since the amplitude of $\theta_p(t)$ is proportional to M, we call M the "dynamical magnification" of the seismograph. A ground motion of amplitude a will produce a maximum pendulum swing of amplitude Ma.

The phase $\beta - \Phi$ also depends on the period of the ground motion and the instrumental parameters. Since M depends on the period $2\pi/p$ of the ground motion, a seismogram showing different prevailing periods in different parts of the trace does not give a picture showing the amplitudes of u in the correct proportion. The frequency-dependent amplitude and phase response of a seismograph is therefore said to introduce amplitude and phase distortion into the recorded signal.

6.4 LINEAR DIFFERENTIAL EQUATIONS WITH VARIABLE COEFFICIENTS

When the coefficients in Eq. (6-3) or (6-4) are no longer all constants, the problem of solving these differential equations becomes more involved. Nevertheless, there are still many general similarities to the case of constant coefficients.

For example, the Laplace and Fourier transform pairs, which always yield solutions to linear differential equations with constant coefficients, can also be used to solve many linear differential equations with variable coefficients. The solution of an inhomogeneous linear differential equation with constant coefficients consists of a complementary function, satisfying the homogeneous equation, plus a particular integral. The same is true even if the coefficients are variable.

A linear differential equation of nth order always has n linearly independent solutions (see Sec. 5-5), regardless of whether the coefficients are variable or not. The solution of a linear differential equation with constant coefficients can always be expressed as a power series. The same is true when the coefficients are variable.

Series solutions and special functions

Certain functions which repeatedly appear in applications are honored by being given special names. For example, e^x is the "name" given to the function of x defined by the infinite power series

$$\sum_{n=0}^{\infty} \frac{x^n}{n!} \tag{6-104}$$

Similarly, $\sin x$ is the "name" of the function defined by the power series

$$\sum_{n=0}^{\infty} (-1)^n \frac{x^{2n+1}}{(2n+1)!} \tag{6-105}$$

The same remarks apply to the remaining dozen or so familiar "elementary" functions, such as $\cos x$, $\tan x$, $\log x$, $\sinh x$, $\cosh x$, and so on.

The point to be emphasized here is that these "elementary" functions satisfy linear differential equations *together with initial conditions*. If we accept the fact that the solution of a differential equation with prescribed initial conditions is unique, then it follows that the differential equation, *together with its initial conditions*, actually defines a special function. Defining a function in this way is as good as defining it by means of a particular power series.

As an example, consider a function $y(x)$ which satisfies

$$\frac{d^2y}{dx^2} - y = 0 \tag{6-106}$$

together with the two initial conditions

$$y(0) = 1 \tag{6-107}$$

$$y'(0) = 1 \tag{6-108}$$

Equations (6-106) to (6-108) uniquely define the function $y = y(x)$. What we shall now see is that $y(x) = e^x$ when e^x is defined by expression (6-104). Hence the exponential function can be defined either through the power series (6-104) or by means of Eqs. (6-106) to (6-108). When we define e^x by means of (6-104), then we say that the power series (6-104) is the solution of Eqs. (6-106) to (6-108). When we define e^x as the solution of Eqs. (6-106) to (6-108), then we say that the solution has the power-series representation (6-104).

The nth derivative of y with respect to x, evaluated at $x = 0$, can be obtained by repeated differentiation of Eq. (6-106). For example,

$$\frac{d^3y}{dx^3} = \frac{dy}{dx} \tag{6-109}$$

evaluated at $x = 0$ gives, using Eq. (6-108),

$$\left(\frac{d^3y}{dx^3}\right)_{x=0} = 1 \tag{6-110}$$

Similarly

$$\frac{d^4y}{dx^4} = \frac{d^2y}{dx^2} = y \tag{6-111}$$

evaluated at $x = 0$ gives

$$\left(\frac{d^4y}{dx^4}\right)_{x=0} = 1 \tag{6-112}$$

with the aid of Eq. (6-107). In general

$$\frac{d^{n+2}y}{dx^{n+2}} = \frac{d^ny}{dx^n} \tag{6-113}$$

for $n = 0, 1, 2, \ldots$ gives

$$y^{(n)}(0) = 1 \qquad n = 0,1,2, \ldots \tag{6-114}$$

after Eqs. (6-107) and (6-108) are applied. The function $y(x)$ satisfying Eqs. (6-106) to (6-108) can be expanded in a Taylor series about $x = 0$. The general result is

$$y(x) = \sum_{n=0}^{\infty} y^{(n)}(0) \frac{x^n}{n!} \tag{6-115}$$

and using Eq. (6-114) to evaluate the derivatives $y^{(n)}(0)$, we find

$$y(x) = \sum_{n=0}^{\infty} \frac{x^n}{n!} = e^x \tag{6-116}$$

as promised.

For a given differential equation each set of initial conditions defines a special function. The corresponding series representation can be obtained by using the differential equation and the initial conditions in the manner just indicated. Thus

$$\frac{d^2y}{dx^2} - y = 0 \tag{6-117}$$

$$y(0) = 1 \tag{6-118}$$

$$y'(0) = 0 \tag{6-119}$$

define the special function

$$y = \cosh x \tag{6-120}$$

and

$$\frac{d^2y}{dx^2} - y = 0 \tag{6-121}$$

$$y(0) = 0 \tag{6-122}$$
$$y'(0) = 1 \tag{6-123}$$

define the special function

$$y = \sinh x \tag{6-124}$$

Obviously, the special function defined by

$$\frac{d^2y}{dx^2} - y = 0 \tag{6-125}$$

$$y(0) = a \tag{6-126}$$
$$y'(0) = b \tag{6-127}$$

can be written as a linear combination of the special functions (6-120) and (6-124). In other words Eqs. (6-125) to (6-127) are satisfied by

$$y = a \cosh x + b \sinh x \tag{6-128}$$

This suggests the idea that we should look upon the cases (6-117) to (6-119) and (6-121) to (6-123) as defining *basic* special functions which may be linearly combined to form the solution of the general problem (6-125) to (6-127). If we now define e^{-x} as the unique solution of

$$\frac{d^2y}{dx^2} - y = 0 \tag{6-129}$$

$$y(0) = 1 \tag{6-130}$$
$$y'(0) = -1 \tag{6-131}$$

it is easy to show, by appropriately choosing a and b in Eqs. (6-125) to (6-128), that

$$e^x = \cosh x + \sinh x \tag{6-132}$$

$$e^{-x} = \cosh x - \sinh x \tag{6-133}$$

6.5 THE SPECIAL FUNCTIONS OF MATHEMATICAL PHYSICS

The special functions of mathematical physics can be defined by stating both the differential equation and the initial conditions which each function must satisfy. In order to prepare a table of numerical values for each special function, it is necessary to have the power-series representation for each such function. The technique of defining a special function is independent of whether the corresponding differential equation has constant or variable coefficients. However, the method of constructing the power-series representation, as explained in Sec. 6-4, no longer applies when the coefficients are variable.

We shall consider the properties, definitions, and series expansions of the special functions next, and we shall relegate the details of how the series expansions are obtained to Appendix B.

6.6 THE GAMMA FUNCTION

The gamma function $\Gamma(z)$ satisfies the simple first-order differential equation

$$\frac{d\Gamma(z)}{dz} - \psi(z)\Gamma(z) = 0 \tag{6-134}$$

together with the initial condition

$$\Gamma(1) = 1 \tag{6-135}$$

The variable coefficient $\psi(z)$ is defined by

$$\psi(z) = -\gamma + \sum_{n=0}^{\infty} \left(\frac{1}{n+1} - \frac{1}{z+n}\right) \tag{6-136}$$

for Re $(z) > 0$ where

$$\gamma = \lim_{n \to \infty} \sum_{k=1}^{n} \left(\frac{1}{k} - \ln n\right) = 0.577215 \ldots \tag{6-137}$$

is called the "Euler-Mascheroni constant." It is easier to write the series expansion for $\ln \Gamma(z)$ and to employ

$$\Gamma(z) = e^{\ln \Gamma(z)} = \sum_{n=0}^{\infty} \frac{[\ln \Gamma(z)]^n}{n!} \tag{6-138}$$

than it is to write the series expansion for $\Gamma(z)$ directly.

It can be shown that

$$\ln \Gamma(z) = (z - \tfrac{1}{2}) \ln z - z + \tfrac{1}{2} \ln 2\pi$$
$$+ \frac{1}{2}\left[\sum_{k=1}^{\infty} \sum_{n=1}^{\infty} \frac{k(z+n)^{-(k+1)}}{(k+1)(k+2)}\right] \tag{6-139}$$

which when used with Eq. (6-138) gives the series expansion for $\Gamma(z)$. The variable coefficient $\psi(z)$ which appears in Eq. (6-134) has an interesting property. Putting $z + 1$ for z in Eq. (6-136) gives

$$\psi(z+1) = -\gamma + \sum_{n=0}^{\infty} \left(\frac{1}{n+1} - \frac{1}{z+n+1}\right) \tag{6-140}$$

and solving Eq. (6-136) for $\displaystyle\sum_{n=0}^{\infty} \frac{1}{n+1}$ gives

$$\sum_{n=0}^{\infty} \frac{1}{n+1} = \psi(z) + \gamma + \sum_{n=0}^{\infty} \frac{1}{z+n} \tag{6-141}$$

Therefore

$$\psi(z + 1) = \psi(z) + \sum_{n=0}^{\infty} \left(\frac{1}{z+n} - \frac{1}{z+n+1} \right) \qquad (6\text{-}142)$$

The series on the right side of Eq. (6-142) "telescopes" to $1/z$ since

$$\frac{1}{z} = \left(\frac{1}{z} - \frac{1}{z+1} \right) + \left(\frac{1}{z+1} - \frac{1}{z+2} \right) + \cdots \qquad (6\text{-}143)$$

and as a result

$$\psi(z + 1) = \psi(z) + \frac{1}{z} \qquad (6\text{-}144)$$

where Re $(z) > 0$.

Equation (6-144) is called a functional equation, and its solution, subject to the condition

$$\psi(1) = -\gamma \qquad (6\text{-}145)$$

is given by Eq. (6-136). Suppose $z = n$ where n is a positive integer. Then it follows from Eq. (6-144) that

$$\psi(n + 1) = -\gamma + 1 + \frac{1}{2} + \frac{1}{3} + \cdots + \frac{1}{n} \qquad (6\text{-}146)$$

Next, using Eq. (6-139), we find that

$$\ln \Gamma(z + 1) = \ln \Gamma(z) + \ln z \qquad (6\text{-}147)$$

and therefore

$$\Gamma(z + 1) = z\Gamma(z) \qquad (6\text{-}148)$$

for Re $(z) > 0$.

The functional equation (6-148), together with the condition $\Gamma(1) = 1$, is sometimes taken as the definition of the gamma function. When $z = n$, where n is a positive integer, Eq. (6-148) gives

$$\begin{aligned} \Gamma(n + 1) = n\Gamma(n) &= n(n-1)\Gamma(n-1) = n(n-1)(n-2)\Gamma(n-2) \\ &= n(n-1)(n-2) \cdots 1\Gamma(1) = n! \qquad (6\text{-}149) \end{aligned}$$

Thus

$$\Gamma(n + 1) = n! \qquad (6\text{-}150)$$

For integer values of n, the gamma function of $n + 1$ is the same as n factorial.

The gamma function is often defined by means of a definite integral. For example,

$$\Gamma(1 + z) = \int_0^{\infty} e^{z \ln u - u} \, du \qquad (6\text{-}151)$$

To use Eq. (6-151) to obtain a power-series representation of the gamma function we can proceed as follows: First we verify that $\Gamma(1) = 1$ by putting $z = 0$ in Eq. (6-151). Then, setting

$$w(z) = \Gamma(1 + z) \qquad (6\text{-}152)$$

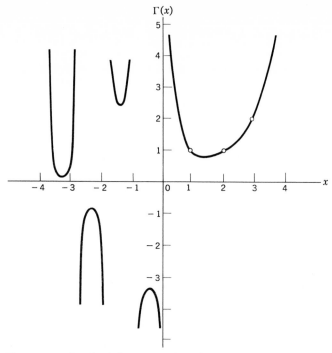

Figure 6-3 Graph of the gamma function.

we expand $w(z)$ in a power series about $z = 0$:

$$w(z) = w(0) + w'(0)z + \cdots + \frac{w^{(n)}(0)}{n!} z^n + \cdots \qquad (6\text{-}153)$$

From Eq. (6-151) we obtain

$$\frac{d^n w}{dz^n} = \int_0^\infty (\ln u)^n e^{z \ln u - u}\, du \qquad (6\text{-}154)$$

Hence

$$\frac{1}{n!}\left(\frac{d^n w}{dz^n}\right)_{z=0} z^n = \int_0^\infty \frac{(z \ln u)^n}{n!} e^{-u}\, du \qquad (6\text{-}155)$$

Now

$$w(z) = \sum_{n=0}^\infty \frac{w^{(n)}(0)}{n!} z^n = \sum_{n=0}^\infty \int_0^\infty \frac{(z \ln u)^n}{n!} e^{-u}\, du \qquad (6\text{-}156)$$

and provided that the order of summation and integration in Eq. (6-156) can be interchanged, we can make use of

$$\sum_{n=0}^\infty \frac{(z \ln u)^n}{n!} = e^{z \ln u} \qquad (6\text{-}157)$$

to regain

$$w(z) = \Gamma(1 + z) = \int_0^\infty e^{z \ln u - u}\, du \qquad (6\text{-}158)$$

The beta function is defined by a definite integral:

$$B(x,y) = \int_0^1 u^{x-1}(1-u)^{y-1}\,du \tag{6-159}$$

for $x > 0$ and $y > 0$. It can be shown that the beta and gamma functions are related according to

$$B(x,y) = \frac{\Gamma(x)\Gamma(y)}{\Gamma(x+y)} \tag{6-160}$$

In particular, if $y = 1 - x$,

$$B(x, 1-x) = \Gamma(x)\Gamma(1-x) = \int_0^1 \frac{u^{x-1}}{(1-u)^x}\,du \tag{6-161}$$

Let

$$w = \frac{u}{1-u} \tag{6-162}$$

$$u = \frac{w}{1+w} \tag{6-163}$$

Then

$$\frac{du}{1-u} = \frac{w}{u}\,du = (1+w)\,d\left(\frac{w}{1+w}\right)$$
$$= \frac{(1+w)\,dw - w\,dw}{1+w} = \frac{dw}{1+w} \tag{6-164}$$

Hence

$$B(x, 1-x) = \int_0^\infty \frac{w^{x-1}}{1+w}\,dw = \frac{\pi}{\sin \pi x} \tag{6-165}$$

for $0 < x < 1$.

The value of the definite integral in Eq. (6-165) comes from a table of definite integrals. However, it could have been obtained directly by use of complex contour integration. Using Eqs. (6-161) and (6-165), we find

$$\Gamma(x)\Gamma(1-x) = \frac{\pi}{\sin \pi x} \tag{6-166}$$

for $0 < x < 1$. This is another functional equation satisfied by the gamma function. If we put $x = \frac{1}{2}$ in Eq. (6-166), then we obtain the occasionally useful result

$$\Gamma(\tfrac{1}{2}) = \sqrt{\pi} \tag{6-167}$$

The definite integral

$$\int_0^\infty \frac{w^{x-1}}{1+w}\,dw = \pi \csc \pi x \tag{6-168}$$

can be evaluated directly by the following elementary method. First, we observe that

$$\pi \csc \pi x = \frac{1}{x} + 2x \sum_{k=1}^\infty \frac{(-1)^{k-1}}{k^2 - x^2} \tag{6-169}$$

Then we expand the integrand of (Eq. 6-168) in a Taylor series, obtaining Eq. (6-169) after term-by-term integration. The details are as follows: Let

$$I = \int_0^\infty \frac{w^{x-1}}{1+w}\, dw = \int_0^1 \frac{w^{x-1}}{1+w}\, dw + \int_1^\infty \frac{w^{x-1}}{1+w}\, dw \tag{6-170}$$

and

$$\frac{1}{1+w} = \sum_{k=0}^\infty (-1)^k w^k \qquad 0 < w < 1 \tag{6-171}$$

Also

$$\frac{1}{1+w} = \frac{1}{w}\frac{1}{1+w^{-1}} = \sum_{k=1}^\infty (-1)^{k-1} w^{-k} \tag{6-172}$$

for $1 < w < \infty$.

Inserting Eqs. (6-171) and (6-172) into Eq. (6-170) and interchanging the orders of summation and integration gives

$$I = \sum_{k=0}^\infty \int_0^1 (-1)^k w^{k+x-1}\, dw + \sum_{k=1}^\infty \int_1^\infty (-1)^{k-1} w^{x-k-1}\, dw \tag{6-173}$$

and

$$\int_0^1 (-1)^k w^{x+k-1}\, dw = \frac{(-1)^k}{x+k} \tag{6-174}$$

provided $k \geq 0$ and $0 < x < 1$. Similarly,

$$\int_1^\infty (-1)^{k-1} w^{x-k-1}\, dw = \frac{(-1)^k}{x-k} \tag{6-175}$$

provided $k \geq 1$ and $0 < x < 1$. Thus

$$I = \sum_{k=0}^\infty \frac{(-1)^k}{x+k} + \sum_{k=1}^\infty \frac{(-1)^k}{x-k} \tag{6-176}$$

which can be rewritten as

$$I = \frac{1}{x} + \sum_{k=1}^\infty (-1)^k \left(\frac{1}{x+k} + \frac{1}{x-k} \right) \tag{6-177}$$

or

$$I = \frac{1}{x} + 2 \sum_{k=1}^\infty \frac{(-1)^k x}{x^2 - k^2} \tag{6-178}$$

and finally

$$I = \frac{1}{x} + 2x \sum_{k=1}^\infty \frac{(-1)^{k-1}}{k^2 - x^2} \tag{6-179}$$

for $0 < x < 1$. It then follows from Eq. (6-169) that

$$\int_0^\infty \frac{w^{x-1}}{1+w}\,dw = \pi \csc \pi x \qquad (6\text{-}180)$$

for $0 < x < 1$.

6-8 THE BESSEL FUNCTIONS

Bessel functions are solutions of Bessel's differential equation

$$\frac{d^2y}{dx^2} + \frac{1}{x}\frac{dy}{dx} + \left(1 - \frac{n^2}{x^2}\right)y = 0 \qquad (6\text{-}181)$$

originally derived by Bessel in connection with studies of planetary motion. Since Bessel's time, this equation has proved to be indispensable for the study, in cylindrical coordinate systems, of problems in acoustics, electromagnetic theory, and heat flow.

The Bessel function of order zero

If we put $n = 0$ in Eq. (6-181), then the equation reduces to

$$\frac{d^2y}{dx^2} + \frac{1}{x}\frac{dy}{dx} + y = 0 \qquad (6\text{-}182)$$

Equation (6-182), *together with the initial conditions*

$$y(0) = 1 \qquad (6\text{-}183)$$

$$y'(0) = 0 \qquad (6\text{-}184)$$

uniquely defines the Bessel function of order zero denoted by $J_0(x)$. The power series which satisfies Eqs. (6-182) to (6-184) is

$$y = J_0(x) = 1 - \frac{x^2}{2^2} + \frac{x^4}{2^4(2!)^2} - \frac{x^6}{2^6(3!)^2} + \cdots \qquad (6\text{-}185)$$

and, in general,

$$J_0(x) = \sum_{k=0}^\infty \frac{(-1)^k x^{2k}}{2^{2k}(k!)^2} \qquad (6\text{-}186)$$

as one can verify by direct substitution of Eq. (6-185) or (6-186) into Eqs. (6-182) to (6-184).

If u_r denotes the rth term of this series,

$$\frac{u_{r+1}}{u_r} = \frac{-x^2}{(2r)^2} \qquad (6\text{-}187)$$

which approaches zero as r becomes infinite for any finite value of x. Consequently, the series converges for all values of x, and since it is a power series, the function $J_0(x)$ and all its derivatives are continuous for all values of x, real or complex.

Notice that

$$\cos x = \sum_{k=0}^\infty \frac{(-1)^k x^{2k}}{(2k)!} \qquad (6\text{-}188)$$

is "something like" $J_0(x)$. This suggests that the graphs of $J_0(x)$ and $\cos x$ should have certain features in common. This is in fact the case. Both $J_0(x)$ and $\cos x$ are unity and have zero slope at $x = 0$. Both oscillate with increasing x; however, $J_0(x)$ is not quite periodic in x, and its peak amplitude decreases slowly from unity as x increases from zero. If we put

$$w = y \sqrt{x} \qquad (6\text{-}189)$$

into Eq. (6-182), we find that w satisfies the equation

$$\frac{d^2w}{dx^2} + \left(1 + \frac{1}{4x^2}\right) w = 0 \qquad (6\text{-}190)$$

For large enough values of x, Eq. (6-190) reduces to

$$\frac{d^2w}{dx^2} + w = 0 \qquad (6\text{-}191)$$

which has the general solution

$$w = A \cos (x - \Phi) \qquad (6\text{-}192)$$

where A and Φ are constants. This together with Eq. (6-189) yields

$$y = \frac{A}{\sqrt{x}} \cos (x - \Phi) \qquad (6\text{-}193)$$

for the general behavior of solutions of Eq. (6-182) as x becomes very large. Notice that by using the transformation (6-189) we have arranged matters so that the coefficient of w in Eq. (6-190) does not vanish as $x \to \infty$. Had we allowed $x \to \infty$ in Eq. (6-182) instead of first transforming with Eq. (6-189), we would have lost the term dy/dx and as a result, the behavior of y for large x would be in error. A more detailed analysis shows that for $x > 0$

$$J_0(x) = \left(\frac{2}{\pi x}\right)^{\frac{1}{2}} \left[\cos \left(x - \frac{\pi}{4}\right) + p(x) \right] \qquad (6\text{-}194)$$

where

$$\lim_{x \to +\infty} p(x) = 0 \qquad (6\text{-}195)$$

For very large positive values of x we write simply

$$J_0(x) \sim \left(\frac{2}{\pi x}\right)^{\frac{1}{2}} \cos \left(x - \frac{\pi}{4}\right) \qquad (6\text{-}196)$$

where the symbol $\sim$ means that $J_0(x)$ is *asymptotically* equal to the expression on the right side of (6-196).

The Bessel functions of positive integral order

Suppose $n = +1$ in Eq. (6-181). The solution of

$$\frac{d^2y}{dx^2} + \frac{1}{x} \frac{dy}{dx} + \left(1 - \frac{1}{x^2}\right) y = 0 \qquad (6\text{-}197)$$

satisfying the initial conditions

$$y(0) = 0 \tag{6-198}$$

$$y'(0) = \tfrac{1}{2} \tag{6-199}$$

is by definition the Bessel function of order one and is given by

$$J_1(x) = \frac{x}{2} - \frac{x^3}{2^2 \cdot 4} + \frac{x^5}{2^2 \cdot 4^2 \cdot 6} - \frac{x^7}{2^2 \cdot 4^2 \cdot 6^2 \cdot 8} + \cdots \tag{6-200}$$

A comparison of the power series for $\sin x$,

$$\sin x = \sum_{k=0}^{\infty} (-1)^k \frac{x^{2k+1}}{(2k+1)!} \tag{6-201}$$

with Eq. (6-200) shows that $J_1(x)$ is similar to $\sin x$. In fact, a comparison of Eq. (6-185) with (6-200) reveals that

$$\frac{dJ_0(x)}{dx} = -J_1(x) \tag{6-202}$$

just as

$$\frac{d}{dx} \cos x = -\sin x \tag{6-203}$$

The function $J_1(x)$ behaves like $\sin x$ vanishing at $x = 0$, and oscillating as x increases. However, the oscillations of $J_1(x)$ are not quite periodic, and the maximum amplitude falls off slowly as x increases. For integer values of $n \geq 2$ the solutions of

$$\frac{d^2y}{dx^2} + \frac{1}{x}\frac{dy}{dx} + \left(1 - \frac{n^2}{x^2}\right)y = 0 \tag{6-204}$$

satisfying the initial conditions

$$y(0) = 0 \tag{6-205}$$

and

$$y'(0) = 0 \tag{6-206}$$

are by definition the Bessel functions of integral order $n \geq 2$. The power-series expansion of a Bessel function of any non-negative integral order including $n = 0$ and $n = 1$ can be written as

$$J_n(x) = \frac{x^n}{2^n n!}\left[1 - \frac{x^2}{2(2n+2)} + \frac{x^4}{2 \cdot 4 \cdot (2n+2)(2n+4)} - \cdots\right] \tag{6-207}$$

or more generally in the form

$$J_n(x) = \sum_{k=0}^{\infty} \frac{(-1)^k x^{n+2k}}{2^{n+2k} k! \Gamma(n+k+1)} \qquad n \neq -1, -2, -3, \ldots \tag{6-208}$$

All the Bessel functions with $n \geq 1$ resemble $\sin x$ in that they begin at zero for $x = 0$ and oscillate as x increases. However, these oscilla-

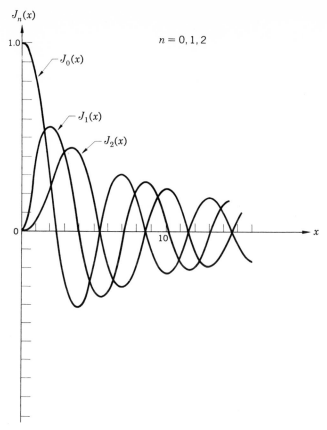

Figure 6-4 Bessel functions of orders 0, 1, and 2.

tions are not periodic, and their peak amplitudes fall off with increasing x.

Bessel functions of negative integral order

When n is an integer, it follows from Eq. (6-208), after some reduction, that

$$J_{-n}(x) = (-1)^n J_n(x) \qquad n = 1,2,3, \ldots \qquad (6\text{-}209)$$

6-9 THE NEUMANN FUNCTIONS

Let us return to Bessel's equation (6-182). The Bessel function $J_0(x)$ of order $n = 0$ is one solution. We should expect to find a second solution which is not simply a constant times $J_0(x)$ because Eq. (6-182) is a second-order differential equation. Such a function is called a "Neumann function of order zero" or a "Bessel function of the second kind of order zero."

Suppose that u is such a function, and let $v = J_0(x)$. Then

$$xu'' + u' + xu = 0 \tag{6-210}$$

$$xv'' + v' + xv = 0 \tag{6-211}$$

Multiplying Eq. (6-210) by v and Eq. (6-211) by u gives on subtraction

$$x(u''v - v''u) + u'v - v'u = 0 \tag{6-212}$$

We can write Eq. (6-212) as

$$\frac{d}{dx}[x(u'v - v'u)] = 0 \tag{6-213}$$

which upon integration gives

$$x(u'v - v'u) = B \tag{6-214}$$

where $B = $ constant. Dividing Eq. (6-214) by $v^2 x$

$$\frac{u'v - v'u}{v^2} = \frac{B}{v^2 x} \tag{6-215}$$

or

$$\frac{d}{dx}\left(\frac{u}{v}\right) = \frac{B}{v^2 x} \tag{6-216}$$

Integration of Eq. (6-216) then gives

$$\frac{u}{v} = A + B\int \frac{dx}{v^2 x} \tag{6-217}$$

and since $v = J_0(x)$,

$$u = AJ_0(x) + BJ_0(x)\int \frac{dx}{xJ_0^2(x)} \tag{6-218}$$

where A and B are arbitrary constants.

Using Eq. (6-185), we find

$$\frac{1}{xJ_0^2(x)} = \frac{1}{x} + \frac{x}{2} + \frac{5x^3}{32} + \cdots \tag{6-219}$$

and as a result

$$J_0(x)\int \frac{dx}{xJ_0^2(x)} = J_0(x)\left(\log x + \frac{x^2}{4} + \frac{5x^4}{128} + \cdots\right) \tag{6-220}$$

Using Eq. (6-185) once more,

$$J_0(x)\int \frac{dx}{xJ_0^2(x)} = J_0(x)\log x$$
$$+ \left(1 - \frac{x^2}{2^2} + \cdots\right)\left(\frac{x^2}{4} + \frac{5x^4}{128} + \cdots\right) \tag{6-221}$$

which leads to

$$u = AJ_0(x) + B\left[J_0(x)\log x + \frac{x^2}{4} - \frac{3x^4}{128} + \cdots\right] \tag{6-222}$$

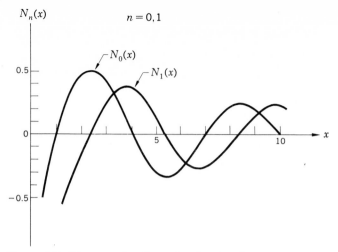

Figure 6-5 Neumann functions of orders 0 and 1.

The Neumann function of order zero is defined by putting

$$A = \frac{-2}{\pi}(\log 2 - \gamma) \tag{6-223}$$

and

$$B = \frac{2}{\pi} \tag{6-224}$$

in Eq. (6-222), where γ is the Euler constant defined in Eq. (6-137). With these substitutions Eq. (6-222) becomes

$$u = N_0(x) = \frac{2}{\pi}\left[J_0(x)\left(\log\frac{x}{2} + \gamma\right)\right]$$
$$+ \frac{2}{\pi}\left(\frac{x^2}{4} - \frac{3x^4}{128} + \cdots\right) \tag{6-225}$$

The complete series can be obtained by other methods and is given by

$$N_0(x) = \frac{2}{\pi}\left[J_0(x)\left(\log\frac{x}{2} + \gamma\right)\right] + \sum_{m=1}^{\infty}\frac{(-1)^{m-1}a_m x^{2m}}{2^{2m}(m!)^2} \tag{6-226}$$

where

$$a_m = 1 + \frac{1}{2} + \frac{1}{3} + \cdots + \frac{1}{m} \tag{6-227}$$

The Neumann function of order zero is also an oscillatory aperiodic function of diminishing peak amplitude. However, instead of remaining finite as $x \to 0$, it approaches $-\infty$ like $\log x$. The logarithmic singularity in Eq. (6-226) also has the effect of requiring x to be non-negative in order that $N_0(x)$ be real. It can be shown that for $x > 0$

$$N_0(x) = \left(\frac{2}{\pi x}\right)^{\frac{1}{2}}\left[\sin\left(x - \frac{\pi}{4}\right) + q(x)\right] \tag{6-228}$$

where

$$\lim_{x \to +\infty} q(x) = 0 \tag{6-229}$$

and consequently, for large positive values of x, we have

$$N_0(x) \sim \left(\frac{2}{\pi x}\right)^{\frac{1}{2}} \left[\sin\left(x - \frac{\pi}{4}\right)\right] \tag{6-230}$$

Neumann functions of positive integral order

In the same way that $N_0(x)$ is the linearly independent companion solution to $J_0(x)$ for Bessel's equation of order zero, there is a linearly independent companion $N_1(x)$ associated with $J_1(x)$, $N_2(x)$ associated with $J_2(x)$, and so on. These Neumann functions are given by

$$N_n(x) = \frac{2}{\pi} J_n(x)\left(\log\frac{x}{2} + \gamma\right)$$

$$+ \frac{x^n}{\pi} \sum_{m=0}^{\infty} \frac{(-1)^{m-1}(a_m + a_{m+n})}{2^{2m+n}m!(m+n)!} x^{2m}$$

$$- \frac{x^{-n}}{\pi} \sum_{m=0}^{n-1} \frac{(n-m-1)!}{2^{2m-n}m!} x^{2m} \qquad x > 0, n = 1,2,3, \ldots \tag{6-231}$$

where

$$a_0 = 1 \tag{6-232}$$

$$a_m = 1 + \frac{1}{2} + \frac{1}{3} + \cdots + \frac{1}{m} \qquad m = 1,2,3, \ldots \tag{6-233}$$

The Neumann functions also satisfy a relation of the form

$$N_{-n}(x) = (-1)^n N_n(x) \qquad n = 1,2,3, \ldots \tag{6-234}$$

The most general solution of Bessel's equation (6-181) when n is an integer is

$$y(x) = A J_n(x) + B N_n(x) \tag{6-235}$$

6-10 BESSEL FUNCTIONS OF ARBITRARY ORDER

Bessel's equation for arbitrary order ν is

$$\frac{d^2y}{dx^2} + \frac{1}{x}\frac{dy}{dx} + \left(1 - \frac{\nu^2}{x^2}\right)y = 0 \tag{6-236}$$

where ν is no longer an integer. The series solution (6-208) still holds when n is replaced by ν. For $n = \frac{1}{2}$, Eq. (6-208) gives

$$J_{\frac{1}{2}}(x) = \sqrt{\frac{2}{\pi x}} \sin x \tag{6-237}$$

and more generally

$$J_{n+\frac{1}{2}}(x) = \sqrt{\frac{2}{\pi}} x^{n+\frac{1}{2}}\left(-\frac{1}{x}\frac{d}{dx}\right)^n \frac{\sin x}{x} \qquad n = 1,2,3, \ldots \tag{6-238}$$

If we put $n = -\nu$ into Eq. (6-208) when ν is no longer an integer, then since Bessel's equation involves ν^2, the functions J_ν and $J_{-\nu}$ must still be solutions of Eq. (6-236) for the same ν. However, for noninteger values of ν, J_ν and $J_{-\nu}$ become linearly independent, since Eq. (6-208) shows that the first term in J_ι is proportional to x^ν while the first term in $J_{-\nu}$ is proportional to $x^{-\nu}$. Consequently (6-208) fails to hold, and the most general solution of Bessel's equation of noninteger order becomes

$$y(x) = A J_\nu(x) + B J_{-\nu}(x) \tag{6-239}$$

Using (6-208), it can be shown that

$$J_{-\frac{1}{2}}(x) = \sqrt{\frac{2}{\pi x}} \cos x \tag{6-240}$$

and, in general,

$$J_{-n-\frac{1}{2}}(x) = \sqrt{\frac{2}{\pi}} x^{n+\frac{1}{2}} \left(\frac{1}{x} \frac{d}{dx} \right)^n \frac{\cos x}{x} \tag{6-241}$$

For example, the most general solution of Bessel's equation of order $\frac{1}{2}$ is

$$y(x) = \sqrt{\frac{2}{\pi x}} (A \sin x + B \cos x) \tag{6-242}$$

Neumann functions of arbitrary order

It appears that the second solution of Bessel's equation is $N_n(x)$ when n is an integer, and $J_{-\nu}(x)$ when ν is not an integer. To eliminate this confusion we define $N_\nu(x)$ for arbitrary values of ν in such a way that it (1) satisfies Bessel's equation, and (2) reduces to $N_n(x)$ as $\nu \to n$. Thus let

$$N_\nu(x) = \frac{1}{\sin \pi \nu} [J_\nu(x) \cos \pi \nu - J_{-\nu}(x)] \tag{6-243}$$

and

$$N_n(x) = \lim_{\nu \to n} N_\nu(x) \tag{6-244}$$

When ν is not an integer, $N_\nu(x)$ satisfies Bessel's equation since $J_\nu(x)$ and $J_{-\nu}(x)$ satisfy it. Furthermore, when ν is not an integer, J_ν and N_ν are linearly independent because of Eq. (6-243) and the linear independence of J_ν and $J_{-\nu}$. Inserting Eq. (6-208) (with n replaced by ν) into Eq. (6-243) and then taking the limit (6-244) yields Eq. (6-231), as expected. Examining (6-231), we see that it contains a logarithmic term which Eq. (6-208) lacks. Therefore $J_n(x)$ and $N_n(x)$ are linearly independent even when n is an integer. Our conclusion is that

$$y(x) = A J_\nu(x) + B N_\nu(x) \tag{6-245}$$

is the general solution of Eq. (6-236) for any real number ν.

The asymptotic formulas (6-196) and (6-230) can be combined to give

$$J_0(x) + iN_0(x) \sim \left(\frac{2}{\pi x}\right)^{1/2} \left[\cos\left(x - \frac{\pi}{4}\right) \right.$$
$$\left. + i \sin\left(x - \frac{\pi}{4}\right) \right] \qquad (6\text{-}246)$$

$$J_0(x) - iN_0(x) \sim \left(\frac{2}{\pi x}\right)^{1/2} \left[\cos\left(x - \frac{\pi}{4}\right) \right.$$
$$\left. - i \sin\left(x - \frac{\pi}{4}\right) \right] \qquad (6\text{-}247)$$

or simply

$$J_0(x) + iN_0(x) \sim \left(\frac{2}{\pi x}\right)^{1/2} e^{i(x - \pi/4)} \qquad (6\text{-}248)$$

$$J_0(x) - iN_0(x) \sim \left(\frac{2}{\pi x}\right)^{1/2} e^{-i(x - \pi/4)} \qquad (6\text{-}249)$$

for $x \gg 0$. The asymptotic forms of these two particular linear combinations of J_0 and N_0 are so useful in applied mathematics that the functions

$$H_0^{(1)}(x) = J_0(x) + iN_0(x) \qquad (6\text{-}250)$$

and

$$H_0^{(2)}(x) = J_0(x) - iN_0(x) \qquad (6\text{-}251)$$

have been tabulated.

The function $H_0^{(1)}(x)$ is called a "Hankel function of the first kind of order zero," and $H_0^{(2)}(x)$ is a "Hankel function of the second kind of order zero." Similarly, one defines

$$H_\nu^{(1)}(x) = J_\nu(x) + iN_\nu(x) \qquad (6\text{-}252)$$

$$H_\nu^{(2)}(x) = J_\nu(x) - iN_\nu(x) \qquad (6\text{-}253)$$

as Hankel functions of the first and second kind of order ν. The functions $H_\nu^{(1)}$ and $H_\nu^{(2)}$ are linearly independent because J_ν and N_ν are. Thus the general solution of Bessel's equation of order ν can be written as

$$y = CH_\nu^{(1)}(x) + DH_\nu^{(2)}(x) \qquad (6\text{-}254)$$

instead of in the form (6-245). Asymptotically,

$$\lim_{x \to +\infty} H_0^{(1)}(x) = \left(\frac{2}{\pi x}\right)^{1/2} e^{i(x - \pi/4)} \qquad (6\text{-}255)$$

$$\lim_{x \to +\infty} H_0^{(2)}(x) = \left(\frac{2}{\pi x}\right)^{1/2} e^{-i(x - \pi/4)} \qquad (6\text{-}256)$$

and using the series representations for J_n and N_n, one can show in addition that

$$\lim_{x \to 0} J_n(x) = \frac{1}{n!} \left(\frac{x}{2}\right)^n \tag{6-257}$$

$$\lim_{x \to \infty} J_n(x) = \left(\frac{2}{\pi x}\right)^{\frac{1}{2}} \cos \left[x - (\pi/2)(n + \frac{1}{2})\right] \tag{6-258}$$

$$\lim_{x \to 0} N_0(x) = \frac{2}{\pi} \left(\log \frac{x}{2} + 0.5772 \cdots\right) \tag{6-259}$$

$$\lim_{x \to 0} N_n(x) = \frac{-(n-1)!}{\pi} \left(\frac{2}{x}\right)^n \qquad n = 1,2,3, \ldots \tag{6-260}$$

$$\lim_{x \to \infty} N_n(x) = \left(\frac{2}{\pi x}\right)^{\frac{1}{2}} \sin \left[x - (\pi/2)(n + \frac{1}{2})\right] \tag{6-261}$$

Therefore

$$\lim_{x \to 0} H_0^{(1)}(x) = \frac{2i}{\pi} \log \frac{x}{2} \tag{6-262}$$

$$\lim_{x \to 0} H_n^{(1)}(x) = \frac{1}{n!} \left(\frac{x}{2}\right)^n$$
$$- \frac{i(n-1)!}{\pi}\left(\frac{2}{x}\right)^n \qquad n = 1,2,3, \ldots \tag{6-263}$$

$$\lim_{x \to +\infty} H_n^{(1)}(x) = \left(\frac{2}{\pi x}\right)^{\frac{1}{2}} e^{i[x-(\pi/2)(n+\frac{1}{2})]} \tag{6-264}$$

give some useful limiting properties of the Hankel function of the first kind. A similar set of limiting relations for $H_n^{(2)}$ are obtained by replacing i by $-i$ in Eqs. (6-262) to (6-264).

6-12 THE HYPERBOLIC BESSEL FUNCTIONS

The hyperbolic Bessel functions (Fig. 6-6) are related to ordinary Bessel functions just as the hyperbolic sines and cosines are related to the ordinary sines and cosines. For example, sin x and cos x satisfy the equation

$$\frac{d^2y}{dx^2} + y = 0 \tag{6-265}$$

and if we replace x by ix in Eq. (6-265), then (6-265) becomes

$$\frac{d^2y}{dx^2} - y = 0 \tag{6-266}$$

which has solutions sinh x and cosh x.

Analogously, let us replace x by ix in Eq. (6-236) which takes the form

$$\frac{d^2y}{dx^2} + \frac{1}{x}\frac{dy}{dx} - \left(1 + \frac{\nu^2}{x^2}\right)y = 0 \tag{6-267}$$

There is a pair of linearly independent solutions of Eq. (6-267) denoted by $I_\nu(x)$ and $K_\nu(x)$, which are called the "hyperbolic" or "modified" Bessel functions of the first and second kind (of order ν), respectively.

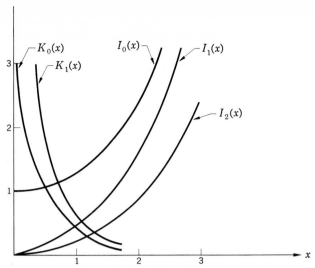

Figure 6-6 Hyperbolic Bessel functions.

In terms of these hyperbolic Bessel functions, the general solution of Eq. (6-267) becomes

$$y = AI_\nu(x) + BK_\nu(x) \tag{6-268}$$

It is apparent from the manner in which Eq. (6-267) is obtained that I_ν and K_ν are related to ordinary Bessel functions of complex argument. In particular,

$$I_\nu(x) = e^{-i\pi\nu/2} J_\nu(ix) \tag{6-269}$$

and

$$K_\nu(x) = \left(\frac{\pi i}{2}\right) e^{i\pi\nu/2} H_\nu{}^{(1)}(ix) \tag{6-270}$$

The hyperbolic Bessel functions of integral order do not oscillate and thus have graphs which differ considerably from those of the ordinary Bessel functions. We might have anticipated this difference because of a similar change between the hyperbolic and ordinary sine and cosine. Some of the important limiting properties of hyperbolic Bessel functions of integral order are

$$\lim_{x \to 0} K_0(x) = -\left(\log \frac{x}{2} + 0.5772 \ldots\right) \tag{6-271}$$

$$\lim_{x \to 0} I_n(x) = \frac{1}{n!} \left(\frac{x}{2}\right)^n \tag{6-272}$$

$$\lim_{x \to \infty} I_n(x) = \frac{e^x}{\sqrt{2\pi x}} \tag{6-273}$$

$$\lim_{x \to 0} K_n(x) = \frac{\Gamma(n)}{2} \left(\frac{2}{x}\right)^n \qquad n \neq 0 \tag{6-274}$$

$$\lim_{x \to \infty} K_n(x) = \left(\frac{\pi}{2x}\right)^{1/2} e^{-x} \tag{6-275}$$

THE HYPERBOLIC BESSEL FUNCTIONS

Associated Legendre functions are solutions of

$$(1 - x^2) \frac{d^2y}{dx^2} - 2x \frac{dy}{dx} + \left[\nu(\nu + 1) - \frac{\mu^2}{1 - x^2} \right] y = 0 \qquad (6\text{-}276)$$

which is known as "Legendre's associated equation." In general, μ and ν are two arbitrary complex constants. This differential equation arises when one attempts to solve wave-propagation, potential, or diffusion problems in spherical coordinates.

Solutions of Eq. (6-276) when μ or ν or both are integers are of special interest, and in particular the case $\mu = 0$ is important. The appearance of a factor $1 - x^2$ in Eq. (6-276) leads one to suspect that for $x = \pm 1$ the solutions behave in some "peculiar" way. This is actually the case. In the range $-1 \le x \le +1$ the general solution is the sum of two linearly independent functions, thus:

$$y = A P_\nu{}^\mu(x) + B Q_\nu{}^\mu(x) \qquad (6\text{-}277)$$

where $P_\nu{}^\mu(x)$ is called an "associated Legendre function of the first kind" and $Q_\nu{}^\mu(x)$ is an "associated Legendre function of the second kind."

For integer values of ν and μ such that $|\nu| \ge |\mu|$ the functions $P_\nu{}^\mu(x)$ and $Q_\nu{}^\mu(x)$ become relatively simple. It is an interesting and important fact that for this particular case, $P_\nu{}^\mu(x)$ can be expressed in terms of $P_\nu{}^0(x)$, and $Q_\nu{}^\mu(x)$ can be expressed in terms of $Q_\nu{}^0(x)$.

The functions $P_\nu{}^0(x)$ and $Q_\nu{}^0(x)$ are solutions of Legendre's differential equation,

$$(1 - x^2) \frac{d^2y}{dx^2} - 2x \frac{dy}{dx} + \nu(\nu + 1)y = 0 \qquad (6\text{-}278)$$

and to simplify the writing, it is customary to omit the zero superscript in $P_\nu{}^0$ and $Q_\nu{}^0$. Thus when ν is an integer, $\nu = n$, the general solution of Eq. (6-278) is written as

$$y = A P_n(x) + B Q_n(x) \qquad (6\text{-}279)$$

The function $P_n(x)$ is a polynomial of degree n in x, and it is called a *Legendre polynomial* of order n. The linearly independent companion solution to $P_n(x)$, i.e., $Q_n(x)$, is *not* a polynomial. It involves a logarithmic term, and most often $Q_n(x)$ is called a Legendre function of the second kind (Fig. 6-7). Since we are concerned with the range $-1 \le x \le 1$, we can define an angle θ with Eq. (6-280):

$$x = \cos \theta \qquad (6\text{-}280)$$

Then in terms of x or $\cos \theta$ the first few Legendre polynomials and

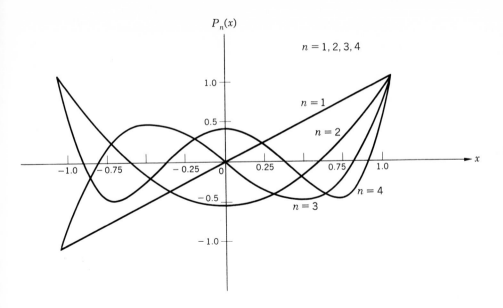

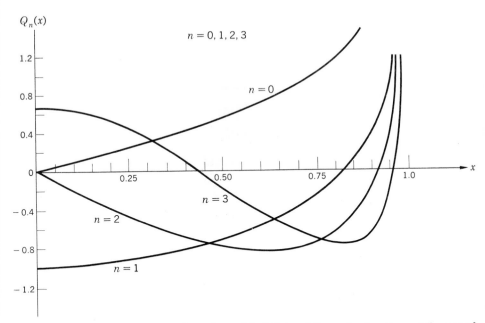

Figure 6-7 Legendre polynomials $P_n(x)$ and Legendre functions of the second kind $Q_n(x)$.

Legendre functions of the second kind are given by

$$P_0(x) = 1 \tag{6-281}$$

$$P_1(x) = x = \cos\theta \tag{6-282}$$

$$P_2(x) = \tfrac{1}{2}(3x^2 - 1) = \tfrac{1}{4}(3\cos 2\theta - 1) \tag{6-283}$$

$$P_3(x) = \tfrac{1}{2}(5x^3 - 3x) = \tfrac{1}{8}(5\cos 3\theta + 3\cos\theta) \tag{6-284}$$

$$Q_0(x) = \tfrac{1}{2}\ln\frac{1+x}{1-x} \tag{6-285}$$

$$Q_1(x) = \frac{x}{2}\ln\frac{1+x}{1-x} - 1 \tag{6-286}$$

$$Q_2(x) = \tfrac{1}{4}(3x^2 - 1)\ln\frac{1+x}{1-x} - \tfrac{3}{2}x \tag{6-287}$$

$$Q_3(x) = \tfrac{1}{4}(5x^3 - 3x)\ln\frac{1+x}{1-x} - \tfrac{5}{2}x^2 + \tfrac{2}{3} \tag{6-288}$$

We can verify by direct substitution into Eq. (6-278) that Eqs. (6-282) through (6-288) are solutions for appropriate values of n. Since the Q's involve logarithms and the P's do not, it follows that for a given value of n, $P_n(x)$ and $Q_n(x)$ are linearly independent.

It is possible to give some very simple general expressions for P_n and Q_n. For example, Rodrigues's formula for $P_n(x)$ is

$$P_n(x) = \frac{1}{2^n n!}\frac{d^n}{dx^n}(x^2 - 1)^n \tag{6-289}$$

and $Q_n(x)$ may then be written as

$$Q_n(x) = \tfrac{1}{2}P_n(x)\ln\frac{1+x}{1-x} - W_{n-1}(x) \tag{6-290}$$

where $n = 0,1,2, \ldots$, and

$$W_{n-1}(x) = \frac{2n-1}{1\cdot n}P_{n-1}(x) + \frac{2n-5}{3\cdot(n-1)}P_{n-3}(x)$$

$$+ \frac{2n-9}{5\cdot(n-2)}P_{n-5}(x) + \cdots \tag{6-291}$$

In Eq. (6-291) $W_{-1}(x) \equiv 0$ and the series for $W_{n-1}(x)$ ends with $P_1(x)$ or $P_0(x)$, depending on the particular value of n.

Legendre polynomials are frequently defined as the expansion coefficients obtained when one expands the function $(1 - 2r\cos\theta + r^2)^{-\frac{1}{2}}$ in powers of r. Thus, for $r < 1$,

$$(1 - 2r\cos\theta + r^2)^{-\frac{1}{2}} = \sum_{n=0}^{\infty} P_n(\cos\theta)r^n \tag{6-292a}$$

while, for $r > 1$,

$$(1 - 2r\cos\theta + r^2)^{-\frac{1}{2}} = \sum_{n=0}^{\infty} P_n\frac{(\cos\theta)}{r^{n+1}} \tag{6-292b}$$

Legendre polynomials are sometimes referred to as "zonal harmonics," and the function $(1 - 2r\cos\theta + r^2)^{-\frac{1}{2}}$ whose power-series expansion generates them is called, appropriately enough, the "generating function" for zonal harmonics. An examination of Eq. (6-292a) for $\theta = 0$ and $\theta = \pi$ shows on comparison with the geometric series that

$$P_n(1) = 1 \qquad n = 0,1,2, \ldots \tag{6-293}$$

and

$$P_n(-1) = (-1)^n \qquad n = 0,1,2, \ldots \tag{6-294}$$

6-14 REPRESENTATION OF ASSOCIATED LEGENDRE FUNCTIONS IN TERMS OF LEGENDRE POLYNOMIALS

When ν and μ take on integer values, Legendre's associated equation becomes

$$(1 - x^2)\frac{d^2y}{dx^2} - 2x\frac{dy}{dx} + \left[n(n + 1) - \frac{m^2}{(1 - x^2)} \right] y = 0 \tag{6-295}$$

This equation has one solution $y = P_n{}^m(x)$ which is a polynomial in x and is related to the ordinary Legendre polynomials $(m = 0)$ through the formula

$$y = P_n{}^m(x) = (1 - x^2)^{m/2} \frac{d^m P_n(x)}{dx^m} \qquad -1 \leq x \leq +1 \tag{6-296}$$

Similarly, Eq. (6-295) possesses a second solution $y = Q_n{}^m(x)$ which is related to the Q_n functions by the expression

$$Q_n{}^m(x) = (1 - x^2)^{m/2} \frac{d^m Q_n(x)}{dx^m} \qquad -1 \leq x \leq +1 \tag{6-297}$$

When n and m are non-negative integers and $|x| \leq 1$, the general solution of Eq. (6-295) is given by

$$y = AP_n{}^m(x) + BQ_n{}^m(x) \tag{6-298}$$

Using Eqs. (6-297) and (6-298), together with the expressions for $P_n(x)$ and $Q_n(x)$ given in Sec. 6-13, we can write

$$P_1{}^1(x) = (1 - x^2)^{1/2} \tag{6-299}$$

$$P_2{}^1(x) = 3x(1 - x^2)^{1/2} \tag{6-300}$$

$$P_2{}^2(x) = 3(1 - x^2) \tag{6-301}$$

$$Q_1{}^1(x) = (1 - x^2)^{1/2} \left(\frac{1}{2} \ln\frac{1 + x}{1 - x} + \frac{x}{1 - x^2} \right) \tag{6-302}$$

$$Q_2{}^1(x) = (1 - x^2)^{1/2} \left(\frac{3}{2}x \ln\frac{1 + x}{1 - x} + \frac{3x^2 - 2}{1 - x^2} \right) \tag{6-303}$$

$$Q_2{}^2(x) = (1 - x^2) \left[\frac{3}{2} \ln\frac{1 + x}{1 - x} + \frac{5x - 3x^3}{(1 - x^2)^2} \right] \tag{6-304}$$

Since the $Q_n{}^m(x)$ contain logarithmic terms whereas the $P_n{}^m(x)$ do not, it follows that $P_n{}^m(x)$ and $Q_n{}^m(x)$ are linearly independent functions for each pair of non-negative integers (n,m). This of course must be the case in order for Eq. (6-298) to be the general solution of Eq. (6-295).

The solutions of Laplace's equation

$$\nabla^2 \varphi = 0 \tag{6-305}$$

are called "harmonic functions." In particular, solutions of Laplace's equation in spherical coordinates are spherical harmonics.

Consider the spherical coordinates (r,θ,φ), where r is the radial distance, φ is longitudinal angle, and θ is the colatitude measured relative to the north pole of the sphere. Laplace's equation expressed in this coordinate system is satisfied by the following expressions:

$$r^n P_n{}^m(\cos\theta)\cos m\varphi \tag{6-306}$$

$$r^n P_n{}^m(\cos\theta)\sin m\varphi \tag{6-307}$$

$$r^{-n-1}P_n{}^m(\cos\theta)\cos m\varphi \tag{6-308}$$

$$r^{-n-1}P_n{}^m(\cos\theta)\sin m\varphi \tag{6-309}$$

and by

$$r^n Q_n{}^m(\cos\theta)\cos m\varphi \tag{6-310}$$

$$r^n Q_n{}^m(\cos\theta)\sin m\varphi \tag{6-311}$$

$$r^{-n-1}Q_n{}^m(\cos\theta)\cos m\varphi \tag{6-312}$$

$$r^{-n-1}Q_n{}^m(\cos\theta)\sin m\varphi \tag{6-313}$$

as well. One can prove that expressions (6-306) to (6-313) are solutions of Eq. (6-305) by direct substitution into (6-305) expressed in spherical coordinates. One then performs the indicated differentiations noticing that $P_n{}^m(\cos\theta)$ and $Q_n{}^m(\cos\theta)$ are solutions of Legendre's associated equation with $x = \cos\theta$.

The expressions (6-306), (6-307), (6-310), and (6-311) are called "solid spherical harmonics of the first kind of degree n and order m." Similarly (6-308), (6-309), (6-312), and (6-313) are "solid spherical harmonics of the second kind of degree $-n - 1$ and order m."

In most applications we are concerned with functions $f(r,\theta,\varphi)$ which are everywhere finite and differentiable on the surface of some sphere. We seek to represent such functions as a sum of solid spherical harmonics. However, the solid spherical harmonics of the second kind involve the functions $Q_n{}^m(\cos\theta)$ which become infinite at the north pole ($\theta = 0$) of any sphere. This happens because of the logarithmic term contained in $Q_n{}^m(\cos\theta)$. For this reason solid spherical harmonics of the second kind are not often of use in representing functions $f(r,\theta,\varphi)$ which must remain finite on the surface of a sphere.

Properties of spherical harmonics

The functions $\cos m\varphi\, P_n{}^m(\cos\theta)$ and $\sin m\varphi\, P_n{}^m(\cos\theta)$ are periodic on the surface of a unit sphere. The locus of points, $\varphi = 0$, on the surface of a unit sphere is a great circle passing through the north and south poles. The spherical harmonic $\sin m\varphi\, P_n{}^m(\cos\theta)$ vanishes

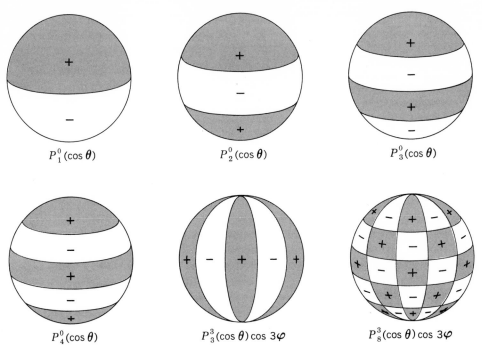

$P_1^0 (\cos \theta)$ $P_2^0 (\cos \theta)$ $P_3^0 (\cos \theta)$

$P_4^0 (\cos \theta)$ $P_3^3 (\cos \theta) \cos 3\varphi$ $P_8^3 (\cos \theta) \cos 3\varphi$

Figure 6-8 Zonal, sectorial, and tesseral harmonics.

at every point of this great circle. Therefore the circular locus $\varphi = 0$ is called a "nodal line" or "nodal circle" associated with sin $m\varphi$ $P_n^m(\cos \theta)$. The indices n and m determine the number of nodal lines associated with sin $m\varphi$ $P_n^m(\cos \theta)$ and cos $m\varphi$ $P_n^m(\cos \theta)$. Let us consider the case $m = 0$ first, and let n range through the non-negative integers. When $m = 0$, the harmonic sin $m\varphi$ $P_n^m(\cos \theta)$ vanishes identically for all values of φ, while

$$\cos m\varphi\ P_n^m(\cos \theta) = P_n^0(\cos \theta) = P_n(\cos \theta)$$

also becomes independent of the longitudinal angle φ. If n is also zero, then cos $m\varphi$ $P_n^m(\cos \theta) = P_0(\cos \theta) = 1$ is everywhere constant on the surface of the sphere. When $m = 0$ and $n = 1$, then cos $m\varphi$ $P_n^m(\cos \theta) = P_1(\cos \theta) = \cos \theta$ has a single nodal line at the equator $(\theta = \pi/2)$ along which the function vanishes. For $m = 0$ and $n = 2$, cos $m\varphi$ $P_n^m(\cos \theta) = P_2(\cos \theta) = \frac{1}{4}(3 \cos 2\theta + 1)$ has two nodal lines following the parallels of latitude at approximately $\theta = 55$ degrees and $\theta = 125$ degrees, so that the sphere is divided into three zones; $P_2(\cos \theta)$ is positive in the polar zones and negative in the equatorial zone.

In general, for $m = 0$, cos $m\varphi$ $P_n^m(\cos \theta) = P_n(\cos \theta)$ and $P_n(\cos \theta)$ has n nodal lines which divide the sphere into $n + 1$ zones within which $P_n(\cos \theta)$ is alternately positive and negative. It is for this reason that $P_n(\cos \theta)$ is called a "zonal harmonic of degree n."

Now suppose that m has an integer value greater than zero, and consider the behavior of $\cos m\varphi\, P_n{}^m(\cos\theta)$ and $\sin m\varphi\, P_n{}^m(\cos\theta)$. We see from Eq. (6-296) that the factor $(1 - x^2)^{m/2}$ ensures that both these harmonics vanish at the north and south poles of the sphere. Since $P_n(x)$ is a polynomial of degree n in x, the equation $P_n(x) = 0$ has n roots $x_1, x_2, \ldots, x_n$, each of which is associated with an angle $\theta_1, \theta_2, \ldots, \theta_n$ corresponding to a nodal line on the sphere. The correspondence is established through the relation $\cos\theta_n = x_n$. This explains why $P_n(x)$ has n nodal lines on the sphere. We see from Eq. (6-296) that $P_n{}^m(x) = 0$ is a polynomial equation of degree $n - m$ in x, the reason being that $P_n(x)$ is differentiated m times. We conclude therefore that the number of nodal lines of $P_n{}^m(\cos\theta)$ parallel to the equator is equal to $n - m$. Also, $\cos m\varphi\, P_n{}^m(\cos\theta)$ and $\sin m\varphi\, P_n{}^m(\cos\theta)$ vanish along lines of longitude determined by the angles φ for which $\cos m\varphi$ and $\sin m\varphi$ vanish. For example, in the range $0 \le \varphi < \pi$, $\sin m\varphi$ vanishes for

$$m\varphi = [0, \pi, 2\pi, \ldots, (m - 1)\pi]$$

Thus $\sin m\varphi$ has m longitudinal nodes which are great circles on the sphere and which intersect the nodal parallels of latitude orthogonally, thus dividing the surface of the sphere into rectangular domains or tesserae, within which $\sin m\varphi\, P_n{}^m(\cos\theta)$ is alternately positive and negative. A similar remark holds for $\cos m\varphi\, P_n{}^m(\cos\theta)$, and for this reason the functions $\sin m\varphi\, P_n{}^m(\cos\theta)$ and $\cos m\varphi\, P_n{}^m(\cos\theta)$ are called "tesseral harmonics" of degree n and order m.

Since $0 \le |m| \le n$, it follows that there are exactly $2n + 1$ tesseral harmonics of degree n.

Spherical surface harmonics

If the tesseral harmonics are multiplied by a set of arbitrary constants and summed, one obtains spherical *surface* harmonics of degree n. Thus

$$Y_n(\theta,\varphi) = \sum_{m=0}^{n} (a_{nm}\cos m\varphi + b_{nm}\sin m\varphi)\, P_n{}^m(\cos\theta) \qquad (6\text{-}314)$$

represents a spherical surface harmonic of degree n.

It can be shown that the tesseral harmonics form a complete set of orthogonal functions on the surface of a sphere.

Using Eqs. (6-288) and (6-296) and integrating by parts, one can show that

$$\int_{-1}^{+1} P_n{}^m(x) P_k{}^m(x)\, dx = 0 \qquad (6\text{-}315)$$

$$\int_{-1}^{+1} P_n{}^m(x) P_n{}^k(x)\, \frac{dx}{1 - x^2} = 0 \qquad (6\text{-}316)$$

when $n \ne k$ or $m \ne k$, respectively, and that

$$\int_{-1}^{+1} [P_n{}^m(x)]^2\, dx = \frac{2}{2n + 1}\, \frac{(n + m)!}{(n - m)!} \qquad (6\text{-}317)$$

$$\int_{-1}^{+1} [P_n{}^m(x)]^2\, \frac{dx}{1 - x^2} = \frac{1}{m}\, \frac{(n + m)!}{(n - m)!} \qquad (6\text{-}318)$$

Using these relations, we can obtain the expansion of an arbitrary function in spherical surface harmonics. The rule is the following: Let $u(\theta,\varphi)$ be an arbitrary function on the surface of a sphere which together with all its first and second derivatives is continuous. Then $u(\theta,\varphi)$ can be represented by an absolutely convergent series of surface harmonics

$$u(\theta,\varphi) = \sum_{n=0}^{\infty} [a_{n0}P_n(\cos\theta) + \sum_{m=1}^{\infty} (a_{nm}\cos m\varphi$$
$$+ b_{nm}\sin m\varphi)P_n{}^m(\cos\theta)] \qquad (6\text{-}319)$$

The expansion coefficients are determined by means of the orthogonality relations (6-315) to (6-318) and are given by

$$a_{n0} = \frac{2n+1}{4\pi} \int_0^{2\pi} \int_0^{\pi} u(\theta,\phi)P_n(\cos\theta)\sin\theta\,d\theta\,d\phi \qquad (6\text{-}320)$$

$$a_{nm} = \frac{2n+1}{2\pi}\frac{(n-m)!}{(n+m)!} \int_0^{2\pi} \int_0^{\pi} u(\theta,\phi)P_n{}^m(\cos\theta)\cos m\phi\sin\theta\,d\theta\,d\phi$$
$$\qquad (6\text{-}321)$$

$$b_{nm} = \frac{2n+1}{2\pi}\frac{(n-m)!}{(n+m)!} \int_0^{2\pi} \int_0^{\pi} u(\theta,\phi)P_n{}^m(\cos\theta)\sin m\phi\sin\theta\,d\theta\,d\phi$$
$$\qquad (6\text{-}322)$$

6-16 SPHERICAL BESSEL FUNCTIONS

Spherical Bessel functions are solutions of the following differential equation:

$$\frac{d^2y}{dr^2} + \frac{2}{r}\frac{dy}{dr} + \left[k^2 - \frac{p(p+1)}{r^2}\right]y = 0 \qquad (6\text{-}323)$$

With the substitution

$$y = \frac{z(r)}{\sqrt{r}} \qquad (6\text{-}324)$$

Eq. (6-323) is transformed into

$$\frac{d^2z}{dr^2} + \frac{1}{r}\frac{dz}{dr} + \left[k^2 - \frac{(p+\frac{1}{2})^2}{r^2}\right]z = 0 \qquad (6\text{-}325)$$

This equation is just Bessel's equation (6-236) with $\nu = p + \frac{1}{2}$ and $x = kr$. Thus the general solution of (Eq. 6-323) can be written as

$$y = \frac{A}{\sqrt{kr}}J_{p+\frac{1}{2}}(kr) + \frac{B}{\sqrt{kr}}N_{p+\frac{1}{2}}(kr) \qquad (6\text{-}326)$$

where A and B are arbitrary constants.

The spherical Bessel functions are defined by

$$j_p(kr) = \left(\frac{\pi}{2kr}\right)^{\frac{1}{2}}J_{p+\frac{1}{2}}(kr) \qquad (6\text{-}327)$$

and the spherical Neumann functions by

$$n_p(kr) = (-1)^{p+1}\left(\frac{\pi}{2kr}\right)^{\frac{1}{2}}J_{-p-\frac{1}{2}}(kr) \qquad (6\text{-}328)$$

In terms of these functions the solution (6-326) becomes

$$y = Cj_p(kr) + Dn_p(kr) \tag{6-329}$$

where C and D are arbitrary constants. We see from Eqs. (6-238) and (6-241) that

$$j_p(x) = (-x)^p \left(\frac{1}{x}\frac{d}{dx}\right)^p \frac{\sin x}{x} \tag{6-330}$$

$$n_p(x) = -(-x)^p \left(\frac{1}{x}\frac{d}{dx}\right)^p \frac{\cos x}{x} \tag{6-331}$$

It is also customary to define spherical Hankel functions as

$$h_p^{(1)}(kr) = j_p(kr) + in_p(kr) \tag{6-332}$$

$$h_p^{(2)}(kr) = j_p(kr) - in_p(kr) \tag{6-333}$$

which permits us to write the general solution of Eq. (6-323) as

$$y = Eh_p^{(1)}(kr) + Fh_p^{(2)}(kr) \tag{6-334}$$

Spherical Bessel functions are important because with their aid we can write solutions of the Helmholtz equation,

$$(\nabla^2 + k^2)\psi = 0 \tag{6-335}$$

in spherical coordinates. Such solutions are given by

$$j_n(kr)P_n^m(\cos\theta)\begin{pmatrix}\cos m\varphi\\\sin m\varphi\end{pmatrix} \tag{6-336}$$

$$n_n(kr)P_n^m(\cos\theta)\begin{pmatrix}\cos m\varphi\\\sin m\varphi\end{pmatrix} \tag{6-337}$$

$$j_n(kr)Q_n^m(\cos\theta)\begin{pmatrix}\cos m\varphi\\\sin m\varphi\end{pmatrix} \tag{6-338}$$

$$n_n(kr)Q_n^m(\cos\theta)\begin{pmatrix}\cos m\varphi\\\sin m\varphi\end{pmatrix} \tag{6-339}$$

As $k \to 0$, $(\nabla^2 + k^2)\psi = 0 \to \nabla^2\psi = 0$, and we should expect the solutions (6-336) to (6-339) to reduce to the corresponding solutions (6-306) to (6-313) of Laplace's equation. It follows from Eqs. (6-330) and (6-331) that

$$\lim_{x\to 0} j_p(x) = \frac{x^p}{(2p+1)!!} \tag{6-340}$$

and

$$\lim_{x\to 0} n_p(x) = -\frac{(2p-1)!!}{x^{p+1}} \tag{6-341}$$

where

$$(2p+1)!! = (2p+1)(2p-1)(2p-3) \cdots 5\cdot3\cdot1 \tag{6-342}$$

Hence apart from unimportant numerical factors, the solutions (6-336) to (6-339) do indeed reduce to the previous solutions of Laplace's equation as $k \to 0$.

The following asymptotic properties of spherical Bessel functions are also frequently useful.

When $x \gg p$,

$$j_p(x) \sim \frac{1}{x} \sin \left(x - \frac{p\pi}{2} \right) \tag{6-343}$$

$$n_p(x) \sim -\frac{1}{x} \cos \left(x - \frac{p\pi}{2} \right) \tag{6-344}$$

$$h_p^{(1)}(x) \sim (-i)^{p+1} \frac{e^{ix}}{x} \tag{6-345}$$

6-17 HERMITE POLYNOMIALS

Hermite polynomials arise in physics when one considers the behavior of a quantum-mechanical harmonic oscillator. The potential energy of an ideal spring whose spring constant is k is given by

$$V(x) = \tfrac{1}{2}kx^2 \tag{6-346}$$

The Hamiltonian, or total energy of a system consisting of the spring plus a particle of kinetic energy $\tfrac{1}{2}mv^2$ coupled to the spring, is

$$H = \tfrac{1}{2}mv^2 + \tfrac{1}{2}kx^2 \tag{6-347}$$

This can also be written as

$$H = \frac{p^2}{2m} + \tfrac{1}{2}m\omega^2 x^2 \tag{6-348}$$

where

$$p = mv \tag{6-349}$$

and

$$\omega = \sqrt{\frac{k}{m}} \tag{6-350}$$

represent the linear momentum of the particle and the classical angular frequency of the oscillator, respectively. The Schrödinger equation for the oscillator becomes

$$H\psi = \left(\frac{p^2}{2m} + V \right) \psi = E\psi \tag{6-351}$$

where now p is replaced by the operator $-i\hbar \, d/dx$.

Thus Eq. (6-351) becomes

$$\frac{-\hbar^2}{2m} \frac{d^2\psi}{dx^2} + \tfrac{1}{2}m\omega^2 x^2 \psi = E\psi \tag{6-352}$$

or

$$\frac{d^2\psi}{dx^2} + (E - \tfrac{1}{2}m\omega^2 x^2)\psi = 0 \tag{6-353}$$

It is customary to put this equation in a standard form by changing both the independent and dependent variables.

First we let

$$z = \sqrt{\frac{m\omega}{\hbar}} \, x \tag{6-354}$$

which reduces Eq. (6-353) to

$$\frac{d^2\psi}{dz^2} + \left(\frac{2E}{\hbar\omega} - z^2\right)\psi = 0 \tag{6-355}$$

Then we set

$$\psi = e^{-z^2/2}v(z) \tag{6-356}$$

in Eq. (6-355), with the result that $v(z)$ must satisfy

$$\frac{d^2v}{dz^2} - 2z\frac{dv}{dz} + 2nv = 0 \tag{6-357}$$

where n is defined by the relation

$$E = \hbar\omega(n + \tfrac{1}{2}) \tag{6-358}$$

Equation (6-357) is known as "Hermite's differential equation." Its general solution is

$$v(z) = Av_1(z) + Bv_2(z) \tag{6-359}$$

where

$$v_1(z) = \left(1 - \frac{2n}{2!}z^2 + \frac{2^2n(n-2)}{4!}z^4 - \frac{2^3n(n-2)(n-4)}{6!}z^6\right.$$
$$\left. + \cdots + (-2)^k\frac{n(n-2)\cdots(n-2k+2)}{(2k)!}z^{2k} + \cdots\right) \tag{6-360}$$

and

$$v_2(z) = z\left[1 - \frac{2(n-1)}{3!}z^2 + 2^2\frac{(n-1)(n-3)}{5!}z^4 - \cdots\right.$$
$$\left. + (-2)^k\frac{(n-1)(n-3)\cdots(n-2k+1)}{(2k+1)!}z^{2k} + \cdots\right] \tag{6-361}$$

When n is not an integer, there is some number K such that all the terms in Eq. (6-360) or (6-361) with $k > K$ have the same sign. A comparison of the series formed by the terms in (6-360) or (6-361) with $k > K$ and the power-series expansion of e^{z^2} shows that

$$v_1(z) \sim e^{z^2} \qquad z \to \pm\infty \tag{6-362}$$

and

$$v_2(z) \sim \pm e^{z^2} \qquad z \to +\infty \tag{6-363}$$

$$v_2(z) \sim \mp e^{z^2} \qquad z \to -\infty \tag{6-364}$$

It is a consequence of expressions (6-362) to (6-364) that no matter how we choose A and B in Eq. (6-359), $v(z)$ will diverge as e^{z^2}, for either large positive or large negative values of z, or both.

This leads to the conclusion that if n is not an integer, then the wave function

$$\psi(z) = e^{-z^2/2}v(z) \tag{6-365}$$

diverges as $e^{z^2/2}$, for either large positive or large negative values of z, or both.

The physical requirement that the probability of finding a bound particle at infinity is zero means that

$$\lim_{|z| \to \infty} \psi(z) = 0 \tag{6-366}$$

Hence solutions of Hermite's equation (6-357) for nonintegral values of n cannot be used to construct wave functions for the harmonic oscillator.

When n is a non-negative even integer, then the series for $v_1(z)$ terminates, and $v_1(z)$ becomes an even polynomial of degree n in z. Similarly, when n is a non-negative odd integer, the series for $v_2(z)$ terminates, and $v_2(z)$ becomes an odd polynomial of degree n in z. Thus we choose

$$\psi_n(z) = A_n e^{-z^2/2} v_1(z) \qquad n = 0,2,4, \ldots \tag{6-367}$$

and

$$\psi_n(z) = B_n e^{-z^2/2} v_2(z) \qquad n = 1,3,5, \ldots \tag{6-368}$$

as the desired forms for our wave functions.

A Hermite polynomial of degree n is defined as

$$H_n(z) = (2z)^n - \frac{n(n-1)}{1!} (2z)^{n-2}$$
$$+ \frac{n(n-1)(n-2)(n-3)}{2!} (2z)^{n-4} - \cdots \tag{6-369}$$

and in terms of it the series (6-360) for $v_1(z)$ becomes

$$v_1(z) = (-1)^{n/2} \frac{(n-2)!}{n!} H_n(z) \qquad n = 0,2,4, \ldots \tag{6-370}$$

while the series (6-361) for $v_2(z)$ takes the form

$$v_2(z) = (-1)^{(n-1)/2} \frac{\left(\frac{n-1}{2}\right)!}{2 \cdot (n!)} H_n(z) \qquad n = 1,3,5 \tag{6-371}$$

Since the A_n's and B_n's in Eqs. (6-367) and (6-368) are arbitrary constants, we can rewrite these equations as a single equation,

$$\psi_n(z) = C_n e^{-z^2/2} H_n(z) \qquad n = 0,1,2,3, \ldots \tag{6-372}$$

by making use of Eqs. (6-370) and (6-371). In Eq. (6-372) the C_n's are arbitrary constants which must be determined by normalizing ψ_n to some constant value. In terms of the original variables,

$$\psi_n(x) = C_n e^{-(m\omega/2\hbar)x^2} H_n\left(\sqrt{\frac{m\omega}{\hbar}} x\right) \tag{6-373}$$

is the energy eigenfunction belonging to the energy eigenvalue

$$E_n = (n + \tfrac{1}{2})\hbar\omega \tag{6-374}$$

Using Eq. (6-239), the first few Hermite polynomials are found to be

$H_0(z) = 1$

$H_1(z) = 2z$

$H_2(z) = 4z^2 - 2$

$H_3(z) = 8z^3 - 12z$

$H_4(z) = 16z^4 - 48z^2 + 12$

$H_5(z) = 32z^5 - 160z^3 + 120z$

Observe that all the Hermite polynomials can be represented by the following formula:

$$H_n(z) = (-1)^n e^{z^2} \frac{d^n}{dz^n} e^{-z^2} \qquad (6\text{-}375)$$

and that

$$H_n(-z) = (-1)^n H_n(z)$$

$$\frac{dH_n}{dz} = 2nH_{n-1}(z) \qquad (6\text{-}376)$$

Orthogonality properties

If we multiply Hermite's equation (6-367) by e^{-z^2}, then we can write it in the form

$$\frac{d}{dz}\left(e^{-z^2}\frac{dH_n}{dz}\right) + 2ne^{-z^2}H_n = 0 \qquad (6\text{-}377)$$

Multiplying Eq. (6-377) by $H_m(z)$ and integrating gives

$$-2n\int_{-\infty}^{+\infty} H_n(z)H_m(z)e^{-z^2}\,dz$$

$$= \int_{-\infty}^{+\infty}\left[\frac{d}{dz}\left(e^{-z^2}\frac{dH_n}{dz}\right)\right]H_m(z)\,dz \qquad (6\text{-}378)$$

Integrating the right side of Eq. (6-378) by parts gives

$$\int_{-\infty}^{+\infty}\left[\frac{d}{dz}\left(e^{-z^2}\frac{dH_n}{dz}\right)\right]H_m(z)\,dz = \left[e^{-z^2}\frac{dH_n}{dz}H_m(z)\right]_{-\infty}^{+\infty}$$

$$-\int_{-\infty}^{+\infty} e^{-z^2}\frac{dH_n}{dz}\frac{dH_m}{dz}\,dz = -\int_{-\infty}^{+\infty} e^{-z^2}\frac{dH_n}{dz}\frac{dH_m}{dz}\,dz \qquad (6\text{-}379)$$

To obtain Eq. (6-379) we have used the fact that the integrated part $e^{-z^2}H_n'H_m$ is e^{-z^2} times a polynomial of degree $n + m - 1$ in z and therefore vanishes as $z \to \pm\infty$.

Now Eq. (6-378) becomes

$$2n\int_{-\infty}^{+\infty} H_n(z)H_m(z)e^{-z^2}\,dz = \int_{-\infty}^{+\infty} e^{-z^2}H_n'(z)H_m'(z)\,dz \qquad (6\text{-}380)$$

If we treat Hermite's equation,

$$\frac{d}{dz}\left(e^{-z^2}\frac{dH_m}{dz}\right) + 2me^{-z^2}H_m = 0 \qquad (6\text{-}381)$$

by exactly the same procedure, we obtain

$$2m \int_{-\infty}^{+\infty} H_n(z)H_m(z)e^{-z^2}\, dz = \int_{-\infty}^{+\infty} e^{-z^2}H_n'(z)H_m'(z)\, dz \tag{6-382}$$

and a comparison of Eqs. (6-380) and (6-382) shows that

$$(n - m) \int_{-\infty}^{+\infty} H_n(z)H_m(z)e^{-z^2}\, dz = 0 \tag{6-383}$$

so that

$$\int_{-\infty}^{+\infty} H_n(z)H_m(z)e^{-z^2}\, dz = 0 \tag{6-384}$$

for $n \neq m$, which shows that the Hermite polynomials form an orthogonal set with respect to the weight function e^{-z^2}.

Generating function for Hermite polynomials

The Hermite polynomials may also be defined by means of a generating function $F(x,y)$ as follows:

$$F(x,y) = e^{-y^2+2xy} = e^{x^2}e^{-(y-x)^2}$$

$$= \sum_{n=0}^{\infty} \frac{H_n(x)}{n!} y^n \tag{6-385}$$

To show that the coefficient $H_n(x)$ is a Hermite polynomial we prove that $H_n(x)$ satisfies Hermite's equation. Differentiating F with respect to x gives

$$\frac{\partial F}{\partial x} = 2yF \tag{6-386}$$

and therefore

$$\sum_{n=0}^{\infty} \frac{H_n'(x)}{n!} y^n = 2 \sum_{n=0}^{\infty} \frac{H_n(x)y^{n+1}}{n!} \tag{6-387}$$

which on equating like powers of y yields

$$H_n'(x) = 2n\, H_{n-1}(x) \tag{6-388}$$

Similarly,

$$\frac{\partial F}{\partial y} = 2(x - y)F \tag{6-389}$$

leads to

$$\sum_{n=0}^{\infty} \frac{nH_n(x)}{n!} y^{n-1} = \sum_{n=0}^{\infty} \frac{2xH_n(x)}{n!} y^n - \sum_{n=0}^{\infty} \frac{2H_n(x)y^{n+1}}{n!} \tag{6-390}$$

Once again equating like powers of y gives

$$H_{n+1} = 2xH_n - 2nH_{n-1} \tag{6-391}$$

or

$$H_{n+1} = 2xH_n - H_n'(x) \tag{6-392}$$

Differentiating Eq. (6-392) with respect to x

$$H'_{n+1} = 2H_n + 2xH'_n - H''_n \tag{6-393}$$

and using

$$H'_{n+1} = 2(n+1)H_n \tag{6-394}$$

we obtain Hermite's equation

$$H''_n - 2xH'_n + 2nH_n = 0 \tag{6-395}$$

From Eqs. (6-377) and (6-388) it follows that

$$2n \int_{-\infty}^{+\infty} e^{-z^2} H_n{}^2(z)\ dz = \int_{-\infty}^{+\infty} e^{-z^2}[H'_n(z)]^2\ dz$$

$$= (2n)^2 \int_{-\infty}^{+\infty} e^{-z^2} H_{n-1}^2(z)\ dz \tag{6-396}$$

Thus

$$\int_{-\infty}^{+\infty} e^{-z^2} H_n{}^2(z)\ dz = 2n \int_{-\infty}^{+\infty} e^{-z^2} H_{n-1}^2(z)\ dz$$

$$= 2n \cdot 2(n-1) \int_{-\infty}^{+\infty} e^{-z^2} H_{n-2}^2(z)\ dz = \cdots$$

$$= 2^n(n!) \int_{-\infty}^{+\infty} e^{-z^2} H_0{}^2(z)\ dz$$

$$= 2^n(n!) \int_{-\infty}^{+\infty} e^{-z^2}\ dz \tag{6-397}$$

In order to complete the evaluation of Eq. (6-397), we must compute

$$I = \int_{-\infty}^{+\infty} e^{-z^2}\ dz \tag{6-398}$$

which can be done by using a well-known trick. Instead of I, consider

$$I^2 = \int_{-\infty}^{+\infty} e^{-x^2}\ dx \int_{-\infty}^{+\infty} e^{-y^2}\ dy = \int_{-\infty}^{+\infty} \int_{-\infty}^{+\infty} e^{-(x^2+y^2)}\ dx\ dy \tag{6-399}$$

and transform to polar coordinates. Then

$$I^2 = \int_0^{2\pi} \int_0^{\infty} e^{-r^2} r\ dr\ d\theta \tag{6-400}$$

$$I^2 = -\pi e^{-r^2} \Big|_0^{\infty} = \pi \tag{6-401}$$

$$I = \sqrt{\pi} \tag{6-402}$$

and therefore

$$\int_{-\infty}^{+\infty} e^{-z^2} H_n{}^2(z)\ dz = 2^n(n!)\ \sqrt{\pi} \tag{6-403}$$

Thus the system of functions

$$\psi_n(z) = \{2^n(n!)\ \sqrt{\pi}\}^{-\frac{1}{2}} e^{-z^2/2} H_n(z) \tag{6-404}$$

satisfies the orthogonality relations

$$\int_{-\infty}^{+\infty} \psi_n(z)\psi_m(z)\ dz = \delta_{nm} \tag{6-405}$$

and forms an orthonormal set on the interval $[-\infty, +\infty]$.

The orthonormal harmonic-oscillator eigenfunctions (Fig. 6-9) are then given by

$$\psi_n(x) = C_n e^{-(m\omega/2\hbar)x^2} H_n\left(\sqrt{\frac{m\omega}{\hbar}}\,x\right) \tag{6-406}$$

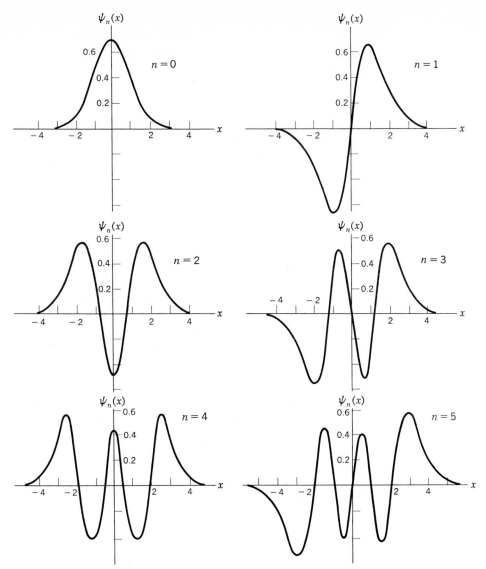

Figure 6-9 Harmonic-oscillator eigenfunctions as functions of $(m\omega/\hbar)^{1/2}x$.

where now
$$C_n = \{2^n(n!) \sqrt{\pi}\}^{-1/2} \tag{6-407}$$

6-18 GENERAL PROPERTIES OF LINEAR SECOND-ORDER DIFFERENTIAL EQUATIONS WITH VARIABLE COEFFICIENTS

Most of the special functions of mathematical physics are solutions of a differential equation of the form

$$\frac{d^2y}{dx^2} + p(x)\frac{dy}{dx} + q(x)y = 0 \tag{6-408}$$

Therefore the general statements which can be made about Eq. (6-408) are of interest to us. We already know that we should expect it to possess two linearly independent solutions, say $y_1(x)$ and $y_2(x)$. The fact that $y_1(x)$ and $y_2(x)$ are linearly independent for all values of x in the interval $a \leq x \leq b$ means that the equation

$$c_1 y_1(x) + c_2 y_2(x) = 0 \qquad (6\text{-}409)$$

cannot be satisfied for all $a \leq x \leq b$ unless $c_1 \equiv 0$ and $c_2 \equiv 0$. Notice that the words "all x between a and b" are really necessary. For example, if $y_2(\frac{1}{2}) \neq 0$, then we can satisfy Eq. (6-409) at $x = \frac{1}{2}$ by choosing $c_1 = 1$ and $c_2 = -y_1(\frac{1}{2})/y_2(\frac{1}{2})$. This, however, tells us nothing about the linear dependence of $y_1(x)$ and $y_2(x)$. In order to conclude that $y_1(x)$ and $y_2(x)$ are linearly dependent on some interval containing the point $x = \frac{1}{2}$, we must verify that Eq. (6-409) holds, not only at $x = \frac{1}{2}$, but at every other point of the chosen interval as well. Moreover, this must happen when c_1 and c_2 are fixed constants, at least one of which is not zero.

Sometimes it is easy to recognize functions which cannot be linearly dependent. For example, we observed in Sec. 6-9 that $N_0(x)$ and $J_0(x)$ must be linearly *independent* functions on any interval $a \leq x \leq b$ because $N_0(x)$ contains a logarithmic term in x whereas $J_0(x)$ does not. In other words, the logarithmic part of $N_0(x)$ guarantees that

$$c_1 J_0(x) + c_2 N_0(x) = 0 \qquad (6\text{-}410)$$

does not hold for all $\{x : a \leq x \leq b\}$ unless $c_1 \equiv 0$ and $c_2 \equiv 0$. Thus for specific functions represented by explicit formulas, the question of linear dependence can often be settled by inspection.

It is also possible to develop a more elegant characterization of linear dependence. Suppose that $y_1(x)$ and $y_2(x)$ are two differentiable functions which are known to be linearly dependent on the interval $a \leq x \leq b$. Then there exist constants c_1 and c_2, not both zero, such that

$$c_1 y_1(x) + c_2 y_2(x) = 0 \qquad (6\text{-}411)$$

Now differentiating Eq. (6-411) gives

$$c_1 y_1'(x) + c_2 y_2'(x) = 0 \qquad (6\text{-}412)$$

Let it be assumed that x is assigned some fixed value, say x_0, in the interval $[a,b]$, and consider Eqs. (6-411) and (6-412) as forming two equations in two unknowns. The unknowns are c_1 and c_2, and the coefficients are $y_1(x_0)$, $y_2(x_0)$, $y_1'(x_0)$, and $y_2'(x_0)$. In other words Eqs. (6-411) and (6-412) are thought of as forming a system analogous to

$$Ax + By = 0 \qquad (6\text{-}413)$$

$$Cx + Dy = 0 \qquad (6\text{-}414)$$

in the sense that x and y are replaced by c_1 and c_2 and $\{A,B,C,D\}$ are replaced by $\{y_1(x_0),\ y_2(x_0),\ y_1'(x_0),\ y_2'(x_0)\}$.

We know from our earlier studies of linear algebraic systems that the condition for the system (6-413) and (6-414) to have a non-trivial solution (i.e., one for which x and y are not both zero) is that the determinant of the system must vanish:

$$\begin{vmatrix} A & B \\ C & D \end{vmatrix} = 0 \tag{6-415}$$

Now c_1 and c_2 play the role of x and y, and it is known that they are not both zero because $y_1(x)$ and $y_2(x)$ are linearly dependent. It follows that the system (6-411) and (6-412) must have a nontrivial solution for the unknowns c_1 and c_2, and therefore that

$$\begin{vmatrix} y_1(x_0) & y_2(x_0) \\ y_1'(x_0) & y_2'(x_0) \end{vmatrix} = 0 \tag{6-416}$$

for any x_0 in the interval $[a,b]$.

The determinant

$$W\{y_1,y_2;x\} = \begin{vmatrix} y_1(x) & y_2(x) \\ y_1'(x) & y_2'(x) \end{vmatrix} \tag{6-417}$$

is called the "Wronskian" of the two functions $y_1(x)$ and $y_2(x)$, and we have just demonstrated that if $y_1(x)$ and $y_2(x)$ are linearly dependent on the interval $a \le x \le b$, then their Wronskian $W\{y_1,y_2;x\}$ vanishes for every x such that $a \le x \le b$.

Notice that although linear dependence implies vanishing of the Wronskian, vanishing of Wronskian does not necessarily imply linear dependence.

For example, inspection of the graphs of $y_1 = x^2$ and $y_2 = x|x|$ shows that these functions cannot be linearly dependent for $-1 \le x \le 1$. Furthermore, they are both differentiable on $-1 \le x \le 1$.

Consider the Wronskian

$$W\{x;x|x|;x\} = \begin{vmatrix} x^2 & x|x| \\ 2x & \dfrac{d}{dx}(x|x|) \end{vmatrix} \tag{6-418}$$

and observe that

$$\frac{d}{dx}(x|x|) = 2|x| \tag{6-419}$$

where Eq. (6-419) becomes obvious on examining the graph of $x|x|$. Thus we have

$$W\{x^2,x|x|;x\} = \begin{vmatrix} x^2 & x|x| \\ 2x & 2|x| \end{vmatrix} \tag{6-420}$$

from which it follows that $W\{x^2,x|x|;x\} = 0$ for every x in the interval $[-1,1]$, even though x^2 and $x|x|$ are not linearly dependent on $[-1,1]$!

In order to ensure that the vanishing of the Wronskian of y_1 and y_2 on some interval guarantees that y_1 and y_2 are linearly dependent on that interval, we need further information.

The type of information required is summarized in the following:

THEOREM: The necessary and sufficient condition for a pair of differentiable functions $y_1(x)$ and $y_2(x)$ to be linearly dependent on an interval $a \leq x \leq b$ is that their Wronskian $W\{y_1, y_2; x\} = 0$ for every value of x on the interval $[a,b]$, *provided* that $y_1(x)$ and $y_2(x)$ are two solutions of the second-order linear equation

$$y'' + p(x)y' + q(x)y = 0 \qquad (6\text{-}421)$$

in which $p(x)$ and $q(x)$ are continuous functions of x for $a \leq x \leq b$.

REMARK: The functions x^2 and $x|x|$ are not covered by this theorem because they do not satisfy a single differential equation of the form (6-421) with continuous $p(x)$ and $q(x)$.

proof of the theorem: To prove necessity we must show that if the Wronskian does not vanish, then $y_1(x)$ and $y_2(x)$ cannot be linearly dependent. But we have already done this because we have demonstrated that whenever $y_1(x)$ and $y_2(x)$ are known to be linearly dependent, their Wronskian must vanish. Therefore, nonvanishing of the Wronskian guarantees that $y_1(x)$ and $y_2(x)$ cannot be linearly dependent. Sufficiency is established by proving that the vanishing of the Wronskian actually does guarantee the linear dependence of $y_1(x)$ and $y_2(x)$.

Assume that $W\{y_1, y_2; x\} = 0$ for every $\{x: a \leq x \leq b\}$. We shall prove that $y_1(x)$ and $y_2(x)$ must be linearly dependent on $[a,b]$. If $y_1(x) = 0$ for every x between a and b, then y_1 and y_2 must be linearly dependent for $a \leq x \leq b$ because in this case $c_1 y_1(x) + c_2 y_2(x) = 0$ on $[a,b]$ with $c_2 = 0$ and $c_1 = 1$.

Therefore we consider the remaining case in which $y_1(x_0) \neq 0$ for some x_0 between a and b. Differentiability of $y_1(x)$ implies that $y_1(x)$ is continuous. Since $y_1(x)$ is continuous, and $y_1(x_0) \neq 0$, we can assert that there is a neighborhood, say $N_\epsilon(x_0)$, containing x_0 such that if x is any point belonging to this neighborhood, then $y_1(x) \neq 0$. By hypothesis, $W = 0$ on $[a,b]$; therefore

$$W\{y_1, y_2; x\} = y_1 y_2' - y_1' y_2 = 0 \qquad (6\text{-}422)$$

for every x belonging to $N_\epsilon(x_0)$. This is true because $N_\epsilon(x_0)$ is itself a subinterval of $[a,b]$. Since $y_1(x) \neq 0$ for x in $N_\epsilon(x_0)$, we can divide Eq. (6-422) by $[y_1(x)]^2$ to obtain

$$\frac{d}{dx}\left[\frac{y_2(x)}{y_1(x)}\right] = \frac{y_1(x)y_2'(x) - y_1'(x)y_2(x)}{[y_1(x)]^2} = 0 \qquad (6\text{-}423)$$

which gives $y_2(x) = A y_1(x)$, where A is a constant.

Suppose we define

$$y_3(x) = y_2(x) - A y_1(x) \qquad (6\text{-}424)$$

for all $\{x: a \leq x \leq b\}$. Then by the result just obtained, $y_3(x) = 0$ for every x belonging to $N_\epsilon(x_0)$. Thus we have not only $y_3(x_0) = 0$ but $y_3'(x_0) = 0$ as well.

Also, since $y_3(x)$ is a linear combination of y_1 and y_2, it follows that y_3 is a solution of Eq. (6-421) which satisfies $y_3(x_0) = 0$ and $y_3'(x_0) = 0$.

Now suppose that $y_4(x)$ is some other function which satisfies Eq. (6-421) and the same initial conditions as y_3, and which in addition vanishes not only over the neighborhood $N_\epsilon(x_0)$ but over the entire interval $a \leq x \leq b$ as well.

Because the solution of Eq. (6-421) which vanishes together with its first derivative at x_0 must be unique, we conclude that

$$y_3(x) = y_4(x) \tag{6-425}$$

for every $\{x : a \leq x \leq b\}$.

Since $y_4(x)$ vanishes over the entire interval $a \leq x \leq b$, so must $y_3(x)$. Thus, by appealing to the uniqueness of a solution of Eq. (6-421) which satisfies given initial conditions at x_0, we have succeeded in extending the result that $y_3(x)$ is zero from the small interval $N_\epsilon(x_0)$ contained in $[a,b]$ to the entire interval $[a,b]$.

Since

$$y_3(x) = y_2(x) - A y_1(x) = 0 \tag{6-426}$$

for every $\{x : a \leq x \leq b\}$, we can write

$$c_1 y_1(x) + c_2 y_2(x) = 0 \tag{6-427}$$

for every $\{x : a \leq x \leq b\}$ by setting $c_1 = -A$, $c_2 = 1$.

This proves that the vanishing of the Wronskian of y_1 and y_2 implies their linear dependence, thus establishing the sufficiency of the condition.

6-19   EVALUATION OF THE WRONSKIAN

The Wronskian $W\{y_1, y_2; x\}$ of the two solutions, $y_1(x)$ and $y_2(x)$, of

$$y'' + p(x)y' + q(x)\, y = 0 \tag{6-428}$$

satisfies an important relation first obtained by the Norwegian mathematician Niels Abel. This relation, known as "Abel's formula" for the Wronskian, can be derived as follows.

Suppose that $p(x)$ and $q(x)$ are both continuous functions of x for $a \leq x \leq b$, and let $y_1(x)$ and $y_2(x)$ be two solutions of Eq. (6-428) valid in the interval $a \leq x \leq b$. By hypothesis

$$y_1'' + p y_1' + q y_1 = 0 \tag{6-429}$$
$$y_2'' + p y_2' + q y_2 = 0 \tag{6-430}$$

Multiplying Eq. (6-429) by $-y_2$ and Eq. (6-430) by y_1 and then adding the results gives

$$y_1 y_2'' - y_2 y_1'' + p(y_1 y_2' - y_2 y_1') = 0 \tag{6-431}$$

However,

$$y_1 y_2'' - y_2 y_1'' = \frac{d}{dx}(y_1 y_2' - y_2 y_1') \tag{6-432}$$

and since

$$W\{y_1,y_2;x\} = \begin{vmatrix} y_1 & y_2 \\ y_1' & y_2' \end{vmatrix} \tag{6-433}$$

Eq. (6-432) can be written as

$$\frac{dW}{dx} + p(x)W = 0 \tag{6-434}$$

In order to integrate Eq. (6-434), let

$$I(x) = \int_{x_0}^{x} p(z)\,dz \tag{6-435}$$

where $a \leq x_0 \leq x \leq b$, and notice that

$$\frac{d}{dx}\left(We^{I(x)}\right) = e^{I(x)}\left(\frac{dW}{dx} + \frac{dI}{dx}W\right) \tag{6-436}$$

On differentiating Eq. (6-435), we find

$$\frac{dI(x)}{dx} = p(x) \tag{6-437}$$

and therefore

$$\frac{d}{dx}\left(We^{I(x)}\right) = e^{I(x)}\left[\frac{dW}{dx} + p(x)W\right] = 0 \tag{6-438}$$

or

$$We^{I(x)} = C \tag{6-439}$$

In order to evaluate the constant of integration C, let $x = x_0$,

$$W\{y_1,y_2;x_0\}e^{I(x_0)} = C \tag{6-440}$$

and since $I(x_0) = 0$,

$$C = W\{y_1,y_2;x_0\} \tag{6-441}$$

Abel's formula for the Wronskian now becomes

$$W\{y_1,y_2;x\} = W\{y_1,y_2;x_0\}e^{-\int_{x_0}^{x} p(z)dz} \tag{6-442}$$

6-20 GENERAL SOLUTION OF A HOMOGENEOUS EQUATION USING ABEL'S FORMULA

In Sec. 6-9 we saw how we can find a second solution of Bessel's equation when we are given one solution. The technique demonstrated there is a particular illustration of the following general method.

Let $p(x)$ and $q(x)$ be continuous for $a \leq x \leq b$, and suppose that one solution $y_1(x)$, of the equation

$$y'' + p(x)y' + q(x)y = 0 \tag{6-443}$$

is already known.

Let $y_2(x)$ be a second solution. Using Eqs. (6-433) and (6-442), one obtains

$$y_1 y_2' - y_2 y_1' = W\{y_1,y_2;x_0\}e^{-I(x)} \tag{6-444}$$

Now if $y_1(x)$ is a nontrivial solution of Eq. (6-443) on $[a,b]$, then it cannot vanish identically on this interval. Let $[a',b']$ be a subinterval of $[a,b]$ with $a \leq a' \leq b' \leq b$, and suppose that $y_1(x) \neq 0$ for any value of x on the subinterval $a' \leq x \leq b'$. We choose x_0 to be a point of the interval $[a',b']$ throughout which $y_1(x)$ does not vanish. Then dividing Eq. (6-444) by $[y_1(x)]^2$ gives

$$\frac{d}{dx}\left[\frac{y_2(x)}{y_1(x)}\right] = \frac{W\{y_1,y_2;x_0\}}{[y_1(x)]^2} e^{-I(x)} \tag{6-445}$$

which holds for every x on $[a',b']$ and in which

$$I(x) = \int_{x_0}^{x} p(z)\, dz \tag{6-446}$$

Integration of Eq. (6-445) yields

$$\frac{y_2(x)}{y_1(x)} = c_1 + W\{y_1,y_2;x_0\} \int_{x_0}^{x} \frac{e^{-I(s)}}{[y_1(s)]^2}\, ds \tag{6-447}$$

or

$$y_2(x) = c_1 y_1(x) + W\{y_1,y_2;x_0\} y_1(x) \int_{x_0}^{x} \frac{e^{-I(s)}}{[y_1(s)]^2}\, ds \tag{6-448}$$

which is valid for every x such that

$$a \leq a' \leq x_0 \leq x \leq b' \leq b \tag{6-449}$$

6-21 SOLUTION OF AN INHOMOGENEOUS EQUATION USING ABEL'S FORMULA

Suppose that $p(x)$, $q(x)$, and $f(x)$ are continuous functions for $a \leq x \leq b$ and that we wish to solve the inhomogeneous equation

$$y'' + p(x)y' + q(x)y = f(x) \tag{6-450}$$

This can be accomplished with the aid of Abel's formula, provided that the two linearly independent solutions, $y_1(x)$ and $y_2(x)$, of the homogeneous problem

$$y'' + p(x)y' + q(x)y = 0 \tag{6-451}$$

are known in advance.

Consider the pair of equations

$$y_1'' + p y_1' + q y_1 = 0 \tag{6-452}$$

$$y'' + p y' + q y = f(x) \tag{6-453}$$

Multiplying Eq. (6-453) by y_1 and Eq. (6-452) by y gives, upon subtracting (6-452) from (6-453),

$$y_1 y'' - y y_1'' + p(x)(y_1 y' - y_1' y) = y_1 f(x) \tag{6-454}$$

or

$$\frac{dW}{dx} + p(x)W = y_1(x)f(x) \tag{6-455}$$

where

$$W = \begin{vmatrix} y_1(x) & y(x) \\ y_1'(x) & y'(x) \end{vmatrix} \tag{6-456}$$

An application of Eq. (6-438) to Eq. (6-455) permits us to write

$$\frac{d}{dx}(We^{I(x)}) = e^{I(x)}\left[\frac{dW}{dx} + p(x)W\right] = y_1(x)f(x)e^{I(x)} \qquad (6\text{-}457)$$

where

$$I(x) = \int_{x_0}^{x} p(z)\,dz \qquad (6\text{-}458)$$

as before.

The general solution of Eq. (6-457) consists of a particular integral plus a complementary function. It is given explicitly by

$$W\{y_1,y;x\}e^{I(x)} = A + \int_{x_0}^{x} y_1(s)f(s)e^{I(s)}\,ds \qquad (6\text{-}459)$$

Since the same argument could have been carried through using y_2 instead of y_1 in Eq. (6-452), we can also write

$$W\{y_2,y;x\}e^{I(x)} = B + \int_{x_0}^{x} y_2(s)f(s)e^{I(s)}\,ds \qquad (6\text{-}460)$$

where A and B are constants.

Suppose we now multiply Eq. (6-459) by $y_2(x)$ and Eq. (6-460) by $-y_1(x)$ and add the results. We obtain thereby

$$[y_2 W\{y_1,y;x\} - y_1 W\{y_2,y;x\}]e^{I(x)} = Ay_2(x) - By_1(x)$$
$$+ \int_{x_0}^{x} f(s)e^{I(s)}[y_1(s)y_2(x) - y_1(x)y_2(s)]\,ds \qquad (6\text{-}461)$$

However,

$$y_2 W\{y_1,y;x\} - y_1 W\{y_2,y;x\} = y_2 \begin{vmatrix} y_1 & y \\ y_1' & y' \end{vmatrix} - y_1 \begin{vmatrix} y_2 & y \\ y_2' & y' \end{vmatrix}$$
$$= y(y_1 y_2' - y_2 y_1') = y W\{y_1,y_2;x\}$$
$$(6\text{-}462)$$

which reduces Eq. (6-461) to

$$y(x)W\{y_1,y_2;x\}e^{I(x)} = Ay_2(x) - By_1(x)$$
$$+ \int_{x_0}^{x} f(s)e^{I(s)}[y_1(s)y_2(x) - y_1(x)y_2(s)]\,ds \qquad (6\text{-}463)$$

Abel's formula (6-442),

$$W\{y_1,y_2;x\}e^{I(x)} = W\{y_1,y_2;x_0\} \qquad (6\text{-}464)$$

is now inserted into Eq. (6-463), giving

$$y(x) = \frac{A}{W\{y_1,y_2;x_0\}}\,y_2(x) - \frac{B}{W\{y_1,y_2;x_0\}}\,y_1(x)$$
$$+ \frac{1}{W\{y_1,y_2;x_0\}}\int_{x_0}^{x} f(s)e^{I(s)}[y_1(s)y_2(x) - y_1(x)y_2(s)]\,ds \qquad (6\text{-}465)$$

Notice that $W\{y_1,y_2;x_0\}$ is a constant. If this constant is zero, then Eq. (6-464), Abel's formula for the Wronskian, shows that the Wronskian of y_1 and y_2 must vanish for every x in the interval $[a,b]$. This contradicts the assumption that $y_1(x)$ and $y_2(x)$ are linearly independent solutions of Eq. (6-451) on $[a,b]$. Consequently,

$W\{y_1,y_2;x_0\} \neq 0$, and we can define new constants c_1 and c_2 such that

$$c_1 = -\frac{B}{W\{y_1,y_2;x_0\}} \tag{6-466}$$

$$c_2 = \frac{A}{W\{y_1,y_2;x_0\}} \tag{6-467}$$

In terms of these new constants, the general solution of Eq. (6-450) becomes

$$y(x) = c_1 y_1(x) + c_2 y_2(x)$$
$$+ \frac{1}{W\{y_1,y_2;x_0\}} \int_{x_0}^x f(s) e^{I(s)} \begin{vmatrix} y_1(s) & y_2(s) \\ y_1(x) & y_2(x) \end{vmatrix} ds \tag{6-468}$$

where

$$I(s) = \int_{x_0}^s p(z)\, dz \tag{6-469}$$

6-22 GREEN'S FUNCTION

Consider the inhomogeneous differential equation

$$g'' + p(x)g' + q(x)g = -\delta(x - x') \tag{6-470}$$

where $\delta(x - x')$ is a Dirac delta function. The general solution of Eq. (6-470) represents the response to a point source concentrated at $x = x'$. Such a response function is called a "Green's function." It can be calculated directly from Eq. (6-468) or by the following alternative method. Let

$$e^{I(x)} = e^{\int_{x_0}^x p(z)\,dz} \tag{6-471}$$

and multiply Eq. (6-470) by Eq. (6-471) to obtain

$$[g'' + p(x)g']e^{I(x)} + q(x)ge^{I(x)} = -\delta(x - x')e^{I(x)} \tag{6-472}$$

or

$$\frac{d}{dx}\left(\frac{dg}{dx}e^{I(x)}\right) + q(x)ge^{I(x)} = -\delta(x - x')e^{I(x)} \tag{6-473}$$

Except at $x = x'$, Eq. (6-470) is homogeneous,

$$g'' + p(x)g' + q(x)g = 0 \tag{6-474}$$

and has two linearly independent solutions, $g_1(x)$ and $g_2(x)$. We can use the linearly independent solutions of Eq. (6-474) to construct a particular integral $G(x|x')$ of Eq. (6-470). Suppose that

$$G = \begin{cases} Ag_1(x) & x < x' \\ Bg_2(x) & x > x' \end{cases} \tag{6-475}$$

is a particular integral of Eq. (6-470). We shall assume that G is *continuous* at $x = x'$; then

$$Ag_1(x') = Bg_2(x') \tag{6-476}$$

If both sides of Eq. (6-473) are now integrated with respect to dx from $x = x' - \epsilon$ to $x = x' + \epsilon$, then, provided $q(x)$ is continuous at

$x = x'$, (6-473) reduces to

$$\lim_{\epsilon \to 0} \frac{dG}{dx} e^{I(x)} \Big|_{x=x'-\epsilon}^{x=x'+\epsilon} = -e^{I(x')} \tag{6-477}$$

Inserting Eq. (6-475) into Eq. (6-477) gives us

$$Bg_2'(x') - Ag_1'(x') = -1 \tag{6-478}$$

and we have obtained two equations

$$\begin{aligned} Bg_2'(x') - Ag_1'(x') &= -1 \\ Bg_2(x') - Ag_1(x') &= 0 \end{aligned} \tag{6-479}$$

for the two unknowns A and B. The solution of the system (6-479) is

$$A = \frac{-g_2(x')}{W\{g_1,g_2;x'\}} \tag{6-480}$$

$$B = \frac{-g_1(x')}{W\{g_1,g_2;x'\}} \tag{6-481}$$

where

$$W\{g_1,g_2;x'\} = \begin{vmatrix} g_1(x') & g_2(x') \\ g_1'(x') & g_2'(x') \end{vmatrix} \tag{6-482}$$

is the Wronskian of g_1 and g_2, evaluated at $x = x'$.

With the aid of Eqs. (6-480) and (6-481), Eq. (6-475) yields

$$G(x|x') = \frac{-g_1(x)g_2(x')}{W\{g_1,g_2;x'\}} \qquad x < x' \tag{6-483}$$

$$G(x|x') = \frac{-g_2(x)g_1(x')}{W\{g_1,g_2;x'\}} \qquad x > x' \tag{6-484}$$

It is possible to write Eqs. (6-483) and (6-484) in the form of a single equation by introducing a new notation commonly used in physics. One writes

$$G(x|x') = \frac{-g_1(x_<)g_2(x_>)}{W\{g_1,g_2;x'\}} \tag{6-485}$$

where $x_>$ is the greater of the two numbers x and x', and $x_<$ is the lesser of x and x'. It is easy to see that when $x < x'$, Eq. (6-485) reduces to (6-483), while for $x > x'$, it reduces to (6-484). The general solution of Eq. (6-470) consists of a complementary function $\{c_1g_1(x) + c_2g_2(x)\}$ which contains two arbitrary constants c_1 and c_2 and satisfies Eq. (6-474), plus the particular integral (6-485) satisfying (6-470). Therefore it is given by

$$g(x|x') = c_1g_1(x) + c_2g_2(x) + G(x|x') \tag{6-486}$$

6-23 USE OF THE GREEN'S FUNCTION $g(x|x')$

Instead of using Abel's formula (6-468) to solve the problem

$$y'' + p(x)y' + q(x)y = -f(x) \tag{6-487}$$

directly, we can represent the solution of Eq. (6-487) in terms of the Green's function $g(x|x')$ specified by (6-486).

To do this, we need to make use of Green's symmetric identity

$$gy'' - yg'' = \frac{d}{dx}\{gy' - yg'\} \qquad (6\text{-}488)$$

The Green's function $g(x|x')$ satisfies

$$g'' + p(x)g' + q(x)g = -\delta(x - x') \qquad (6\text{-}489)$$

and using Eqs. (6-487) and (6-489) together, one finds

$$g\{y'' + py' + qy\} - y\{g'' + pg' + q\}g = -gf(x) + y(x)\,\delta(x - x')$$
$$= \{gy'' - yg''\} + p\{gy' - yg'\} \qquad (6\text{-}490)$$

With the aid of Eq. (6-488) this result becomes

$$\frac{d}{dx}\{gy' - yg'\} + p\{gy' - yg'\} = -gf + y\,\delta(x - x') \qquad (6\text{-}491)$$

and recognizing that $\{gy' - yg'\} = W$ is the Wronskian of g and y, Eq. (6-491) can be written as

$$\frac{dW}{dx} + p(x)W\{g,y;x\} = -g(x|x')f(x) + y(x)\,\delta(x - x') \qquad (6\text{-}492)$$

We can now set

$$\frac{d}{dx}\left(We^{I(x)}\right) = e^{I(x)}\left[\frac{dW}{dx} + p(x)W\right]$$
$$= -g(x|x')e^{I(x)}f(x) + y(x)e^{I(x)}\,\delta(x - x') \qquad (6\text{-}493)$$

where as usual

$$I(x) = \int_{x_0}^{x} p(z)\,dz \qquad (6\text{-}494)$$

Integrating each term in Eq. (6-493) with respect to x, between the fixed limits $x = a$ and $x = b$, one obtains

$$\int_a^b y(x)e^{I(x)}\,\delta(x - x')\,dx = \int_a^b g(x|x')f(x)e^{I(x)}\,dx + We^{I(x)}\Big|_a^b \qquad (6\text{-}495)$$

and if $a < x' < b$, Eq. (6-495) reduces to

$$y(x') = \int_a^b g(x|x')f(x)e^{-\{I(x')-I(x)\}}\,dx + W\{g,y\}e^{-\{I(x')-I(x)\}}\Big|_{x=a}^{x=b} \qquad (6\text{-}496)$$

The last term in Eq. (6-496), when written out, is

$$W\{g,y\}e^{-\{I(x')-I(x)\}}\Big|_a^b = \{g(b|x')y'(b) - g'(b|x')y(b)\}e^{-\{I(x')-I(b)\}}$$
$$- \{g(a|x')y'(a) - g'(a|x')y(a)\}e^{-\{I(x')-I(a)\}} \qquad (6\text{-}497)$$

We see that formula (6-496) represents $y(x')$ at an interior point x' of the interval $[a,b]$ in terms of the boundary values of y and its first derivative y' at a and b, and in terms of a convolution integral involving the forcing function $f(x)$ and the Green's function $g(x|x')$. The introduction of the boundary values of y and y' at $x = a$ and $x = b$ is an important feature of Eq. (6-496). It is precisely this property of the Green's-function technique which makes it so useful in the solution of boundary-value problems.

As a rule, $y(x)$ and $y'(x)$ are not both specified at the end points of $[a,b]$. Usually we are given only $y(a)$ and $y(b)$ or only $y'(a)$ and $y'(b)$. However, in some problems a linear combination $y' + \mu y$ is specified at the end points of the interval $[a,b]$.

In each case one must eliminate the unspecified terms from Eq. (6-496). For example, suppose we are required to solve the problem

$$y'' + p(x)y' + q(x)y = -f(x) \tag{6-498}$$

subject to the boundary conditions

$$y(a) = \alpha \tag{6-499}$$

$$y(b) = \beta \tag{6-500}$$

The Green's function $g(x|x')$ for Eq. (6-498) satisfies

$$g'' + p(x)g' + q(x)g = -\delta(x - x') \tag{6-501}$$

and the general solution of Eq. (6-501) consists of a complementary function plus a particular integral

$$g(x|x') = c_1 g_1(x) + c_2 g_2(x) - \frac{g_1(x_<)g_2(x_>)}{W\{g_1,g_2;x'\}} \tag{6-502}$$

By properly choosing the constants c_1 and c_2 in Eq. (6-502), we can make the solution of Eq. (6-501) satisfy the homogeneous boundary conditions

$$g(a|x') = 0 \tag{6-503}$$

$$g(b|x') = 0 \tag{6-504}$$

For this case, Eq. (6-496) reduces to

$$y(x') = \int_a^b g(x|x')f(x)e^{-\{I(x')-I(x)\}}\,dx$$
$$- \{\beta g'(b|x')e^{I(b)} - \alpha g'(a|x')e^{I(a)}\}e^{-I(x')} \tag{6-505}$$

which is an expression involving only known quantities in the right member. The problem

$$y'' + p(x)y' + q(x)y = -f(x) \tag{6-506}$$

$$y'(a) = \alpha \tag{6-507}$$

$$y'(b) = \beta \tag{6-508}$$

is solved by choosing a Green's function $g(x|x')$ which satisfies the homogeneous boundary conditions

$$g'(a|x') = 0 \tag{6-509}$$

$$g'(b|x') = 0 \tag{6-510}$$

The solution (6-496) now becomes

$$y(x') = \int_a^b g(x|x')f(x)e^{-\{I(x')-I(x)\}}\,dx$$
$$+ \{\beta g(b|x')e^{I(b)} - \alpha g(a|x')e^{I(a)}\}e^{-I(x')} \tag{6-511}$$

Finally, in order to solve the problem

$$y'' + p(x)y' + q(x)y = -f(x) \tag{6-512}$$

$$y(a) + \mu y'(a) = \alpha \tag{6-513}$$

$$y(b) + \mu y'(b) = \beta \tag{6-514}$$

where μ is some constant, we choose a Green's function $g(x|x')$ satisfying homogeneous boundary conditions of the form

$$g(a|x') + \mu g'(a|x') = 0 \tag{6-515}$$

$$g(b|x') + \mu g'(b|x') = 0 \tag{6-516}$$

The corresponding solution (6-496) is now

$$y(x') = \int_a^b g(x|x')f(x)e^{-\{I(x')-I(x)\}} \, dx$$
$$- \{\beta g'(b|x')e^{I(b)} - \alpha g'(a|x')e^{I(a)}\}e^{-I(x')} \tag{6-517}$$

Notice that in each of the three cases that we have just examined the Green's function $g(x|x')$ satisfies a homogeneous boundary condition of the same form as the inhomogeneous boundary condition satisfied by $y(x)$.

6-24 THE STURM-LIOUVILLE PROBLEM

Many of the differential equations occurring in physics can be written in the form

$$\frac{d}{dx}\left[p(x)\frac{dy}{dx}\right] + [q(x) + \lambda r(x)]y = 0 \tag{6-518}$$

where p, q, and r are real functions of x such that p has a continuous derivative, q and r are continuous, and the parameter λ is independent of x. For example, if $p(x) = 1 - x^2$, $q(x) = 0$, $r(x) = 1$, and $\lambda = \nu(\nu + 1)$, then Eq. (6-518) reduces to Legendre's equation (6-278). If $p(x) = 1 - x^2$, $q(x) = -m^2/(1 - x^2)$, $r(x) = 1$, and $\lambda = \nu(\nu + 1)$, then it reduces to Legendre's associated equation (6-276). Finally, Bessel's equation in the variable kx can be written as

$$\frac{d}{dx}\left(x\frac{dy}{dx}\right) + \left(k^2x - \frac{\nu^2}{x}\right)y = 0 \tag{6-519}$$

and Eq. (6-519) is seen to be in the Sturm-Liouville form with $p(x) = x$, $q(x) = -\nu^2/x$, $r(x) = x$, and $\lambda = k^2$.

The so-called Sturm-Liouville problem is to solve Eq. (6-518) subject to the boundary conditions

$$Ay(a) + By'(a) = 0 \tag{6-520}$$

$$Cy(b) + Dy'(b) = 0 \tag{6-521}$$

where A, B, C, and D are real constants such that A and B are not both zero and C and D are not both zero. Two special cases are very important, namely the case in which Eqs. (6-520) and (6-521) become

$$y(a) = 0 \tag{6-522}$$

$$y(b) = 0 \tag{6-523}$$

and the case in which (6-520) and (6-521) reduce to

$$y'(a) = 0 \tag{6-524}$$

$$y'(b) = 0 \tag{6-525}$$

A simple and familiar example of a Sturm-Liouville problem is the following: Solve

$$y'' + \lambda y = 0 \qquad (6\text{-}526)$$

subject to the boundary conditions

$$y(0) = 0 \qquad (6\text{-}527)$$

$$y(b) = 0 \qquad (6\text{-}528)$$

The general solution of Eq. (6-526) is

$$y = A \sin \sqrt{\lambda}\, x + B \cos \sqrt{\lambda}\, x \qquad (6\text{-}529)$$

and the particular solution of (6-526) which satisfies the boundary conditions (6-527) and (6-528) is

$$y = A \sin \frac{n\pi x}{b} \qquad (6\text{-}530)$$

provided that

$$\lambda = \left(\frac{n\pi}{b}\right)^2 \qquad n = 1,2,3, \ldots \qquad (6\text{-}531)$$

There are now three features to note. First of all, in order for the Sturm-Liouville problem (6-526) to (6-528) to have a nontrivial solution, λ must be restricted to certain characteristic values or eigenvalues specified by Eq. (6-531).

Secondly, the eigenfunctions (6-530) belonging to different eigenvalues (6-531) are orthogonal over $[0,b]$. This follows from

$$\int_0^b \sin \frac{n\pi x}{b} \sin \frac{m\pi x}{b}\, dx = \frac{2}{b}\, \delta_{nm} \qquad (6\text{-}532)$$

Finally, we observe from the discussion following Eq. (5-251) that the eigenfunctions (6-530) form a complete set on the interval $[0,b]$.

Actually, these features of the simple problem (6-526) to (6-528) are also characteristic of the general problem (6-518), (6-520), and (6-521). More formally, we can state that the general problem defined by (6-518), (6-520), and (6-521) exhibits the following properties:

1. The eigenvalues λ_n associated with (6-518), (6-520), and (6-521) form a countably infinite set called a "spectrum." The spectrum of eigenvalues can be arranged in a monotonic-increasing sequence $\lambda_1 < \lambda_2 < \cdots$ such that $\lambda_n \to \infty$ as $n \to \infty$.

2. Corresponding to each eigenvalue λ_n, there is an eigenfunction y_n defined for $a \le x \le b$.

3. Any two eigenfunctions belonging to the same eigenvalue, say λ_n, are linearly dependent.

4. Any two eigenfunctions belonging to different eigenvalues, say λ_n and λ_m, are orthogonal with respect to the weight function $r(x)$ on the interval $a \le x \le b$. This means that

$$\int_a^b y_n(x)y_m(x)r(x)\, dx = C_{nm}\delta_{nm} \qquad (6\text{-}533)$$

5. Any function $A(x)$ which satisfies the same boundary conditions as $y_1, y_2, \ldots, y_n(x), \ldots$ can be formally expanded in an orthogonal series:

$$A(x) = \text{l.i.m.} \sum_{k=1}^{n} a_k y_k(x) \qquad (6\text{-}534)$$
$$\quad n \to \infty$$

Equation (6-534) means that $\sum_{k=1}^{n} a_k y_k(x)$ converges to $A(x)$ in the

mean-square sense, or in other words, that

$$\lim_{n \to \infty} \int_a^b \left[A - \sum_{k=1}^{n} a_k y_k(x) \right]^2 r(x) \, dx = 0 \qquad (6\text{-}535)$$

This type of convergence has already been extensively discussed in Sec. 5-6.

Orthogonality of Sturm-Liouville eigenfunctions

Suppose that y_m is a solution of Eq. (6-518) corresponding to the eigenvalue λ_m, and let y_n be a solution when λ has a different eigenvalue, say λ_n. Then,

$$(py_m')' + (q + \lambda_m r)y_m = 0 \qquad (6\text{-}536)$$
$$(py_n')' + (q + \lambda_n r)y_n = 0 \qquad (6\text{-}537)$$

If we multiply Eq. (6-536) by y_n and Eq. (6-537) by y_m and then subtract one from the other, the result is

$$[y_n(py_m')' - y_m(py_n')'] + (\lambda_m - \lambda_n)ry_ny_m = 0 \qquad (6\text{-}538)$$

However,

$$y_n(py_m')' - y_m(py_n')' = p'(y_ny_m' - y_my_n')$$
$$+ p(y_ny_m'' - y_my_n'') = \frac{d}{dx}[p(y_ny_m' - y_my_n')] \qquad (6\text{-}539)$$

and Eq. (6-539) reduces (6-538) to

$$\frac{d}{dx}[p(y_ny_m' - y_my_n')] = (\lambda_n - \lambda_m)ry_ny_m \qquad (6\text{-}540)$$

Integrating Eq. (6-540) from a to b then gives

$$(\lambda_n - \lambda_m) \int_a^b y_n(x)y_m(x)r(x) \, dx = p(x)(y_ny_m' - y_my_n') \Big|_a^b \qquad (6\text{-}541)$$

The two eigenfunctions $y_n(x)$ and $y_m(x)$ must each satisfy the boundary conditions (6-520) and (6-521), and this fact, together with Eq. (6-541), permits us to conclude that

$$(\lambda_n - \lambda_m) \int_a^b y_n(x)y_m(x)r(x) \, dx = 0 \qquad (6\text{-}542)$$

Given $n \neq m$, we assume $\lambda_n \neq \lambda_m$, and therefore

$$\int_a^b y_n(x)y_m(x)r(x) \, dx = 0 \qquad n \neq m \qquad (6\text{-}543)$$

This proves that the eigenfunctions y_n and y_m are orthogonal with respect to the weighting function $r(x)$ on $[a,b]$.

EXAMPLE 6-1: *Legendre's Equation.* We can now show that the Legendre polynomials are orthogonal on the interval $[-1,1]$. These polynomials satisfy a Sturm-Liouville equation of the form

$$[(1 - x^2)P_n']' + n(n + 1)P_n(x) = 0 \tag{6-544}$$

where $\lambda_n = n(n + 1)$, $r(x) = 1$, and $p(x) = 1 - x^2$. Equation (6-541) gives, for the case at hand,

$$[n(n + 1) - m(m + 1)] \int_{-1}^{+1} P_n(x)P_m(x)\ dx$$
$$= (1 - x^2)[P_n P_m' - P_m P_n'] \tag{6-545}$$

and since $1 - x^2$ vanishes at $x = \pm 1$, we find

$$\int_{-1}^{+1} P_n(x)P_m(x)\ dx = 0 \qquad n \neq m \tag{6-546}$$

When $n = m$, we shall prove that

$$\int_{-1}^{+1} P_n^2(x)\ dx = \frac{2}{2n + 1} \tag{6-547}$$

To see this, let us recall Rodrigues's formula,

$$P_n(x) = \frac{1}{2^n n!} \frac{d^n}{dx^n} (x^2 - 1)^n \tag{6-548}$$

and set

$$y_n = (x^2 - 1)^n \tag{6-549}$$

Now consider $\int_{-1}^{+1} y_n^{(n)}(x)y_n^{(n)}(x)\ dx$, and integrate by parts. The result is

$$\int_{-1}^{+1} y_n^{(n)}(x)y_n^{(n)}(x)\ dx = -\int_{-1}^{+1} y_n^{(n-1)}y_n^{(n+1)}\ dx = \cdots$$
$$= (-1)^n \int_{-1}^{+1} y_n y_n^{(2n)}\ dx = (2n)! \int_{-1}^{+1} (1 - x)^n(1 + x)^n\ dx$$
$$= \frac{n}{n + 1} (2n)! \int_{-1}^{+1} (1 - x)^{n-1}(1 + x)^{n+1}\ dx$$
$$= \frac{n!(2n)!}{(n + 1)(n + 2)\ \cdots\ 2n} \int_{-1}^{+1} (1 + x)^{2n}\ dx$$
$$= \frac{(n!)^2}{2n + 1} 2^{2n+1} \tag{6-550}$$

Therefore

$$2^{2n}(n!)^2 \int_{-1}^{+1} P_n^2(x)\ dx = 2^{2n}(n!)^2 \frac{2}{2n + 1} \tag{6-551}$$

and consequently

$$\int_{-1}^{+1} P_n(x)P_m(x)\ dx = \frac{2}{2n + 1} \delta_{nm} \tag{6-552}$$

EXAMPLE 6-2: *Bessel's Equation.* Equation (6-519) is the Sturm-Liouville form of Bessel's equation with $p(x) = x$, $q(x) = -\nu^2/x$, $r(x) = x$, and $\lambda = k^2$.

Suppose that the sequence of numbers $k_1, k_2, \ldots$ are the distinct positive roots of the equation

$$J_\nu(ka) = 0 \qquad (6\text{-}553)$$

so that $J_\nu(k_n a) = 0$ for $n = 1,2,3, \ldots$. We shall demonstrate that the eigenfunctions $y_n(x) = J_\nu(k_n x)$ are orthogonal on the interval $[0,a]$ with respect to the weight function x.

Let $y_n(x) = J_\nu(kx)$ and $y_m(x) = J_\nu(k_m x)$ in Eq. (6-541) which then becomes

$$(k^2 - k_m{}^2) \int_0^a J_\nu(kx) J_\nu(k_m x) x \, dx$$
$$= x \left[J_\nu(kx) \frac{d}{dx} J_\nu(k_m x) - J_\nu(k_m x) \frac{d}{dx} J_\nu(kx) \right] \Big|_0^a \qquad (6\text{-}554)$$

Since $J_\nu(k_m a) = 0$, Eq. (6-554) reduces to

$$(k^2 - k_m{}^2) \int_0^a J_\nu(kx) J_\nu(k_m x) x \, dx = k_m a J_\nu(ka) J_\nu'(k_m a) \qquad (6\text{-}555)$$

If we now insert $k = k_n$ in Eq. (6-555), assuming that $k_n \neq k_m$, we obtain

$$\int_0^a J_\nu(k_n x) J_\nu(k_m x) x \, dx = 0 \qquad n \neq m \qquad (6\text{-}556)$$

since $J_\nu(k_n a) = 0$.

Finally, differentiating Eq. (6-555) with respect to k yields

$$2k \int_0^a J_\nu(kx) J_\nu(k_m x) x \, dx + (k^2 - k_m{}^2) \int_0^a x^2 J_\nu'(kx) J_\nu(k_m x) \, dx$$
$$= k_m a^2 J_\nu'(ka) J_\nu'(k_m a) \qquad (6\text{-}557)$$

and setting $k = k_m$, we find

$$2 \int_0^a [J_\nu(k_m x)]^2 x \, dx = a^2 [J_\nu'(k_m a)]^2 \qquad (6\text{-}558)$$

We can summarize Eqs. (6-556) and (6-558) by a single orthogonality relation of the form

$$\int_0^a J_\nu(k_n x) J_\nu(k_m x) x \, dx = \frac{a^2}{2} [J_\nu'(k_m a)]^2 \, \delta_{nm} \qquad (6\text{-}559)$$

6-25 SOLUTION OF ORDINARY DIFFERENTIAL EQUATIONS WITH VARIABLE COEFFICIENTS BY TRANSFORM METHODS

In Chap. 5 we saw how a differential equation with constant coefficients could be converted into an algebraic equation by transforming with a Fourier or Laplace transform. We shall now learn how the Laplace or Fourier transform can be used to transform a differential equation with variable coefficients into another more easily solvable differential equation, also having variable coefficients. The method which we shall describe is applicable to most differential equations having polynomial coefficients and is based on the following two integral formulas,

$$\int_{-\infty}^{+\infty} x^n A^{(m)}(x) e^{-ikx} \, dx = i^{(n+m)} \frac{d^n}{dk^n} [k^m \bar{A}(k)] \qquad (6\text{-}560)$$

where

$$\bar{A}(k) = \int_{-\infty}^{+\infty} A(x)e^{-ikx}\,dx \qquad (6\text{-}561)$$

and

$$\int_0^\infty x^n A^{(m)}(x)e^{-sx}\,dx = (-1)^n \frac{d^n}{ds^n}\,[s^m \bar{A}(s) - s^{m-1}A(0)$$
$$- s^{m-2}A'(0) - \cdots - A^{(m-1)}(0)] \qquad (6\text{-}562)$$

where

$$\bar{A}(s) = \int_0^\infty A(x)e^{-sx}\,dx \qquad (6\text{-}563)$$

proof: To prove Eq. (6-560) let us assume that $\int_{-\infty}^{+\infty} A^{(m)}(x)e^{-ikx}\,dx$ converges uniformly so that differentiation under the integral sign is permissible; then

$$\frac{d^n}{d(-ik)^n}\int_{-\infty}^{+\infty} A^{(m)}(x)e^{-ikx}\,dx = \int_{-\infty}^{+\infty} x^n A^{(m)}(x)e^{-ikx}\,dx \qquad (6\text{-}564)$$

It follows from Eq. (5-406) that

$$\int_{-\infty}^{+\infty} A^{(m)}(x)e^{-ikx}\,dx = (ik)^m \int_{-\infty}^{+\infty} A(x)e^{-ikx}\,dx \qquad (6\text{-}565)$$

and therefore

$$\int_{-\infty}^{+\infty} x^n A^{(m)}(x)e^{-ikx}\,dx = \frac{(i)^m}{(-i)^n}\frac{d^n}{dk^n}\,[k^m \bar{A}(k)] \qquad (6\text{-}566)$$

Observing that

$$\frac{i^m}{(-i)^n} = \frac{i^{m+n}}{(i)^n(-i)^n} = i^{m+n} \qquad (6\text{-}567)$$

then proves Eq. (6-560).

To prove Eq. (6-562) consider

$$\frac{d^n}{ds^n}\int_0^\infty A^{(m)}(x)e^{-sx}\,dx = (-1)^n \int_0^\infty x^n A^{(m)}(x)e^{-sx}\,dx \qquad (6\text{-}568)$$

Using Eq. (5-495), we have

$$\int_0^\infty A^{(m)}(x)e^{-sx}\,dx = s^m \bar{A}(s) - s^{m-1}A(0) - s^{m-2}A'(0)$$
$$- \cdots - A^{(m-1)}(0) \qquad (6\text{-}569)$$

which together with Eq. (6-568) gives

$$\int_0^\infty x^n A^{(m)}(x)e^{-sx}\,dx = (-1)^n \frac{d^n}{ds^n}\,[s^m \bar{A}(s) - s^{m-1}A(0) - s^{m-2}A'(0)$$
$$- \cdots - A^{(m-1)}(0)] \qquad (6\text{-}570)$$

thus proving Eq. (6-562).

EXAMPLE 6-3: *Modified Bessel's Equation of Order Zero.* Let us construct a solution of

$$x\frac{d^2y}{dx^2} + \frac{dy}{dx} - xy = 0 \qquad (6\text{-}571)$$

with the aid of the Fourier transform. We have, using Eq. (6-560),

$$\int_{-\infty}^{+\infty} \left(x \frac{d^2 y}{dx^2} + \frac{dy}{dx} - xy \right) e^{-ikx}$$

$$= -i \left[(k^2 + 1) \frac{d\bar{y}}{dk} + k\bar{y} \right] = 0 \qquad (6\text{-}572)$$

where

$$\bar{y}(k) = \int_{-\infty}^{+\infty} y(x) e^{-ikx}\, dx \qquad (6\text{-}573)$$

The equation

$$(k^2 + 1) \frac{d\bar{y}}{dk} + k\bar{y} = 0 \qquad (6\text{-}574)$$

is easier to solve than Bessel's equation (6-571). Its solution is given by

$$\int \frac{d\bar{y}}{\bar{y}} = -\frac{1}{2} \int \frac{2k}{k^2 + 1}\, dk + \text{const} \qquad (6\text{-}575)$$

which integrates to

$$\bar{y}(k) = \frac{c}{\sqrt{k^2 + 1}} \qquad (6\text{-}576)$$

where c is an arbitrary constant.

Use of the inversion theorem (5-320) for Fourier transforms now gives

$$y(x) = \frac{c}{2\pi} \int_{-\infty}^{+\infty} \frac{e^{ikx}}{\sqrt{k^2 + 1}}\, dk \qquad (6\text{-}577)$$

which is an integral representation of a particular solution of Eq. (6-571). Consulting a table of Fourier transforms, we find

$$\frac{1}{\pi} K_0(|x|) = \frac{1}{2\pi} \int_{-\infty}^{+\infty} \frac{e^{ikx}}{\sqrt{k^2 + 1}}\, dk \qquad (6\text{-}578)$$

Consequently, the solution (6-577) must be

$$y(x) = c K_0(|x|)$$

as expected.

EXAMPLE 6-4: *Solution of Bessel's Equation of Order Zero by Use of the Laplace Transform.* As before, we wish to solve

$$x \frac{d^2 y}{dx^2} + \frac{dy}{dx} + xy = 0 \qquad (6\text{-}579)$$

but now subject to the initial conditions

$$y(0) = 1 \qquad (6\text{-}580)$$
$$y'(0) = 0 \qquad (6\text{-}581)$$

Taking the Laplace transform of Eq. (6-579) gives, with the aid of Eqs. (6-562), (6-580), and (6-581),

$$\int_{0}^{\infty} \left(x \frac{d^2 y}{dx^2} + \frac{dy}{dx} + xy \right) e^{-sx} = -\left[(s^2 + 1) \frac{d\bar{y}}{ds} + s\bar{y}(s) \right] = 0$$

$$(6\text{-}582)$$

where

$$\bar{y}(s) = \int_0^\infty y(x)e^{-sx}\, dx \tag{6-583}$$

The general solution of

$$\frac{d\bar{y}}{ds} + \frac{s}{s^2 + 1}\,\bar{y}(s) = 0 \tag{6-584}$$

is

$$\bar{y}(s) = \frac{c}{\sqrt{s^2 + 1}} \tag{6-585}$$

where c is an arbitrary constant. Applying the inversion theorem (5-473) to Eq. (6-585) yields a solution of the form

$$y(x) = \frac{c}{2\pi i} \int_{\sigma_0 - i\infty}^{\sigma_0 + i\infty} \frac{e^{sx}}{\sqrt{s^2 + 1}}\, ds \tag{6-586}$$

in which σ_0 is an arbitrarily small positive number.

From a table of Laplace transforms, one sees that

$$J_0(x) = \frac{1}{2\pi i} \int_{\sigma_0 - i\infty}^{\sigma_0 + i\infty} \frac{e^{sx}}{\sqrt{s^2 + 1}}\, ds \tag{6-587}$$

and consequently

$$y(x) = cJ_0(x) \tag{6-588}$$

Since $J_0(0) = 1$, the initial condition (6-580) requires $c = 1$ and the solution of Eqs. (6-579) to (6-581) reduces to

$$y(x) = J_0(x) \tag{6-589}$$

as expected.

6-26 PROBLEMS AND APPLICATIONS

Find the general solutions of:

1. $y'' - 2y' + y = 0$
2. $y'' + \omega^2 y = 0$
3. $y'' - k^2 y = 0$
4. $y'' - 4y' + 5y = 0$
5. $y'' - 5y' + 6y = 0$
6. $y'' = 0$
7. $y'' + 2y' = 0$
8. $yy' = 0$
9. $y'' - 4y' + 4y = 0$
10. $Ly'' + Ry' + \dfrac{1}{C}y = 0$
11. $y''' + y'' - 7y' - 15y = 0$
12. $y'''' + 2y'' + y = 0$
13. $y'' + 3y' + 2y = 2e^x$
14. $y'' + 2y' + y = e^{-x}$
15. $y'' + 3y' + 2y = 1 + 2x$

16. $y'' - 2y' + y = xe^x$

17. $y'' - k^2y = e^{\alpha x}$

18. $y'' + \omega^2 y = A \cos \omega_0 x$

19. $3y'' + 2y' - 8y = 5 \cos x$

20. $y'' - 4y = 16x^2 e^{2x^2}$

Solve each of the following equations subject to the given conditions.

21. $y'' + y = 0$, $y(0) = 1$, $y'(0) = 0$

22. $y'' - y = 0$, $y(0) = 1$, $y'(0) = 0$

23. $y'' = -g$, $y'(0) = v_0$, $y(0) = y_0$

24. $y'' + y = x^3 + x$, $y(0) = a$, $y'(0) = b$

25. $y'' + 5y' + 4y = e^x$, $y(0) = 0$, $y'(0) = -1$

Find the general solution of the following systems of equations.

26. $\dfrac{dy}{dt} = 2y + 3x$

$\dfrac{dx}{dt} = 2y + x$

Hint: Let $y = Ae^{\lambda t}$ and $x = Be^{\lambda t}$ be trial solutions. This leads to a certain matrix eigenvalue problem. By solving this problem you can find the eigenvalues λ and then the eigenvectors which correspond to different values of λ. Your final answer should be

$$y = c_1 e^{-t} + c_2 e^{4t} \qquad x = -c_1 e^{-t} + \tfrac{2}{3} c_2 e^{4t}$$

27. $\dfrac{dy}{dt} = y + x$

$\dfrac{dx}{dt} = 4y + x$

28. $m_2 \dfrac{d^2y}{dt^2} = -k_2(y - x)$

$m_1 \dfrac{d^2x}{dt^2} = k_2(y - x) - k_1 x$

29. $\dfrac{d^2y}{dt^2} = x$

$\dfrac{d^2x}{dt^2} = y$

30. $\dfrac{dx}{dt} + 2x - 2y = t$

$\dfrac{dy}{dt} - 3x + y = e^t$

Hint: First find the general solution of the homogeneous form of this pair. Then to find the particular integrals, operate on the second equation with $\frac{1}{3}(d/dt + 2)$, and add the result to the first equation. This gives an equation for y alone, for which a particular integral can be found. The result for y is now substituted into the first equation to obtain an equation in x alone.

31. Consider a particle of mass m moving in a straight line under the influence of an attractive force whose magnitude varies inversely as the distance of the particle from the center of attraction. In such a force field the equation of motion is

$$m \frac{d^2y}{dt^2} = \frac{-k}{y}$$

If the velocity of the particle is zero when $y = y_0$, prove that the time it takes for the particle to travel from $y = y_0$ to the center of attraction at $y = 0$ is given by

$$T = y_0 \sqrt{\frac{m}{2k}} \; \Gamma(\tfrac{1}{2}) = y_0 \sqrt{\frac{m\pi}{2k}} \qquad \text{sec}$$

32. Prove that

$$\int_0^\infty x^a e^{-bx^c} \, dx = \frac{\Gamma\left(\dfrac{a+1}{c}\right)}{cb^{(a+1)/c}}$$

where b and c are positive constants and $a > -1$.
Hint: Let $bx^c = y$.

33. The equation of motion for a simple pendulum of mass m and length L is

$$m \frac{d^2\theta}{dt^2} + \frac{g}{L} \sin \theta = 0$$

Given the initial conditions

$$\theta(0) = \theta_0 \qquad \frac{d\theta}{dt}\bigg|_{t=0} = 0$$

show that the time it takes the pendulum bob to swing from $\theta = 0$ to $\theta = \theta_0$ is

$$T = \sqrt{\frac{L}{2g}} \int_0^{\theta_0} \frac{d\theta}{\sqrt{\cos \theta - \cos \theta_0}}$$

Use the change of variable

$$\sin \frac{\theta}{2} = \sin \frac{\theta_0}{2} \sin \Phi = k \sin \Phi$$

together with the identity

$$\cos \theta = 1 - 2 \sin^2 \frac{\theta}{2}$$

to reduce the formula for T to

$$T = \sqrt{\frac{L}{g}} \int_0^{\pi/2} \frac{d\Phi}{\sqrt{1 - k^2 \sin^2 \Phi}}$$

The function

$$F(k,\Phi) = \int_0^\Phi \frac{d\Phi}{\sqrt{1 - k^2 \sin^2 \Phi}} \qquad k^2 < 1$$

is called an "elliptic integral of the first kind." In terms of it, the exact period of the pendulum becomes $P = 4T$ or

$$P = 4\sqrt{\frac{L}{g}} F\left(k, \frac{\pi}{2}\right)$$

34. Expand $F(k,\Phi)$ in a power series, and use this power-series expansion to show that

$$P = 2\pi \sqrt{\frac{L}{g}} \left\{1 + \left(\frac{1}{2}\right) k^2 + \left(\frac{1 \cdot 3}{2 \cdot 4}\right)^2 k^4 + \cdots \right\}$$

35. Prove that the beta function can be expressed in the form

$$B(x,y) = \int_0^{\pi/2} 2 \sin^{2x-1} \theta \cos^{2y-1} \theta \, d\theta$$

36. Use the results of Probs. 33 and 35 to show that the time it takes a pendulum to swing through 90 degrees is

$$T = \frac{1}{2} \sqrt{\frac{L}{2g}} B\left(\frac{1}{2}, \frac{1}{4}\right)$$

37. Prove that Bessel functions satisfy the following recursion relations:

$$J_{n-1}(x) + J_{n+1}(x) = \frac{2n}{x} J_n(x)$$

$$J_{n-1}(x) - J_{n+1}(x) = 2J_n'(x)$$

$$J_{n-1}(x) = \frac{n}{x} J_n(x) + J_n'(x)$$

$$J_{n+1}(x) = \frac{n}{x} J_n(x) - J_n'(x)$$

$$J_0'(x) = -J_1(x)$$

38. Prove that the Wronskian of $J_\nu(x)$ and $J_{-\nu}(x)$ is

$$W\{J_\nu, J_{-\nu}; x\} = \frac{-2 \sin \nu\pi}{\pi x}$$

39. Prove that

$$e^{(x/2)(u-1/u)} = \sum_{n=-\infty}^{n=+\infty} u^n J_n(x)$$

40. Use Prob. 39 to prove that

$$J_n(x + y) = \sum_{k=-\infty}^{+\infty} J_k(x) J_{n-k}(x)$$

41. Use Prob. 39 to prove that

$$e^{ix \sin\theta} = \sum_{n=-\infty}^{+\infty} J_n(x) e^{in\theta}$$

and from this obtain the formula

$$J_n(x) = \frac{1}{\pi} \int_0^\pi \cos(x \sin \theta - n\theta) \, d\theta$$

42. Prove that the hyperbolic Bessel functions satisfy recursion relations of the form

$$K_0'(x) = -K_1(x)$$
$$I_0'(x) = I_1(x)$$

$$I_{\nu-1}(x) - I_{\nu+1}(x) = \frac{2\nu}{x} I_\nu(x)$$

$$K_{\nu-1}(x) - K_{\nu+1}(x) = \frac{-2\nu}{x} K_\nu(x)$$

$$I_{\nu-1}(x) + I_{\nu+1}(x) = 2I_\nu'(x)$$
$$K_{\nu-1}(x) + K_{\nu+1}(x) = -2K_\nu'(x)$$

43. Show that as $r \to \infty$,

$$H_0{}^{(1)}(kr)e^{-i\omega t} \to \text{const} \frac{e^{i(kr-\omega t)}}{\sqrt{kr}}$$

and

$$H_0{}^{(2)}(kr)e^{-i\omega t} \to \text{const} \frac{e^{-i(kr+\omega t)}}{\sqrt{kr}}$$

44. Prove that the general solution of

$$y'' + \frac{1 - 2a}{x} y' + \left\{ (bcx^{c-1})^2 + \frac{a^2 - n^2c^2}{x^2} \right\} y = 0$$

is given by

$$y = x^a\{AJ_n(bx^c) + BN_n(bx^c)\}$$

where A and B are arbitrary constants. Use this result to show that the general solution of

$$y'' + xy = 0$$

is

$$y = x^{1/2}\left\{ AJ_{1/3}\left(\frac{2x^{3/2}}{3}\right) + BN_{1/3}\left(\frac{2x^{3/2}}{3}\right) \right\}$$

and that the general solution of

$$y'' + \frac{(2n + 1)y'}{x} + y = 0$$

is

$$y = x^{-n}\{AJ_n(x) + BN_n(x)\}$$

45. Derive the following recurrence relations for Legendre polynomials:

$$(n + 1)P_{n+1}(x) - (2n + 1)xP_n(x) + nP_{n-1}(x) = 0$$
$$xP_n'(x) - P_{n-1}'(x) = nP_n(x)$$
$$P_{n+1}'(x) - P_{n-1}'(x) = (2n + 1)P_n(x)$$

46. Prove that

$$\int_{-1}^{+1} x^m P_n(x) \, dx = \begin{cases} 0 & m \le n - 1 \\ 2^{n+1}(n!)^2/(n + 1)! & m = n \end{cases}$$

and

$$\int_{-1}^{+1} x^m P_n(x)\,dx = \frac{m!\,\Gamma\left(\dfrac{m-n+1}{2}\right)}{2^n (m-n)!\,\Gamma\left(\dfrac{m+n+3}{2}\right)}$$

when m and n are positive integers or zero such that $m \geq n$ and $m - n = 2k$ for $k = 0,1,2, \ldots .$
    Also show that

$$\int_{-1}^{+1} x^m P_n(x)\,dx = 0$$

when $m - n = 2k + 1$ for $k = 0,1,2, \ldots$ or when $m < n$.
Hint: Use Rodrigues's formula, and integrate by parts. Then use the definition of the beta function.

47. Prove that

$$\int_{-1}^{+1} e^{ikx} P_n(x)\,dx = i^n \left(\frac{2\pi}{k}\right)^{\frac{1}{2}} J_{n+\frac{1}{2}}(k)$$

Hint: Expand e^{ikx} in a power series, and integrate term by term, using the result obtained in Prob. 46 to evaluate the integrals. Next make use of the formula $\Gamma(n + \frac{1}{2})/(2n)! = \sqrt{\pi}/(2^{2n}n!)$ to identify the power-series expansion for $J_{n+\frac{1}{2}}(k)$.

48. Derive the formula

$$e^{ikz} \equiv e^{ikr\cos\theta} = \sum_{n=0}^{\infty} i^n(2n+1)P_n(\cos\theta)j_n(kr)$$

where $j_n(kr)$ is a spherical Bessel function of the first kind.

Hint: Expand $e^{ikr\cos\theta}$ in a series of the form $\displaystyle\sum_{n=0}^{\infty} C_n(r)P_n(\cos\theta)$, and solve for $C_n(r)$, using the orthogonality relations for $P_n(\cos\theta)$.

49. Prove that

$$\int_{-1}^{1} P_n{}^m(x)P_k{}^m(x)\,dx = \frac{2}{2n+1}\frac{(n+m)!}{(n-m)!}\,\delta_{nk}$$

$$\int_{-1}^{+1} P_n{}^m(x)P_n{}^k(x)\,\frac{dx}{1-x^2} = \frac{1}{m}\frac{(n+m)!}{(n-m)!}\,\delta_{mk}$$

Hint: Integrate by parts, using Eqs. (6-289) and (6-296).

50. Consider a pair of points on the surface of a unit sphere. Let the first point have spherical coordinates $(x,y,z) = (\sin\theta\cos\phi,\ \sin\theta\sin\phi,\ \cos\theta)$ and the second point the coordinates $(x',y',z') = (\sin\theta'\cos\phi',\ \sin\theta'\sin\phi',\ \cos\theta')$. The angle between the position vectors of the two points is given by

$$\cos\gamma = xx' + yy' + zz' = \sin\theta\sin\theta'\cos(\phi - \phi') + \cos\theta\cos\theta'$$

Prove the addition formula for Legendre polynomials,

$$P_n(\cos\gamma) = P_n(\cos\theta)P_n(\cos\theta')$$

$$+ 2\sum_{m=1}^{n} \frac{(n-m)!}{(n+m)!} P_n{}^m(\cos\theta)P_n{}^m(\cos\theta')\cos m(\phi - \phi')$$

Hint: Assume an expansion for $P_n(\cos \gamma)$ of the form

$$P_n(\cos \gamma) = \frac{a_0}{2} P_n(\cos \theta) + \sum_{m=1}^{n} (a_m \cos m\phi + b_m \sin m\phi) P_n{}^m(\cos \theta)$$

Then determine the unknown coefficients by means of the orthogonality relations (Prob. 49).

51. Show that spherical Bessel functions satisfy

$$\int_{-\infty}^{+\infty} j_n(x) j_m(x)\, dx = \frac{\pi}{2} \frac{1}{2n+1} \delta_{nm}$$

provided that n and m are non-negative integers.

52. Prove that spherical Bessel functions satisfy the recursion formulas

$$\frac{2n+1}{x} j_n(x) = j_{n-1}(x) + j_{n+1}(x)$$

$$j_n'(x) = \frac{1}{2n+1} \{n j_{n-1}(x) - (n+1) j_{n+1}(x)\}$$

and that their Wronskians satisfy

$$W\{j_n, n_n\} = \frac{1}{i} W\{j_n, h_n{}^{(1)}\} = -W\{n_n, h_n{}^{(1)}\} = \frac{1}{x^2}$$

53. Consider a positive point charge q located at the point $x = 0, y = 0, z = 1$. Show that the electric potential Φ at the point (x,y,z) is given by

$$\Phi(\mathbf{r}) = \frac{q}{4\pi\epsilon_0} \sum_{n=0}^{\infty} \frac{P_n(\cos \theta)}{r^{n+1}}$$

where

$$r = (x^2 + y^2 + z^2)^{1/2}$$

and

$$\theta = \cos^{-1} \frac{z}{r}$$

54. Show that

$$Q_n(x) = P_n(x) \int \frac{dx}{(1 - x^2)[P_n(x)]^2}$$

is a second solution of Legendre's differential equation.

55. Consider an arbitrary scalar function $F(R)$ which depends only on the distance $R = [(x_1 - x_1')^2 + (x_2 - x_2')^2 + (x_3 - x_3')^2]^{1/2} = |\mathbf{r} - \mathbf{r}'|$ between the two points $\mathbf{r}$ and $\mathbf{r}'$. Derive the Taylor-series expansion for $F(R)$ about the point $\mathbf{r} = (x_1, x_2, x_3)$,

$$F(R) = \sum_{n=0}^{\infty} \frac{(-1)^n}{n!} (\mathbf{r}' \cdot \nabla)^n F(r) \Big|_{r=(x_1,x_2,x_3)}$$

where

$$(\mathbf{r}' \cdot \nabla)^n = \left(x_1' \frac{\partial}{\partial x_1} + x_2' \frac{\partial}{\partial x_2} + x_3' \frac{\partial}{\partial x_3} \right)^n$$

56. Suppose that electric charge is distributed throughout some finite volume of space, say V', with a density $\rho(\mathbf{r}')$ coul/m^3. It is shown in electromagnetic theory that the electric potential generated by $\rho(\mathbf{r}')$ is given by

$$\Phi(\mathbf{r}) = \frac{1}{4\pi\epsilon_0} \int_{V'} \frac{\rho(\mathbf{r}')}{R} \, dV'$$

where $dV' = dx_1' \, dx_2' \, dx_3'$ and

$$R = |\mathbf{r} - \mathbf{r}'| = [(x_1 - x_1')^2 + (x_2 - x_2')^2 + (x_3 - x_3')^2]^{1/2}$$

Prove that

$$\frac{(r')^n P_n(\cos\gamma)}{r^{n+1}} = \frac{(-1)^n}{n!} \left(x_1' \frac{\partial}{\partial x_1} + x_2' \frac{\partial}{\partial x_2} + x_3' \frac{\partial}{\partial x_3} \right)^n \frac{1}{r}$$

where $r = (x_1^2 + x_2^2 + x_3^2)^{1/2}$, $r' = [(x_1')^2 + (x_2')^2 + (x_3')^2]^{1/2}$, and $\cos\gamma = (x_1 x_1' + x_2 x_2' + x_3 x_3')/rr'$. Hence, show that

$$\Phi(\mathbf{r}) = \sum_{n=0}^{\infty} \Phi^{(n)}(\mathbf{r})$$

where

$$\Phi^{(n)}(\mathbf{r}) = \frac{1}{4\pi\epsilon_0} \frac{1}{r^{n+1}} \int_{V'} P_n(\cos\gamma)(r')^n \rho(\mathbf{r}') \, dV'$$

Suppose that the volume V' is a cylinder of radius r_0 and length L. Show that the potential $\Phi^{(n)}(\mathbf{r})$ at any point $\mathbf{r}$ which is far away from the cylinder is approximately

$$\Phi^{(n)}(\mathbf{r}) = \frac{1}{4\pi\epsilon_0} M^{(n)} \frac{P_n(\cos\theta)}{r^{n+1}}$$

where θ is the angle between the direction of r and the axis of the cylinder, and

$$M^{(n)} = \int_{V'} (r')^n \rho(\mathbf{r}') \, dV'$$

Can you interpret these results physically?

57. Show that

$$\Phi(\mathbf{r}) = \sum_{n=0}^{\infty} \Phi^{(n)}(\mathbf{r})$$

where

$$\Phi^{(n)}(\mathbf{r}) = \frac{1}{4\pi\epsilon_0} \frac{(-1)^n}{n!} \sum_{i_1=1}^{3} \sum_{i_2=1}^{3} \cdots \sum_{i_n=1}^{3} M_{i_1 i_2 \cdots i_n} \frac{\partial^n}{\partial x_{i_1} \partial x_{i_2} \cdots \partial x_{i_n}} \left(\frac{1}{r}\right)$$

$$M_{i_1 i_2 \cdots i_n} = \int_{V'} \rho(\mathbf{r}') x_{i_1}' x_{i_2}' x_{i_3}' \cdots x_{i_n}' \, dV$$

for $n \geq 1$; and for $n = 0$,

$$\Phi^{(0)}(\mathbf{r}) = \frac{1}{4\pi\epsilon_0} \frac{Q}{r}$$

where

$$Q = \int_{V'} \rho(\mathbf{r}') \, dV$$

Hint: First prove that

$$(y_1 + y_2 + y_3)^n = \sum_{i_1=1}^{3} \sum_{i_2=1}^{3} \cdots \sum_{i_n=1}^{3} y_{i_1} y_{i_2} \cdots y_{i_n}$$

Then let

$$y_1 = x_1' \frac{\partial}{\partial x_1} \qquad y_2 = x_2' \frac{\partial}{\partial x_2} \qquad \text{etc.}$$

Can you interpret these results physically?

58. Prove that

$$\int_{-\infty}^{+\infty} x e^{-x^2} H_n(x) H_m(x) \, dx = \sqrt{\pi} \, [2^{n-1}(n!) \delta_{m,n-1} + 2^n(n+1)! \delta_{m,n+1}]$$

Hint: Use the generating function for Hermite polynomials.

59. Show that the Green's function $g(x|x')$ which satisfies

$$\frac{d}{dx} \left[p(x) \frac{dg}{dx} \right] + q(x)g(x) = -\delta(x - x')$$

together with the boundary conditions $g_2(a|x') = 0$ and $g_1(b|x') = 0$ is

$$g(x|x') = -\frac{g_1(x_>)g_2(x_<)}{p(x')W\{g_1, g_2; x'\}}$$

provided that g_1 and g_2 are linearly independent solutions of

$$\frac{d}{dx} \left[p(x) \frac{dy}{dx} \right] + q(x)g(x) = 0$$

that satisfy $g_1(b) = 0$, $g_2(a) = 0$.

60. Obtain the following Green's function solutions:

$$\frac{d^2g}{dx^2} = -\delta(x - x')$$

$$g(0) = 0 \qquad g(1) = 0$$

Ans. $\quad g(x|x') = (1 - x_>)x_<$

$$\frac{d^2g}{dx^2} + k^2g = -\delta(x - x')$$

$$g(0) = 0 \qquad g(1) = 0$$

Ans. $\quad g(x|x') = \dfrac{\sin k(1 - x_>) \sin kx_<}{k \sin k}$

$$\frac{d^2g}{dx^2} - k^2g = -\delta(x - x')$$

$$g(0) = 0 \qquad g(1) = 0$$

Ans. $\quad g(x|x') = \dfrac{\sinh k(1 - x_>) \sinh kx_<}{k \sinh k}$

61. Show that Hermite's differential equation can be written in Sturm-Liouville form, and from this deduce the orthogonality properties of Hermite polynomials.

62. Suppose that a function $f(x)$ defined on the interval $-1 \leq x \leq 1$ is expanded in a Fourier-Legendre series

$$f(x) = \sum_{n=0}^{\infty} a_n P_n(x)$$

Derive a formula for the expansion coefficients a_k. What can you say about the convergence of this series?

63. Suppose that a function $f(x)$ defined on the interval $0 \leq x \leq a$ is expanded in a Fourier-Bessel series

$$f(x) = \sum_{n=0}^{\infty} a_n J_\nu(k_n x)$$

where k_n, $n = 0,1,2, \ldots$, denotes the roots of $J_\nu(k_n a) = 0$. Derive a formula for the expansion coefficients a_k. Discuss the convergence of this series.

64. Use the Fourier transform to solve Bessel's equation

$$\frac{d^2 y}{dx^2} + \frac{1}{x} \frac{dy}{dx} + \left(1 - \frac{\nu^2}{x^2}\right) y = 0$$

65. Use a Laplace transform to show that the solution of

$$x \frac{d^2 y}{dx^2} - \frac{dy}{dx} - xy = 0$$

is

$$y = Ax I_1(x) + Bx K_1(x)$$

Hint: Use a table of Laplace transforms to invert the transform.

66. Solve the equation

$$x \frac{d^2 y}{dx^2} + (1 + 2x) \frac{dy}{dx} + y = 0$$

with the aid of a Laplace transform. The answer should be

$$y = e^{-x}\{A I_0(x) + B K_0(x)\}$$

partial differential equations

7-1 INTRODUCTION

In many physical problems the fundamental object under investigation is a vector or scalar field and the desired end is to be able to predict the behavior of this field throughout all space and for all time given initially only the local behavior of the field.

One method of specifying this local behavior is to give a relation which must hold at each point of space and time and which interrelates, at any given point, the rates of change of the field in different directions.

Such a relation is known as a "partial differential equation," and the problem of predicting the behavior of the field throughout all space and for all time amounts to integrating this partial differential equation.

In this chapter we shall not treat the general theory of partial differential equations at all. Rather, we shall confine our attention to certain partial differential equations of interest in physics and to the methods used to integrate them.

7-2 THE ROLE OF THE LAPLACIAN

The Laplacian operator ∇^2 appears in a partial differential equation whenever the difference between the local value of a function at a point and the average value of the function in a neighborhood of the point governs the further space-time evolution of the function.

To see why this is true let us consider a cube with sides of length a centered at the origin of coordinates $x = 0$, $y = 0$, $z = 0$. A scalar field defined throughout space may take on different values throughout the interior of the cube, and in particular the value $\phi_0 = \phi(0,0,0)$ is taken on at the center of the cube. The average value $\bar{\phi}$ of ϕ in the interior of the cube is given by the mean-value theorem:

$$\bar{\phi} = \frac{1}{a^3} \int_{-a/2}^{a/2} \int_{-a/2}^{a/2} \int_{-a/2}^{a/2} \phi(x,y,z)\ dx\ dy\ dz \tag{7-1}$$

If the function $\phi(x,y,z)$ is now expanded in a Taylor series about

$x = 0$, $y = 0$, $z = 0$, then

$$\phi(x,y,z) = \phi_0 + \left(\frac{\partial\phi}{\partial x}\right)_0 x + \left(\frac{\partial\phi}{\partial y}\right)_0 y + \left(\frac{\partial\phi}{\partial z}\right)_0 z$$
$$+ \frac{1}{2}\left[\left(\frac{\partial^2\phi}{\partial x^2}\right)_0 x^2 + \left(\frac{\partial^2\phi}{\partial y^2}\right)_0 y^2 + \left(\frac{\partial^2\phi}{\partial z^2}\right)_0 z^2\right]$$
$$+ \left(\frac{\partial^2\phi}{\partial x\,\partial y}\right)_0 xy + \left(\frac{\partial^2\phi}{\partial y\,\partial z}\right)_0 yz + \left(\frac{\partial^2\phi}{\partial z\,\partial x}\right)_0 zx + \cdots \qquad (7\text{-}2)$$

Inserting Eq. (7-2) into Eq. (7-1) and carrying out the integrations from $-a/2$ to $a/2$, we find that the odd functions cancel out while from the squared terms we obtain

$$\frac{1}{a^3}\int_{-a/2}^{+a/2}\int_{-a/2}^{a/2}\int_{-a/2}^{a/2}\frac{1}{2}\left(\frac{\partial^2\phi}{\partial x^2}\right)_0 x^2\,dx\,dy\,dz = \frac{a^2}{24}\left(\frac{\partial^2\phi}{\partial x^2}\right)_0 \qquad (7\text{-}3)$$

etc. Hence,

$$\bar{\phi} = \phi_0 + \frac{a^2}{24}\left(\frac{\partial^2\phi}{\partial x^2} + \frac{\partial^2\phi}{\partial y^2} + \frac{\partial^2\phi}{\partial z^2}\right)_0 + \text{higher-order terms} \qquad (7\text{-}4)$$

For an infinitesimal cube we have to have a good approximation,

$$\bar{\phi} - \phi_0 = \frac{a^2}{24}(\nabla^2\phi)_0 \qquad (7\text{-}5)$$

and therefore the quantity $\nabla^2\phi$ is a measure of the difference between the value of the scalar ϕ at a point and the average value of ϕ in an infinitesimal neighborhood of the point.

7-3 LAPLACE'S EQUATION

Whenever a scalar field $\phi(x,y,z)$ has the property that its value at a point equals its average value throughout a neighborhood of the point, then according to Eq. (7-5), that field must satisfy Laplace's equation:

$$\nabla^2\phi = 0 \qquad (7\text{-}6)$$

The scalar potentials associated with gravitational, electrostatic, and magnetostatic fields are examples of functions which must satisfy Laplace's equation.

7-4 POISSON'S EQUATION

According to Gauss' law, the total electric charge contained within a volume V enclosed by a surface $S(V)$ is given by the flux of electric displacement through the surface $S(V)$, or, in other words,

$$\int_{S(V)} \mathbf{D} \cdot d\mathbf{S} = q \qquad (7\text{-}7)$$

In this case the flux of $\mathbf{D}$ must have the dimensions of electric charge. Using the three-dimensional divergence theorem, we can also write

$$\int_V \nabla \cdot \mathbf{D}\,dV = \int_{S(V)} \mathbf{D} \cdot d\mathbf{S} = q \qquad (7\text{-}8)$$

where the divergence of $\mathbf{D}$ represents the flux per unit volume in V. Thus $\boldsymbol{\nabla} \cdot \mathbf{D}$ has the dimensions of charge per unit volume and therefore represents the charge density in V. This is expressed by writing

$$\int_V \boldsymbol{\nabla} \cdot \mathbf{D} \, dV = \int_V \rho \, dV = q \tag{7-9}$$

which, if it is to hold for all arbitrary volumes contained within V, implies that

$$\boldsymbol{\nabla} \cdot \mathbf{D} = \rho \tag{7-10}$$

throughout V. If the electric displacement field is now expressed as the gradient of a scalar function ϕ then

$$\mathbf{D} = -\epsilon_0 \boldsymbol{\nabla} \phi \tag{7-11}$$

and consequently the scalar function ϕ must satisfy *Poisson's equation*,

$$\nabla^2 \phi = -\frac{\rho}{\epsilon_0} \tag{7-12}$$

throughout V. For example, the presence of a net positive electric charge smeared out through the interior of volume V forces the value of the potential at any point in V to be greater than its average value over a small neighborhood of the point. At any point at which the charge density vanishes, Poisson's equation reduces to Laplace's equation.

7-5 THE DIFFUSION EQUATION

The scalar fields which satisfy Laplace's or Poisson's equation are generally, through not always, time-independent. However, there are a number of physical processes in which the value of a scalar function ϕ at any point may be different from its average value in the neighborhood at some time, but not for all values of time. In stable situations this difference causes a tendency toward equalization with time. In other words, for stable behavior the local value of ϕ will approach the average value of ϕ at a rate proportional to the difference between the average and local values. In quantitative terms, this relationship is expressed by means of the *diffusion equation*,

$$\frac{\partial \phi}{\partial t} = \alpha \, \nabla^2 \phi \tag{7-13}$$

where the parameter α is known as the *diffusivity*. Thus the larger the diffusivity, the more rapidly the difference between the average and local values of ϕ is equalized.

The conduction of heat through a solid is a classical example of such a tendency toward equalization. Since heat flows from higher to lower temperatures in a solid, the heat current density due to a temperature field T is given by

$$\mathbf{q} = -k \, \boldsymbol{\nabla} T \tag{7-14}$$

where k is called the "thermal conductivity" of the solid and is measured in calories per centimeter per second per degree centigrade. If H represents the heat per unit volume in the solid, then thermodynamics tells us that

$$dH = \rho c \, dT \qquad (7\text{-}15)$$

where ρ is the density in grams per cubic centimeter, and c is the specific heat of the solid in calories per gram per degree centigrade. This equation means that a change in temperature dT is produced by the addition of an amount of heat $dH/\rho c$ to the solid; thus,

$$\frac{dH}{dt} = \rho c \frac{dT}{dt} \qquad (7\text{-}16)$$

If the solid remains fixed and rigid, then $\mathbf{v} = 0$, and Eq. (7-16) reduces to

$$\frac{\partial H}{\partial t} = \rho c \frac{\partial T}{\partial t} \qquad (7\text{-}17)$$

The total decrease in heat in the region V per unit time is given by

$$- \int_V \frac{\partial H}{\partial t} \, dV \qquad (7\text{-}18)$$

and if heat is to be conserved, then

$$- \int_V \frac{\partial H}{\partial t} \, dV = \int_{S(V)} d\mathbf{S} \cdot \mathbf{q} \qquad (7\text{-}19)$$

which states that the rate of decrease of heat in region V is equal to the flux of heat current emerging from the boundary of V. Inserting Eqs. (7-14) and (7-17) into (7-19) and applying the three-dimensional divergence theorem yields

$$- \int_V \rho c \frac{\partial T}{\partial t} \, dV = - \int_{S(V)} d\mathbf{S} \cdot (k \, \boldsymbol{\nabla} T)$$

$$= - \int_V \boldsymbol{\nabla} \cdot (k \, \boldsymbol{\nabla} T) \, dV \qquad (7\text{-}20)$$

or

$$\int_V \left[\rho c \frac{\partial T}{\partial t} - \boldsymbol{\nabla} \cdot (k \, \boldsymbol{\nabla} T) \right] dV = 0 \qquad (7\text{-}21)$$

and if Eq. (7-21) is to hold for all volumes contained in V, then at each point in V,

$$\rho c \frac{\partial T}{\partial t} = \boldsymbol{\nabla} \cdot (k \, \boldsymbol{\nabla} T) \qquad (7\text{-}22)$$

which is the equation governing the temperature distribution in the solid. When the thermal conductivity k is a constant, Eq. (7-22) reduces to

$$\nabla^2 T = \frac{1}{\alpha} \frac{\partial T}{\partial t} \qquad (7\text{-}23)$$

in which the diffusivity α is given by

$$\alpha = \frac{k}{\rho c} \tag{7-24}$$

Thus we see that, as expected, the greater the thermal conductivity of a solid, the more rapidly temperature differences are smoothed out.

7-6 THE WAVE EQUATION

In an elastic medium which is at rest, each point may be thought of as occupying a position of stable equilibrium. Then wave motion takes place when the particles comprising the medium undergo the following kind of collective interaction. Suppose a given particle is disturbed from its position of stable equilibrium. As a result of elastic coupling, its nearest neighbors will also be displaced from their equilibrium positions. They in turn will displace their nearest neighbors, and so on, causing the original disturbance to spread or propagate through the medium. The remarkable feature of this phenomenon is that despite the essentially unlimited distance over which it can propagate energy, no particle of the medium undergoes more than a small deviation from its position of stable equilibrium!

For example, consider a stretched elastic membrane such as a drumhead. If a point on the drumhead, say $x = 0$, $y = 0$, is given a displacement $\phi_0 = \phi(0,0,t)$ above or below its equilibrium plane, then because of elastic coupling, the points near $x = 0$, $y = 0$ will also be displaced from their equilibrium positions, though not by the same amount ϕ_0. Let the average displacement in an infinitesimal neighborhood of $x = 0$, $y = 0$ be called $\bar{\phi}$. Then $\bar{\phi}$ and ϕ_0 are unequal, and the membrane acts in such a way as to reduce the difference between $\bar{\phi}$ and ϕ_0. As a result, the mass at $x = 0$, $y = 0$ will be accelerated back toward the plane in which $\phi_0 = \bar{\phi}$. This acceleration continues, decreasing to zero as the difference between ϕ_0 and $\bar{\phi}$ vanishes. As the mass at $x = 0$, $y = 0$ passes through the plane in which $\bar{\phi}$ and ϕ_0 are equal, its acceleration vanishes. However, its velocity is now a maximum, and therefore inertia will cause it to overshoot this plane. Consequently, ϕ_0 will deviate from $\bar{\phi}$ once again. Apparently ϕ_0 will oscillate about the value $\bar{\phi}$ with some characteristic frequency ω. We can write for the acceleration of the mass at $x = 0$, $y = 0$,

$$\frac{1}{\omega^2}\frac{\partial^2 \phi_0}{\partial t^2} + \phi_0 = \bar{\phi} \tag{7-25}$$

and using Eq. (7-5), this becomes

$$\frac{\partial^2 \phi_0}{\partial t^2} = \omega^2(\bar{\phi} - \phi_0) = \frac{\omega^2 a^2}{24}(\nabla^2 \phi)_0 \tag{7-26}$$

Since $\omega^2 a^2/24 = c^2$ has the dimensions of a velocity squared, we shorten the expression for the acceleration of the piece of membrane at $x = 0$, $y = 0$ to

$$\left(\frac{\partial^2 \phi}{\partial t^2}\right)_0 = c^2 (\nabla^2 \phi)_0 \tag{7-27}$$

However, the point $x = 0$, $y = 0$ is arbitrary, and therefore the acceleration of the mass at any point (x,y) must satisfy the *wave equation*

$$\frac{\partial^2 \phi}{\partial t^2} = c^2 \nabla^2 \phi \tag{7-28}$$

A more precise analysis of the vibrations of a membrane shows that

$$c = \sqrt{\frac{T}{\rho}} \tag{7-29}$$

where T is the tension or force per unit length in the membrane, and ρ is the surface density in grams per square centimeter. We see that, as expected, the greater the tension in the membrane, the more rapidly its particles oscillate about their equilibrium positions.

7-7 A FEW GENERAL REMARKS

The four partial differential equations which we have just derived in a more or less heuristic manner are of major importance in classical theoretical physics, and for this reason we shall give a detailed discussion of how they can be solved. One point to be emphasized is that the same general procedures apply to each of the four equations.

What do we really wish to do? For Laplace's equation and Poisson's equation we want to construct time-independent solutions in two and three space dimensions. For the time-dependent wave and diffusion equations we seek solutions which depend on one time coordinate and one, two, or three space coordinates. Furthermore, we want to construct not just any solution but rather a solution which satisfies certain specified conditions. For example, in the vibrating drumhead problem we may wish to find a function which not only satisfies the two-dimensional wave equation but also represents, together with its time derivative, the initial displacement and velocity of each point in the drumhead at $t = 0$. Even this may not be enough. If the drumhead is finite and rigidly clamped along the edge of the drum, then we may also demand that our displacement function, in addition to satisfying the wave equation and initial conditions, also reduce to zero on the edge of the drum for all time. A problem of this type is called a "mixed initial- and boundary-value problem" for the two-dimensional wave equation. Similarly, if the ends of a metal rod of finite length are maintained at two different temperatures, and the initial temperature distribution in the rod is specified at $t = 0$, then we obtain a mixed initial- and boundary-value problem for the one-dimensional diffusion equation.

PARTIAL DIFFERENTIAL EQUATIONS

Finally, the problem of the electric potential due to a point charge external to a grounded conducting spherical shell leads to a boundary-value problem for the three-dimensional Laplace equation. Here the potential must vanish on the boundary of the shell.

The solution of a partial differential equation subject to initial and boundary conditions is a complete problem as opposed to an incomplete problem of merely writing down arbitrary solutions of a given equation. Physical phenomena invariably lead to complete problems for the corresponding partial differential equations. The student will do well to get accustomed from the beginning to thinking in terms of solving not merely the partial differential equation but also the complete problem, together with all of its accessory conditions.

For the equations of potential theory, wave propagation, and diffusion, the process of solving a complete problem can always be broken down into two steps. The first step consists of representing the complete solution in terms of integrals involving the product of the accessory data with a Green's function. The Green's function is a particular solution of the given partial differential equation. It represents the response to a delta-function source term. The first step is generally accomplished with the aid of an appropriate Green's identity. The second step involves the actual construction of the Green's function, and it is here that the true practical difficulties are encountered.

7-8 SOLUTION OF POTENTIAL PROBLEMS IN TWO DIMENSIONS

As our first example, consider the problem of computing the electric potential due to a line charge of linear density q coul/m located between a pair of grounded parallel metal plates (Fig. 7-1). The line charge runs from $z = -\infty$ to $z = +\infty$ parallel to the z axis and passes through the x, y plane at $x = 0$, $y = d$. The lower plate is at $y = 0$, and the upper plate is at $y = a$. This example leads us to a complete problem for Poisson's equation in which the charge density due to the line charge is $\rho(x,y) = q\delta(x)\delta(y - d)$ coul/m³, and δ is the Dirac delta function.

We are to solve Poisson's equation,

$$\nabla^2\phi = -\frac{\rho(x,y)}{\epsilon_0} \tag{7-30}$$

subject to the boundary conditions

$$\phi(x,0) = 0 \qquad -\infty \leq x \leq +\infty \tag{7-31}$$

$$\phi(x,a) = 0 \qquad -\infty \leq x \leq +\infty \tag{7-32}$$

stating that the two parallel plates are grounded and therefore at zero potential. The problem will be solved by executing steps 1 and 2 of Sec. 7-7. Step 1 calls for us to express the solution of Eqs. (7-30) to (7-32) in terms of integrals involving the product of the accessory

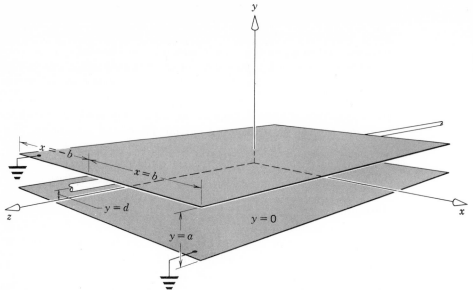

Figure 7-1 A line charge located between a pair of grounded parallel plates.

data (7-31) and (7-32) with a Green's function which will be defined below. To do this we need to develop an appropriate form of Green's identity. Since this is a two-dimensional problem, we begin with the two-dimensional divergence theorem:

$$\int_S \mathbf{\nabla} \cdot \mathbf{A} \, dS = \int_{C(S)} d\mathbf{\delta} \cdot \mathbf{A} \tag{7-33}$$

Let $\mathbf{A} = G \, \mathbf{\nabla}\phi$ in Eq. (7-33), and then let $\mathbf{A} = \phi \, \mathbf{\nabla}G$ as well. Subtracting the second result from the first gives the desired form of Green's symmetric identity,

$$\int_S \{G \, \nabla^2\phi - \phi \, \nabla^2 G\} \, dS = \int_{C(S)} \left\{ G \frac{\partial \phi}{\partial n} - \phi \frac{\partial G}{\partial n} \right\} \, ds \tag{7-34}$$

Here $\partial\phi/\partial n$ represents the rate of change of ϕ along the outward normal to $C(S)$, and ds represents the element of arc length on $C(S)$. In the problem at hand, S represents the interior of the rectangle given by

$$0 \le y \le a \tag{7-35}$$

$$-b \le x \le +b \tag{7-36}$$

and $C(S)$ represents its perimeter. Eventually, the sides of the rectangle at $x = \pm b$ will be allowed to recede to infinity.

The Green's function for Poisson's equation is defined as the solution of

$$\nabla^2 G = -\delta(x - x') \, \delta(y - y') \tag{7-37}$$

and using Eqs. (7-37), (7-34), and (7-30) together gives

$$\int_0^a \int_{-b}^b \phi(x,y)\, \delta(x - x')\, \delta(y - y')\, dx\, dy$$

$$= \int_0^a \int_{-b}^b G(x,x';y,y')\, \frac{\rho(x,y)}{\epsilon_0}\, dx\, dy$$

$$+ \int_{C(S)} \left\{ G \frac{\partial \phi}{\partial n} - \phi \frac{\partial G}{\partial n} \right\}\, ds \qquad (7\text{-}38)$$

The first term in Eq. (7-38) gives

$$\int_0^a \int_{-b}^b \phi(x,y)\, \delta(x - x')\, \delta(y - y')\, dx\, dy$$

$$= \phi(x',y') \int_0^a \int_{-b}^b \delta(x - x')\, \delta(y - y')\, dx\, dy$$

$$= \begin{cases} \phi(x',y') & (x',y') \text{ contained in } S \\ 0 & (x',y') \text{ outside } S \end{cases} \qquad (7\text{-}39)$$

Thus, assuming that (x',y') is a point contained in the rectangle S, Eq. (7-38) becomes

$$\phi(x',y') = \int_0^a \int_{-b}^b G(x,x';y,y')\, \frac{\rho(x,y)}{\epsilon_0}\, dx\, dy$$

$$+ \int_{C(S)} \left\{ G \frac{\partial \phi}{\partial n} - \phi \frac{\partial G}{\partial n} \right\}\, ds \qquad (7\text{-}40)$$

We must now simplify the line-integral contribution to Eq. (7-40) as much as possible, and if possible, eliminate it entirely. The boundary conditions (7-31) and (7-32) eliminate the term $\phi\, \partial G/\partial n$ on the portions $y = 0$ and $y = a$ of $C(S)$. We do not have any information regarding the behavior of $\phi(x,y)$ on $x = \pm b;\ 0 \leq y \leq a$. However, since the line charge is located at $x = 0$, $y = d$, it is reasonable to assume that, provided there are no line sources at infinity, the greater b is, the smaller the potential at (b,y) will be. Thus we assume that

$$\lim_{\substack{x \to \pm \infty \\ 0 < y < a}} \phi(x,y) = 0 \qquad (7\text{-}41)$$

and that as a result, the contributions to the second line-integral term in Eq. (7-40) arising from integrating $\phi\, \partial G/\partial n$ over the ends of the rectangle at $x = \pm b$ vanishes as these ends recede to infinity. Under these circumstances Eq. (7-40) may be replaced by

$$\phi(x',y') = \int_0^a \int_{-b}^{+b} G(x,x';y,y')\, \frac{\rho(x,y)}{\epsilon_0}\, dx\, dy + \int_{C(S)} G \frac{\partial \phi}{\partial n}\, ds$$

$$(7\text{-}42)$$

and if we assume that

$$G(x,0) = 0 \qquad -\infty \leq x \leq +\infty \qquad (7\text{-}43)$$

$$G(x,a) = 0 \qquad -\infty \leq x \leq +\infty \qquad (7\text{-}44)$$

$$\lim_{\substack{x \to \pm \infty \\ 0 < y < a}} G(x,y) = 0 \qquad (7\text{-}45)$$

as well, then the remaining line integral also vanishes as the ends of the rectangle recede to infinity, leaving us with

$$\phi(x',y') = \int_0^a \int_{-\infty}^{+\infty} G(x,x';y,y') \frac{\rho(x,y)}{\epsilon_0} \, dx \, dy \qquad (7\text{-}46)$$

Equation (7-46) is the formal solution of problem (7-30) to (7-32), and we can simplify (7-46) even further by recalling that in our special case

$$\rho(x,y) = q \, \delta(x) \, \delta(y - d) \qquad (7\text{-}47)$$

where $0 < d < a$. Therefore (7-46) reduces to

$$\begin{aligned}
\phi(x',y') &= \frac{q}{\epsilon_0} \int_0^a \int_{-\infty}^{+\infty} G(x,x';y,y') \, \delta(x) \, \delta(y - d) \, dx \, dy \\
&= \frac{q}{\epsilon_0} G(0,x';d,y') \int_0^a \int_{-\infty}^{+\infty} \delta(x) \, \delta(y - d) \, dx \, dy \\
&= q \frac{G(0,x';d,y')}{\epsilon_0} \qquad (7\text{-}48)
\end{aligned}$$

Consequently,

$$\phi(x',y') = q \frac{G(0,x';d,y')}{\epsilon_0} \qquad (7\text{-}49)$$

represents the electric potential at the point (x',y') due to a line source of charge of linear density q located at $x = 0$, $y = d$. By analogy, $qG(x,x';y,y')/\epsilon_0$ must represent the electric potential at (x',y') due to a line source of charge of linear density q located at (x,y). This observation permits us to interpret (7-46). Equation (7-46) states that the *potential* at the *point* (x',y') due to an *arbitrary charge density distribution* $\rho(x,y)$ *may be represented as a superposition of the potentials generated by an infinity of line sources*, the line source at the point (x,y) having a linear charge density $\rho(x,y) \, dx \, dy$ coul/m. It is only because Poisson's equation is a *linear partial differential equation* that we may represent the potential due to $\rho(x,y)$ as the superposition of the potentials due to appropriately placed line charges having the correct linear charge density.

To complete the solution of problem (7-30) to (7-32) we must perform step 2 of Sec. 7-7, which requires that we actually construct the Green's function $G(x,x';y,y')$ which satisfies

$$\nabla^2 G = -\delta(x - x') \, \delta(y - y') \qquad (7\text{-}50)$$

$$G = 0 \text{ on } y = 0 \qquad -\infty \le x \le +\infty \qquad (7\text{-}51)$$

$$G = 0 \text{ on } y = a \qquad -\infty \le x \le +\infty \qquad (7\text{-}52)$$

$$\lim_{|x| \to \infty} G = 0 \qquad 0 < y < a \qquad (7\text{-}53)$$

At this point the student may wonder why we bothered with step 1 at all, since we are left with the task of solving Eqs. (7-50) to (7-53), which is the original problem. There are three reasons. First of all, if instead of a line charge, we are given distributed charge density $\rho(x,y)$, then step 1 is necessary to obtain Eq. (7-46). Secondly, although in this problem the two line integrals in Eq. (7-40) vanish, there are many other problems in which they do not both vanish, and this possibility must be kept in mind. Finally, we are interested in developing a general technique of attacking boundary-value problems in potential theory, wave propagation, and diffusion, and the Green's function method is one of the most powerful and most general techniques available.

Construction of the Green's function

The easiest and fastest way to construct the Green's function which satisfies Eqs. (7-50) to (7-53) is to employ integral transforms, particularly since these have already been introduced in Chap. 5. Another more classical but clumsier way to construct the solution is based on the method of separation of variables, and we shall illustrate both methods for purposes of comparison. The integral transform method can immediately take the boundary conditions (7-51) and (7-52) into account. Thus the vanishing of G on $y = 0$ and $y = a$ suggests that we take a finite sine transform of Eq. (7-50). Multiplying (7-50) through by $\sin n\pi y/a$, integrating twice by parts with respect to y from 0 to a, and then eliminating the integrated parts with the aid of Eqs. (7-51) and (7-52) gives an ordinary differential equation,

$$\frac{d^2\bar{G}}{dx^2} - \left(\frac{n\pi}{a}\right)^2 \bar{G} = -\delta(x - x') \sin\frac{n\pi y'}{a} \tag{7-54}$$

for the determination of $\bar{G}$. Here

$$\bar{G} = \int_0^a G \sin\frac{n\pi y}{a}\, dy \tag{7-55}$$

is the finite sine transform of G. The ordinary differential equation (7-54) has already been encountered in both Chaps. 5 and 6, and its general solution is

$$\bar{G} = Ae^{n\pi x/a} + Be^{-n\pi x/a} + \frac{e^{-n\pi x_>/a}e^{n\pi x_</a}}{W\{e^{-n\pi x'/a},e^{n\pi x'/a};x'\}} \sin\frac{n\pi y'}{a} \tag{7-56}$$

where the reader will recall that

$$x_> = \text{greater of } (x,x') \tag{7-57}$$

$$x_< = \text{lesser of } (x,x') \tag{7-58}$$

and that $W\{e^{-n\pi x'/a},e^{n\pi x'/a};x'\}$ is the Wronskian of $e^{-n\pi x/a}$ and $e^{n\pi x/a}$ which is defined by

$$W = \begin{vmatrix} e^{-n\pi x'/a} & e^{n\pi x'/a} \\ -\dfrac{n\pi}{a}e^{-n\pi x'/a} & \dfrac{n\pi}{a}e^{n\pi x'/a} \end{vmatrix} = \frac{2\pi n}{a} \tag{7-59}$$

The boundary condition (7-53) stating that $\bar{G}$ must vanish as $x \to \pm\infty$ means that we must set both A and B equal to zero in Eq. (7-56), leaving

$$\bar{G} = \frac{a}{2\pi n} \sin\frac{n\pi y'}{a} e^{-n\pi x_>/a}e^{n\pi x_</a} \tag{7-60}$$

The inversion theorem for the finite sine transform,

$$G = \frac{2}{a} \sum_{n=1}^{\infty} \bar{G} \sin \frac{n\pi y}{a} \tag{7-61}$$

then gives

$$G(x,x';y,y') = \frac{1}{\pi} \sum_{n=1}^{\infty} \frac{1}{n} \sin \frac{n\pi y'}{a} \sin \frac{n\pi y}{a} e^{-n\pi x_> / a} e^{n\pi x_< / a} \tag{7-62}$$

which is the desired Green's-function solution of Eqs. (7-50) to (7-53). From Eq. (7-49),

$$\phi(x',y') = \frac{q}{\epsilon_0} G(0,x';d,y') \tag{7-63}$$

we recover the expression for the potential at (x',y') due to the line source at $x = 0$, $y = d$. Thus, putting $x = 0$, $y = d$ in Eq. (7-62), we find

$$\phi(x',y') = \frac{q}{\pi\epsilon_0} \sum_{n=1}^{\infty} \frac{1}{n} \sin \frac{n\pi d}{a} e^{-n\pi x' / a} \sin \frac{n\pi y'}{a} \tag{7-64}$$

for $x' > 0$ and

$$\phi(x',y') = \frac{q}{\pi\epsilon_0} \sum_{n=1}^{\infty} \frac{1}{n} \sin \frac{n\pi d}{a} e^{n\pi x' / a} \sin \frac{n\pi y'}{a} \tag{7-65}$$

for $x' < 0$. Notice that the character of the solution of Eq. (7-54) has forced a division of the space between the plates into two regions according to whether x' is greater or less than the coordinate $x = 0$ of the source.

This is not the only way in which the space between the plates may be subdivided. We may also separate the space between the plates into two regions according to whether y' is greater or less than the y coordinate of the source.

To do this we observe that the x subdivision occurs when a finite sine transform on y is used to solve Eq. (7-50). Hence we expect that a subdivision in y should occur when a transform with respect to x is used to solve (7-50). Since, in this problem, the x coordinate has the infinite range $-\infty \leq x \leq +\infty$, the complex Fourier transform is the most appropriate one to use.

Multiplying Eq. (7-50) through by e^{-ikx} and integrating twice by parts with respect to x from $x = -\infty$ to $x = +\infty$ gives us

$$\frac{d^2\bar{G}}{dy^2} - k^2\bar{G} = -e^{-ikx'} \delta(y - y') \tag{7-66}$$

where $\bar{G} = \int_{-\infty}^{+\infty} G e^{-ikx} \, dx$ and provided that

$$\lim_{|x| \to \infty} \left(\frac{\partial G}{\partial x} + ikG \right) = 0 \tag{7-67}$$

Equation (7-67) may be reasonably expected to hold because Eq. (7-53) implies that the potential very far from any sources is zero, and therefore the electric field, which is the gradient of the potential, should also vanish at such remote places.

The general solution of Eq. (7-66) is given by

$$\bar{G} = A \sinh ky + B \cosh ky$$
$$+ \frac{\sinh ky_> \cosh ky_<}{W\{\sinh ky', \cosh ky';y'\}} e^{-ikx'} \qquad (7\text{-}68)$$

and the Wronskian of $\sinh ky'$ and $\cosh ky'$ is

$$W = \begin{vmatrix} \sinh ky' & \cosh ky' \\ k \cosh ky' & k \sinh ky' \end{vmatrix} = -k \qquad (7\text{-}69)$$

Therefore

$$\bar{G} = A \sinh ky + B \cosh ky - (\sinh ky_> \cosh ky_<)\frac{e^{-ikx'}}{k} \qquad (7\text{-}70)$$

We must now satisfy the boundary conditions (7-51) and (7-52). On $y = 0, \bar{G} = 0$, and so

$$B = \frac{\sinh ky'}{k} e^{-ikx'} \qquad (7\text{-}71)$$

On $y = a, \bar{G} = 0$ gives

$$A \sinh ka + B \cosh ka - \sinh ka \cosh ky' \frac{e^{-ikx'}}{k} = 0 \qquad (7\text{-}72)$$

and combining Eqs. (7-71) and (7-72), we find

$$A = \frac{\sinh k(a - y')}{k \sinh ka} e^{-ikx'} \qquad (7\text{-}73)$$

$$B = \sinh ky' \frac{e^{-ikx'}}{k} \qquad (7\text{-}74)$$

Therefore $\bar{G}$ becomes

$$\bar{G} = \frac{e^{-ikx'}}{k} \left[\frac{\sinh k(a - y')}{\sinh ka} \sinh ky + \sinh ky' \cosh ky \right.$$
$$\left. - \sinh ky_> \cosh ky_< \right] \qquad (7\text{-}75)$$

Equation (7-75) provides us with a natural subdivision of the space between the two plates into two regions according to whether y is greater or less than y'.

For $y < y'$,

$$\bar{G} = \frac{e^{-ikx'}}{k} \left[\frac{\sinh k(a - y')}{\sinh ka} \sinh ky \right] \qquad (7\text{-}76)$$

whereas for $y > y'$,

$$\bar{G} = \frac{e^{-ikx'}}{k} \left[\frac{\sinh k(a - y')}{\sinh ka} \sinh ky - \sinh k(y - y') \right] \qquad (7\text{-}77)$$

The inversion theorem (5-320) for Fourier transforms now gives us the following expressions for the Green's function:

$$G(x,x';y,y') = \frac{1}{2\pi} \int_{-\infty}^{+\infty} e^{ik(x-x')} \frac{\sinh k(a - y')}{k \sinh ka} \sinh ky \, dk \qquad (7\text{-}78)$$

for $y < y'$, and

$$G(x,x';y,y') = \frac{1}{2\pi} \int_{-\infty}^{+\infty} e^{ik(x-x')} \, dk \left[\frac{\sinh k(a - y')}{k \sinh ka} \sinh ky - \frac{\sinh k(y - y')}{k} \right] \qquad (7\text{-}79)$$

for $y > y'$. The potentials for $y' > d$ and $y' < d$ are obtained from Eq. (7-49), and they are given by

$$\phi(x',y') = \frac{q}{2\pi\epsilon_0} \int_{-\infty}^{+\infty} e^{-ikx'} \frac{\sinh k(a - y')}{k \sinh ka} \sinh kd \, dk \qquad (7\text{-}80)$$

for $d \leq y' \leq a$ and

$$\phi(x',y') = \frac{q}{2\pi\epsilon_0} \int_{-\infty}^{+\infty} e^{-ikx'} \, dk \left[\frac{\sinh k(a - y')}{k \sinh ka} \sinh kd - \frac{\sinh k(d - y')}{k} \right] \qquad (7\text{-}81)$$

for $0 \leq y \leq d$.

The expressions (7-80) and (7-81) represent the electric potential at the point (x',y') due to a line source at $x = 0$, $y = d$. These expressions for the potentials can be simplified even further. For example, the integrand in (7-81) can be shortened by using the identity

$$\frac{\sinh k(a - y')}{k \sinh ka} \sinh kd - \frac{\sinh k(d - y')}{k}$$
$$= \frac{\sinh k(a - y') \sinh kd - \sinh ka \sinh k(d - y')}{k \sinh ka}$$
$$= \frac{\sinh k(a - d)}{k \sinh ka} \sinh ky' \qquad (7\text{-}82)$$

Next we recall that $e^{-ikx'} = \cos kx' - i \sin kx'$, and observing that the integrands in Eqs. (7-80) and (7-81), exclusive of the factor $e^{-ikx'}$, are strictly even in k, we conclude that only the real parts of (7-80) and (7-81) are nonzero. This happens because the $i \sin kx'$ contributions to (7-80) and (7-81), being odd, integrate to zero over the symmetric k interval $[-\infty, +\infty]$. Thus we are left with

$$\phi(x',y') = \frac{q}{2\pi\epsilon_0} \int_{-\infty}^{+\infty} \frac{\sinh kd}{k \sinh ka} \cos kx' \sinh k(a - y') \, dk \qquad (7\text{-}83)$$

for $d \leq y' \leq a$, and

$$\phi(x',y') = \frac{q}{2\pi\epsilon_0} \int_{-\infty}^{+\infty} \frac{\sinh k(a - d)}{k \sinh ka} \cos kx' \sinh ky' \, dk \qquad (7\text{-}84)$$

which holds for $0 \leq y' \leq d$.

The existence of two alternative ways to divide the space between the plates is not unique to this problem. In fact, most two-dimensional problems in potential theory, wave propagation, and diffusion exhibit a similar phenomenon when a Green's function must be determined.

How can we decide which of the two forms of the solution (7-64) and (7-65) or (7-83) and (7-84) is better? The solution (7-64) and (7-65) leaves us with the problem of summing a pair of infinite series, while (7-83) and (7-84) asks us to evaluate two complicated integrals.

When the coordinate $x = x'$ of the observer differs markedly from the coordinate $x = 0$ of the source, then the exponential factor $e^{-n\pi|x'|/a}$ occurring in Eqs. (7-64) and (7-65) is very small to begin with, and grows even smaller as n increases. Thus (7-64) and (7-65) are rapidly converging alternating series, the first few terms of which will give an excellent approximation to $\phi(x',y')$. On the other hand, when $|x'|$ is large, the $\cos kx'$ factor appearing in both (7-83) and (7-84) causes the integrands to oscillate very rapidly with changing k. As a result, the integrals will converge only very slowly to $\phi(x',y')$. Obviously, when the x coordinate of the observer differs markedly from the x coordinate of the source, the best solution to use is (7-64) and (7-65). If instead of the x coordinate, it is the y coordinate of the observer which differs markedly from the y coordinate of the source, then the situation is reversed. The exponential terms in (7-64) and (7-65), while still assisting convergence, are not so effective as before, and the two series will converge to $\phi(x',y')$ much more slowly than previously. At the same time, the factor $\cos kx'$ no longer oscillates as rapidly with changing k as it did before. Consequently, the integrals (7-83) and (7-84) will converge more rapidly to $\phi(x',y')$ than before. Hence, when the y coordinate of the observer differs markedly from the y coordinate of the source, the best solution to use is (7-83) and (7-84). We can summarize these results in the form of a *rule:*

In two-dimensional problems in potential theory, wave propagation, and diffusion, there will exist two distinct representations of the Green's function. One such representation will be found by taking an integral transform with respect to the y coordinate, and the other one by taking an integral transform with respect to the x coordinate.

When the x coordinate of the observer differs markedly from the x coordinate of the source, the Green's function found by using the integral transform on y converges the most rapidly. When the y coordinate of the observer differs markedly from the y coordinate of the source, the Green's function found by using the integral transform on x converges the most rapidly.

Reciprocity principle

The Green's function $G(x,x';y,y')$ represents, apart from the constant factor of q/ϵ_0, the potential at the point (x',y') due to a line source at

(x,y). We shall see that the Green's function satisfies the *reciprocity relation*

$$G(x,x';y,y') = G(x',x;y',y) \tag{7-85}$$

and consequently $G(x,x';y,y')$ must also represent the potential at (x,y) due to a line source at (x',y').

In other words, the points (x,y) and (x',y') are completely reciprocal in the sense that the potential at the second point due to a source at the first point is the same as the potential at the first point due to the same source placed at the second point.

To see that (Eq. 7-85) is true, let us begin with the identity

$$2 \sin \frac{n\pi y'}{a} \sin \frac{n\pi y}{a} = \cos \frac{n\pi}{a} (y - y') - \cos \frac{n\pi}{a} (y + y') \tag{7-86}$$

Inserting Eq. (7-86) into (7-62) and making use of the fact that

$$e^{-n\pi x_>/a} e^{n\pi x_</a} = e^{(-n\pi/a)|x-x'|} \tag{7-87}$$

we can reduce (7-62) to

$$G(x,x';y,y') = \frac{1}{2\pi} \sum_{n=1}^{\infty} \left[\cos \frac{n\pi}{a} (y - y') \right.$$

$$\left. - \cos \frac{n\pi}{a} (y + y') \right] e^{(-n\pi/a)|x-x'|} \tag{7-88}$$

and since $|x - x'| = |x' - x|$ and the cosine is an even function, we have shown that

$$G(x,x';y,y') = G(x',x;y',y)$$

Similarly, Eqs. (7-78) and (7-79) can be reduced to the single equation,

$$G(x,x';y,y') = \frac{1}{2\pi} \int_{-\infty}^{+\infty} \frac{\sinh k(a - y_>)}{k \sinh ka} \sinh ky_< \cos k(x - x') \, dk \tag{7-89}$$

by using the identity

$$\frac{\sinh k(a - y) \sinh ky}{k \sinh ka} - \frac{\sinh k(y - y')}{k}$$

$$= \frac{\sinh ky' \sinh k(a - y)}{k \sinh ka} \tag{7-90}$$

and remembering that since the integrand, apart from the factor $e^{ik(x-x')} = \cos k(x - x') + i \sin k(x - x')$, is even in k, only the cosine term will survive the integration from $-\infty$ to $+\infty$. Finally, we observe that since

$$\sinh k(a - y_>) \sinh ky_< = \cosh k[a - (y_> - y_<)]$$

$$- \cosh k[a - (y_> + y_<)] \tag{7-91}$$

and

$$y_> - y_< = |y - y'| \tag{7-92}$$

Eq. (7-89) becomes

$$G(x,x';y,y')$$
$$= \frac{1}{2\pi} \int_{-\infty}^{+\infty} \frac{\cosh k(a - |y - y'|) - \cosh k[a - (y + y')]}{k \sinh ka}$$
$$\cosh k(x - x') \, dk \qquad (7\text{-}93)$$

and once again we have demonstrated that

$$G(x,x';y,y') = G(x',x;y',y)$$

7-9 SEPARATION OF VARIABLES

An alternative to using integral transforms to construct the Green's function defined by

$$\nabla^2 G = -\delta(x - x') \, \delta(y - y') \qquad (7\text{-}94)$$

$$G = 0 \text{ on } y = 0 \qquad -\infty \leq x \leq +\infty \qquad (7\text{-}95)$$

$$G = 0 \text{ on } y = a \qquad -\infty \leq x \leq +\infty \qquad (7\text{-}96)$$

$$\lim_{|x| \to \infty} G = 0 \qquad 0 < y < a \qquad (7\text{-}97)$$

is to use the classical method of separation of variables.

This method begins with the observation that except at the point $x = x'$, $y = y'$ the Green's function G must satisfy Laplace's equation:

$$\nabla^2 G = 0 \qquad (7\text{-}98)$$

One then seeks a trial solution of Eq. (7-98) of the form

$$G = X(x) Y(y) \qquad (7\text{-}99)$$

Substituting Eq. (7-99) into Eq. (7-98) gives

$$YX'' + XY'' = 0 \qquad (7\text{-}100)$$

and on dividing both sides of Eq. (7-100) by Eq. (7-99), we find

$$\frac{X''(x)}{X(x)} + \frac{Y''(y)}{Y(y)} = 0 \qquad (7\text{-}101)$$

Since x and y vary independently, the only condition under which Eq. (7-101) can hold is that $X''(x)/X(x)$ and $Y''(y)/Y(y)$ are both constants. In particular, we can write

$$\frac{X''(x)}{X(x)} = -\frac{Y''(y)}{Y(y)} = C \qquad (7\text{-}102)$$

where the parameter C is called the separation constant. This separation of variables gives rise to two ordinary differential equations,

$$X''(x) - CX(x) = 0 \qquad (7\text{-}103)$$

and

$$Y''(y) + CY(y) = 0 \qquad (7\text{-}104)$$

which determine X and Y.

If there are no restrictions on the separation constant C, the product of the general solutions of the ordinary differential equations forms a fairly general solution of the two-dimensional Laplace equation.

As we shall see, the boundary conditions of the problem limit both the nature of the solution and the values of the separation constant C. For our purposes, it is convenient to let

$$C = \pm k^2 \tag{7-105}$$

so that the ordinary differential equations become

$$X'' \pm k^2 X = 0 \tag{7-106}$$

and

$$Y'' \pm k^2 Y = 0 \tag{7-107}$$

When $C = +k^2$, the general solutions of Eqs. (7-105) and (7-106) are

$$X(x) = D(k)e^{kx} + E(k)e^{-kx} \tag{7-108}$$

$$Y(y) = A(k) \sin ky + B(k) \cos ky \tag{7-109}$$

and for $C = -k^2$, the corresponding general solutions may be written in the form

$$X(x) = D(k) \cos kx + E(k) \sin kx \tag{7-110}$$

$$Y(y) = A(k) \sinh ky + B(k) \cosh ky \tag{7-111}$$

Thus both

$$G = X(x)Y(y) = \{D(k)e^{kx} + E(k)e^{-kx}\}\{A(k) \sin ky + B(k) \cos ky\} \tag{7-112}$$

and

$$G = X(x)Y(y) = \{D(k) \cos kx + E(k) \sin kx\}$$
$$\{A(k) \sinh ky + B(k) \cosh ky\} \tag{7-113}$$

are possible solutions of Laplace's equation $\nabla^2 G = 0$. The arbitrary parameters A, B, D, and E may depend on the separation constant k, and on x' and y', but not on x or y.

Both solutions (7-112) and (7-113) can be tailored to satisfy the boundary conditions at $y = 0$ and $y = a$. For example, consider Eq. (7-112). Let $k = n\pi/a$ where n is an integer, and choose $B = 0$. Then G_n vanishes at the upper and lower plates, and (7-112) reduces to

$$G_n = X_n(x) \sin \frac{n\pi y}{a} \tag{7-114}$$

where

$$X_n(x) = A\{De^{n\pi x/a} + Ee^{-n\pi x/a}\} \tag{7-115}$$

Since Laplace's equation is linear and Eq. (7-114) is a solution of it for arbitrary integer values of n, a superposition

$$G = \sum_{n=1}^{\infty} X_n(x) \sin \frac{n\pi y}{a} \tag{7-116}$$

of the solutions (7-114) will also satisfy $\nabla^2 G = 0$.

The functions $X_n(x)$ and $Y_n(y) = \sin n\pi y/a$ are called the "eigenfunctions" of the separated equations,

$$X_n'' = \left(\frac{n\pi}{a}\right)^2 X_n \qquad (7\text{-}117)$$

$$Y_n'' = -\left(\frac{n\pi}{a}\right)^2 Y_n \qquad (7\text{-}118)$$

obtained by applying the method of separation of variables to Laplace's equation. The numbers $n\pi/a$ are the corresponding eigenvalues associated with the eigenfunctions $X_n(x)$ and $Y_n(y)$. Whenever a linear operator acting on a function yields a constant times the function, the constant is called an "eigenvalue," the function is called an "eigenfunction," and the resulting equation is known as an "eigenvalue equation."

In the method of separation of variables, the allowed values of the separation constant generate the eigenvalues, the separation process gives the eigenvalue equations, and their solutions provide the corresponding eigenfunctions. The allowed values of the separation constant are usually determined by the boundary conditions. Here, for example, setting $k = n\pi/a$, where n is an integer, allows G to vanish at the upper and lower plates.

Equation (7-116) represents a solution of Laplace's equation as an expansion in products of eigenfunctions of the separated equations. Although (7-116) vanishes at $y = 0$ and $y = a$, it does not yet satisfy the boundary condition (7-97) at infinity. Furthermore, (7-116) is a solution of the homogeneous equation $\nabla^2 G = 0$, and what we really want is a solution of the inhomogeneous equation $\nabla^2 G = -\delta(x - x')$ $\delta(y - y')$. Our problem, therefore, is to choose $X_n(x)$ so that it satisfies three conditions. These are that it must be a solution of Eq. (7-117), except perhaps at $x = x'$; it must be such that

$$G = \sum_{n=1}^{\infty} X_n(x) \sin \frac{n\pi y}{a} \qquad (7\text{-}119)$$

is a solution of $\nabla^2 G = -\delta(x - x')\,\delta(y - y')$; and finally, $X_n(x)$ must satisfy

$$\lim_{|x| \to \infty} X_n(x) = 0 \qquad (7\text{-}120)$$

To fix these X_n's, let us treat them as essentially undetermined coefficients in the expansion (7-119). If we can expand $-\delta(x - x')$ $\delta(y - y')$ in terms of $\sin n\pi y/a$, then we can use Eq. (7-94) to determine the X_n's. Assuming an expansion

$$-\delta(x - x')\,\delta(y - y') = -\sum_{n=1}^{\infty} \delta(x - x')A_n \sin \frac{n\pi y}{a} \qquad (7\text{-}121)$$

we multiply Eq. (7-121) through by $\sin m\pi y/a$ and integrate with respect to y from 0 to a using

$$\int_0^a \sin \frac{n\pi y}{a} \sin \frac{m\pi y}{a}\, dy = \frac{a}{2}\, \delta_{nm} \qquad (7\text{-}122)$$

to find

$$A_n = \frac{2}{a} \sin \frac{n\pi y'}{a} \tag{7-123}$$

and as a result

$$-\delta(x - x') \delta(y - y') = \frac{-2}{a} \sum_{n=1}^{\infty} \delta(x - x') \sin \frac{n\pi y'}{a} \sin \frac{n\pi y}{a} \tag{7-124}$$

It follows from Eqs. (7-119) and (7-124) that $\nabla^2 G = -\delta(x - x') \delta(y - y')$ yields

$$\sum_{n=1}^{\infty} \left[\frac{d^2 X_n}{dx^2} - \left(\frac{n\pi}{a} \right)^2 X_n \right] \sin \frac{n\pi y}{a}$$

$$= \frac{-2}{a} \sum_{n=1}^{\infty} \delta(x - x') \sin \frac{n\pi y'}{a} \sin \frac{n\pi y}{a} \tag{7-125}$$

and on equating the coefficients of $\sin n\pi y/a$ on both sides of Eq. (7-125), we obtain

$$\frac{d^2 X_n}{dx^2} - \left(\frac{n\pi}{a} \right)^2 X_n = \frac{-2}{a} \sin \frac{n\pi y'}{a} \delta(x - x') \tag{7-126}$$

This equation is essentially Eq. (7-54), and its particular integral is

$$X_n(x) = \frac{1}{n\pi} \sin \frac{n\pi y'}{a} e^{-n\pi x_>/a} e^{n\pi x_</a} \tag{7-127}$$

We see from Eq. (7-127) that except at $x = x'$, $X_n(x)$ satisfies Eq. (7-117) and has the correct behavior (7-120) at infinity. Inserting (7-127) into Eq. (7-119) gives

$$G(x,x';y,y') = \frac{1}{\pi} \sum_{n=1}^{\infty} \frac{1}{n} \sin \frac{n\pi y'}{a} \sin \frac{n\pi y}{a} e^{-n\pi x_>/a} e^{n\pi x_</a} \tag{7-128}$$

and we have recovered Eq. (7-62).

Instead of beginning with Eq. (7-112), we could have used (7-113). However, since the hyperbolic sine and cosine are not periodic functions, we can no longer make G vanish on $y = 0$ and $y = a$ by choosing $k = n\pi/a$. Thus the separation constant k must remain a continuous parameter. Application of the principle of superposition permits us to write solutions of Laplace's equation like

$$G = \int_{-\infty}^{+\infty} \{ D(k) \cos kx + E(k) \sin kx \}$$
$$\{ A(k) \sinh ky + B(k) \cosh ky \} \, dk \tag{7-129}$$

wherein the summation over a discrete separation parameter such as $n\pi/a$ is replaced by an integration over the continuous separation parameter k.

Our problem now is to determine the coefficients A, B, D, and E in such a way that Eqs. (7-94) through (7-97) are satisfied. One clue as to how to proceed is based on the Fourier integral representation of the Dirac delta function:

$$\delta(x - x') = \frac{1}{2\pi} \int_{-\infty}^{+\infty} \cos k(x - x') \, dk \tag{7-130}$$

Using Eq. (7-130), we can write $-\delta(x - x')\,\delta(y - y')$ as

$$-\delta(x - x')\,\delta(y - y') = -\frac{1}{2\pi} \int_{-\infty}^{+\infty} \delta(y - y') \cos k(x - x') \, dk \tag{7-131}$$

and this is the present equivalent of (7-124). Since Eq. (7-131) depends on $\cos k(x - x')$, we choose D and E in Eq. (7-129) in such a way that Eq. (7-129) takes the form

$$G = \int_{-\infty}^{+\infty} Y(k,y) \cos k(x - x') \, dk \tag{7-132}$$

where

$$Y(k,y) = \{A(k) \sinh ky + B(k) \cosh ky\} \tag{7-133}$$

It follows from Eqs. (7-130) and (7-132) that $\nabla^2 G = -\delta(x - x')\,\delta(y - y')$ yields

$$\int_{-\infty}^{+\infty} \left(\frac{d^2 Y}{dy^2} - k^2 Y\right) \cos k(x - x') \, dk$$
$$= \frac{-1}{2\pi} \int_{-\infty}^{+\infty} \delta(y - y') \cos k(x - x') \, dk \tag{7-134}$$

as the analogue of Eq. (7-125). Equating the coefficients of $\cos k(x - x')$ on each side of Eq. (7-134) gives us

$$\frac{d^2 Y}{dy^2} - k^2 Y = -\frac{1}{2\pi} \delta(y - y') \tag{7-135}$$

for the determination of $Y(k,y)$.

The solution of Eq. (7-135) which satisfies the boundary conditions

$$Y = 0 \text{ on } y = 0 \tag{7-136}$$

and

$$Y = 0 \text{ on } y = a \tag{7-137}$$

can be written as

$$Y(k,y) = \frac{\sinh k(a - y_>) \sinh ky_<}{2\pi k \sinh ka} \tag{7-138}$$

and inserting this expression into Eq. (7-132) gives

$$G(x,x';y,y') = \frac{1}{2\pi} \int_{-\infty}^{+\infty} \frac{\sinh k(a - y_>) \sinh ky_<}{k \sinh ka} \cos k(x - x') \, dk \tag{7-139}$$

As expected, we have recovered the result of Eq. (7-89).

Consider the problem of computing a potential function $\phi(x,y)$ throughout a half space $x \geq 0$, in such a way that it reduces to a specific function, say $f(y)$, on $x = 0$. In mathematical terms, we want to find a solution of

$$\nabla^2 \phi = 0 \tag{7-140}$$

for $x \geq 0$ that satisfies the following conditions:

$$\phi(0,y) = f(y) \text{ on } x = 0 \tag{7-141}$$

$$\lim_{x \to \infty} \phi(x,y) = 0 \tag{7-142}$$

for any real y, and

$$\lim_{|y| \to \infty} \phi(x,y) = 0 \tag{7-143}$$

for all $x \geq 0$.

This problem can be solved with the general Green's-function technique outlined in Sec. 7-8. The computation begins with Green's symmetric identity:

$$\int_S \{g \nabla^2 \phi - \phi \nabla^2 g\} \, dS = \int_{C(S)} \left\{ g \frac{\partial \phi}{\partial n} - \phi \frac{\partial g}{\partial n} \right\} ds \tag{7-144}$$

In Eq. (7-144), S represents the portion of the half plane $x \geq 0$ enclosed by the curve $C(S)$. This curve is formed by the y axis and the circumference of a semicircle of very large (actually infinite) radius located in the right half plane. It is reasonable to assume that the potential vanishes everywhere along the infinite semicircle. Under these circumstances only the line integral along y contributes to Eq. (7-144), which becomes

$$\int_0^{+\infty} \int_{-\infty}^{+\infty} \{g \nabla^2 \phi - \phi \nabla^2 g\} \, dx \, dy = \int_{-\infty}^{+\infty} \left\{ g \frac{\partial \phi}{\partial n} \right.$$
$$\left. - \phi \frac{\partial g}{\partial n} \right\} dy \tag{7-145}$$

The line integral on the right side of Eq. (7-145) is understood to be computed along the line $x = 0$, in other words, along the y axis. Since we have not been given any information about $\partial \phi / \partial n$ on $x = 0$, the term in which it appears must be eliminated. We eliminate it by choosing g so that

$$g = 0 \text{ on } x = 0 \tag{7-146}$$

One way of satisfying Eq. (7-146) is to let g be a special "half-space" Green's function which has odd symmetry with respect to x. If g is such a function, then it must satisfy

$$g(-x,x';y,y') = -g(x,x';y,y') \tag{7-147}$$

and consequently g will vanish on $x = 0$. Suppose that

$$g(x,x';y,y') = G(x,x';y,y') - G(-x,x';y,y') \tag{7-148}$$

and that $G(x,x';y,y')$ satisfies

$$\nabla^2 G = -\delta(x - x') \, \delta(y - y') \tag{7-149}$$

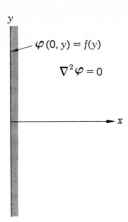

$\varphi(0, y) = f(y)$

$\nabla^2 \varphi = 0$

Figure 7-2 The potential problem for a half space.

Then G represents the potential at (x',y') due to a line source of unit positive charge density located at (x,y). Obviously g, as given by Eq. (7-148), has property (7-147) and thus satisfies Eq. (7-146). Furthermore, (7-148) gives us a physical interpretation for g. Because of Eq. (7-149), g must satisfy

$$\nabla^2 g = -\delta(x - x') \, \delta(y - y') + \delta(x + x') \, \delta(y - y') \qquad (7\text{-}150)$$

with

$$g = 0 \text{ on } x = 0 \qquad (7\text{-}151)$$

and therefore $g(x,x';y,y')$ must represent the potential at the point (x',y') when there is a grounded conducting plane, halfway between a line source of unit positive charge density located at (x,y) and a line source of unit negative charge density located at $(-x,y)$. In electromagnetic theory, this solution is described by saying that in order to determine the potential due to a positive line charge in the presence of a grounded conducting plane, it is necessary to introduce a *fictitious image line charge* of the opposite sign. The location of the image charge is chosen so that it is the geometrical reflection in the grounded plane of the original line charge. It follows that, by symmetry, the grounded plane must be at zero potential.

We are now ready to return to Eq. (7-145). Since $\partial g/\partial n$ represents the rate of change of g along the *outward* normal to $C(S)$, we must have

$$\frac{\partial g}{\partial n} = -\frac{\partial g}{\partial x} \text{ on } x = 0 \qquad (7\text{-}152)$$

Taking note of (7-140), (7-141), and (7-150) to (7-152), Eq. (7-145) gives us

$$\int_0^\infty \int_{-\infty}^{+\infty} \phi(x,y)[\delta(x - x') \, \delta(y - y') - \delta(x + x') \, \delta(y - y')] \, dx \, dy$$

$$= \int_{-\infty}^{+\infty} f(y) \frac{\partial g}{\partial x} \, dy \qquad (7\text{-}153)$$

Only the first term in Eq. (7-153) contributes to the left side because x is always positive, and as a result

$$\phi(x',y') = \int_{-\infty}^{+\infty} f(y) \frac{\partial g}{\partial x} \, dy \tag{7-154}$$

is the formal solution of our problem. Equation (7-154) represents $\phi(x',y')$ in terms of the half-space Green's function. As usual, the real problem is to construct the Green's function itself.

Construction of the half-space Green's function

Once again let us consider the problem of solving

$$\nabla^2 G = -\delta(x - x') \, \delta(y - y') \tag{7-155}$$

subject to the condition that very far away from the source, G and its derivatives approach zero. Multiplying Eq. (7-155) by e^{-iky} and integrating over y from $y = -\infty$ to $y = +\infty$ gives

$$\frac{d^2\bar{G}}{dx^2} - k^2\bar{G} = -\delta(x - x')e^{-iky'} \tag{7-156}$$

where

$$\bar{G} = \int_{-\infty}^{+\infty} G e^{-iky} \, dy \tag{7-157}$$

assuming that

$$\lim_{|y| \to \infty} \left(\frac{\partial G}{\partial y} + ikG \right) = 0 \tag{7-158}$$

We have already encountered both Eq. (7-156) and its general solution in Eqs. (7-66) and (7-68). However, it is also enlightening to obtain a particular integral of (7-156) by a different technique. Thus, consider

$$\bar{G} = Ae^{-|k|(x-x')} \qquad x > x' \tag{7-159}$$

and

$$\bar{G} = Be^{|k|(x-x')} \qquad x < x' \tag{7-160}$$

Both Eqs. (7-159) and (7-160) satisfy (7-156) when $x \neq x'$. The solution (7-159) has the property that as the source coordinate $x \to +\infty$, the disturbance $\bar{G}$ at x' goes to zero as it should, because then the source and observer are infinitely removed from each other. Similarly, as $x \to -\infty$ in Eq. (7-160), the disturbance at x' also vanishes. Each "half" of the solution gives the correct behavior at x' as the source recedes to ∞ in the appropriate direction. Out of these two pieces, (7-159) and (7-160), we shall manufacture a single continuous solution of Eq. (7-156).

Continuity of Eqs. (7-159) and (7-160) at $x = x'$ requires that $A = B$, and therefore

$$\bar{G} = Ae^{-|k|(x-x')} \qquad x > x' \tag{7-161}$$

and

$$\bar{G} = Ae^{|k|(x-x')} \qquad x < x' \tag{7-162}$$

together, form a single continuous solution of Eq. (7-156). The object now is to choose A so that Eqs. (7-161) and (7-162) satisfy (7-156) not only for $x > x'$ and $x < x'$, respectively, but for $x \geq x'$ and $x \leq x'$ as well. To do this, suppose that we integrate (7-156) about a small interval of length 2ϵ centered on $x = x'$,

$$\int_{x=x'-\epsilon}^{x=x'+\epsilon} \frac{d^2\bar{G}}{dx^2}\, dx - k^2 \int_{x=x'-\epsilon}^{x=x'+\epsilon} \bar{G}\, dx = -e^{-iky'} \int_{x=x'-\epsilon}^{x=x'+\epsilon} \delta(x-x')\, dx \tag{7-163}$$

and then take the limit of Eq. (7-163) as $\epsilon \to 0$. The result is

$$\lim_{\epsilon \to 0} \frac{d\bar{G}}{dx} \Big|_{x=x'-\epsilon}^{x=x'+\epsilon} = -e^{-iky'} \tag{7-164}$$

The second term on the left side of Eq. (7-163) vanishes as $\epsilon \to 0$ because $\bar{G}$ is constructed to be continuous at $x = x'$. The result (7-164) tells us that the derivative of $\bar{G}$ must be discontinuous at $x = x'$ and that the *jump* or *saltus* in $d\bar{G}/dx$ must be equal to $-e^{-iky'}$. It is this condition which permits us to determine A in Eqs. (7-161) and (7-162), for by differentiation we find

$$\frac{d}{dx} A e^{-|k|(x-x')} = -|k| A e^{-|k|(x-x')} \qquad x > x' \tag{7-165}$$

and

$$\frac{d}{dx} A e^{|k|(x-x')} = |k| A e^{|k|(x-x')} \qquad x < x' \tag{7-166}$$

Therefore

$$\frac{d\bar{G}}{dx} \Big|_{x=x'-\epsilon}^{x=x'+\epsilon} = -|k| A e^{-|k|\epsilon} - |k| A e^{-|k|\epsilon} = -2|k| A e^{-|k|\epsilon} \tag{7-167}$$

gives us

$$\lim_{\epsilon \to 0} \frac{d\bar{G}}{dx} \Big|_{x=x'-\epsilon}^{x=x'+\epsilon} = -2|k| A = -e^{-iky'} \tag{7-168}$$

so that

$$A = \frac{e^{-iky'}}{2|k|} \tag{7-169}$$

We can represent the two formulas (7-161) and (7-162) as a single equation by using $|x - x'|$ in the exponential; then

$$\bar{G} = \frac{e^{-iky'-|k||x-x'|}}{2|k|} \tag{7-170}$$

is the desired solution of Eq. (7-156). The Fourier transform of the half-space Green's function (7-148) must satisfy

$$\bar{g}(x,x';y';k) = \bar{G}(x,x';y';k) - \bar{G}(-x,x';y';k) \tag{7-171}$$

where

$$\bar{g}(x,x';y';k) = \int_{-\infty}^{+\infty} g(x,x';y,y') e^{-iky}\, dy \tag{7-172}$$

Using Eq. (7-170), we conclude that

$$\bar{g}(x,x';y';k) = e^{-iky'}\left(\frac{e^{-|k||x-x'|} - e^{-|k||x+x'|}}{2|k|}\right) \qquad (7\text{-}173)$$

and applying Fourier's inversion formula (5-348) to Eq. (7-173) gives

$$g(x,x';y,y') = \frac{1}{2\pi}\int_{-\infty}^{+\infty} e^{ik(y-y')}\frac{e^{-|k||x-x'|} - e^{-|k||x+x'|}}{2|k|}\,dk \qquad (7\text{-}174)$$

The formula (7-154) for $\phi(x',y')$,

$$\phi(x',y') = \int_{-\infty}^{+\infty} f(y)\frac{\partial g}{\partial x}\,dy \qquad (7\text{-}175)$$

can now be simplified if we remember that $\partial g/\partial x$ is to be evaluated on $x = 0$.

Differentiating Eq. (7-174) under the integral sign gives us

$$\frac{\partial g}{\partial x} = \frac{1}{2\pi}\int_{-\infty}^{+\infty} e^{-k(y-y')}\frac{-|k|e^{-|k||x-x'|} + |k|e^{-|k||x+x'|}}{2|k|}\,dk$$
$$x > x' > 0 \qquad (7\text{-}176)$$

and

$$\frac{\partial g}{\partial x} = \frac{1}{2\pi}\int_{-\infty}^{+\infty} e^{ik(y-y')}\frac{|k|e^{-|k||x-x'|} + |k|e^{-|k||x+x'|}}{2|k|}\,dk$$
$$x' > x > 0 \qquad (7\text{-}177)$$

We must select the appropriate expression for $\partial g/\partial x$ as $x \to 0$ from the two possible choices (7-176) and (7-177). Since the observer is assumed to be located in the physical half space $x' > 0$, the inequality $x > x' > 0$ associated with (7-176) eliminates this expression from contention when $x = 0$. Therefore we are left with (7-177), which reduces to

$$\left(\frac{\partial g}{\partial x}\right)_{x=0} = \frac{1}{2\pi}\int_{-\infty}^{+\infty} e^{ik(y-y')-|k||x'|}\,dk \text{ on } x = 0 \qquad (7\text{-}178)$$

The integral in Eq. (7-178) can be integrated directly to give

$$\int_{-\infty}^{+\infty} e^{ik(y-y')-|k||x'|}\,dk = \int_{-\infty}^{0} e^{ik(y-y')-|k||x'|}\,dk$$
$$+ \int_{0}^{\infty} e^{ik(y-y')-|k||x'|}\,dk = \int_{0}^{\infty} e^{-ik(y-y')-|k||x'|}\,dk$$
$$+ \int_{0}^{\infty} e^{ik(y-y')-|k|x'|}\,dk = \frac{-1}{-i(y-y') - |x'|}$$
$$- \frac{1}{i(y-y') - |x'|} = \frac{+2|x'|}{(x')^2 + (y-y')^2} \qquad (7\text{-}179)$$

and consequently

$$\left(\frac{\partial g}{\partial x}\right)_{x=0} = \frac{1}{\pi}\frac{|x'|}{(x')^2 + (y-y')^2} \qquad (7\text{-}180)$$

Thus, the problem of computing a potential function which satisfies Laplace's equation in the half space $x' \geq 0$ and which reduces to

$f(y')$ on $x' = 0$ is solved by the formula

$$\phi(x',y') = \frac{x'}{\pi} \int_{-\infty}^{+\infty} \frac{f(y)}{(x')^2 + (y - y')^2} \, dy \qquad (7\text{-}181)$$

REMARK: The problem of solving $\nabla^2\phi = 0$ for some domain in such a way that ϕ reduces to a given function on the boundary of the domain is known as "Dirichlet's problem." One says that ϕ obeys an inhomogeneous Dirichlet condition on the boundary. For example, Eq. (7-181) is the solution of Dirichlet's problem for the half space $x' \geq 0$, and $\phi(x',y')$ satisfies the inhomogeneous Dirichlet condition $\phi(0,y') = f(y')$ on the boundary $x' = 0$ of the half space.

7-11 LAPLACE'S EQUATION IN POLAR COORDINATES

In plane polar coordinates (r,θ), Laplace's equation becomes

$$\nabla^2\phi = \frac{1}{r}\frac{\partial}{\partial r}\left(r\frac{\partial\phi}{\partial r}\right) + \frac{1}{r^2}\frac{\partial^2\phi}{\partial\theta^2} = 0 \qquad (7\text{-}182)$$

The Green's-function technique of solving boundary-value problems for Eq. (7-182) applies in general. It is only in constructing the Green's function itself, that one must deal with particular coordinate systems. Thus Eq. (7-34) gives us the formal solution of (7-182),

$$\phi(r',\theta') = \int_{C(S)}\left\{G\frac{\partial\phi}{\partial n} - \phi\frac{\partial G}{\partial n}\right\} ds \qquad (7\text{-}183)$$

where now the Green's function $G(r,r';\theta,\theta')$ appearing in Eq. (7-183) is defined as the solution of

$$\nabla^2 G = \frac{-\delta(r - r')\,\delta(\theta - \theta')}{r} \qquad (7\text{-}184)$$

A few comments regarding Eqs. (7-183) and (7-184) are in order. Formula (7-183) represents the potential ϕ at the point (r',θ') in terms of the boundary values of ϕ and $\partial\phi/\partial n$ on a curve $C(S)$ enclosing (r',θ').

This actually overdetermines the problem, because ϕ and $\partial\phi/\partial n$ cannot be independently assigned on $C(S)$. To see why this is true, consider the one-dimensional analogue of Laplace's equation,

$$\frac{d^2\phi}{dx^2} = 0 \text{ on } a \leq x \leq b \qquad (7\text{-}185)$$

Corresponding to Eq. (7-183), we have

$$\phi(x') = \left\{G\frac{d\phi}{dx} - \phi\frac{dG}{dx}\right\}_{x=a}^{x=b} \qquad (7\text{-}186)$$

where $G(x|x')$ is the solution of

$$\frac{d^2 G}{dx^2} = -\delta(x - x') \qquad (7\text{-}187)$$

Formula (7-186) asks us to specify both ϕ and $d\phi/dx$ at $x = a$ and at $x = b$. However, the solution of Eq. (7-185) must be a straight line. Having specified ϕ and $d\phi/dx$ at $x = a$, these quantities are completely determined at $x = b$ and cannot be arbitrarily assigned. One remedy for this impasse is to choose G so that it vanishes at $x = a$ and $x = b$. Then Eq. (7-186) involves only the values of ϕ at a and b, and these can indeed be arbitrarily assigned.

The same sort of argument shows that ϕ and $\partial\phi/\partial n$ cannot both be arbitrarily specified on $C(S)$. This difficulty is now resolved as before. One solves Eq. (7-184) subject to a *homogeneous Dirichlet condition*, $G = 0$ on $C(S)$, obtaining in the process

$$\phi(r',\theta') = -\int_{C(S)} \phi \frac{\partial G}{\partial n}\, ds \tag{7-188}$$

It is also possible to solve Eq. (7-184) subject to a *homogeneous Neumann condition*, $\partial G/\partial n = 0$ on $C(S)$; then

$$\phi(r',\theta') = \int_{C(S)} G \frac{\partial \phi}{\partial n}\, ds \tag{7-189}$$

Other possibilities exist as well, but we shall not treat these here.

Returning to (7-184), we notice that the right side contains the expression $-\delta(\theta - \theta')\,\delta(r - r')/r$. The $1/r$ factor arises because the element of area in polar coordinates is $dS = r\, dr\, d\theta$, and we must have

$$\int_S \delta(\mathbf{r} - \mathbf{r}')\, dS = \iint_S \delta(x - x')\,\delta(y - y')\, dx\, dy$$

$$= \iint_S \frac{\delta(r - r')}{r}\, \delta(\theta - \theta')r\, dr\, d\theta$$

$$= \begin{cases} 1 & (r',\theta')\ \text{contained in area } S \\ 0 & (r',\theta')\ \text{outside of area } S \end{cases} \tag{7-190}$$

7-12 CONSTRUCTION OF A GREEN'S FUNCTION IN POLAR COORDINATES

The real problem in using Eq. (7-188) or (7-189) is the actual construction of an appropriate Green's function. We shall apply the method of separation of variables for this purpose. One sets

$$\phi = R(r)\Theta(\theta) \tag{7-191}$$

into

$$\nabla^2\phi = \frac{\partial^2\phi}{\partial r^2} + \frac{1}{r}\frac{\partial\phi}{\partial r} + \frac{1}{r^2}\frac{\partial^2\phi}{\partial\theta^2} = 0 \tag{7-192}$$

to obtain

$$r^2\frac{d^2R/dr^2 + (1/r)\, dR/dr}{R} = -\frac{d^2\Theta/d\theta^2}{\Theta} \tag{7-193}$$

Since the left side of Eq. (7-193) is a function of r alone, while the right side depends only on θ, both sides must be equal to one and the same constant, say n^2. Then

$$-\frac{d^2\Theta/d\theta^2}{\Theta} = n^2 \tag{7-194}$$

$$r^2 \frac{d^2R/dr^2 + (1/r)\, dR/dr}{R} = n^2 \tag{7-195}$$

give the separated equations

$$\frac{d^2\Theta}{d\theta^2} + n^2\Theta = 0 \tag{7-196}$$

and

$$\frac{d^2R}{dr^2} + \frac{1}{r}\frac{dR}{dr} - \frac{n^2}{r^2}R = 0 \tag{7-197}$$

When n is an integer, Θ is periodic in θ with period 2π. The solutions of Eqs. (7-196) and (7-197) always separate into two groups according to whether n is zero or not.

If n is not zero,

$$\Theta_n(\theta) = A_n \cos n\theta + B_n \sin n\theta \tag{7-198}$$

and

$$R_n(r) = C_n r^n + D_n r^{-n} \tag{7-199}$$

are the general solutions of Eqs. (7-196) and (7-197). For $n = 0$ the solutions become

$$\Theta_0 = A_0\theta + B_0 \tag{7-200}$$

$$R_0(r) = C_0 \log r + D_0 \tag{7-201}$$

Assuming that n is an integer, an infinite sum of these separated solutions gives the general solution of $\nabla^2\phi = 0$ in polar coordinates:

$$\phi(r,\theta) = \sum_{n=0}^{\infty} R_n(r)\Theta_n(\theta) = (A_0\theta + B_0)(C_0 \log r + D_0)$$

$$+ \sum_{n=0}^{\infty} \{A_n \cos n\theta + B_n \sin n\theta\}\{C_n r^n + D_n r^{-n}\} \tag{7-202}$$

The term $\{A_n \cos n\theta + B_n \sin n\theta\}\{C_n r^n + D_n r^{-n}\}$ is called a "circular harmonic of degree n," and $\{A_0\theta + B_0\}\{C_0 \log r + D_0\}$ is called a "circular harmonic of degree zero."

Construction of the Green's function

The Green's function must satisfy

$$\nabla^2 G = -\frac{\delta(r - r')\, \delta(\theta - \theta')}{r} \tag{7-203}$$

and if we want to solve Dirichlet's problem for a circle using Eq. (7-188), then G must also satisfy the boundary condition

$$G = 0 \text{ on } r = a \qquad 0 \leq \theta \leq 2\pi \tag{7-204}$$

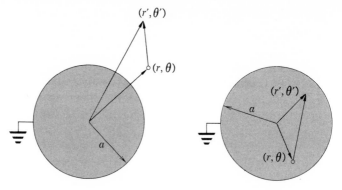

Exterior Dirichlet problem   Interior Dirichlet problem

Figure 7-3   The exterior and interior Dirichlet problems for a circle.

The Green's function $G(r,r';\theta,\theta')$ defined by Eq. (7-203) represents the potential at (r',θ') due to a line source of positive charge located at (r,θ). Equation (7-204) expresses the presence of a grounded conducting cylinder of radius $r = a$. If $r < a$, $r' < a$, both source and observer are inside the circle $r = a$, and (7-203) and (7-204) form an interior Dirichlet problem. If $r > a$, $r' > a$, then the reverse is true, and (7-203) and (7-204) constitute an exterior Dirichlet problem for the circle (Fig. 7-3).

Following the procedure of Eqs. (7-119) to (7-128), let us represent the solution of

$$\nabla^2 G = \frac{-\delta(r - r')\,\delta(\theta - \theta')}{r} \tag{7-205}$$

in terms of an expansion in eigenfunctions of the separated equation (7-196):

$$G = \sum_{n=-\infty}^{+\infty} R_n(r)e^{in\theta} \tag{7-206}$$

The right side of Eq. (7-205) must also be expanded in these eigenfunctions, and we write

$$\frac{\delta(r - r')\,\delta(\theta - \theta')}{r} = \sum_{n=-\infty}^{+\infty} \frac{\delta(r - r')}{r}\,C_n e^{in\theta} \tag{7-207}$$

To compute the C_n's, multiply Eq. (7-207) through by $e^{-im\theta}$, and integrate both sides with respect to θ, using

$$\int_{-\pi}^{\pi} e^{i(n-m)\theta}\,d\theta = 2\pi\delta_{nm} \tag{7-208}$$

This gives $C_n = (1/2\pi)e^{-in\theta'}$, and therefore

$$\frac{\delta(r - r')\,\delta(\theta - \theta')}{r} = \frac{1}{2\pi} \sum_{n=-\infty}^{+\infty} \frac{\delta(r - r')}{r}\,e^{in(\theta-\theta')} \tag{7-209}$$

Equations (7-206) and (7-209) are now substituted into (7-205) to give us

$$\sum_{n=-\infty}^{+\infty} \left(\frac{d^2 R_n}{dr^2} + \frac{1}{r} \frac{dR_n}{dr} - \frac{n^2}{r^2} R_n \right) e^{in\theta}$$

$$= \frac{-1}{2\pi} \frac{\delta(r - r')}{r} \sum_{n=-\infty}^{+\infty} e^{in(\theta - \theta')} \qquad (7\text{-}210)$$

Equating the coefficients of $e^{in\theta}$ on both sides of Eq. (7-210) determines R_n. It must be a solution of

$$\frac{d^2 R_n}{dr^2} + \frac{1}{r} \frac{dR_n}{dr} - \frac{n^2}{r^2} R_n = - \frac{1}{2\pi} \frac{\delta(r - r')}{r} e^{-in\theta'} \qquad (7\text{-}211)$$

We shall solve Eq. (7-211) using the technique of Eq. (7-159). Let r' be a fixed positive number, and suppose that $n \neq 0$ and $r \neq r'$. Then (7-211) is satisfied by

$$R_n = A r^{|n|} \qquad 0 \le r < r' < \infty \qquad (7\text{-}212)$$

and

$$R_n = B r^{-|n|} \qquad r' < r < \infty \qquad (7\text{-}213)$$

The absolute-value signs around n in Eqs. (7-212) and (7-213) guarantee that R_n will always remain finite for $r = 0$ and $r = \infty$, regardless of whether n is a positive or a negative integer.

Continuity of R_n at $r = r'$ requires that

$$A(r')^{|n|} = B(r')^{-|n|} \qquad (7\text{-}214)$$

The determination of A and B is completed by integrating Eq. (7-211) with respect to r from $r = r' - \epsilon$ to $r = r' + \epsilon$, where ϵ is some small positive number. We have

$$\frac{1}{r} \frac{d}{dr} \left(r \frac{dR_n}{dr} \right) - \frac{n^2}{r^2} R_n = - \frac{1}{2\pi} \frac{\delta(r - r')}{r} e^{-in\theta'} \qquad (7\text{-}215)$$

and therefore

$$\int_{r'-\epsilon}^{r'+\epsilon} \frac{d}{dr} \left(r \frac{dR_n}{dr} \right) dr - n^2 \int_{r'-\epsilon}^{r'+\epsilon} \frac{R_n}{r} dr = - \frac{1}{2\pi} e^{-in\theta'} \qquad (7\text{-}216)$$

Suppose we take the limit in Eq. (7-216) as $\epsilon \to 0$. Since R_n has been made continuous at $r = r'$, the second term in (7-216) vanishes, and we are left with

$$\lim_{\epsilon \to 0} r \frac{dR_n}{dr} \Big|_{r=r'-\epsilon}^{r=r'+\epsilon} = - \frac{1}{2\pi} e^{-in\theta'} \qquad (7\text{-}217)$$

Combined with Eqs. (7-212) and (7-213), Eq. (7-217) gives

$$-|n| B(r')^{-|n|} - |n| A(r')^{|n|} = - \frac{1}{2\pi} e^{-in\theta'} \qquad (7\text{-}218)$$

Solving Eqs. (7-218) and (7-214) simultaneously determines A and B:

$$A = \frac{e^{-in\theta'}}{4\pi |n| (r')^{|n|}} \qquad (7\text{-}219)$$

$$B = \frac{(r')^{|n|} e^{-in\theta'}}{4\pi |n|} \qquad (7\text{-}220)$$

For $n \neq 0$,

$$R_n = \frac{1}{4\pi|n|} \left(\frac{r}{r'}\right)^{|n|} e^{-in\theta'} \qquad 0 \leq r \leq r' \qquad (7\text{-}221)$$

and

$$R_n = \frac{1}{4\pi|n|} \left(\frac{r'}{r}\right)^{|n|} e^{-in\theta'} \qquad r' \leq r < \infty \qquad (7\text{-}222)$$

These two formulas can be written as usual as a single equation:

$$R_n = \frac{1}{4\pi|n|} \left(\frac{r_<}{r_>}\right)^{|n|} e^{-in\theta'} \qquad n \neq 0 \qquad (7\text{-}223)$$

For the case where $n = 0$, Eq. (7-215) reduces to

$$\frac{1}{r}\frac{d}{dr}\left(r\frac{dR_n}{dr}\right) = -\frac{1}{2\pi}\frac{\delta(r-r')}{r} e^{-in\theta} \qquad (7\text{-}224)$$

In order to construct the desired particular integral of Eq. (7-224) we need two linearly independent solutions of the homogeneous version of (7-224). These solutions are $C_0 \log r$ and a constant, D_0. If G is to remain finite at the origin $r = 0$, then one must choose

$$R_0(r) = D_0 \qquad 0 \leq r < r' \qquad (7\text{-}225)$$

$$R_0(r) = C_0 \log r \qquad r' < r < \infty \qquad (7\text{-}226)$$

Continuity of $R_0(r)$ at $r = r'$ requires

$$C_0 \log r' = D_0 \qquad (7\text{-}227)$$

and for $n = 0$, Eq. (7-217) becomes

$$\lim_{\epsilon \to 0} r \frac{dR_0}{dr} \Big|_{r=r'-\epsilon}^{r=r'+\epsilon} = -\frac{1}{2\pi} \qquad (7\text{-}228)$$

which gives $C_0 = -1/2\pi$. Thus

$$R_0(r) = -\frac{1}{2\pi} \log r' \qquad 0 \leq r \leq r' \qquad (7\text{-}229)$$

$$R_0(r) = -\frac{1}{2\pi} \log r \qquad r' \leq r < \infty \qquad (7\text{-}230)$$

is the solution of Eq. (7-215) for $n = 0$. As before, we can express Eqs. (7-229) and (7-230) as a single equation:

$$R_0(r) = -\frac{1}{2\pi} \log r_> \qquad (7\text{-}231)$$

From Eq. (7-206), using (7-223) and (7-231), we obtain the eigenfunction expansion of the infinite-medium Green's function:

$$G_\infty(r,r';\theta,\theta') = -\frac{1}{2\pi} \log r_> + \frac{1}{4\pi} \sum_{n=-\infty}^{+\infty}{}' \left(\frac{r_<}{r_>}\right)^{|n|} \frac{e^{in(\theta-\theta')}}{|n|} \qquad (7\text{-}232)$$

The prime on the summation sign in Eq. (7-232) means that the value $n = 0$ is excluded. Using Euler's identity, (7-232) reduces to

$$G_\infty(r,r';\theta,\theta') = -\frac{1}{2\pi} \log r_> + \frac{1}{2\pi} \sum_{n=1}^{\infty}{}' \left(\frac{r_<}{r_>}\right)^{n} \frac{\cos n(\theta - \theta')}{n} \qquad (7\text{-}233)$$

where as usual

$$r_> = \text{greater of } (r,r') \tag{7-234}$$

$$r_< = \text{lesser of } (r,r') \tag{7-235}$$

The infinite-medium Green's function (7-233) is a particular integral of Eq. (7-205). It represents the potential due to a line source of unit positive charge density, provided no boundaries are present.

Green's function for the interior Dirichlet problem

The Green's function for the interior Dirichlet problem is the solution of Eq. (7-205) corresponding to a line source of positive charge contained inside the grounded conducting cylinder $r = a$. We write it as

$$G = G_i + G_\infty \tag{7-236}$$

where G_∞ represents the potential in the absence of the cylinder, and the induced potential G_i is a solution of

$$\nabla^2 G_i = 0 \tag{7-237}$$

which remains finite inside the cylinder. The condition that the cylinder be grounded requires that

$$G = G_i + G_\infty = 0 \text{ on } r = a \tag{7-238}$$

From our previous analysis it follows that

$$G_i = \sum_{n=-\infty}^{+\infty} C_n r^{|n|} e^{in\theta} + \frac{1}{2\pi} \log a \tag{7-239}$$

where the constants C_n are to be determined from Eq. (7-238). For the interior Dirichlet problem, when $r = a$, we must have $r' < r = a$. Using Eqs. (7-232) and (7-239) in (7-238) gives

$$C_n a^{|n|} + \frac{1}{4\pi} \left(\frac{r'}{a}\right)^{|n|} \frac{e^{-in\theta'}}{|n|} = 0 \tag{7-240}$$

or

$$C_n = -\frac{1}{4\pi} \left(\frac{r'}{a^2}\right)^{|n|} \frac{e^{-in\theta'}}{|n|} \tag{7-241}$$

The additive constant $(1/2\pi) \log a$ in Eq. (7-239) is so chosen that when it is combined with $-(1/2\pi) \log r_>$ in G_∞, it reduces to $(1/2\pi)$ $\log a/r_>$ which vanishes on $r = a$.

Our solution for the interior Green's function is

$$G(r,r';\theta,\theta') = \frac{1}{2\pi} \log \frac{a}{r_>} + \frac{1}{4\pi} \sum_{n=-\infty}^{+\infty}{}' \left[\left(\frac{r_<}{r_>}\right)^{|n|}\right.$$
$$\left. - \left(\frac{r_> r_<}{a^2}\right)^{|n|}\right] \frac{e^{in(\theta-\theta')}}{|n|} \tag{7-242}$$

or

$$G(r,r';\theta,\theta') = \frac{1}{2\pi} \log \frac{a}{r_>} + \frac{1}{2\pi} \sum_{n=1}^{\infty} \left[\left(\frac{r_<}{r_>} \right)^n \right.$$
$$\left. - \left(\frac{r_> r_<}{a^2} \right)^n \right] \frac{\cos n(\theta - \theta')}{n} \qquad (7\text{-}243)$$

One can readily verify that G vanishes on $r = a$ when $r' < a$.

Interpretation of $G(r,r';\theta,\theta')$

Suppose that $r' < r$; then from Eq. (7-233),

$$G_\infty(r,r';\theta,\theta') = -\frac{1}{2\pi} \log r + \frac{1}{2\pi} \sum_{n=1}^{\infty} \left(\frac{r'}{r} \right)^n \frac{\cos n(\theta - \theta')}{n} \qquad (7\text{-}244)$$

and replacing r by a^2/r in Eq. (7-244), we find

$$G_\infty \left(\frac{a^2}{r}, r';\theta,\theta' \right) = \frac{-1}{2\pi} \log \frac{a^2}{r} + \frac{1}{2\pi} \sum_{n=1}^{\infty} \left(\frac{rr'}{a^2} \right)^n \frac{\cos n(\theta - \theta')}{n} \qquad (7\text{-}245)$$

Subtracting Eq. (7-245) from (7-244) gives

$$G_\infty(r,r';\theta,\theta') - G_\infty \left(\frac{a^2}{r}, r';\theta,\theta' \right) = \frac{1}{2\pi} \log \left(\frac{a}{r} \right)^2$$
$$+ \frac{1}{2\pi} \sum_{n=1}^{\infty} \left[\left(\frac{r'}{r} \right)^n - \left(\frac{rr'}{a^2} \right)^n \right] \frac{\cos n(\theta - \theta')}{n} \qquad (7\text{-}246)$$

and from Eq. (7-243) we find

$$G(r,r';\theta,\theta') = \frac{1}{2\pi} \log \frac{a}{r} + \frac{1}{2\pi} \sum_{n=1}^{\infty} \left[\left(\frac{r'}{r} \right)^n \right.$$
$$\left. - \left(\frac{rr'}{a^2} \right)^n \right] \frac{\cos n(\theta - \theta')}{n} \qquad (7\text{-}247)$$

Now comparing Eqs. (7-246) and (7-247), we see that

$$G(r,r';\theta,\theta') = G_\infty(r,r';\theta,\theta') - G_\infty \left(\frac{a^2}{r}, r';\theta,\theta' \right) - \frac{1}{2\pi} \log \frac{a}{r} \qquad (7\text{-}248)$$

for $r' < r \leq a$. The first two terms in Eq. (7-248) represent the potentials at (r',θ') due to a positive line source at (r,θ) and a negative line source at $(a^2/r,\theta)$. The points (r,θ) and $(a^2/r,\theta)$ are images of each other in the circle $r = a$. When the original positive line charge is inside the circle $r = a$, then its negative image charge lies outside the circle, on the same diameter, and at a distance a^2/r from the center $(r = 0)$ of the circle.

If we set $r' = 0$ in Eq. (7-244), then

$$G_\infty = -\frac{1}{2\pi} \log r \qquad (7\text{-}249)$$

represents the potential at a distance r units away from a unit positive line charge. Therefore, we may also write

$$G_\infty = -\frac{1}{2\pi} \log R \tag{7-250}$$

in which

$$R = |\mathbf{r}' - \mathbf{r}| = [(r)^2 + (r')^2 - 2rr' \cos(\theta - \theta')]^{\frac{1}{2}} \tag{7-251}$$

measures the distance between the line source and the observer. One immediate consequence of Eqs. (7-250) and (7-233) is the expansion

$$G_\infty(r,r';\theta,\theta') = \frac{1}{2\pi} \log \frac{1}{R} = -\frac{1}{2\pi} \log r_>$$
$$+ \frac{1}{2\pi} \sum_{n=1}^\infty \left(\frac{r_<}{r_>}\right)^n \frac{\cos n(\theta - \theta')}{n} \tag{7-252}$$

With the aid of (7-252), Eq. (7-248) reduces to

$$G(r,r';\theta,\theta') = \frac{1}{2\pi} \log \frac{rR'}{aR} \tag{7-253}$$

where

$$R' = \left| \mathbf{r}' - \frac{a^2}{r^2}\mathbf{r} \right| = \left[\frac{a^4}{r^2} + (r')^2 - 2a^2 \frac{r'}{r} \cos(\theta - \theta') \right]^{\frac{1}{2}} \tag{7-254}$$

determines the distance between the point of observation $\mathbf{r}'$ and the image charge at $(a^2/r^2)\mathbf{r}$. Combining Eqs. (7-251), (7-253), and (7-254) we obtain

$$G(r,r';\theta,\theta') = \frac{1}{4\pi} \log \frac{a^2 + (rr'/a)^2 - 2rr' \cos(\theta - \theta')}{(r')^2 + (r)^2 - 2rr' \cos(\theta - \theta')} \tag{7-255}$$

for the closed-form expression of the interior Green's function.

The potential ϕ at (r',θ') inside the circle is given in terms of its boundary values on the circle $r = a$ by Eq. (7-188):

$$\phi(r',\theta') = -\int_{r=a} \phi(a,\theta) \frac{\partial G}{\partial n} ds \tag{7-256}$$

Since the outward normal to the circle $r = a$ is along the radius r, we have

$$\left(\frac{\partial G}{\partial n}\right)_{r=a} = \left(\frac{\partial G}{\partial r}\right)_{r=a} = \frac{1}{2\pi} \frac{(r')^2 - a^2}{a[a^2 - 2ar' \cos(\theta - \theta') + (r')^2]} \tag{7-257}$$

On the circle $r = a$, the element of arc length is $ds = a\, d\theta$; therefore Eqs. (7-256) and (7-257) yield

$$\phi(r',\theta') = \frac{a^2 - (r')^2}{2\pi} \int_0^{2\pi} \frac{\phi(a,\theta)\, d\theta}{a^2 - 2ar' \cos(\theta - \theta') + (r')^2} \tag{7-258}$$

which solves the problem. Formula (7-258) is known as Poisson's integral solution of the interior Dirichlet problem for a circle.

For the interior Dirichlet problem, we constructed an infinite-medium Green's function G_∞ with the property that if $r \to 0$ and $r' \neq 0$, the G_∞ remains finite. This is physically reasonable. It says that the potential r' units away from a line source is finite. For the exterior Dirichlet problem, both source and observer are located outside the circle $r = a$. If one allows the source to recede to infinity, i.e., $r \to \infty$, while keeping the point of observation fixed at a distance r' from the origin of coordinates, then the potential at r' must also remain finite. This condition requires an alteration of Eq. (7-233) which otherwise diverges logarithmically as $r \to \infty$. Instead of (7-233), one has

$$G_\infty(r,r';\theta,\theta') = -\frac{1}{2\pi} \log r_<$$

$$+ \frac{1}{2\pi} \sum_{n=1}^{\infty} \left(\frac{r_<}{r_>}\right)^n \frac{\cos n(\theta - \theta')}{n} \qquad (7\text{-}259)$$

This form of the infinite-medium Green's function satisfies Eq. (7-205) and remains finite as $r \to \infty$.

The Green's function for the exterior Dirichlet problem is the solution of Eq. (7-205) corresponding to a line source of positive charge contained outside the grounded conducting cylinder $r = a$. The exterior Green's function is written as

$$G = G_i + G_\infty \qquad (7\text{-}260)$$

where G_∞ is given by Eq. (7-259) and represents the potential in the absence of the cylinder. The induced potential G_i is a solution

$$\nabla^2 G_i = 0 \qquad (7\text{-}261)$$

which remains finite as $r \to \infty$ and which satisfies the boundary condition

$$G = G_i + G_\infty = 0 \text{ on } r = a \qquad (7\text{-}262)$$

The function G_i must be of the form

$$G_i = \sum_{n=1}^{\infty} C_n r^{-n} \cos n(\theta - \theta') + \frac{1}{2\pi} \log a \qquad (7\text{-}263)$$

since Eq. (7-263) satisfies Eq. (7-261) and behaves correctly as $r \to \infty$. The constant term in (7-263) is chosen to cancel the term $-(1/2\pi) \log r_<$ in G_∞ when $r = a$. It follows, using Eqs. (7-259), (7-263), and (7-262) to compute the C_n's, that the exterior Green's function for a circle is

$$G(r,r';\theta,\theta') = \frac{1}{2\pi} \log \left(\frac{r_<}{a}\right) + \frac{1}{2\pi} \sum_{n=1}^{\infty} \left[\left(\frac{r_<}{r_>}\right)^n \right.$$

$$\left. - \left(\frac{a^2}{r_>r_<}\right)^n \right] \frac{\cos n(\theta - \theta')}{n} \qquad (7\text{-}264)$$

Interpretation of $G(r,r';\theta,\theta')$

Suppose that $a \leq r < r'$; then Eq. (7-264) gives us

$$G(r,r';\theta,\theta') = \frac{1}{2\pi} \log \frac{r}{a} + \frac{1}{2\pi} \sum_{n=1}^{\infty} \left[\left(\frac{r}{r'}\right)^n \right.$$
$$\left. - \left(\frac{a^2}{rr'}\right)^n \right] \frac{\cos n(\theta - \theta')}{n} \qquad (7\text{-}265)$$

Recalling Eq. (7-252), we have

$$\frac{1}{2\pi} \log R = -\frac{1}{2\pi} \log r' = \frac{1}{2\pi} \sum_{n=1}^{\infty} \left(\frac{r}{r'}\right)^n \frac{\cos n(\theta - \theta')}{n} \qquad (7\text{-}266)$$

and

$$\frac{1}{2\pi} \log R' = -\frac{1}{2\pi} \log r' + \frac{1}{2\pi} \sum_{n=1}^{\infty} \left(\frac{a^2}{rr'}\right)^n \frac{\cos n(\theta - \theta')}{n} \qquad (7\text{-}267)$$

where

$$R = |\mathbf{r}' - \mathbf{r}| \qquad (7\text{-}268)$$

The distance R' is formed from R by replacing r with a^2/r:

$$R' = \left| \mathbf{r}' - \frac{a^2}{r^2} \mathbf{r} \right| \qquad (7\text{-}269)$$

Comparing Eqs. (7-265) through (7-267) shows that

$$G(r,r';\theta,\theta') = \frac{1}{2\pi} \log \frac{1}{R} - \frac{1}{2\pi} \log \frac{1}{R'} + \frac{1}{2\pi} \log \frac{r}{a} \qquad (7\text{-}270)$$

Hence

$$G(r,r';\theta,\theta') = \frac{1}{2\pi} \log \frac{rR'}{aR} \qquad (7\text{-}271)$$

and this result coincides with Eq. (7-253). The potential ϕ at a point (r',θ') outside of the circle $r = a$ is given in terms of its boundary values on the circle by Eq. (7-188):

$$\phi(r',\theta') = - \int_{r=a} \phi(a,\theta) \frac{\partial G}{\partial n} ds \qquad (7\text{-}272)$$

One must now observe that since we are calculating the potential in the exterior region $r' > a$, the outward normal on the boundary of the circle $r = a$ points toward the center of the circle. With this remark, Eq. (7-272) gives us

$$\phi(r',\theta') = \frac{(r')^2 - a^2}{2\pi} \int_0^{2\pi} \frac{\phi(a,\theta) \, d\theta}{(r')^2 - 2ar' \cos (\theta - \theta') + a^2} \qquad (7\text{-}273)$$

for $a < r'$. The integrand in Eq. (7-273) can be expanded in a power series in a/r' when $a < r'$. The result is

$$\frac{(r')^2 - a^2}{(r')^2 - 2ar' \cos (\theta - \theta') + a^2} = 1 + 2 \sum_{n=1}^{\infty} \left(\frac{a}{r'}\right)^n \cos n(\theta - \theta')$$
$$= \sum_{n=1}^{\infty} \epsilon_n \left(\frac{a}{r'}\right)^n \cos n(\theta - \theta') \qquad (7\text{-}274)$$

where

$$\epsilon_n = \begin{cases} 2 & n = 1,2, \ldots \\ 1 & n = 0 \end{cases} \tag{7-275}$$

With the aid of Eq. (7-274) the potential $\phi(r',\theta')$ can be expressed as

$$\phi(r',\theta') = \frac{1}{2\pi} \sum_{n=0}^{\infty} \left(\frac{a}{r'}\right)^n \epsilon_n \int_0^{2\pi} \phi(a,\theta) \cos n(\theta - \theta') \, d\theta \tag{7-276}$$

and this completes our solution of the problem.

7-14 LAPLACE'S EQUATION IN CYLINDRICAL COORDINATES

In cylindrical coordinates (r,θ,z), Laplace's equation takes the form

$$\nabla^2\phi = \frac{1}{r}\frac{\partial}{\partial r}\left(r\frac{\partial\phi}{\partial r}\right) + \frac{1}{r^2}\frac{\partial^2\phi}{\partial\theta^2} + \frac{\partial^2\phi}{\partial z^2} = 0 \tag{7-277}$$

The Green's function corresponding to Eq. (7-277) is the solution of

$$\nabla^2 G = \frac{-\delta(r - r')\,\delta(\theta - \theta')\,\delta(z - z')}{r} \tag{7-278}$$

and $G(r,r';\theta,\theta';z,z')$ represents the potential at (r',θ',z') due to a unit positive *point* charge located at (r,θ,z).

As usual, we begin by applying the method of separation of variables to (7-277). Let $\phi = R(r)\Theta(\theta)Z(z)$ in Eq. (7-277). Then divide the result by $R\Theta Z/r^2$ to obtain

$$\frac{r}{R}\frac{d}{dR}\left(r\frac{dR}{dr}\right) + \frac{r^2}{Z}\frac{d^2Z}{dz^2} = -\frac{1}{\Theta}\frac{d^2\Theta}{d\theta^2} \tag{7-279}$$

The right side of Eq. (7-279) depends only on θ while the left side depends on r and z. Consequently, the right side of (7-279) must be constant, and one writes

$$-\frac{1}{\Theta}\frac{d^2\Theta}{d\theta^2} = n^2 \tag{7-280}$$

We are left with

$$\frac{1}{rR}\frac{d}{dr}\left(r\frac{dR}{dr}\right) - \frac{n^2}{r^2} = \frac{-1}{Z}\frac{d^2Z}{dz^2} \tag{7-281}$$

where again the left side of Eq. (7-281) depends only on r while the right side depends only on z. It follows that both sides of (7-281) must be equal to one and the same constant. This we write as k^2, and therefore

$$\frac{1}{Z}\frac{d^2Z}{dz^2} = k^2 \tag{7-282}$$

$$\frac{1}{r}\frac{d}{dr}\left(r\frac{dR}{dr}\right) + \left(k^2 - \frac{n^2}{r^2}\right)R = 0 \tag{7-283}$$

By separating variables, we have reduced Eq. (7-277) to three ordinary differential equations,

$$\frac{d^2Z}{dz^2} - k^2 Z = 0 \tag{7-284}$$

$$\frac{d^2\Theta}{d\theta^2} + n^2\Theta = 0 \tag{7-285}$$

$$\frac{d^2R}{dr^2} + \frac{1}{r}\frac{dR}{dr} + \left(k^2 - \frac{n^2}{r^2}\right)R = 0 \tag{7-286}$$

containing two separation parameters n and k. The solution of Eq. (7-285) for the Θ factor is either $\sin n\theta$ or $\cos n\theta$ or some linear combination of these such as $e^{in\theta}$. Ultimately, the allowed values of the separation parameters n and k will be determined by the nature of the boundary conditions which ϕ must satisfy. For example, if there are no plane boundaries for $\theta = $ constant but θ is allowed to go from 0 to 2π, then n must be zero or an integer; otherwise ϕ will not have 2π as a period. Equation (7-284) has as solutions either trigonometric or hyperbolic functions, depending on whether k is real or imaginary.

If one wishes ϕ or $\partial\phi/\partial z$ to vanish on the flat ends of a cylinder while taking on a specified z dependence along the curved portion, then ϕ should be periodic in z, and k must be imaginary. On the other hand, if one wishes to specify the dependence of ϕ on r at one or both flat ends of the cylinder while ϕ remains constant on the curved part, then k should be real.

The equation for $R(r)$ is a Bessel equation with solutions $J_n(kr)$ and $N_n(kr)$ when k is real. The Bessel function $J_n(kr)$ is finite at the origin; so it must be used if the cylindrical axis is inside the boundary surface, where the solution is to be computed. The Neumann function $N_n(kr)$ is the second solution. It is infinite at the origin $r = 0$. When k is imaginary, the solutions of Eq. (7-286) are the hyperbolic Bessel functions $I_n(kr)$ and $K_n(kr)$. Of these, $I_n(kr)$ is finite at the origin and infinite at infinity, while $K_n(kr)$ is infinite at the origin and vanishes at infinity.

Complete solutions of Eqs. (7-284) through (7-286) for real nonzero k are

$$Z(kz) = Ce^{kz} + De^{-kz} = C'\cosh kz + D'\sinh kz \tag{7-287}$$

$$\Theta(n\theta) = Ae^{in\theta} + Be^{-in\theta} = A'\cos n\theta + B'\sin n\theta \tag{7-288}$$

$$R_n(kr) = EJ_n(kr) + FN_n(kr) = E'H_n{}^{(1)}(kr) + F'H_n{}^{(2)}(kr) \tag{7-289}$$

while for imaginary nonzero k,

$$Z(kz) = C\cos kz + D\sin kz = C'e^{ikz} + D'e^{-ikz} \tag{7-290}$$

$$\Theta(n\theta) = Ae^{in\theta} + Be^{-in\theta} = A'\cos n\theta + B'\sin n\theta \tag{7-291}$$

$$R_n(kr) = EK_n(kr) + FI_n(kr) \tag{7-292}$$

If $k = 0$, and n is real and nonzero,

$$Z(z) = Cz + D \tag{7-293}$$

$$\Theta(n\theta) = A \cos n\theta + B \sin \theta \tag{7-294}$$

$$R_n(r) = Er^n + Fr^{-n} \tag{7-295}$$

whereas if $k = 0$, and n is imaginary and nonzero,

$$Z(z) = Cz + D \tag{7-296}$$

$$\Theta(n\theta) = A \cosh n\theta + B \sinh n\theta \tag{7-297}$$

$$R(r) = E \cos (n \log r) + F \sin (n \log r) \tag{7-298}$$

Finally, if both k and n are zero,

$$Z(z) = Cz + D \tag{7-299}$$

$$\Theta(\theta) = A\theta + B \tag{7-300}$$

$$R(r) = E \log r + F \tag{7-301}$$

Each expression of the form

$$\phi = R_n(kr)\Theta(n\theta)Z(kz) \tag{7-302}$$

is a solution of Laplace's equation in cylindrical coordinates. For this reason, expressions such as Eq. (7-302) are called "cylindrical harmonics." By summing or integrating over the separation parameters k and n, one can form more general cylindrical harmonics which satisfy Laplace's equation.

7-15   CONSTRUCTION OF THE GREEN'S FUNCTION

The Green's function must satisfy

$$\nabla^2 G = \frac{-\delta(r - r')\,\delta(\theta - \theta')\,\delta(z - z')}{r} \tag{7-303}$$

and we shall construct G by expanding it in terms of the separated solutions of Eq. (7-277); thus let

$$G = \sum_{n=-\infty}^{\infty} \int_{-\infty}^{+\infty} R_n(kr)e^{i(n\theta+kz)}\,dk \tag{7-304}$$

The right side of Eq. (7-303) must also be expanded in terms of the same separated solutions, and therefore we write

$$\frac{\delta(r - r')\,\delta(\theta - \theta')\,\delta(z - z')}{r}$$

$$= \sum_{n=-\infty}^{\infty} \int_{-\infty}^{+\infty} \frac{\delta(r - r')}{r} C_n(k)e^{i(n\theta+kz)}\,dk \tag{7-305}$$

To calculate the coefficients $C_n(k)$, multiply both sides of Eq. (7-305) by $e^{-i(m\theta+hz)}$, and then integrate with respect to θ and z, using

$$\int_{-\pi}^{\pi} e^{i(n-m)\theta}\,d\theta = 2\pi\delta_{nm} \tag{7-306}$$

and

$$\int_{-\infty}^{+\infty} e^{i(k-h)z}\, dz = 2\pi\delta(k - h) \tag{7-307}$$

This gives

$$C_n(k) = \frac{1}{4\pi^2} e^{-i(n\theta'+kz')} \tag{7-308}$$

and consequently

$$\frac{\delta(r - r')\,\delta(\theta - \theta')\,\delta(z - z')}{r}$$

$$= \frac{1}{4\pi^2} \sum_{n=-\infty}^{+\infty} \int_{-\infty}^{+\infty} \frac{\delta(r - r')}{r} e^{i[n(\theta-\theta')+k(z-z')]}\, dk \tag{7-309}$$

Now we substitute Eqs. (7-304) and (7-309) into (7-303) to obtain

$$\sum_{n=-\infty}^{+\infty} \int_{-\infty}^{+\infty} \left[\frac{d^2R_n}{dr^2} + \frac{1}{r}\frac{dR_n}{dr} - \left(k^2 + \frac{n^2}{r^2} \right) R_n \right] e^{i(n\theta+kz)}\, dk$$

$$= -\frac{1}{4\pi^2} \sum_{n=-\infty}^{+\infty} \int_{-\infty}^{+\infty} \frac{\delta(r - r')}{r} e^{i[n(\theta-\theta')+k(z-z')]}\, dk \tag{7-310}$$

and on equating the coefficients of $e^{i(n\theta+kz)}$ on both sides of Eq. (7-310), we obtain the equation for $R_n(kr)$:

$$\frac{d^2R_n}{dr^2} + \frac{1}{r}\frac{dR_n}{dr} - \left(k^2 + \frac{n^2}{r^2} \right) R_n = \frac{-\delta(r - r')}{4\pi^2 r^2} e^{-i(n\theta'+kz')} \tag{7-311}$$

To solve Eq. (7-311) for $k \neq 0$, we notice that when $r \neq r'$,

$$R_n(kr) = \begin{cases} AI_n(kr) \\ BK_n(kr) \end{cases} \tag{7-312}$$

are linearly independent solutions of Eq. (7-311). Since the source is presumably neither at the origin $r = 0$ nor at infinity, the Green's function should remain finite at $r = 0$ and $r = \infty$. This forces us to assign the two solutions (7-312) so that

$$R_n = AI_n(kr) \qquad 0 \le r < r' \tag{7-313}$$

$$R_n = BK_n(kr) \qquad r' < r < \infty \tag{7-314}$$

Continuity of Eqs. (7-313) and (7-314) at $r = r'$ requires that

$$AI_n(kr') = BK_n(kr') \tag{7-315}$$

which yields one equation for A and B. A second equation is obtained by integrating Eq. (7-311) with respect to r from $r = r' - \epsilon$ to $r = r' + \epsilon$ where ϵ is a small positive number. We have

$$\frac{1}{r}\frac{d}{dr}\left(r\frac{dR_n}{dr} \right) - \left(k^2 + \frac{n^2}{r^2} \right) R_n = -\frac{\delta(r - r')}{4\pi^2 r} e^{-i(n\theta'+kz')} \tag{7-316}$$

and therefore

$$\int_{r'-\epsilon}^{r'+\epsilon} \frac{d}{dr}\left(r\frac{dR_n}{dr} \right) dr - \int_{r'-\epsilon}^{r'+\epsilon} \left(k^2 + \frac{n^2}{r^2} \right) R_n\, dr$$

$$= -\frac{1}{4\pi^2} e^{-i(n\theta'+kz')} \tag{7-317}$$

Taking the limit of Eq. (7-317) as $\epsilon \to 0$ and remembering that the second term in (7-317) vanishes as $\epsilon \to 0$ because of continuity, it follows that

$$\lim_{\epsilon \to 0} r \frac{dR_n}{dr} \Big|_{r=r'-\epsilon}^{r=r'+\epsilon} = -\frac{1}{4\pi^2} e^{-i(n\theta'+kz')} \tag{7-318}$$

Equations (7-318), (7-313), and (7-314) give us our second equation for A and B,

$$\lim_{\epsilon \to 0} (kr) \frac{dR_n}{d(kr)} \Big|_{r=r'-\epsilon}^{r=r'+\epsilon} = Bx \frac{dK_n(x)}{dx} - Ax \frac{dI_n(x)}{dx} \tag{7-319}$$

where $x = kr'$. Our equations for A and B now read

$$AI_n(x) - BK_n(x) = 0 \tag{7-320}$$

$$AxI'_n(x) - BxK'_n(x) = \frac{1}{4\pi^2} e^{-i(n\theta'+kz')} \tag{7-321}$$

The determinant of the system is

$$\Delta = \begin{vmatrix} I_n(x) & -K_n(x) \\ xI'_n(x) & -xK'_n(x) \end{vmatrix} = -x(I_n K'_n - K_n I'_n) \tag{7-322}$$

which is almost the Wronskian of I_n and K_n, i.e.,

$$\Delta = -xW\{I_n, K_n; x\} \tag{7-323}$$

Abel's formula (6-442) for the Wronskian shows that

$$xW\{I_n, K_n; x\} = x_0 W\{I_n, K_n; x_0\} \tag{7-324}$$

Since the left side of Eq. (7-324) is a function of x alone while the right side is a function of x_0 alone, (7-324) can hold only if each side is equal to one and the same constant; thus

$$W\{I_n, K_n; x\} = \frac{\text{const}}{x} \tag{7-325}$$

The constant in Eq. (7-325) is determined by evaluating the Wronskian at some arbitrary but definite point. The easiest points to use are $x = 0$ or $x = \infty$ because at these points the formulas for $I_n(kr)$ and $K_n(kr)$ become especially simple. For example, using Eqs. (6-273) and (6-274), we find

$$x\{I_n K'_n - K_n I'_n\} = x \left\{ \frac{\pi e^x}{\sqrt{2\pi x}} \frac{d}{dx} \left(\frac{e^{-x}}{\sqrt{2\pi x}} \right) \right.$$
$$\left. - \frac{\pi e^{-x}}{\sqrt{2\pi x}} \frac{d}{dx} \left(\frac{e^x}{\sqrt{2\pi x}} \right) \right\} \tag{7-326}$$

or

$$x\{I_n K' - K_n I'_n\} = -1 \tag{7-327}$$

which gives the Wronskian of I_n and K_n as

$$W\{I_n, K_n; x\} = -\frac{1}{x} \tag{7-328}$$

The system (7-320) and (7-321) can now be solved for A and B to yield

$$A = \frac{1}{4\pi^2} K_n(kr')e^{-i(n\theta'+kz')} \tag{7-329}$$

$$B = \frac{1}{4\pi^2} I_n(kr')e^{-i(n\theta'+kz')} \tag{7-330}$$

Therefore the solution for R_n becomes

$$R_n = \frac{1}{4\pi^2} I_n(kr)K_n(kr')e^{-i(n\theta'+kz')} \qquad 0 \le r \le r' \tag{7-331}$$

$$R_n = \frac{1}{4\pi^2} I_n(kr')K_n(kr)e^{-i(n\theta'+kz')} \qquad r' \le r \le \infty \tag{7-332}$$

As usual, we can combine Eqs. (7-331) and (7-332) in a single formula by writing

$$R_n = \frac{1}{4\pi^2} I_n(kr_<)K_n(kr_>)e^{-i(n\theta'+kz')} \tag{7-333}$$

With the aid of (7-333), Eq. (7-304) is written as

$$G_\infty(r,r';\theta,\theta';z,z')$$
$$= \frac{1}{4\pi^2} \sum_{n=-\infty}^{+\infty} \int_{-\infty}^{+\infty} I_n(kr_<)K_n(kr_<)e^{i[n(\theta-\theta')+k(z-z')]} \, dk \tag{7-334}$$

which is the same as either

$$G_\infty(r,r';\theta,\theta';z,z')$$
$$= \frac{1}{2\pi^2} \sum_{n=-\infty}^{+\infty} \int_0^{+\infty} I_n(kr_<)K_n(kr_>)e^{in(\theta-\theta')} \cos k(z - z') \, dk \tag{7-335}$$

or

$$G_\infty = \frac{1}{\pi^2} \left\{ \int_0^\infty \cos k(z - z') \, dk \left[\frac{1}{2} I_0(kr_<)K_0(kr_>) \right. \right.$$
$$\left. \left. + \sum_{n=1}^\infty I_n(kr_<)K_n(kr_>) \cos n(\theta - \theta') \right] \right\} \tag{7-336}$$

On the other hand, we know that Eq. (7-303) is also satisfied by

$$G_\infty = \frac{1}{4\pi R} = \frac{1}{4\pi[(x - x')^2 + (y - y')^2 + (z - z')^2]^{1/2}} \tag{7-337}$$

since (7-337) represents the potential at a distance R units away from a unit positive point charge; consequently

$$\frac{1}{4\pi R} = \frac{1}{\pi^2} \left\{ \int_0^\infty \cos k(z - z') \, dk \left[\frac{I_0(kr_<)K_0(kr_>)}{2} \right. \right.$$
$$\left. \left. + \sum_{n=1}^\infty I_n(kr_<)K_n(kr_>) \cos n(\theta - \theta') \right] \right\} \tag{7-338}$$

must follow. Suppose that we let $x' = 0$, $y' = 0$, $z' = 0$ in Eq. (7-338); then since

$$I_n(0) = \begin{cases} 1 & n = 0 \\ 0 & n = 1,2,3, \ldots \end{cases} \tag{7-339}$$

Eq. (7-338) reduces to

$$\frac{1}{4\pi \sqrt{r^2 + z^2}} = \frac{1}{2\pi^2} \int_0^\infty \cos kz\, K_0(kr)\, dk \tag{7-340}$$

If r^2 in Eq. (7-340) is replaced by $R^2 = r^2 + (r')^2 - 2rr' \cos(\theta - \theta')$, then the left side of (7-340) becomes just $1/[(x - x')^2 + (y - y')^2 + z^2]^{\frac{1}{2}}$ where $r^2 = x^2 + y^2$ and $(r')^2 = (x')^2 + (y')^2$. We can write

$$\left(\frac{1}{4\pi R}\right)_{z'=0} = \frac{1}{2\pi^2} \int_0^\infty \cos kz\, K_0(kR)\, dk \tag{7-341}$$

but from Eq. (7-338) we can also write

$$\left(\frac{1}{4\pi R}\right)_{z'=0} = \frac{1}{2\pi^2} \left\{ \int_0^\infty \cos kz\, dk \left[I_0(kr_<) K_0(kr_>) \right. \right.$$
$$\left. \left. + 2 \sum_{n=1}^\infty I_n(kr_<) K_n(kr_>) \cos n(\theta - \theta') \right] \right\} \tag{7-342}$$

so that on comparison of Eqs. (7-341) and (7-342),

$$K_0(kR) = I_0(kr_<) K_0(kr_>) + 2 \sum_{n=1}^\infty I_n(kr_<) K_n(kr_>) \cos n(\theta - \theta') \tag{7-343}$$

where

$$R = [r^2 + (r')^2 - 2rr' \cos(\theta - \theta')]^{\frac{1}{2}} \tag{7-344}$$

If one takes the limit of Eq. (7-343) as $k \to 0$, then the result of Eq. (7-233),

$$G_\infty = \frac{1}{2\pi} \log \frac{1}{R} = \frac{1}{2\pi} \log \frac{1}{r_>} + \frac{1}{2\pi} \sum_{n=1}^\infty \left(\frac{r_<}{r_>}\right)^n \frac{\cos n(\theta - \theta')}{n} \tag{7-345}$$

is recovered.

7-16 AN ALTERNATIVE METHOD OF SOLVING BOUNDARY-VALUE PROBLEMS

Having constructed the infinite-medium Green's function (7-334) to (7-336) for Laplace's equation in cylindrical coordinates, we could now construct the Green's functions which satisfy homogeneous Dirichlet or Neumann boundary conditions, say on a cylinder $r = a$, by merely adding to G_∞ appropriate solutions of $\nabla^2 G_i = 0$ chosen so that $G = G_\infty + G_i = 0$ on $r = a$ or $\partial G/\partial n = 0$ on $r = a$. The solutions of the Dirichlet and Neumann problems are then given by

$$\phi(r', \theta', z') = -\int_{S(V)} \phi \frac{\partial G}{\partial n}\, dS \tag{7-346}$$

Figure 7-4 Electric field configuration for a grounded conducting cylinder placed in an initially uniform electric field.

and

$$\phi(r',\theta',z') = \int_{S(V)} G\,\frac{\partial\phi}{\partial n}\,dS \qquad (7\text{-}347)$$

respectively.

When there is a great deal of symmetry in the problem, or when the source is at infinity, an alternative procedure is sometimes simpler. For example, we may wish to determine the potential at any point outside of an infinitely long, grounded conducting cylinder when it is in a uniform electric field $\mathbf{E}_0$ whose direction is perpendicular to the axis of the cylinder (Fig. 7-4). By symmetry, the electric field and the potential should depend only on the distance r from the center of the cylinder and on the angle θ relative to the initially uniform field $\mathbf{E}_0$. Thus ϕ should be independent of z, and we must solve

$$\nabla^2\phi = \frac{1}{r}\frac{\partial}{\partial r}\left(r\frac{\partial\phi}{\partial r}\right) + \frac{1}{r^2}\frac{\partial^2\phi}{\partial\theta^2} = 0 \tag{7-348}$$

subject to the boundary condition

$$\phi = 0 \text{ on } r = a \tag{7-349}$$

Let ϕ_0 represent the potential of the initially uniform electric field $\mathbf{E}_0$ in which the cylinder is placed. We have $\phi_0 = E_0 x = E_0 r \cos\theta$ corresponding to a uniform field $\mathbf{E}_0 = -E_0\mathbf{e}_x$ directed along the negative x axis. The potential ϕ must consist of two parts, an induced portion ϕ_i due to the presence of the cylinder, and the original uniform field ϕ_0. Consequently

$$\phi = \phi_0 + \phi_i \tag{7-350}$$

must satisfy Eqs. (7-348) and (7-349). The potential ϕ_i must represent the effect of the cylinder so that in addition to satisfying $\nabla^2\phi_i = 0$, it must vanish very far away from the cylinder. In other words,

$$\lim_{r\to\infty} \phi_i(r,\theta) = 0 \tag{7-351}$$

An expression of the form

$$\phi(r,\theta) = E_0 r\cos\theta + \sum_{n=1}^{\infty} r^{-n}(C_n\cos n\theta + D_n\sin C\theta) \tag{7-352}$$

is a good trial solution since it satisfies Eq. (7-348) and behaves correctly at infinity.

The symmetry of the problem can be used to eliminate the sine terms from Eq. (7-352). By symmetry

$$\phi(r,\theta) = \phi(r, -\theta) \tag{7-353}$$

and Eq. (7-353) cannot hold unless $D_n = 0$ for $n = 1,2,3, \ldots$. This leaves us with

$$\phi(r,\theta) = E_0 r\cos\theta + \sum_{n=1}^{\infty} C_n r^{-n}\cos n\theta \tag{7-354}$$

Applying Eq. (7-349) to (7-354) gives

$$0 = aE_0\cos\theta + \sum_{n=1}^{\infty} C_n a^{-n}\cos n\theta \tag{7-355}$$

and therefore

$$C_1 = -a^2 E_0, \; C_2 = 0, \; C_3 = 0, \; \ldots, \; C_n = 0, \; \ldots$$

Our result is

$$\phi(r,\theta) = E_0 r\cos\theta - \frac{a^2 E_0}{r}\cos\theta = \left(1 - \frac{a^2}{r^2}\right)E_0 r\cos\theta \tag{7-356}$$

and $\mathbf{E} = -\nabla\phi$ gives us

$$E_r = -\frac{\partial\phi}{\partial r} = -\left(1 + \frac{a^2}{r^2}\right)E_0 \cos\theta \tag{7-357}$$

$$E_\theta = \frac{-1}{r}\frac{\partial\phi}{\partial\theta} = \left(1 - \frac{a^2}{r^2}\right)E_0 \sin\theta \tag{7-358}$$

as the radial and tangential components of the electric field.

7.17 LAPLACE'S EQUATION IN SPHERICAL COORDINATES

Laplace's equation in spherical coordinates (r,θ,ϕ) becomes

$$\nabla^2\psi = \frac{1}{r^2}\frac{\partial}{\partial r}\left(r^2\frac{\partial\psi}{\partial r}\right) + \frac{1}{r^2 \sin\theta}\frac{\partial}{\partial\theta}\left(\sin\theta\frac{\partial\psi}{\partial\theta}\right)$$
$$+ \frac{1}{r^2 \sin^2\theta}\frac{\partial^2\psi}{\partial\phi^2} = 0 \tag{7-359}$$

The Green's function for Eq. (7-359) is the solution of

$$\nabla^2 G = \frac{-\delta(r - r')\,\delta(\theta - \theta')\,\delta(\phi - \phi')}{r^2 \sin\theta} \tag{7-360}$$

and $G(r,r';\theta,\theta';\phi,\phi')$ represents the potential at (r',θ',ϕ') due to a unit positive *point* charge located at (r,θ,ϕ). The factor $1/r^2 \sin\theta$ appearing in Eq. (7-360) is required because an element of volume in spherical coordinates is $dV = r^2 \sin\theta\, dr\, d\theta\, d\phi$ and the volume integral of the right side of (7-360) must be normalized to unity when the source is inside in the region of integration.

To apply the method of separation of variables, we seek solutions of Eq. (7-359) of the form $\psi(r,\theta,\phi) = R(r)\Theta(\theta)\Phi(\phi)$. On substituting $\psi = R\Theta\Phi$ into (7-359) and dividing the result by $R\Theta\Phi/r^2 \sin^2\theta$, we obtain

$$\frac{\sin^2\theta}{R}\frac{d}{dr}\left(r^2\frac{dR}{dr}\right) + \frac{\sin\theta}{\Theta}\frac{d}{d\theta}\left(\sin\theta\frac{d\Theta}{d\theta}\right) = -\frac{1}{\Phi}\frac{d^2\Phi}{d\phi^2} \tag{7-361}$$

The right side of Eq. (7-361) depends only on ϕ while the left side depends on r and θ. Consequently, the right side of (7-361) must be a constant, and one writes

$$-\frac{1}{\Phi}\frac{d^2\Phi}{d\phi^2} = m^2 \tag{7-362}$$

We are left with

$$\frac{1}{R}\frac{d}{dr}\left(r^2\frac{dR}{dr}\right) = -\left[\frac{1}{\Theta \sin\theta}\frac{d}{d\theta}\left(\sin\theta\frac{d\Theta}{d\theta}\right) - \frac{m^2}{\sin^2\theta}\right] \tag{7-363}$$

where again the left side of Eq. (7-363) depends only on r while the right side depends only on θ. It follows that both sides must be equal to one and the same constant, say k. Thus

$$\frac{d}{dr}\left(r^2\frac{dR}{dr}\right) - kR = 0 \tag{7-364}$$

$$\frac{1}{\sin\theta}\frac{d}{d\theta}\left(\sin\theta\frac{d\Theta}{d\theta}\right) + \left(k - \frac{m^2}{\sin^2\theta}\right)\Theta = 0 \tag{7-365}$$

and by separating variables, we have reduced Eq. (7-359) to three ordinary differential equations,

$$\frac{d^2\Phi}{d\phi^2} + m^2\Phi = 0 \tag{7-366}$$

$$\frac{1}{\sin\theta}\frac{d}{d\theta}\left(\sin\theta\frac{d\Theta}{d\theta}\right) + \left(k - \frac{m^2}{\sin^2\theta}\right)\Theta = 0 \tag{7-367}$$

$$\frac{d}{dr}\left(r^2\frac{dR}{dr}\right) - kR = 0 \tag{7-368}$$

containing two separation parameters m and k. The allowed values of these separation parameters depend on the boundary conditions which ψ must satisfy. For example, if there are no boundary planes for $\phi = $ constant, and ϕ is allowed to run from 0 to 2π, then $\psi(r,\theta,\phi)$ should be periodic in ϕ with period 2π. This requires m to be a positive or a negative integer.

Suppose we let $R(r) = r^\lambda$ in Eq. (7-368). The result is that $R = r^\lambda$ satisfies (7-368) provided that

$$\lambda^2 + \lambda - k = 0 \tag{7-369}$$

If we choose $\lambda = n$ in Eq. (7-369), then $k = n(n+1)$. However, if $\lambda = -(n+1)$, Eq. (7-369) still gives $k = n(n+1)$. Therefore, when $k = n(n+1)$, Eq. (7-368) has r^n and $r^{-(n+1)}$ as linearly independent solutions. So far, n is still an arbitrary parameter. To further restrict n we must examine Eq. (7-367) more closely. Let $x = \cos\theta$ and $\Theta(\theta) = y(x)$ in (7-367). Then since $\dfrac{d}{d\theta} = \dfrac{dx}{d\theta}\dfrac{d}{dx}$, we find

$$\frac{1}{\sin\theta}\frac{d}{d\theta}\left(\sin\theta\frac{d\Theta}{d\theta}\right) = \frac{d}{dx}\left[(1-x^2)\frac{dy}{dx}\right] \tag{7-370}$$

With the aid of Eq. (7-370), the system (7-364) to (7-368) can be reduced to

$$\frac{d^2\Phi}{d\phi^2} + m^2\Phi = 0 \tag{7-371}$$

$$\frac{d}{dx}\left[(1-x^2)\frac{dy}{dx}\right] + \left[n(n+1) - \frac{m^2}{1-x^2}\right]y(x) = 0 \tag{7-372}$$

$$\frac{d}{dr}\left(r^2\frac{dR}{dr}\right) - n(n+1)R = 0 \tag{7-373}$$

Equation (7-371) has either trigonometric or hyperbolic solutions, depending on whether m is real or imaginary, and the solutions of Eq. (7-373) are already known to be r^n and $r^{-(n+1)}$. Now Eq. (7-372) is recognized as Legendre's associated differential equation. Its solutions are $P_n{}^m(x)$ and $Q_n{}^m(x)$. Consequently, the complete solutions of Eqs. (7-371) to (7-373) become

$$R(r) = Ar^n + Br^{-(n+1)} \tag{7-374}$$

$$\Theta(\theta) = CP_n{}^m(\cos\theta) + DQ_n{}^m(\cos\theta) \tag{7-375}$$

$$\Phi(\phi) = E\cos m\phi + F\sin m\phi \tag{7-376}$$

We have already seen that m must be an integer if $\psi(r,\theta,\phi)$ is to be periodic in ϕ. In most problems $\psi(r,\theta,\phi)$ must also remain finite over any sphere of finite radius. Therefore Eq. (7-375) must remain finite for $0 \le \theta \le \pi$, i.e., for $-1 \le \cos\theta \le 1$. This requires D to vanish and n to take only integer values in (7-375). The reason is that $Q_n{}^m(x)$ is singular at ± 1 and $P_n{}^m(x)$ remains finite for $-1 \le x \le 1$ only when n and m are both integers and $n \ge m$. For the singular case $m > 0$, $n = 0$, Eqs. (7-374) to (7-376) reduce to

$$R(r) = A + Br^{-1} \tag{7-377}$$

$$\Theta(\theta) = C \cot^m \frac{\theta}{2} + D \tan^m \frac{\theta}{2} \tag{7-378}$$

$$\Phi(\phi) = E \cos m\phi + F \sin m\phi \tag{7-379}$$

and for $n = 0$, $m = 0$,

$$R(r) = A + Br^{-1} \tag{7-380}$$

$$\Theta(\theta) = C \log \tan \frac{\theta}{2} + D \tag{7-381}$$

$$\Theta(\phi) = D\phi + E \tag{7-382}$$

7-18   CONSTRUCTION OF THE GREEN'S FUNCTION

The Green's function satisfies

$$\nabla^2 G = \frac{-\delta(r - r')\,\delta(\theta - \theta')\,\delta(\phi - \phi')}{r^2 \sin\theta} \tag{7-383}$$

and is constructed by making an expansion in terms of the separated solutions of Eq. (7-359) and then substituting the expansion into Eq. (7-383) to determine the expansion coefficients. Thus let

$$G = \sum_{n=0}^{\infty} \sum_{m=-n}^{+n} R_n{}^{|m|}(r) P_n{}^{|m|}(\cos\theta) e^{im\phi} \tag{7-384}$$

and corresponding to Eq. (7-384), choose

$$\frac{\delta(r - r')\,\delta(\theta - \theta')\,\delta(\phi - \phi')}{r^2 \sin\theta} = \sum_{n=0}^{\infty} \sum_{m=-n}^{+n} C_n{}^{|m|} P_n{}^{|m|}(\cos\theta) e^{im\phi} \tag{7-385}$$

To compute the expansion coefficients $C_n{}^{|m|}$, multiply both sides of Eq. (7-385) by $P_\lambda{}^{|\mu|}(\cos\theta) e^{-i\mu\phi} \sin\theta\, d\theta\, d\phi$, and then integrate θ and ϕ over the surface of a unit sphere, using

$$\int_0^{2\pi} \int_0^{\pi} P_n{}^{|m|}(\cos\theta) P_\lambda{}^{|\mu|}(\cos\theta) e^{i(m-\mu)\phi} \sin\theta\, d\theta\, d\phi$$

$$= \frac{4\pi}{2n + 1} \frac{(n + |m|)!}{(n - |m|)!} \delta_{n\lambda} \delta_{m\mu} \tag{7-386}$$

This gives $C_n{}^{|m|}$ as

$$C_n{}^{|m|} = \frac{\delta(r - r')}{4\pi r^2} \frac{(n - |m|)!}{(n + |m|)!} (2n + 1) P_m{}^{|m|}(\cos\theta') e^{-im\phi'} \tag{7-387}$$

and consequently

$$\frac{\delta(r - r')\,\delta(\theta - \theta')\,\delta(\phi - \phi')}{r^2 \sin \theta}$$

$$= \frac{1}{4\pi} \sum_{n=0}^{\infty} \sum_{m=-n}^{+n} \frac{\delta(r - r')}{r^2} \frac{(n - |m|)!}{(n + |m|)!}$$
$$(2n + 1)P_n^{|m|}(\cos \theta)P_n^{|m|}(\cos \theta')e^{im(\phi-\phi')} \qquad (7\text{-}388)$$

Substituting Eqs. (7-384) and (7-388) into (7-383) gives us

$$\sum_{n=0}^{\infty} \sum_{m=-n}^{+n} \left[\frac{1}{r^2} \frac{d}{dr}\left(r^2 \frac{dR_n^{|m|}}{dr}\right) - \frac{n(n + 1)}{r^2} R_n^{|m|} \right] P_n^{|m|}(\cos \theta)e^{im\phi}$$

$$= -\frac{1}{4\pi} \sum_{n=0}^{\infty} \sum_{m=-n}^{+n} \frac{\delta(r - r')}{r^2} \frac{(n - |m|)!}{(n + |m|)!}$$
$$(2n + 1)P_n^{|m|}(\cos \theta)P_n^{|m|}(\cos \theta')e^{im(\phi-\phi')} \qquad (7\text{-}389)$$

and on equating the coefficients of $P_n^{|m|}(\cos \theta)e^{im\phi}$ on both sides of Eq. (7-389), we obtain the equation determining $R_n^{|m|}(r)$:

$$\frac{1}{r^2} \frac{d}{dr}\left(r^2 \frac{dR_n^{|m|}}{dr}\right) - \frac{n(n + 1)}{r^2} R_n^{|m|}$$

$$= \frac{-\delta(r - r')}{4\pi r^2} \frac{(n - |m|)!}{(n + |m|)!} (2n + 1)P_n^{|m|}(\cos \theta')e^{-im\phi'} \qquad (7\text{-}390)$$

To solve Eq. (7-390) one notes that when $r \neq r'$,

$$R_n^{|m|} = \begin{cases} Ar^n \\ Br^{-(n+1)} \end{cases} \qquad (7\text{-}391)$$

are linearly independent solutions of (7-390). When the source is neither at the origin $r = 0$ nor at infinity, the Green's function should remain finite at $r = 0$ and $r = \infty$. Thus the pair of solutions in Eq. (7-391) are assigned so that

$$R_n^{|m|}(r) = Ar^n \qquad 0 \leq r < r' \qquad (7\text{-}392)$$

$$R_n^{|m|}(r) = Br^{-(n+1)} \qquad r' < r < \infty \qquad (7\text{-}393)$$

Continuity of Eqs. (7-392) and (7-393) at $r = r'$ requires that

$$A(r')^n = B(r')^{-(n+1)} \qquad (7\text{-}394)$$

giving us one equation for A and B. A second equation is obtained by integrating Eq. (7-390) with respect to r from $r = r' - \epsilon$ to $r = r' + \epsilon$ where ϵ is a small positive number. We can write (7-390) as

$$\frac{1}{r^2} \frac{d}{dr}\left(r^2 \frac{dR_n^{|m|}}{dr}\right) - \frac{n(n + 1)}{r^2} R_n^{|m|} = -Q \frac{\delta(r - r')}{r^2} \qquad (7\text{-}395)$$

where

$$Q = \frac{2n + 1}{4\pi} \frac{(n - |m|)!}{(n + |m|)!} P_n^{|m|}(\cos \theta')e^{-im\phi} \qquad (7\text{-}396)$$

and therefore

$$\int_{r'-\epsilon}^{r'+\epsilon} \frac{d}{dr}\left(r^2 \frac{dR_n^{|m|}}{dr}\right) dr - n(n + 1) \int_{r'-\epsilon}^{r'+\epsilon} R_n^{|m|}\, dr = -Q \qquad (7\text{-}397)$$

Taking the limit of Eq. (7-397) as $\epsilon \to 0$ and remembering that the second term vanishes as $\epsilon \to 0$ because of continuity, it follows that

$$\lim_{\epsilon \to 0} r^2 \frac{dR_n^{|m|}}{dr}\Big|_{r=r'-\epsilon}^{r=r'+\epsilon} = -Q \qquad (7\text{-}398)$$

Equations (7-398), (7-392), and (7-393) give us the second equation for A and B:

$$An(r')^{n+1} + B(n+1)(r')^{-n} = Q \qquad (7\text{-}399)$$

The system of equations determining A and B is therefore

$$A(r')^n - B(r')^{-(n+1)} = 0 \qquad (7\text{-}400)$$

$$An(r')^{n+1} + B(n+1)(r')^{-n} = Q \qquad (7\text{-}401)$$

Solving this system for A and B, one finds

$$A = \frac{Q}{2n+1}(r')^{-(n+1)} \qquad (7\text{-}402)$$

$$B = \frac{Q}{2n+1}(r')^n \qquad (7\text{-}403)$$

and therefore Eqs. (7-392) and (7-393) reduce to

$$R_n^{|m|}(r) = \frac{Q}{2n+1}\frac{r^n}{(r')^{n+1}} \qquad 0 \le r \le r' \qquad (7\text{-}404)$$

$$R_n^{|m|}(r) = \frac{Q}{2n+1}\frac{(r')^n}{(r)^{n+1}} \qquad r' \le r < \infty \qquad (7\text{-}405)$$

In terms of a single formula, Eqs. (7-404) and (7-405) combine to give

$$R_n^{|m|}(r) = \frac{Q}{2n+1}\frac{(r_<)^n}{(r_>)^{n+1}} \qquad (7\text{-}406)$$

and using Eqs. (7-406), (7-396), and (7-384), the infinite-medium Green's function is found to be

$$G_\infty = \frac{1}{4\pi}\sum_{n=0}^{\infty}\sum_{m=-n}^{+n}\frac{(r_<)^n}{(r_>)^{n+1}}\frac{(n-|m|)!}{(n+|m|)!}$$
$$P_n^{|m|}(\cos\theta)P_n^{|m|}(\cos\theta')e^{im(\phi-\phi')} \qquad (7\text{-}407)$$

Equation (7-407) is the same as

$$G_\infty(r,r';\theta,\theta';\phi,\phi')$$
$$= \frac{1}{4\pi}\sum_{n=0}^{\infty}\sum_{m=1}^{\infty}\frac{(r_<)^n}{(r_>)^{n+1}}\left[P_n(\cos\theta)P_n(\cos\theta')\right.$$
$$\left. + \frac{2(n-|m|)!}{(n+|m|)!}P_n^{|m|}(\cos\theta)P_n^{|m|}(\cos\theta')\cos m(\phi-\phi')\right] \qquad (7\text{-}408)$$

However, we also know that

$$G_\infty = \frac{1}{4\pi R} = \frac{1}{4\pi|\mathbf{r}-\mathbf{r}'|} = \frac{1}{4\pi\sqrt{r^2+(r')^2-2rr'\cos\gamma}} \qquad (7\text{-}409)$$

where $r = |\mathbf{r}| = (x^2+y^2+z^2)^{1/2}$, $r' = |\mathbf{r}'| = [(x')^2+(y')^2+(z')^2]^{1/2}$, and $\cos\gamma = \mathbf{r}\cdot\mathbf{r}'/|\mathbf{r}|\,|\mathbf{r}'|$ is the cosine of the angle between $\mathbf{r}$ and $\mathbf{r}'$.

Equation (7-409) can be expanded as a power series,

$$G_\infty = \frac{1}{4\pi R} = \frac{1}{4\pi} \sum_{n=0}^{\infty} \frac{(r_<)^n}{(r_>)^{n+1}} P_n(\cos \gamma) \qquad (7\text{-}410)$$

by noticing that Eq. (7-409) is a generating formula for Legendre polynomials. A comparison of Eqs. (7-408) and (7-410) then yields the addition formula for Legendre polynomials,

$$P_n(\cos \gamma) = P_n(\cos \theta) P_n(\cos \theta')$$
$$+ 2 \sum_{m=1}^{\infty} \frac{(n-m)!}{(n+m)!} P_n{}^m(\cos \theta) P_n{}^m(\cos \theta') \cos m(\phi - \phi') \qquad (7\text{-}411)$$

where the spherical coordinates of $\mathbf{r}$ and $\mathbf{r}'$ are (r,θ,ϕ) and (r',θ',ϕ'), respectively.

7-19 SOLUTION OF THE INTERIOR AND EXTERIOR DIRICHLET PROBLEMS FOR A GROUNDED CONDUCTING SPHERE

Let us construct the Green's function for the interior problem, of a unit charge inside a grounded conducting sphere of radius $r = a$. We set

$$G = G_\infty - G_i \qquad (7\text{-}412)$$

where G satisfies Eq. (7-383), together with the boundary condition

$$G = 0 \text{ on } r = a \qquad (7\text{-}413)$$

The induced potential G_i is a solution of Laplace's equation,

$$\nabla^2 G_i = 0 \qquad (7\text{-}414)$$

and, for the interior problem, G_i must be regular throughout the interior of the sphere $r = a$. Therefore we choose

$$G = \frac{1}{4\pi R} - \frac{1}{4\pi} \sum_{n=0}^{\infty} \sum_{m=0}^{\infty} A r^n \epsilon_m \frac{(n-m)!}{(n+m)!}$$
$$P_n{}^m(\cos \theta) P_n{}^m(\cos \theta') \cos m(\phi - \phi') \qquad (7\text{-}415)$$

where

$$\epsilon_m = \begin{cases} 1 & m = 0 \\ 2 & m = 1,2,3 \end{cases} \qquad (7\text{-}416)$$

and where A is to be determined through the boundary condition (7-413). With the aid of (7-408), Eq. (7-415) becomes

$$G = \frac{1}{4\pi} \sum_{n=0}^{\infty} \sum_{m=0}^{\infty} \left(\frac{r_<{}^n}{r_>{}^{n+1}} - A r^n \right)$$
$$\epsilon_m \frac{(n-m)!}{(n+m)!} P_n{}^m(\cos \theta) P_n{}^m(\cos \theta') \cos m(\phi - \phi') \qquad (7\text{-}417)$$

and on applying Eq. (7-413), keeping in mind that both r' and r must be less than or equal to a in the interior problem, we obtain

$$\frac{(r')^n}{a^{n+1}} = A a^n \tag{7-418}$$

or

$$A = \frac{(r')^n}{a^{2n+1}} \tag{7-419}$$

Thus the Green's function for the interior Dirichlet problem is

$$G = \frac{1}{4\pi R} - \frac{1}{4\pi} \sum_{n=0}^{\infty} \sum_{m=0}^{\infty} \epsilon_m \frac{(rr')^n}{a^{2n+1}}$$
$$P_n^m(\cos\theta) P_n^m(\cos\theta') \cos m(\phi - \phi') \tag{7-420}$$

The exterior Green's function is obtained in the same way except that now the point charge is located outside of the grounded conducting sphere and the induced potential G_i must remain finite as $r \to \infty$ instead of as $r \to 0$.

Therefore we choose

$$G = \frac{1}{4\pi R} - \frac{1}{4\pi} \sum_{n=0}^{\infty} \sum_{m=0}^{\infty} \frac{A \epsilon_m}{r^{n+1}} \frac{(n-m)!}{(n+m)!}$$
$$P_n^m(\cos\theta) P_n^m(\cos\theta') \cos m(\phi - \phi') \tag{7-421}$$

and with the aid of Eq. (7-408), this becomes

$$G = \frac{1}{4\pi} \sum_{n=0}^{\infty} \sum_{m=0}^{\infty} \left(\frac{r_<^n}{r_>^{n+1}} - \frac{A}{r^{n+1}} \right)$$
$$\epsilon_m \frac{(n-m)!}{(n+m)!} P_n^m(\cos\theta) P_n^m(\cos\theta') \cos m(\phi - \phi') \tag{7-422}$$

On equating G to zero on $r = a$, remembering that both r' and r are greater than or equal to a in the exterior problem, Eq. (7-422) yields

$$\frac{a^n}{(r')^{n+1}} = \frac{A}{a^{n+1}} \tag{7-423}$$

Hence

$$A = \frac{a^{2n+1}}{(r')^{n+1}} \tag{7-424}$$

and the Green's function for the exterior Dirichlet problem must be

$$G = \frac{1}{4\pi R} - \frac{1}{4\pi} \sum_{n=0}^{\infty} \sum_{m=0}^{\infty} \frac{\epsilon_m a^{2n+1} (n-m)!}{(rr')^{n+1} (n+m)!}$$
$$P_n^m(\cos\theta) P_n^m(\cos\theta') \cos m(\phi - \phi') \tag{7-425}$$

The additional term in expression (7-425), which causes G to vanish on $r = a$, is identical with that which would arise from an image charge of magnitude a/r' at the point $r = a^2/r'$, $\theta = \theta'$, $\phi = \phi'$.

If we compare Eqs. (7-425) and (7-420), we see that the image of a point charge q at point (r', θ', ϕ') in a grounded spherical surface at $r = a$ (with a either larger or smaller than r') is a charge $q(a/r')$ at the point $(a^2/r',\theta',\phi')$. When the charge is outside the surface $(r' > a)$, the image is inside the surface and is smaller than the original; if the charge is inside, the image is outside and larger than the original.

According to this discussion, both the interior and exterior Green's functions can be represented by

$$G = \frac{1}{4\pi R} - \frac{a/r'}{4\pi R'} \qquad (7\text{-}426)$$

where

$$R = |\mathbf{r} - \mathbf{r}'| = [r^2 + (r')^2 - 2rr' \cos \gamma]^{\frac{1}{2}} \qquad (7\text{-}427)$$

$$R' = \left| \mathbf{r} - \left(\frac{a}{r'}\right)^2 \mathbf{r}' \right| = \left[r^2 + \frac{a^4}{(r')^2} - \frac{2a^2 r}{r'} \cos \gamma \right]^{\frac{1}{2}} \qquad (7\text{-}428)$$

and

$$\frac{r'R'}{a} = \left[a^2 + \frac{(rr')^2}{a^2} - 2rr' \cos \gamma \right]^{\frac{1}{2}} \qquad (7\text{-}429)$$

With the aid of these expressions G reduces to

$$G = \frac{1}{4\pi[r^2 + (r')^2 - 2rr' \cos \gamma]^{\frac{1}{2}}}$$
$$- \frac{1}{4\pi[a^2 + (rr')^2/a^2 - 2rr' \cos \gamma]^{\frac{1}{2}}} \qquad (7\text{-}430)$$

The interior Dirichlet problem for Laplace's equation in a sphere requires us to determine a function $\psi(r,\theta,\phi)$, satisfying the conditions

$$\nabla^2\psi = 0 \qquad r < a \qquad (7\text{-}431)$$

$$\psi = \psi(a,\theta,\phi) \text{ on } r = a \qquad (7\text{-}432)$$

The solution is easily obtained if we insert Eqs. (7-430) and (7-431) into Green's symmetric identity:

$$\int_V \{G \nabla^2\psi - \psi \nabla^2 G\} \, dV = \int_{S(V)} \left\{ G \frac{\partial \psi}{\partial n} - \psi \frac{\partial G}{\partial n} \right\} dS \qquad (7\text{-}433)$$

In Eq. (7-431) V is the region enclosed by a sphere of radius $r = a$ and boundary surface $S(V)$. If we note that the outward normals to $S(V)$ point radially away from the center of the sphere $r = a$, it follows that $(\partial G/\partial n)_{r=a} = (\partial G/\partial r)_{r=a}$ on $S(V)$. Since $\nabla^2\psi = 0$ in V and $G = 0$ on $S(V)$, Eq. (7-433) gives us

$$\psi(r',\theta',\phi') = -\int_0^{2\pi} \int_0^{\pi} \psi(a,\theta,\phi) \left(\frac{\partial G}{\partial r}\right)_{r=a} a^2 \sin \theta \, d\theta \, d\phi \qquad (7\text{-}434)$$

and differentiating Eq. (7-430) partially with respect to r,

$$\left(\frac{\partial G}{\partial r}\right)_{r=a} = \frac{1}{4\pi a} \frac{(r')^2 - a^2}{[a^2 + (r')^2 - 2ar' \cos \gamma]^{\frac{3}{2}}} \qquad (7\text{-}435)$$

Therefore

$$\psi(r',\theta',\phi') = \frac{a[a^2 - (r')^2]}{4\pi} \int_0^{2\pi} \int_0^{\pi} \frac{\psi(a,\theta,\phi) \sin\theta \, d\theta \, d\phi}{[a^2 + (r')^2 - 2ar' \cos\gamma]^{3/2}}$$

(7-436)

is the required solution of Eqs. (7-431) and (7-432).

The exterior Dirichlet problem asks us to construct a function which is harmonic *outside* of the sphere $r = a$ and which assumes prescribed values on the spherical boundary. The problem is exactly the same as (7-431) and (7-432) except that the inequality in (7-431) is reversed. The solutions of the interior and exterior Dirichlet problems are identical apart from a minus sign which enters because the outward normal for the exterior region points toward instead of away from the center of the sphere $r = a$. Thus $(\partial G/\partial n)_{r=a} = - (\partial G/\partial r)_{r=a}$, and consequently

$$\psi(r',\theta',\phi') = \frac{a[(r')^2 - a^2]}{4\pi} \int_0^{2\pi} \int_0^{\pi} \frac{\psi(a,\theta,\phi) \sin\theta \, d\theta \, d\phi}{[a^2 + (r')^2 - 2ar' \cos\gamma]^{3/2}}$$

(7-437)

replaces Eq. (7-436). Solutions (7-436) and (7-437) are known as "Poisson's solution" of the Dirichlet problem. Double integrals like those appearing in (7-436) and (7-437) are called "Poisson's integrals," and they play an important role in potential theory.

7-20 THE ONE-DIMENSIONAL WAVE EQUATION

Suppose that a flexible, elastic string is stretched between two supports on the x axis (Fig. 7-5). Let $u(x,t)$ be the vertical displacement of the string as measured from the x axis. The mass of a length ds of string located between x and $x + dx$ is

$$dm = \rho \, ds$$

(7-438)

where ρ represents the mass per unit length of the string. The vertical component of force acting on dm can be resolved into two parts:

$$F_V = F_T + F_E$$

(7-439)

In Eq. (7-439), F_T represents the vertical component of force exerted on dm due to tension in the string, and F_E represents the vertical component of all other external forces acting on dm, such as gravity and so on. The vertical component of acceleration of dm is $\partial^2 u/\partial t^2$, and therefore

$$F_V = \rho \, ds \, \frac{\partial^2 u}{\partial t^2}$$

(7-440)

To compute F_T, let T be the tension in the string, and let θ be the angle between the tension vector and the x axis; then

$$F_T = (T \sin\theta)_{x+dx} - (T \sin\theta)_x$$

(7-441)

If the *external force per unit length* acting vertically on the string is

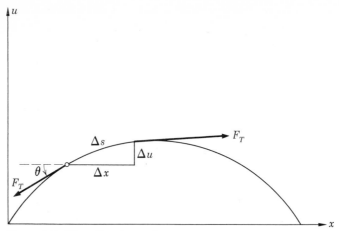

Figure 7-5 The vibrating string.

given by $F(x,t)$, then the amount of external force acting on dm is

$$F_E = F(x,t)\ ds \tag{7-442}$$

and we have obtained

$$F_V = [(T \sin \theta)_{x+dx} - (T \sin \theta)_x] + F(x,t)\ ds \tag{7-443}$$

A further simplification can be effected by assuming that the displacement $u(x,t)$ is always small, for then θ is never a large angle, and the small-angle approximation

$$\sin \theta \cong \tan \theta = \frac{\partial u}{\partial x} \tag{7-444}$$

is applicable. Moreover, since

$$ds = \left[1 + \left(\frac{\partial u}{\partial x}\right)^2\right]^{\frac{1}{2}} dx \tag{7-445}$$

the small-angle approximation $\left|\dfrac{\partial u}{\partial x}\right| \ll 1$ permits us to use dx in place of ds. As a result, Eqs. (7-440) and (7-443) reduce to

$$\rho\ dx\ \frac{\partial^2 u}{\partial t^2} = \frac{\partial}{\partial x}\left(T\ \frac{\partial u}{\partial x}\right) dx + F(x,t)\ dx \tag{7-446}$$

The tension T and linear density ρ are constants. Therefore, on setting

$$c^2 = \frac{T}{\rho} \tag{7-447}$$

the one-dimensional inhomogeneous wave equation,

$$\frac{\partial^2 u}{\partial t^2} = c^2 \frac{\partial^2 u}{\partial x^2} + \frac{F(x,t)}{\rho} \tag{7-448}$$

follows from Eq. (7-446). Since T has the dimensions of force and ρ the dimensions of mass per unit length, the quantity c defined in

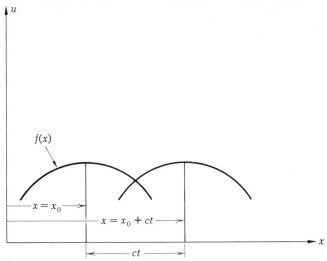

Figure 7-6 The curve $u = f(x)$ is caused to propagate to the right at speed c by substituting $x - ct$ for x.

Eq. (7-447) must have the dimensions of a velocity. Indeed, we shall see presently that c is just the speed with which the displacement $u(x,t)$ *propagates* along the string.

Consider a curve $u = f(x)$ in the (u,x) plane. So far this curve is static, but if x is now replaced by $x - ct$, then the possibility of motion exists. The new function, $u = f(x - ct)$, has the property that when t increases, the argument $x - ct$ may be kept constant by increasing x proportionately. This corresponds to translating the entire curve $u = f(x)$ to the right with a constant velocity equal to c (Fig. 7-6). In other words, a point which was at position x_0 at time $t = 0$ and is at position $x = x_0 + ct$ at time t will always be assigned the same fixed amplitude $u = f(x_0)$.

Had we replaced x in $f(x)$ with $x + ct$ instead of $x - ct$, the same argument would still prevail except that $u = f(x)$ would now translate to the left instead of to the right. This happens because as t increases, x must decrease proportionately in order to keep $x + ct$ constant. A point at $x = x_0$ at time $t = 0$ and at $x = x_0 - ct$ at time t would always be assigned the same fixed amplitude $u = f(x_0)$.

This discussion suggests that in the absence of external forces $F(x,t)$, we should expect Eq. (7-448) to have a general solution of the form

$$u(x,t) = f(x - ct) + g(x + ct) \tag{7-449}$$

wherein f and g are arbitrary functions of their arguments. It is easy to verify that this is actually the case. Let $r = x - ct$ and

$s = x + ct$; then

$$\frac{\partial u}{\partial x} = \frac{\partial f}{\partial r}\frac{\partial r}{\partial x} + \frac{\partial g}{\partial s}\frac{\partial s}{\partial x} = \frac{\partial f}{\partial r} + \frac{\partial g}{\partial s}$$

$$\frac{\partial^2 u}{\partial x^2} = \frac{\partial^2 f}{\partial r^2} + \frac{\partial^2 g}{\partial s^2}$$

$$\frac{\partial u}{\partial t} = \frac{\partial f}{\partial r}\frac{\partial r}{\partial t} + \frac{\partial g}{\partial s}\frac{\partial s}{\partial t} = -c\frac{\partial f}{\partial r} + c\frac{\partial g}{\partial s}$$

$$\frac{\partial^2 u}{\partial t^2} = c^2\left(\frac{\partial^2 f}{\partial r^2} + \frac{\partial^2 g}{\partial s^2}\right)$$

so that

$$c^2\frac{\partial^2 u}{\partial x^2} = \frac{\partial^2 u}{\partial t^2} \tag{7-450}$$

is indeed satisfied by Eq. (7-449).

The initial-value problem

The initial-value problem for the one-dimensional wave equation is to solve Eq. (7-450) for a string of unlimited length, given that the initial shape of the string is

$$u(x,0) = F(x) \tag{7-451}$$

and that the initial velocity of each point on the string is

$$\frac{\partial u}{\partial t}(x,0) = G(x) \tag{7-452}$$

From Eqs. (7-449), (7-451), and (7-452) it follows that

$$F(x) = f(x) + g(x) \tag{7-453}$$

$$G(x) = -cf'(x) + cg'(x) \tag{7-454}$$

and therefore

$$2cg'(x) = G(x) + cF'(x) \tag{7-455}$$

$$-2cf'(x) = G(x) - cF'(x) \tag{7-456}$$

Integrating Eqs. (7-455) and (7-456) directly, one finds

$$f(x) = \tfrac{1}{2}F(x) - \frac{1}{2c}\int^x G(s)\,ds + \text{const} \tag{7-457}$$

$$g(x) = \tfrac{1}{2}F(x) + \frac{1}{2c}\int^x G(s)\,ds + \text{const} \tag{7-458}$$

On replacing x by $x - ct$ in Eq. (7-457) and by $x + ct$ in Eq. (7-458), and then adding the results, there follows:

$$u(x,t) = f(x - ct) + g(x + ct) = \tfrac{1}{2}F(x - ct)$$
$$+ \tfrac{1}{2}F(x + ct) + \frac{1}{2c}\int_{x-ct}^{x+ct} G(s)\,ds + \text{const} \tag{7-459}$$

The constant in Eq. (7-459) is evaluated by setting $t = 0$ and noting that because of Eq. (7-451), the constant must be zero. Thus

$$u(x,t) = \tfrac{1}{2}F(x - ct) + \tfrac{1}{2}F(x + ct) + \frac{1}{2c} \int_{x-ct}^{x+ct} G(s)\, ds \qquad (7\text{-}460)$$

which is d'Alembert's solution of the initial-value problem, gives the motion of a string subjected to arbitrary initial displacements and velocities.

Mixed boundary- and initial-value problems

In general, strings are not infinitely long, and external forces are not always zero. Hence we frequently want to find a solution of

$$\frac{\partial^2 u}{\partial t^2} = c^2 \frac{\partial^2 u}{\partial x^2} + \frac{1}{\rho} f(x,t) \qquad (7\text{-}461)$$

which satisfies not only the initial conditions,

$$u(x,0) = F(x) \qquad (7\text{-}462)$$

$$\frac{\partial u}{\partial t}(x,0) = G(x) \qquad (7\text{-}463)$$

but the boundary conditions,

$$u(0,t) = 0 \qquad (7\text{-}464)$$

$$u(a,t) = 0 \qquad (7\text{-}465)$$

at $x = 0$ and $x = a$ as well. This mixed initial- and boundary-value problem deals with the forced vibrations of a flexible elastic string supported between rigid walls at $x = 0$ and $x = a$.

One of the easiest ways to solve Eq. (7-461) is to employ the finite sine transform introduced in Sec. 5-10. This transform is particularly well suited to the present problem because, as one notes from Eq. (5-176), the boundary conditions (7-464) and (7-465) are exactly the ones useful for the finite sine transform.

Equation (7-461) is multiplied through by $\sin n\pi x/a$ and then integrated by parts with respect to x from $x = 0$ to $x = a$, using Eqs. (5-176), (7-464), and (7-465). The result is that

$$\frac{d^2 \bar{u}_s}{dt^2}(n,t) + \left(\frac{n\pi c}{a}\right)^2 \bar{u}_s(n,t) = \frac{1}{\rho} \bar{f}_s(n,t) \qquad (7\text{-}466)$$

where

$$\bar{u}_s(n,t) = \int_0^a u(x,t) \sin \frac{n\pi x}{a}\, dx \qquad (7\text{-}467)$$

$$\bar{f}_s(n,t) = \int_0^a f(x,t) \sin \frac{n\pi x}{a}\, dx \qquad (7\text{-}468)$$

are finite sine transforms of u and f. Equation (7-466) must be solved subject to the transformed initial conditions,

$$\bar{u}_s(n,0) = \bar{F}_s(n) \qquad (7\text{-}469)$$

$$\frac{\partial \bar{u}_s}{\partial t}(n,0) = \bar{G}_s(n) \qquad (7\text{-}470)$$

obtained by multiplying Eqs. (7-462) and (7-463) by $\sin n\pi x/a$ and then integrating with respect to x from $x = 0$ to $x = a$.

The solution of Eq. (7-466) subject to (7-469) and (7-470) is given in Sec. 5-24 in the form

$$\bar{u}_s(n,t) = \bar{F}_s(n) \cos \omega_n t + \bar{G}_s(n) \frac{\sin \omega_n t}{\omega_n}$$

$$+ \frac{1}{\rho \omega_n} \int_0^t \bar{f}_s(n,\tau) \sin \omega_n(t - \tau)\, d\tau \qquad (7\text{-}471)$$

where $\omega_n = n\pi c/a$. To obtain $u(x,t)$, the inversion theorem (5-151) must be applied to Eq. (7-471). When this is done, we obtain

$$u(x,t) = \frac{2}{a} \sum_{n=1}^{\infty} \left\{ \bar{F}_s(n) \cos \omega_n t + \bar{G}_s(n) \frac{\sin \omega_n t}{\omega_n} \right\} \sin k_n x$$

$$+ \frac{2}{\rho a} \sum_{n=1}^{\infty} \frac{\sin k_n x}{\omega_n} \int_0^t \bar{f}_s(n,\tau) \sin \omega_n(t - \tau)\, d\tau \qquad (7\text{-}472)$$

where $k_n = n\pi/a$. Equation (7-472) expresses the solution of the mixed initial- and boundary-value problem for the one-dimensional wave equation in terms of the Fourier coefficients of the external force and the Fourier coefficients of the initial conditions.

It is instructive to examine the form of solution (7-472). It can be written as the sum of a complementary function $u_C(x,t)$ and a particular integral $u_P(x,t)$:

$$u(x,t) = u_C(x,t) + u_P(x,t) \qquad (7\text{-}473)$$

The complementary function u_C satisfies the homogeneous wave equation,

$$\frac{\partial^2 u_C}{\partial t^2} = c^2 \frac{\partial^2 u_C}{\partial x^2} \qquad (7\text{-}474)$$

the initial conditions,

$$u_C(x,0) = F(x) \qquad (7\text{-}475)$$

$$\frac{\partial u_C}{\partial t}(x,0) = G(x) \qquad (7\text{-}476)$$

and the boundary conditions,

$$u_C(0,t) = 0 \qquad (7\text{-}477)$$

$$u_C(a,t) = 0 \qquad (7\text{-}478)$$

The particular integral u_P satisfies the inhomogeneous wave equation,

$$\frac{\partial^2 u_P}{\partial t^2} = c^2 \frac{\partial^2 u_P}{\partial x^2} + \frac{1}{\rho} f(x,t) \qquad (7\text{-}479)$$

the initial conditions,

$$u_P(x,0) = 0 \qquad (7\text{-}480)$$

$$\frac{\partial u_P}{\partial t}(x,0) = 0 \qquad (7\text{-}481)$$

and the boundary conditions,

$$u_P(0,t) = 0 \qquad\qquad\qquad\qquad (7\text{-}482)$$

$$u_P(a,t) = 0 \qquad\qquad\qquad\qquad (7\text{-}483)$$

Notice that u_P and u_C satisfy the boundary conditions at $x = 0$ and $x = a$ independently of each other. The reason is that the initial conditions and the force term have both been expanded in terms of the same eigenfunctions, namely $\sin n\pi x/a$, and these eigenfunctions all vanish at $x = 0$ and $x = a$.

7-21 THE TWO-DIMENSIONAL WAVE EQUATION

The inhomogeneous scalar wave equation appears most frequently in the form

$$\left(\nabla^2 - \frac{1}{c^2}\frac{\partial^2}{\partial t^2}\right) u(\mathbf{r},t) = -F(\mathbf{r},t) \qquad\qquad (7\text{-}484)$$

where ∇^2 is the two-dimensional Laplacian operator. One basic procedure employed in solving Eq. (7-484) depends on the nature of the source term $F(\mathbf{r},t)$. If $F(\mathbf{r},t)$ is defined for all positive and negative time, then it is possible to represent $F(\mathbf{r},t)$ as a Fourier integral,

$$F(\mathbf{r},t) = \frac{1}{2\pi}\int_{-\infty}^{+\infty} \bar{F}(\mathbf{r},\omega)e^{i\omega t}\,d\omega \qquad\qquad (7\text{-}485)$$

and because Eq. (7-484) is a linear equation, it is reasonable to expect that the solution of (7-484) will also be a superposition of the same form:

$$u(\mathbf{r},t) = \frac{1}{2\pi}\int_{-\infty}^{+\infty} \bar{u}(\mathbf{r},\omega)e^{i\omega t}\,d\omega \qquad\qquad (7\text{-}486)$$

Inserting Eqs. (7-485) and (7-486) into (7-484) gives as a partial differential equation for the Fourier transform of u:

$$(\nabla^2 + k^2)\bar{u}(\mathbf{r},\omega) = -\bar{F}(\mathbf{r},\omega) \qquad k = \frac{\omega}{c} \qquad (7\text{-}487)$$

Equation (7-487) is called the "inhomogeneous Helmholtz equation."

A more realistic situation is one in which $u(\mathbf{r},t)$, together with all of its partial derivatives, is identically zero up to a certain instant, say $t = 0$. At $t = 0$, the source term $F(\mathbf{r},t)$ is suddenly "turned on," and the initial values of u and $\partial u/\partial t$ are prescribed. One then determines the later evolution of the solution $u(\mathbf{r},t)$. This type of problem is readily attacked with the aid of a Laplace transform. One multiplies Eq. (7-484) by e^{-st}, integrates twice by parts with respect to t from $t = 0$ to $t = \infty$, and obtains thereby

$$(\nabla^2 - k^2)\bar{u}(\mathbf{r},s) = -\bar{F}(\mathbf{r},s) - \frac{1}{c^2}\left(\frac{\partial u}{\partial t} + su\right)_{t=0} \qquad (7\text{-}488)$$

which is a Helmholtz type of equation for the Laplace transform of u. In Eq. (7-487) it is assumed that

$$\bar{u}(\mathbf{r},s) = \int_0^\infty u(\mathbf{r},t)e^{-st}\, dt \tag{7-489}$$

$$\bar{F}(\mathbf{r},s) = \int_0^\infty F(\mathbf{r},t)e^{-st}\, dt \tag{7-490}$$

$$\lim_{t \to \infty} \left[\frac{\partial u}{\partial t} + su(\mathbf{r},t) \right] e^{-st} = 0 \tag{7-491}$$

and that $k = s/c$.

If u and $\partial u/\partial t$ evolve continuously from the quiescent state $u \equiv 0$, then initially we must have

$$u(\mathbf{r},0) = 0 \tag{7-492}$$

$$\left(\frac{\partial u}{\partial t} \right)_{t=0} = 0 \tag{7-493}$$

and Eq. (7-487) reduces to

$$(\nabla^2 - k^2)\bar{u}(\mathbf{r},s) = -\bar{F}(\mathbf{r},s) \tag{7-494}$$

We see that the Fourier or Laplace transform of the time-dependent wave equation leads, under appropriate circumstances, to a Helmholtz equation which must be solved.

The required solution can be obtained with the aid of the by now familiar Green's-function technique. Consider the problem of solving

$$(\nabla^2 + k^2)\bar{u}(\mathbf{r},\omega) = -\bar{F}(\mathbf{r},\omega) \tag{7-495}$$

We first introduce a Green's function, defined as the solution of

$$(\nabla^2 + k^2)\bar{G}(\mathbf{r}|\mathbf{r}') = -\delta(\mathbf{r} - \mathbf{r}') \tag{7-496}$$

where the Dirac delta function has the property that

$$\int_V \bar{F}(\mathbf{r})\, \delta(\mathbf{r} - \mathbf{r}')\, dV = \begin{cases} \bar{F}(\mathbf{r}') & \text{if } \mathbf{r}' \text{ is the position vector} \\ & \text{of a point in } V \\ 0 & \text{if } \mathbf{r}' \text{ lies outside of } V \end{cases} \tag{7-497}$$

Next we observe that Green's symmetric identity can always be written as

$$\int_V \{\bar{G}(\nabla^2 + k^2)\bar{u} - \bar{u}(\nabla^2 + k^2)\bar{G}\}\, dV$$
$$= \int_{S(V)} \left\{ \bar{G}\frac{\partial \bar{u}}{\partial n} - \bar{u}\frac{\partial \bar{G}}{\partial n} \right\} dS \tag{7-498}$$

which is useful in connection with Eqs. (7-495) and (7-496). With the aid of these equations, (7-498) reduces to

$$\bar{u}(\mathbf{r}',\omega) = \int_V \bar{G}(\mathbf{r}|\mathbf{r}')\bar{F}(\mathbf{r},\omega)\, dV + \int_{S(V)} \left\{ \bar{G}\frac{\partial \bar{u}}{\partial n} - \bar{u}\frac{\partial \bar{G}}{\partial n} \right\} dS \tag{7-499}$$

Here V represents the volume of a closed region of space, $\mathbf{r}'$ is the position vector of a point in V, and $S(V)$ is the surface enclosing V.

When we are concerned with a two-dimensional problem, Eq. (7-499) is replaced by

$$\bar{u}(\mathbf{r}',\omega) = \int_S \bar{G}(\mathbf{r}|\mathbf{r}')\bar{F}(\mathbf{r},\omega)\, dS + \int_{C(S)} \left\{ \bar{G}\frac{\partial u}{\partial n} - \bar{u}\frac{\partial \bar{G}}{\partial n} \right\} ds \qquad (7\text{-}500)$$

Here S represents the area of a bordered surface, $\mathbf{r}'$ is a point of S, and $C(S)$ is the complete boundary curve bordering S. For example, if S is the surface of an annulus or "washer," then $\mathbf{r}'$ is a point on the washer, S is the surface of the washer, and $C(S)$ consists of the inner and outer circumference of the washer.

If we replace k^2 by $-k^2$ in Eqs. (7-496) and (7-498), then we can write the three-dimensional solution of (7-494) as

$$\bar{u}(\mathbf{r}',s) = \int_S \bar{G}(\mathbf{r}|\mathbf{r}')\bar{F}(\mathbf{r},s)\, dV + \int_{S(V)} \left\{ \bar{G}\frac{\partial \bar{u}}{\partial n} - \bar{u}\frac{\partial \bar{G}}{\partial n} \right\} dS \qquad (7\text{-}501)$$

and the corresponding two-dimensional solution becomes

$$\bar{u}(\mathbf{r}',s) = \int_S \bar{G}(\mathbf{r}|\mathbf{r}')\bar{F}(\mathbf{r},s)\, dS + \int_{C(S)} \left\{ \bar{G}\frac{\partial \bar{u}}{\partial n} - \bar{u}\frac{\partial \bar{G}}{\partial n} \right\} d\sigma \qquad (7\text{-}502)$$

In order to avoid confusion with the Laplace transform parameter s, the element of arc length in Eq. (7-502) has been changed from ds to $d\sigma$. Equations (7-499) to (7-502) are formal solutions of Eqs. (7-487) and (7-494). In order to make them useful, one must know, not only the Green's function $\bar{G}$, but also the boundary values of $\bar{u}$ and $\partial \bar{u}/\partial n$. The solution in this form is overspecified, since one cannot arbitrarily assign both $\bar{u}$ and $\partial \bar{u}/\partial n$ on $C(S)$. When $\bar{u}$ is a known function on $C(S)$, it is convenient to eliminate $\partial \bar{u}/\partial n$ from the solution by making the Green's function satisfy a homogeneous Dirichlet condition, $\bar{G} = 0$ on $C(S)$. Similarly, if it is $\partial \bar{u}/\partial n$ that is to be assigned on $C(S)$, the boundary values of $\bar{u}$ can be eliminated by making $\partial \bar{G}/\partial n$ satisfy a homogeneous Neumann condition, $\partial \bar{G}/\partial n = 0$ on $C(S)$. Occasionally, one wishes to specify a linear combination such as $\partial \bar{u}/\partial n + \alpha\bar{u} = f$ on $C(S)$. This can be done by making $\bar{G}$ and $\partial \bar{G}/\partial n$ satisfy a so-called "impedance" boundary condition $\partial \bar{G}/\partial n + \alpha\bar{G} = 0$ on $C(S)$.

Properties of the Green's function

The Green's function satisfying Eq. (7-496) must have the following properties:

1. $(\nabla^2 + k^2)\bar{G}(\mathbf{r}|\mathbf{r}') = 0$ except at $\mathbf{r} = \mathbf{r}'$.
2. $\bar{G}(\mathbf{r}|\mathbf{r}')$ is continuous except at $\mathbf{r} = \mathbf{r}'$.
3. $\bar{G}(\mathbf{r}|\mathbf{r}')$ satisfies homogeneous boundary conditions on $C(S)$.
4. The Green's function satisfies the reciprocity relation $\bar{G}(\mathbf{r}|\mathbf{r}') = \bar{G}(\mathbf{r}'|\mathbf{r})$ obtained by interchanging $\mathbf{r}$ and $\mathbf{r}'$.

Let us consider the reciprocity property of the Green's function. It says, for example, that if a point source of sound is placed in the center of a room and a point recorder is placed in one corner of the room, the record obtained is exactly the same as that which would be obtained if the source and recorder were interchanged. This is not particularly obvious. One might expect the corner to affect the source and recorder differently. Reciprocity guarantees that there will be absolutely no difference on interchanging the source and recorder.

To prove the reciprocity property, consider $\bar{G}(\mathbf{r}|\mathbf{r}')$, the solution at the point $\mathbf{r}$ for an applied impulse at $\mathbf{r}'$, and also $\bar{G}(\mathbf{r}|\mathbf{r}'')$, the solution at $\mathbf{r}$ when the impulse is located at another point $\mathbf{r}''$, subject to the same *homogeneous* boundary condition. Then

$$\int_S \{\bar{G}(\mathbf{r}|\mathbf{r}') \, \nabla^2 \bar{G}(\mathbf{r}|\mathbf{r}'') - \bar{G}(\mathbf{r}|\mathbf{r}'') \, \nabla^2 \bar{G}(\mathbf{r}|\mathbf{r}')\} \, dS$$

$$= \int_{C(S)} \left\{ \bar{G}(\mathbf{r}|\mathbf{r}'') \frac{\partial \bar{G}(\mathbf{r}|\mathbf{r}'')}{\partial n} - \bar{G}(\mathbf{r}|\mathbf{r}'') \frac{\partial \bar{G}(\mathbf{r}|\mathbf{r}')}{\partial n} \right\} ds \qquad (7\text{-}503)$$

Now if $\bar{G}(\mathbf{r}|\mathbf{r}')$ vanishes on $C(S)$, then so does $\bar{G}(\mathbf{r}|\mathbf{r}'')$, by hypothesis. Similarly, if $\partial\bar{G}(\mathbf{r}|\mathbf{r}')/\partial n$ vanishes on $C'(S)$, then so does $\partial\bar{G}(\mathbf{r}|\mathbf{r}'')/\partial n$, again by hypothesis. In either case,

$$\int_S \{\bar{G}(\mathbf{r}|\mathbf{r}') \, \nabla^2 \bar{G}(\mathbf{r}|\mathbf{r}'') - \bar{G}(\mathbf{r}|\mathbf{r}'') \, \nabla^2 \bar{G}(\mathbf{r}|\mathbf{r}')\} \, dS = 0 \qquad (7\text{-}504)$$

However,

$$\nabla^2 \bar{G}(\mathbf{r}|\mathbf{r}') = -k^2 \bar{G}(\mathbf{r}|\mathbf{r}') - \delta(\mathbf{r} - \mathbf{r}') \qquad (7\text{-}505)$$

and

$$\nabla^2 \bar{G}(\mathbf{r}|\mathbf{r}'') = -k^2 \bar{G}(\mathbf{r}|\mathbf{r}'') - \delta(\mathbf{r} - \mathbf{r}'') \qquad (7\text{-}506)$$

yield

$$\int_S \{\bar{G}(\mathbf{r}|\mathbf{r}') \, \delta(\mathbf{r} - \mathbf{r}'') - \bar{G}(\mathbf{r}|\mathbf{r}'') \, \delta(\mathbf{r} - \mathbf{r}')\} \, dS = 0 \qquad (7\text{-}507)$$

from which we obtain

$$\bar{G}(\mathbf{r}''|\mathbf{r}') = \bar{G}(\mathbf{r}'|\mathbf{r}'') \qquad (7\text{-}508)$$

proving the reciprocity principle.

The two-dimensional Green's function for an infinite medium

The two-dimensional infinite-medium Green's function for a line source is defined as the solution of

$$(\nabla^2 + k^2)\bar{G}(\mathbf{r}|\mathbf{r}') = -\delta(\mathbf{r} - \mathbf{r}') \qquad (7\text{-}509)$$

in polar coordinates. The Green's function $\bar{G}(\mathbf{r}|\mathbf{r}')$ represents the disturbance at $\mathbf{r}$ due to a line source passing through the point $\mathbf{r}'$ or vice versa. In a medium of unlimited extent, $\bar{G}$ should depend *only* on the distance between the source and receiver. Therefore

$$\bar{G}(\mathbf{r}|\mathbf{r}') = \bar{G}(|\mathbf{r} - \mathbf{r}'|) = \bar{G}(R) \qquad (7\text{-}510)$$

and (7-509) can be written as

$$(\nabla^2 + k^2)\bar{G}(R) = -\delta(\mathbf{r} - \mathbf{r}') \qquad (7\text{-}511)$$

It is convenient to choose a polar coordinate system centered at the source; then $r = R$ and $r' = 0$. In this coordinate system

$dS = R \, dR \, d\theta$, and

$$\delta(\mathbf{r} - \mathbf{r}') = \frac{\delta(R)}{R} \, \delta(\theta) \qquad (7\text{-}512)$$

in order that

$$\int_0^\infty \int_{-\pi}^\pi \delta(\mathbf{r} - \mathbf{r}') R \, dR \, d\theta = 1 \qquad (7\text{-}513)$$

Consequently Eq. (7-511) may be written as

$$\frac{1}{R} \frac{\partial}{\partial R} \left(R \frac{\partial \bar{G}}{\partial R} \right) + k^2 \bar{G}(R) = \frac{-\delta(R)}{R} \, \delta(\theta) \qquad (7\text{-}514)$$

Equation (7-514) is now multiplied through by $d\theta$, and both sides are integrated from $\theta = -\pi$ to $\theta = \pi$ to give

$$\frac{1}{R} \frac{\partial}{\partial R} \left(R \frac{\partial \bar{G}}{\partial R} \right) + k^2 \bar{G}(R) = \frac{-\delta(R)}{2\pi R} \qquad (7\text{-}515)$$

Integrating each side of Eq. (7-515) with respect to dR from $R = -\epsilon$ to $R = \epsilon$ and letting $\epsilon \to 0$ then yields

$$\frac{\partial \bar{G}}{\partial R} = -\frac{1}{2\pi R} \qquad (7\text{-}516)$$

Equation (7-515) is recognized as Bessel's equation of order zero, and thus its solutions must be found among $J_0(kR)$, $N_0(kR)$, $H_0^{(1)}(kR)$, or $H_0^{(2)}(kR)$. To see which one is appropriate, we must recall from Eq. (7-486) that

$$G(R,t) = \frac{1}{2\pi} \int_{-\infty}^{+\infty} \bar{G}(R,\omega) e^{i\omega t} \, d\omega \qquad (7\text{-}517)$$

is supposed to represent the disturbance generated by a *source* at $R = 0$. Thus as time increases, the disturbance must move *away* from the source. The asymptotic expansions in Sec. 6-11 lead to the conclusion that $H_0^{(2)}(kR)$ is the correct function to use, since for very large kR,

$$H_0^{(2)}(kR) e^{i\omega t} \sim \left(\frac{2}{\pi kR} \right)^{1/2} e^{i\pi/4} e^{-i(kR-\omega t)} \qquad (7\text{-}518)$$

In other words, for very large kR, $H_0^{(2)}(kR) e^{i\omega t}$ reduces to a plane wave moving *away* from the source. Thus $\bar{G}$ is chosen as

$$\bar{G}(kR) = A H_0^{(2)}(kR) \qquad (7\text{-}519)$$

where the constant A is determined from Eq. (7-516) and the results in Sec. 6-11. One finds

$$\frac{d}{dR} [\lim_{R \to 0} A H_0^{(2)}(kR)] = \frac{2iA}{\pi} \frac{d}{dR} (\log R) = \frac{-1}{2\pi R} \qquad (7\text{-}520)$$

or

$$A = \frac{i}{4} \qquad (7\text{-}521)$$

and therefore

$$\bar{G}(kR) = \frac{i}{4} H_0^{(2)}(kR) \qquad (7\text{-}522)$$

THE TWO-DIMENSIONAL WAVE EQUATION

In the same way we can show that the infinite-medium Green's function for

$$(\nabla^2 - k^2)\bar{G}(\mathbf{r}|\mathbf{r}') = -\delta(\mathbf{r} - \mathbf{r}') \tag{7-523}$$

is given by

$$\bar{G}(kR) = \frac{1}{2\pi} K_0(kR) \tag{7-524}$$

where as before

$$R = |\mathbf{r} - \mathbf{r}'| = [(x - x')^2 + (y - y')^2]^{1/2} \tag{7-525}$$

7-22 THE HELMHOLTZ EQUATION IN CYLINDRICAL COORDINATES

In this section we shall examine the problem of solving

$$(\nabla^2 + k^2)\bar{G} = -\delta(\mathbf{r} - \mathbf{r}') \tag{7-526}$$

in cylindrical coordinates (r,θ,z). If we recall that $dV = r\,dr\,d\theta\,dz$, the delta function becomes

$$\delta(\mathbf{r} - \mathbf{r}') = \frac{\delta(r - r')\,\delta(\theta - \theta')\,\delta(z - z')}{r} \tag{7-527}$$

If we set $\phi = \theta - \theta'$, then Eq. (7-526) may be written as

$$\frac{1}{r}\frac{\partial}{\partial r}\left(r\frac{\partial \bar{G}}{\partial r}\right) + \frac{1}{r^2}\frac{\partial^2 \bar{G}}{\partial \phi^2} + \frac{\partial^2 \bar{G}}{\partial z^2} + k^2 \bar{G}$$
$$= \frac{-\delta(r - r')\,\delta(\phi)\,\delta(z - z')}{r} \tag{7-528}$$

and a solution of Eq. (7-528) may be sought in the form

$$\bar{G} = \frac{1}{2\pi} \sum_{n=-\infty}^{+\infty} \bar{G}_n e^{in\phi} \tag{7-529}$$

Let Eq. (7-528) be multiplied through by $e^{-in\phi}$ and both sides integrated with respect to ϕ from $\phi = -\pi$ to $\phi = \pi$. First of all,

$$\int_{-\pi}^{\pi} \frac{\partial^2 \bar{G}}{\partial \phi^2} e^{-in\phi}\,d\phi = e^{-in\phi}\left(\frac{\partial \bar{G}}{\partial \phi} + in\bar{G}\right)\Big|_{-\pi}^{\pi} - n^2 \int_{-\pi}^{\pi} \bar{G}e^{-in\phi}\,d\phi \tag{7-530}$$

and in an unbounded medium, $\bar{G}$ should be periodic in $\phi = \theta - \theta'$, so that the integrated part in Eq. (7-530) vanishes. Because of the orthogonality properties of $e^{-in\phi}$,

$$\bar{G}_n = \int_{-\pi}^{\pi} \bar{G}e^{-in\phi}\,d\phi \tag{7-531}$$

and thus

$$\frac{1}{r}\frac{\partial}{\partial r}\left(r\frac{\partial \bar{G}_n}{\partial r}\right) + \left(k^2 - \frac{n^2}{r^2}\right)\bar{G}_n + \frac{\partial^2 \bar{G}_n}{\partial z^2}$$
$$= \frac{-\delta(r - r')\,\delta(z - z')}{r} \tag{7-532}$$

where $n = 0, \pm 1, \pm 2, \ldots$. The z dependence in Eq. (7-532) is now eliminated by taking a Fourier transform of (7-532) with respect to z. Let (7-532) be multiplied through by e^{-ihz} and integrated with respect to z from $z = -\infty$ to $z = \infty$. The result is

$$\frac{1}{r} \frac{\partial}{\partial r} \left(r \frac{\partial \bar{F}_n}{\partial r} \right) - \frac{n^2}{r^2} \bar{F}_n + (k^2 - h^2) \bar{F}_n = \frac{-\delta(r - r')}{r} e^{-ihz'} \qquad (7\text{-}533)$$

where

$$\bar{F}_n = \int_{-\infty}^{+\infty} \bar{G}_n e^{-ihz} \, dz \qquad (7\text{-}534)$$

and

$$\bar{G}_n = \frac{1}{2\pi} \int_{-\infty}^{+\infty} \bar{F}_n e^{ihz} \, dh \qquad (7\text{-}535)$$

In obtaining Eq. (7-533) we have assumed that

$$\left(\frac{\partial \bar{G}_n}{\partial z} + ih\bar{G}_n \right) e^{-ihz} \Big|_{z=-\infty}^{z=+\infty} = 0 \qquad (7\text{-}536)$$

and this will have to be justified later on.

Application of the Hankel transform

In order to solve Eq. (7-533) it is convenient to introduce a new transform based on the orthogonality and completeness properties of Bessel functions. Just as trigonometric functions serve to generate the Fourier integral theorem,

$$f(x) = \frac{2}{\pi} \int_0^\infty \cos xu \, du \int_0^\infty f(y) \cos uy \, dy \qquad (7\text{-}537)$$

so Bessel functions may be expected to provide a similar result.

In fact, if $f(x)$ is an arbitrary function subject only to mild restrictions, it can be shown that for $\nu \geq -\frac{1}{2}$,

$$f(x) = \int_0^\infty J_\nu(xu)(xu)^{1/2} \, du \int_0^\infty f(y) J_\nu(uy)(uy)^{1/2} \, dy \qquad (7\text{-}538)$$

In order for Eq. (7-538) to hold, it is sufficient that $\int_0^\infty |f(y)| \, dy$ converge and that $f(y)$ be of bounded variation in the neighborhood of x. If $f(x)$ is discontinuous at x, then the left side of (7-538) is replaced by $\frac{1}{2}[f(x + 0) + f(x - 0)]$.

It is customary to use $x^{1/2}f(x)$ instead of $f(x)$ in (7-538) and to write the result in terms of a transform and an inversion theorem. Thus

$$H_\nu(u) = \int_0^\infty yf(y)J_\nu(uy) \, dy \qquad (7\text{-}539)$$

is referred to as a Hankel transform of order ν of $f(y)$, and

$$f(x) = \int_0^\infty uH_\nu(u)J_\nu(ux) \, du \qquad (7\text{-}540)$$

is the corresponding inversion theorem.

Returning to Eq. (7-533), let

$$\bar{H}_n(\lambda, r', h) = \int_0^\infty \bar{F}_n(r, r', h) J_n(\lambda r) r \, dr \tag{7-541}$$

be a Hankel transform of order n of the solution of Eq. (7-533), and let

$$\bar{F}_n(r, r', h) = \int_0^\infty \bar{H}_n(\lambda, r', h) J_n(\lambda r) \lambda \, d\lambda \tag{7-542}$$

be the corresponding inversion formula. The usual transform method calls for us to multiply (7-533) on both sides by $J_n(\lambda r) r \, dr$ and then integrate both sides from $r = 0$ to $r = \infty$. This task is facilitated by taking note of Bessel's equation (Sec. 6-8), which yields

$$\frac{1}{r} \frac{\partial}{\partial r} \left(r \frac{\partial J_n}{\partial r} \right) - \frac{n^2}{r^2} J_n(\lambda r) = -\lambda^2 J_n(\lambda r) \tag{7-543}$$

and therefore

$$\int_0^\infty \left[\frac{1}{r} \frac{\partial}{\partial r} \left(r \frac{\partial \bar{F}_n}{\partial r} \right) - \left(\frac{n^2}{r^2} + h^2 - k^2 \right) \bar{F}_n \right] J_n(\lambda r) r \, dr$$

$$= r \left[J_n(\lambda r) \frac{\partial \bar{F}_n}{\partial r} - \lambda \bar{F}_n J_n'(\lambda r) \right] \Big|_{r=0}^{r=\infty} - (\lambda^2 + h^2 - k^2) \bar{H}_n$$

$$= -J_n(\lambda r') e^{-ihz'} \tag{7-544}$$

The integrated term

$$r \left[J_n(\lambda r) \frac{\partial \bar{F}_n}{\partial r} - \lambda \bar{F}_n J_n'(\lambda r) \right] \Big|_{r=0}^{r=\infty} \tag{7-545}$$

vanishes automatically at the lower limit $r = 0$. At the upper limit $r = \infty$, we recall that we have assumed a priori that $\int_0^\infty |\bar{F}_n| \sqrt{r} \, dr$ exists in order to use the Hankel transform. Therefore, $\bar{F}_n$ must vanish faster than $r^{-1/2}$. However, for large r,

$$J_n(\lambda r) \sim \left(\frac{2}{\pi r \lambda} \right)^{1/2} \cos \left(\lambda r - \frac{n\pi}{2} - \frac{\pi}{4} \right) \tag{7-546}$$

and as a result, both $J_n(\lambda r) \, \partial \bar{F}_n / \partial r$ and $\bar{F}_n J_n'(\lambda r)$ vanish faster than r^{-1}; hence the integrated part vanishes as $r \to \infty$, and Eq. (7-544) reduces to

$$\bar{H}_n(\lambda, r', h, z') = \frac{J_n(\lambda r') e^{-ihz'}}{\lambda^2 + h^2 - k^2} \tag{7-547}$$

The inversion formulas (7-542) and (7-535) are now applied to Eq. (7-547) to obtain

$$\bar{G}_n(r, r'; z - z') = \frac{1}{2\pi} \int_{-\infty}^{+\infty} e^{ih(z-z')} \, dh \int_0^\infty \frac{J_n(\lambda r) J_n(\lambda r') \lambda \, d\lambda}{h^2 + (\lambda^2 - k^2)} \tag{7-548}$$

Interchanging the order of integration in Eq. (7-548) and factoring the denominator permits us to write

$$\bar{G}_n = \int_0^\infty J_n(\lambda r) J_n(\lambda r') \lambda \, d\lambda$$

$$\cdot \frac{1}{2\pi} \int_{-\infty}^{+\infty} \frac{e^{ih(z-z')} \, dh}{(h + i\sqrt{\lambda^2 - k^2})(h - i\sqrt{\lambda^2 - k^2})} \tag{7-549}$$

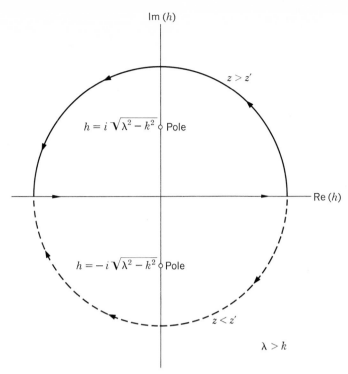

Figure 7-7 The complex h plane.

We wish to evaluate the integral

$$\frac{1}{2\pi} \int_{-\infty}^{+\infty} \frac{e^{ih(z-z')}\, dh}{(h + i\sqrt{\lambda^2 - k^2})\,(h - i\sqrt{\lambda^2 - k^2})} \tag{7-550}$$

by the method of residues (Sec. 4-18). Apparently the integrand in (7-550) has first-order poles at

$$h = \pm i\sqrt{\lambda^2 - k^2} \tag{7-551}$$

in the complex h plane (Fig. 7-7). Two cases, $z > z'$ and $z < z'$, must be considered. Suppose first that $z > z'$. In order to use the residue theorem (4-187), we must close the path of integration in (7-550) with a semicircle whose radius approaches infinity. This semicircle must lie in either the upper or lower half of the complex h plane. The choice is made in such a way that on the semicircular path $e^{ih(z-z')} \to 0$ as $|h| \to \infty$. This is accomplished, when $z > z'$, by choosing the semicircle to lie in the upper half plane, so that on it Im $(h) > 0$. The pole which contributes to (7-550) is the one which lies in the upper half of the complex h plane. In order to fix this pole, we choose the branch of $\sqrt{\lambda^2 - k^2}$ in (7-550) which satisfies

$$\text{Re}\,(\sqrt{\lambda^2 - k^2}) > 0 \tag{7-552}$$

Then the residue contribution to (7-550) comes from the pole at

$$h = i\sqrt{\lambda^2 - k^2} \tag{7-553}$$

and we have

$$\frac{1}{2\pi} \int_{-\infty}^{+\infty} \frac{e^{ih(z-z')}\,dh}{(h + i\sqrt{\lambda^2 - k^2})(h - i\sqrt{\lambda^2 - k^2})}$$
$$= \frac{e^{-\sqrt{\lambda^2 - k^2}(z - z')}}{2\sqrt{\lambda^2 - k^2}} \qquad (7\text{-}554)$$

Suppose next that $z < z'$. For this case, the path of integration in (7-550) should be closed with a semicircle in the lower half plane Im $(h) < 0$. Then the residue contribution to (7-550) comes from the pole at $h = -i\sqrt{\lambda^2 - k^2}$, provided we keep the branch of the radical selected in inequality (7-552). Keeping in mind that the pole at $h = -i\sqrt{\lambda^2 - k^2}$ is encircled in the negative (clockwise) direction, we have

$$\frac{1}{2\pi} \int_{-\infty}^{+\infty} \frac{e^{ih(z-z')}\,dh}{(h + i\sqrt{\lambda^2 - k^2})(h - i\sqrt{\lambda^2 - k^2})}$$
$$= \frac{e^{-\sqrt{\lambda^2 - k^2}(z' - z)}}{2\sqrt{\lambda^2 - k^2}} \qquad (7\text{-}555)$$

Both Eqs. (7-554) and (7-555) can be combined into a single formula by taking the absolute value of $z - z'$. The result is

$$\frac{1}{2\pi} \int_{-\infty}^{+\infty} \frac{e^{ih(z-z')}\,dh}{h^2 + \lambda^2 - k^2} = \frac{e^{-\sqrt{\lambda^2 - k^2}|z - z'|}}{2\sqrt{\lambda^2 - k^2}} \qquad (7\text{-}556)$$

and thus Eq. (7-548) reduces to

$$\bar{G}_n(r,r',z,z') = \frac{1}{2} \int_0^\infty \frac{J_n(\lambda r)J_n(\lambda r')e^{-\sqrt{\lambda^2 - k^2}|z - z'|}}{\sqrt{\lambda^2 - k^2}}\,\lambda\,d\lambda \qquad (7\text{-}557)$$

where Re $(\sqrt{\lambda^2 - k^2}) > 0$. Finally, using Eq. (7-529), the solution of Eq. (7-528) becomes

$$\bar{G}(r, r', \theta - \theta', |z - z'|)$$
$$= \frac{1}{4\pi} \sum_{n=-\infty}^{+\infty} e^{in(\theta - \theta')} \int_0^\infty \frac{J_n(\lambda r)J_n(\lambda r')e^{-\sqrt{\lambda^2 - k^2}|z - z'|}}{\sqrt{\lambda^2 - k^2}}\,\lambda\,d\lambda \qquad (7\text{-}558)$$

The Green's function (7-558) can be regarded as the result of superposing separated solutions of the Helmholtz equation:

$$(\nabla^2 + k^2)\psi = 0 \qquad (7\text{-}559)$$

Let

$$\psi_{n>} = J_n(\lambda r_>)e^{in\theta_> - \sqrt{\lambda^2 - k^2}\,z_>} \qquad (7\text{-}560)$$

and

$$\psi_{n<} = J_n(\lambda r_<)e^{-in\theta_< + \sqrt{\lambda^2 - k^2}\,z_<} \qquad (7\text{-}561)$$

where the notation $>$ is as in Eq. (6-485). Equations (7-560) and (7-561) are separated solutions of Eq. (7-559) with separation parameters n and λ. Using (7-560) and (7-561), the Green's function (7-558) assumes the form

$$\bar{G} = \frac{1}{4\pi} \sum_{n=-\infty}^{n=+\infty} \int_0^\infty \psi_{n>}\psi_{n<} \frac{\lambda\,d\lambda}{\sqrt{\lambda^2 - k^2}} \qquad (7\text{-}562)$$

If one considers a plane passing through the source perpendicular to the z axis, then Eq. (7-562) corresponds to expanding the Green's function $\bar{G}$ in exponentially attentuated standing-wave solutions of Helmholtz's equation. The exponential attenuation takes place along the z axis as one recedes from the source plane.

Independent representation of the Green's function for a point source

In spherical coordinates the Green's function for a point source should be spherically symmetric and thus should depend only on the radial coordinate R. We have

$$(\nabla^2 + k^2)\bar{G}(R) = -\delta(R) \tag{7-563}$$

or

$$\frac{1}{R} \frac{\partial^2}{\partial R^2}[R\bar{G}(R)] + k^2\bar{G}(R) = -\delta(R) \tag{7-564}$$

When $R \neq 0$, Eq. (7-564) is solved by

$$R\bar{G}(R) = Ae^{ikR} + Be^{-ikR} \tag{7-565}$$

where $k = \omega/c$.

Since

$$G(R,t) = \frac{1}{2\pi} \int_{-\infty}^{+\infty} \bar{G}(R)e^{i\omega t}\,d\omega \tag{7-566}$$

only the Be^{-ikR} term corresponds to a disturbance traveling *away* from the source at $R = 0$ as time increases. Consequently, A is equated to zero, and there remains only

$$\bar{G}(R) = \frac{Be^{-ikR}}{R} \tag{7-567}$$

To determine B, let Eq. (7-563) be integrated over a sphere of volume V centered at $R = 0$, and then let V shrink to zero. Since

$$\int_V \delta(R)\,dV = \underset{\text{Sphere}}{\iiint} \delta(x)\,\delta(y)\,\delta(z)\,dx\,dy\,dz = 1 \tag{7-568}$$

we have

$$\int_V (\nabla^2 + k^2)\bar{G}(R)\,dV = -1 \tag{7-569}$$

and using the divergence theorem, Eq. (7-569) becomes

$$\int_{S(V)} \frac{\partial\bar{G}}{\partial R}\,dS + k^2 \int_V \bar{G}(R)\,dV = -1 \tag{7-570}$$

In terms of the element of solid angle $d\Omega$ we have $dS = R^2\,d\Omega$ and $dV = R^2 d\Omega\,dR$ so that Eqs. (7-567) and (7-570) become

$$B \int_{S(V)} \frac{\partial}{\partial R}\left(\frac{e^{-ikR}}{R}\right) R^2\,d\Omega + k^2 B \int_V e^{-ikR}R\,d\Omega\,dR = -1 \tag{7-571}$$

The volume of the sphere is now permitted to shrink to zero by letting $R \to 0$. Since

$$\lim_{R \to 0} k^2 B \int_V e^{-ikR}R\,d\Omega\,dR = 0 \tag{7-572}$$

and

$$\lim_{R \to 0} B \int_{S(V)} \frac{\partial}{\partial R} \left(\frac{e^{-ikR}}{R} \right) R^2 \, d\Omega = -4\pi B \qquad (7\text{-}573)$$

Eq. (7-571) yields

$$B = \frac{1}{4\pi} \qquad (7\text{-}574)$$

and thus

$$\bar{G}(R) = \frac{e^{-ikR}}{4\pi R} \qquad (7\text{-}575)$$

is another important expression for the Green's function for a point source. On comparison of Eqs. (7-575) and (7-558), which both represent the Green's function for a point source, the expansion

$$\frac{e^{-ikR}}{4\pi R} = \frac{1}{4\pi} \sum_{n=-\infty}^{+\infty} e^{in(\theta-\theta')} \int_0^\infty \frac{J_n(\lambda r) J_n(\lambda r') e^{-\sqrt{\lambda^2-k^2}|z-z'|}}{\sqrt{\lambda^2 - k^2}} \lambda \, d\lambda \qquad (7\text{-}576)$$

is obtained. In Eq. (7-576) (r,θ,z) are cylindrical coordinates, and R is the distance $R = [(x - x')^2 + (y - y')^2 + (z - z')^2]^{\frac{1}{2}}$ between the source point (r',θ',z') and the point of observation (r,θ,z). A number of interesting results can be derived from (7-576). For example, in the static limit $k \to 0$, and (7-576) becomes

$$\frac{1}{R} = \sum_{n=-\infty}^{n=+\infty} e^{in(\theta-\theta')} \int_0^\infty e^{-\lambda|z-z'|} J_n(\lambda r) J_n(\lambda r') \, d\lambda \qquad (7\text{-}577)$$

for a static source at the origin $r' = 0$ and $z' = 0$. Since $J_n(0) = 0$ when $n \neq 0$, Eq. (7-577) reduces to

$$\frac{1}{\sqrt{r^2 + z^2}} = \int_0^\infty e^{-\lambda|z|} J_0(\lambda r) \, d\lambda \qquad (7\text{-}578)$$

which is called the "Lipshitz integral." If $r = 1$ in Eq. (7-578), then the equation takes the form of the Laplace transform of $J_0(\lambda)$. The inversion theorem (5-473) for the Laplace transform can then be applied to (7-578) to give an integral representation for J_0: i.e.,

$$J_0(x) = \frac{1}{2\pi i} \int_{\sigma_0-i\infty}^{\sigma_0+i\infty} \frac{e^{sx}}{\sqrt{1+s^2}} \, ds \qquad (7\text{-}579)$$

For a nonstatic source $(k \neq 0)$ at the origin, the previous remarks show that Eq. (7-576) yields

$$\frac{e^{-ikR}}{4\pi R} = \frac{1}{4\pi} \int_0^\infty e^{-\sqrt{\lambda^2-k^2}|z|} \frac{J_0(\lambda r) \lambda \, d\lambda}{\sqrt{\lambda^2 - k^2}} \qquad (7\text{-}580)$$

where $R = (x^2 + y^2 + z^2)^{\frac{1}{2}} = (r^2 + z^2)^{\frac{1}{2}}$. Equation (7-580) has the form of a Hankel transform of order zero of $e^{-\sqrt{\lambda^2-k^2}|z|}/\sqrt{\lambda^2 - k^2}$. Therefore, using the Hankel-transform inversion theorem (7-542) we obtain Sommerfeld's integral,

$$\frac{e^{-\sqrt{\lambda^2 - k^2}|z|}}{\sqrt{\lambda^2 - k^2}} = \int_0^\infty \frac{e^{-ikR}}{R} J_0(\lambda r) r \, dr \qquad (7\text{-}581)$$

where, as in all of these formulas, $\text{Re}\,(\sqrt{\lambda^2 - k^2}) > 0$.

We are now able to return to the matter of justifying Eq. (7-536):

$$\left(\frac{\partial \bar{G}_n}{\partial z} + ih\bar{G}_n\right) e^{-ihz} \Big|_{z=-\infty}^{z=+\infty} = 0 \qquad (7\text{-}582)$$

With the aid of Eq. (7-531),

$$\left(\frac{\partial \bar{G}_n}{\partial z} + ih\bar{G}_n\right) e^{-ihz} \Big|_{z=-\infty}^{z=+\infty}$$
$$= \int_{-\pi}^{\pi} e^{-in\phi} \left(\frac{\partial \bar{G}}{\partial z} + ih\bar{G}\right) e^{-ihz} \Big|_{z=-\infty}^{z=+\infty} d\phi \qquad (7\text{-}583)$$

However

$$\bar{G}(R) = \frac{e^{-ikR}}{4\pi R} \qquad (7\text{-}584)$$

and thus

$$\left(\frac{\partial \bar{G}_n}{\partial z} + ih\bar{G}_n\right) e^{-ihz} \Big|_{z=-\infty}^{z=+\infty}$$
$$= -\int_{\pi}^{\pi} e^{-in\phi} \frac{z(1 + ikR)e^{-i(kR+hz)}}{4\pi R^3} \Big|_{z=-\infty}^{z=+\infty} d\phi \qquad (7\text{-}585)$$

Since for very large z the radial distance $R \sim z$, it follows that

$$\lim_{z \to \infty} \frac{z(1 + ikR)}{4\pi R^3} = 0 \qquad (7\text{-}586)$$

and therefore Eq. (7-582) must hold.

According to the remarks following Eq. (7-84), we should expect that there are two alternative ways to divide up the space around the source. One way, which we have just used, is to divide space up with a plane passing through the source perpendicular to the z axis. The other way, which we shall examine now, is to divide up space with a cylinder passing through the source and having generators parallel to the z axis. For this purpose, let us go back to Eq. (7-533),

$$\frac{1}{r}\frac{\partial}{\partial r}\left(r\frac{\partial \bar{F}_n}{\partial r}\right) - \frac{n^2}{r^2}\bar{F}_n + (k^2 - h^2)\bar{F}_n = \frac{-\delta(r - r')}{r} e^{-ihz'} \qquad (7\text{-}587)$$

which is just Bessel's equation. Instead of using a Hankel transform on Eq. (7-587) we can solve it directly as in Eq. (7-311). When $r \neq r'$,

$$\bar{F}_n = \begin{cases} A J_n(\sqrt{k^2 - h^2}\, r) \\ B H_n^{(2)}(\sqrt{k^2 - h^2}\, r) \end{cases} \qquad (7\text{-}588)$$

provides linearly independent solutions of (7-587). When the source is neither at the origin nor at infinity, the Green's function should remain finite at $r = 0$ and $r = \infty$. One therefore chooses

$$\bar{F}_n = A J_n(\sqrt{k^2 - h^2}\, r) \qquad 0 \le r < r' \tag{7-589}$$

$$\bar{F}_n = B H_n{}^{(2)}(\sqrt{k^2 - h^2}\, r) \qquad r' < r < \infty \tag{7-590}$$

The choice of $H_n{}^{(2)}$ is made instead of $H_n{}^{(1)}$ for the reason mentioned in connection with Eq. (7-560). The constants A and B are determined as in Sec. 7-15, and the result is that

$$\bar{F}_n = - \frac{J_n(\sqrt{k^2 - h^2}\, r_<) H_n{}^{(2)}(\sqrt{k^2 - h^2}\, r_>) e^{-ihz'}}{\sqrt{k^2 - h^2}\, r' W\{J_n, H_n{}^{(2)}; r'\}} \tag{7-591}$$

where

$$W\{J_n, H_n{}^{(2)}; r'\}$$

denotes the Wronskian of J_n and $H_n{}^{(2)}$. The Wronskian can be evaluated as in Sec. 7-15 to give

$$W\{J_n, H_n{}^{(2)}; r'\} = \frac{-2i}{\pi \sqrt{k^2 - h^2}\, r'} \tag{7-592}$$

so that Eq. (7-591) becomes

$$\bar{F}_n = \frac{-i\pi}{2} J_n(\sqrt{k^2 - h^2}\, r_<) H_n{}^{(2)}(\sqrt{k^2 - h^2}\, r_>) e^{-ihz'} \tag{7-593}$$

Consequently, Eqs. (7-529), (7-535), and (7-593) yield

$$\bar{G}(R) = \frac{e^{-ikR}}{4\pi R} = \frac{-i}{8\pi} \sum_{n=-\infty}^{+\infty} e^{in(\theta-\theta')}$$

$$\int_{-\infty}^{+\infty} J_n(\sqrt{k^2 - h^2}\, r_<) H_n{}^{(2)}(\sqrt{k^2 - h^2}\, r_>) e^{ih(z-z')}\, dh \tag{7-594}$$

for the infinite-medium Green's function.

The Green's function (7-594) can be regarded as the result of superposing separated solutions of Helmholtz's equation:

$$(\nabla^2 + k^2)\psi = 0 \tag{7-595}$$

Let

$$\psi_{n<} = J_n(\sqrt{k^2 - h^2}\, r_<) e^{i(n\theta < + hz <)} \tag{7-596}$$

and

$$\psi_{n>} = H_n{}^{(2)}(\sqrt{k^2 - h^2}\, r_>) e^{-i(n\theta > + hz >)} \tag{7-597}$$

These are separated solutions of Eq. (7-595) with separation parameters n and h. Using (7-596) and (7-597), the Green's function (7-594) becomes

$$\bar{G} = \frac{-i}{8\pi} \sum_{n=-\infty}^{+\infty} \int_{-\infty}^{+\infty} \psi_{n>} \psi_{n<}\, dh \tag{7-598}$$

If one considers a cylinder passing through the source at (r', θ', z') and having generators parallel to the z axis, then Eq. (7-598) divides space into two regions, one inside and one outside the cylinder. The expansion (7-598) corresponds to expanding the Green's function in a set of waves which propagate along z instead of decaying exponentially along z.

Just as for Eq. (7-576), a number of interesting formulas can be obtained from (7-594). For example, in the static limit $k \to 0$, (7-594) reduces to

$$\frac{1}{R} = \frac{-i}{2} \sum_{n=-\infty}^{+\infty} e^{in(\theta-\theta')}$$

$$\int_{-\infty}^{+\infty} J_n(-i|h|r_<)H_n{}^{(2)}(-i|h|r_>)e^{ih(z-z')}\,dh \qquad (7\text{-}599)$$

The limiting form (7-599) arises because the branch of $\sqrt{k^2 - h^2}$ in (7-594) is determined by the requirement that

$$\text{Im}\,(\sqrt{k^2 - h^2}) < 0 \qquad (7\text{-}600)$$

To see why inequality (7-600) must hold, notice that

$$\lim_{x\to\infty} \frac{1}{R} = \lim_{x\to\infty} \frac{1}{[(x - x')^2 + (y - y')^2 + (z - z')^2]^{1/2}} = 0 \qquad (7\text{-}601)$$

must apply to both sides of Eq. (7-599). As $x \to \infty$,

$$\lim_{x\to\infty} H_n{}^{(2)}(-i|h|r_>) \to \sqrt{\frac{-2}{\pi|h|x}}\; e^{-i\left\{-i|h|x - \frac{n\pi}{2} - \frac{\pi}{4}\right\}} \to 0 \qquad (7\text{-}602)$$

has the correct behavior; however, if

$$\text{Im}\,(\sqrt{k^2 - h^2}) > 0 \qquad (7\text{-}603)$$

then for $k \to 0$, $\sqrt{k^2 - h^2} \to i|h|$, and the right side of Eq. (7-594) will diverge when x is allowed to become infinite. It is left as an exercise for the reader to show that

$$\frac{e^{ikR}}{4\pi R} = \frac{i}{8\pi} \sum_{n=-\infty}^{+\infty} e^{in(\theta-\theta')}$$

$$\int_{-\infty}^{+\infty} J_n(\sqrt{k^2 - h^2}\,r_<)H_n{}^{(1)}(\sqrt{k^2 - h^2}\,r_>)e^{ih(z-z')}\,dh \qquad (7\text{-}604)$$

In the static limit $k = 0$, the asymptotic form of $H_n{}^{(1)}(\sqrt{k^2 - h^2}\,r_>)$ as $x \to \infty$ requires that

$$\text{Im}\,(\sqrt{k^2 - h^2}) > 0 \qquad (7\text{-}605)$$

and consequently, Eq. (7-604) gives

$$\frac{1}{R} = \frac{i}{2} \sum_{n=-\infty}^{+\infty} e^{in(\theta-\theta')} \int_{-\infty}^{+\infty} J_n(i|h|r_<)H_n{}^{(1)}(i|h|r_>)e^{ih(z-z')}\,dh$$

$$(7\text{-}606)$$

Since

$$J_n(i|h|r_<) = e^{in\pi/2}I_n(|h|r_<) \qquad (7\text{-}607)$$

and

$$H_n{}^{(1)}(i|h|r_>) = \frac{2}{\pi i}\, e^{-in\pi/2}K_n(|h|r_>) \qquad (7\text{-}608)$$

we can write Eq. (7-606) as

$$\frac{1}{R} = \frac{1}{\pi} \sum_{n=-\infty}^{+\infty} e^{in(\theta-\theta')} \int_{-\infty}^{+\infty} I_n(|h|r_<) K_n(|h|r_>) e^{ih(z-z')} \, dh \qquad (7\text{-}609)$$

which is the same as Eq. (7-334). The static limit, $k = 0$, with the source at the origin, $r' = 0$, $z' = 0$, yields

$$\frac{1}{R} = \frac{1}{\sqrt{r^2 + z^2}} = \frac{1}{\pi} \int_{-\infty}^{+\infty} e^{ihz} K_0(hr) \, dh \qquad (7\text{-}610)$$

or

$$\frac{1}{\sqrt{r^2 + z^2}} = \frac{2}{\pi} \int_0^{+\infty} K_0(hr) \cos hz \, dh \qquad (7\text{-}611)$$

This corresponds to Eq. (7-340). When there is a source of spherical waves at the origin, then $k \neq 0$, $r' = 0$, $z' = 0$, $R = (r^2 + z^2)^{\frac{1}{2}}$, and

$$\frac{e^{ikR}}{R} = \frac{i}{2} \int_{-\infty}^{+\infty} H_0^{(1)}(\sqrt{k^2 - h^2}\, r) e^{ihz} \, dh \qquad (7\text{-}612)$$

This last result is called "Weyrich's formula."

7-23 THE HELMHOLTZ EQUATION IN RECTANGULAR CARTESIAN COORDINATES

Consider the problem of solving

$$(\nabla^2 + k^2)\bar{G} = -\delta(r - r') = -\delta(x - x')\,\delta(y - y')\,\delta(z - z')$$
$$(7\text{-}613)$$

in rectangular Cartesian coordinates. We already know that one solution is

$$\bar{G}(R) = \frac{e^{-ikR}}{4\pi R} \qquad (7\text{-}614)$$

However, it is of some interest to derive this result on its own merits by applying a triple Fourier transform. Beginning with

$$\left[\left(\frac{\partial^2}{\partial x^2} + \frac{\partial^2}{\partial y^2} + \frac{\partial^2}{\partial z^2} \right) + k^2 \right] \bar{G}$$
$$= -\delta(x - x')\,\delta(y - y')\,\delta(z - z') \qquad (7\text{-}615)$$

we multiply this by $e^{-i\xi x}\, dx\, e^{-i\eta y}\, dy\, e^{-i\zeta z}\, dz$ and integrate both sides from $x = -\infty$ to $x = \infty$, $y = -\infty$ to $y = \infty$, $z = -\infty$ to $z = \infty$ by parts to obtain

$$[(\xi^2 + \eta^2 + \zeta^2) - k^2]\bar{F}(\xi,\eta,\zeta) = e^{-i(\xi x' + \eta y' + \zeta z')} \qquad (7\text{-}616)$$

on the assumption that

$$\left(\frac{\partial G}{\partial x} + i\xi\bar{G} \right) e^{-i\xi x} \left.\right|_{x=-\infty}^{x=+\infty} = 0 \qquad (7\text{-}617)$$

$$\left(\frac{\partial \bar{G}}{\partial y} + i\eta\bar{G} \right) e^{-i\eta y} \left.\right|_{y=-\infty}^{y=+\infty} = 0 \qquad (7\text{-}618)$$

$$\left(\frac{\partial \bar{G}}{\partial z} + i\zeta\bar{G} \right) e^{-i\zeta z} \left.\right|_{z=-\infty}^{z=+\infty} = 0 \qquad (7\text{-}619)$$

Equations (7-617) to (7-619) are justified in the same way as Eq. (7-582). The triple Fourier transform of $\bar{G}$ is therefore given by

$$\bar{F}(\xi,\eta,\zeta) = \frac{e^{-i(\xi x' + \eta y' + \zeta z')}}{(\xi^2 + \eta^2 + \zeta^2) - k^2} \tag{7-620}$$

where

$$\bar{F}(\xi,\eta,\zeta) = \int_{-\infty}^{+\infty} \int_{-\infty}^{+\infty} \int_{-\infty}^{+\infty} \bar{G} e^{-i(\xi x + \eta y + \zeta z)} \, dx \, dy \, dz \tag{7-621}$$

The corresponding inversion theorem (5-373) is

$$\bar{G} = \frac{1}{(2\pi)^3} \int_{-\infty}^{+\infty} \int_{-\infty}^{+\infty} \int_{-\infty}^{+\infty} \bar{F}(\xi,\eta,\zeta) e^{i(\xi x + \eta y + \zeta z)} \, d\xi \, d\eta \, d\zeta \tag{7-622}$$

and thus

$$\bar{G} = \frac{1}{(2\pi)^3} \int_{-\infty}^{+\infty} \int_{-\infty}^{+\infty} \int_{-\infty}^{+\infty} \frac{e^{i[\xi(x-x') + \eta(y-y') + \zeta(z-z')]}}{(\xi^2 + \eta^2 + \zeta^2) - k^2} \, d\xi \, d\eta \, d\zeta \tag{7-623}$$

represents the Green's-function solution of Eq. (7-615). In Eq. (7-623) we regard (ξ,η,ζ) as forming a right-handed rectangular Cartesian coordinate system in **K** space.

Equation (7-623) can be written more compactly by observing that

$$\mathbf{K} = (\xi,\eta,\zeta) \tag{7-624}$$

$$K^2 = |\mathbf{K}|^2 = \xi^2 + \eta^2 + \zeta^2 \tag{7-625}$$

$$\mathbf{R} = [(x - x'), (y - y'), (z - z')] \tag{7-626}$$

$$R^2 = |\mathbf{R}|^2 = (x - x')^2 + (y - y')^2 + (z - z')^2 \tag{7-627}$$

$$dV_K = d\xi \, d\eta \, d\zeta \tag{7-628}$$

$$\mathbf{K} \cdot \mathbf{R} = \xi(x - x') + \eta(y - y') + \zeta(z - z') \tag{7-629}$$

so that Eq. (7-623) reduces to

$$\bar{G}(R) = \frac{1}{(2\pi)^3} \int_{\text{All } K \text{ space}} \frac{e^{i\mathbf{K} \cdot \mathbf{R}}}{K^2 - k^2} \, dV_K \tag{7-630}$$

The evaluation of Eq. (7-630) is simplified by the following tricks. First of all, we imagine **R** to be a fixed vector in space. Then we rotate the (ξ,η,ζ) coordinate system until the ζ axis coincides with the direction of **R**. Next, we introduce spherical coordinates (K,α,β) into (ξ,η,ζ) space (Fig. 7-8). In these coordinates α is the colatitude measured with respect to the ζ axis, β is the colongitude measured from the ξ axis, and K is the radial distance from the origin of coordinates. The transformation from (ξ,η,ζ) to (K,α,β) is therefore

$$\xi = K \sin \alpha \cos \beta \tag{7-631}$$

$$\eta = K \sin \alpha \sin \beta \tag{7-632}$$

$$\zeta = K \cos \alpha \tag{7-633}$$

The volume element $dV_K = d\xi \, d\eta \, d\zeta$ is replaced by

$$dV_K = K^2 \sin \alpha \, dK \, d\alpha \, d\beta \tag{7-634}$$

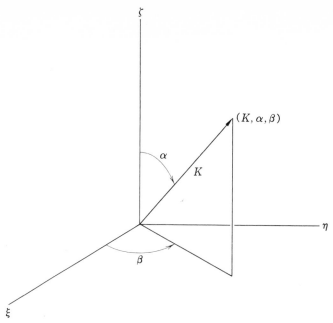

Figure 7-8 Spherical coordinates in (ξ, η, ζ) space.

and since we have chosen the ζ axis to coincide with the direction of **R**, the colatitude angle α of **K** is just the angle between **K** and **R**; thus

$$\mathbf{K} \cdot \mathbf{R} = KR \cos \alpha \qquad (7\text{-}635)$$

With these remarks Eq. (7-630) reduces to

$$\bar{G}(R) = \frac{1}{(2\pi)^3} \int_0^\infty \int_0^\pi \int_0^{2\pi} \frac{e^{iKR \cos \alpha}}{K^2 - k^2} K^2 \sin \alpha \, dK \, d\alpha \, d\beta \qquad (7\text{-}636)$$

The integrations over α and β can be performed immediately using

$$\int_0^\pi e^{ikR \cos \alpha} \sin \alpha \, d\alpha = \frac{e^{iKR} - e^{-iKR}}{iKR} \qquad (7\text{-}637)$$

and

$$\int_0^{2\pi} d\beta = 2\pi \qquad (7\text{-}638)$$

The result is

$$\bar{G}(R) = \frac{1}{(2\pi)^2} \int_0^\infty \frac{e^{iKR} - e^{-iKR}}{iR(K^2 - k^2)} K \, dK \qquad (7\text{-}639)$$

or

$$\bar{G}(R) = \frac{1}{(2\pi)^2} \int_0^\infty \frac{e^{iKR}}{iR(K^2 - k^2)} K \, dK$$
$$- \frac{1}{(2\pi)^2} \int_0^\infty \frac{e^{-iKR}}{iR(K^2 - k^2)} K \, dK \qquad (7\text{-}640)$$

Suppose that we replace K by $-K$ in the first term of Eq. (7-640) and then reverse the limits of integration. We obtain

$$\bar{G}(R) = \frac{-1}{(2\pi)^2} \int_{-\infty}^{+\infty} \frac{e^{-iKR}}{iR(K^2 - k^2)} K \, dK \qquad (7\text{-}641)$$

which must be evaluated by the method of residues (Sec. 4-18). The integrand in Eq. (7-641) has simple first-order poles at $K = k$ and $K = -k$. When k is real, these poles lie on the path of integration, which complicates the evaluation of (7-641). One way to resolve this difficulty is to replace k by $k + i\epsilon$ in (7-641). Then the poles are at $K = k + i\epsilon$ and $K = -k - i\epsilon$, and no longer fall on the path of integration. The evaluation of (7-641) by residues gives a definite result which depends on ϵ and can be evaluated for $\epsilon = 0$. A similar procedure based on replacing k by $k - i\epsilon$ in (7-641) also leads to a definite but different result as $\epsilon \to 0$. One of these two results is then eliminated on the basis of physical considerations.

Thus, consider

$$\bar{G}(R) = -\frac{1}{(2\pi)^2} \lim_{\epsilon \to 0} \int_{-\infty}^{+\infty} \frac{e^{-iKR}}{iR[K^2 - (k + i\epsilon)^2]} K \, dK \qquad (7\text{-}642)$$

where ϵ is a small positive number. Notice that R is a distance and is always non-negative; also, $K = \text{Re}\,(K) + i\,\text{Im}\,(K)$, so that

$$|e^{-iKR}| = e^{R\,\text{Im}\,(K)} \qquad (7\text{-}643)$$

In order to integrate (7-643) by residues, the path of integration must be closed with a semicircle of infinite radius. Equation (7-643) shows that the semicircle must lie in the lower half of the complex K plane (Fig. 7-9). Then $\text{Im}\,(K) < 0$ on the semicircle, and its contribution to Eq. (7-642) vanishes exponentially. The pole in the lower half plane occurs at $K = -k - i\epsilon$ and is encircled in the negative (clockwise) direction. Using Eqs. (4-191) and (4-195), we find

$$\bar{G}(R) = \lim_{\epsilon \to 0} \frac{e^{i(k+i\epsilon)}}{4\pi R} = \frac{e^{ikR}}{4\pi R} \qquad (7\text{-}644)$$

Next, let k be replaced by $k - i\epsilon$; then Eq. (7-641) becomes

$$\bar{G}(R) = \frac{1}{(2\pi)^2} \lim_{\epsilon \to 0} \int_{-\infty}^{+\infty} \frac{e^{-iKR}}{iR[K^2 - (k - i\epsilon)^2]} K \, dK \qquad (7\text{-}645)$$

However, Eq. (7-643) still applies, and the path of integration must be completed with a semicircle in the *lower* half plane. The pole in the lower half plane now occurs at $K = k - i\epsilon$, and the residue theorem gives

$$\bar{G}(R) = \lim_{\epsilon \to 0} \frac{e^{-i(k-i\epsilon)R}}{4\pi R} = \frac{e^{-ikR}}{4\pi R} \qquad (7\text{-}646)$$

To see whether (7-644) or (7-646) is correct, let us evaluate $G(R,t)$ itself. We have

$$G(R,t) = \frac{1}{2\pi} \int_{-\infty}^{+\infty} \bar{G}(R,\omega) e^{i\omega t} \, d\omega \qquad (7\text{-}647)$$

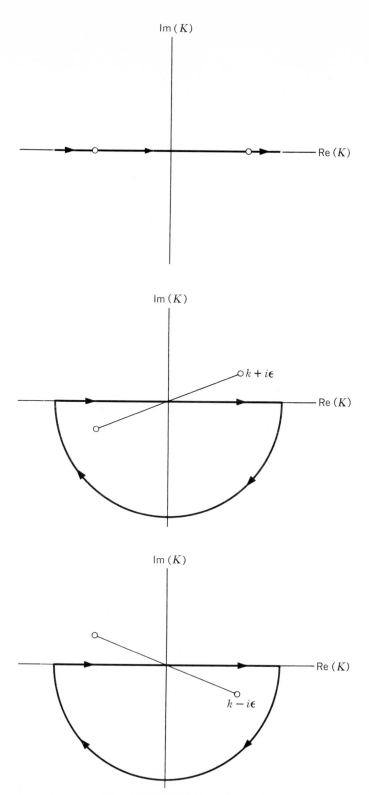

Figure 7-9 Integration contours in the complex K plane.

and therefore Eq. (7-644) gives

$$G(R,t) = \frac{1}{4\pi R} \cdot \frac{1}{2\pi} \int_{-\infty}^{+\infty} e^{i\omega(R/c+t)} \, d\omega \qquad (7\text{-}648)$$

where $k = \omega/c$. Recalling (5-331), Eq. (7-648) becomes

$$G(R,t) = \frac{\delta(t + R/c)}{4\pi R} \qquad (7\text{-}649)$$

while Eq. (7-646) leads to

$$G(R,t) = \frac{\delta(t - R/c)}{4\pi R} \qquad (7\text{-}650)$$

We see that Eq. (7-649) corresponds to a spherical pulse which contracts toward the origin $R = 0$ as time increases, while (7-650) corresponds to a spherical pulse which expands away from the origin $R = 0$ as time increases. The physical behavior of a point source at $R = 0$ fired off at $t = 0$ corresponds to (7-650) and not to (7-649). Therefore,

$$\bar{G}(R) = \frac{e^{-ikR}}{4\pi R} \qquad (7\text{-}651)$$

is the correct result provided that the inverse Fourier transform of $\bar{G}(R)$ is defined as in Eq. (7-647).

Instead of using spherical coordinates, we can deal directly with Eq. (7-623):

$$\bar{G}(R) = \frac{1}{(2\pi)^3} \int_{-\infty}^{+\infty} \int_{-\infty}^{+\infty} \int_{-\infty}^{+\infty} \frac{e^{i[\xi(x-x')+\eta(y-y')+\zeta(z-z')]}}{(\xi^2 + \eta^2 + \zeta^2) - k^2} \, d\xi \, d\eta \, d\zeta \qquad (7\text{-}652)$$

Let us perform the integration over $d\zeta$ by residues; we write Eq. (7-652) as

$$\bar{G} = \frac{1}{(2\pi)^3} \int_{-\infty}^{+\infty} \frac{e^{i\zeta(z-z')} \, d\zeta}{\{\gamma^2 + \zeta^2\}} \int_{-\infty}^{+\infty} \int_{-\infty}^{+\infty} e^{i[\xi(x-x')+\eta(y-y')]} \, d\xi \, d\eta \qquad (7\text{-}653)$$

where

$$\gamma^2 = (\xi^2 + \eta^2) - k^2 \qquad (7\text{-}654)$$

The integrand of the $d\zeta$ integral in Eq. (7-653) has first-order poles at $\zeta = \pm i\gamma$. Suppose that $z > z'$, and let $\zeta = \text{Re}\,(\zeta) + i\,\text{Im}\,(\zeta)$; then

$$|e^{i\zeta(z-z')}| = e^{-(z-z')\,\text{Im}\,(\zeta)} \qquad (7\text{-}655)$$

shows that in order to obtain exponential decay of the semicircular contribution to (7-653), the semicircle must lie in the upper half, $\text{Im}\,(\zeta) > 0$, of the complex ζ plane (Fig. 7-10). The path of integration in

$$\int_{-\infty}^{+\infty} \frac{e^{i\zeta(z-z')}}{\gamma^2 + \zeta^2} \, d\zeta \qquad (7\text{-}656)$$

is closed with a semicircle on which $\text{Im}\,(\zeta) > 0$, and the branch of

$$\gamma = \sqrt{(\xi^2 + \eta^2) - k^2} \qquad (7\text{-}657)$$

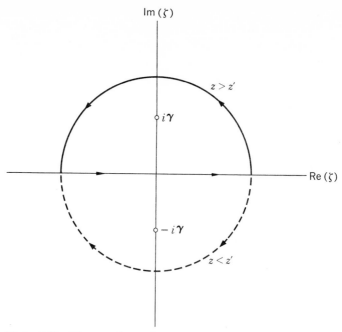

Figure 7-10 The complex ζ plane.

in (7-656) is fixed by choosing it so that

$$\text{Re}\,(\gamma) > 0 \tag{7-658}$$

With these conventions, the pole in the upper half of the complex ζ plane occurs at $\zeta = i\gamma$, provided that the radicand in Eq. (7-657) is real and positive. When $z > z'$, the residue theorem (4-191) and (4-195) applied to (7-656) yields

$$\int_{-\infty}^{+\infty} \frac{e^{i\zeta(z-z')}}{\gamma^2 + \zeta^2}\,d\zeta = \frac{\pi e^{-\gamma(z-z')}}{\gamma} \tag{7-659}$$

with $\text{Re}\,(\gamma) > 0$.

If $z < z'$, then the path of integration in (7-656) must be closed with a semicircle in the lower half plane $\text{Im}\,(\zeta) < 0$. For this case the pole $\zeta = -i\gamma$ is encircled in the negative (clockwise) direction, and

$$\int_{-\infty}^{+\infty} \frac{e^{i\zeta(z-z')}}{\gamma^2 + \zeta^2}\,d\zeta = \frac{\pi e^{-\gamma(z'-z)}}{\gamma} \tag{7-660}$$

where again $\text{Re}\,(\gamma) > 0$. Combining Eqs. (7-659) and (7-660) into one expression, we write

$$\int_{-\infty}^{+\infty} \frac{e^{i\zeta(z-z')}}{\gamma^2 + \zeta^2}\,d\zeta = \pi \frac{e^{-\gamma|z-z'|}}{\gamma} \tag{7-661}$$

With the aid of (7-661), Eq. (7-653) reduces to

$$\bar{G} = \frac{1}{8\pi^2} \int_{-\infty}^{+\infty} \int_{-\infty}^{+\infty} \frac{e^{-\gamma|z-z'|}}{\gamma} e^{i[\xi(x-x')+\eta(y-y')]}\,d\xi\,d\eta \tag{7-662}$$

and this represents $\bar{G}e^{i\omega t}$ as a superposition of plane waves, propagating along x and y and exponentially attenuated along z. To further evaluate Eq. (7-662), we transform it to plane polar coordinates, using

$$x - x' = r \cos \theta \tag{7-663}$$

$$y - y' = r \sin \theta \tag{7-664}$$

$$\xi = \lambda \cos \phi \tag{7-665}$$

$$\eta = \lambda \sin \phi \tag{7-666}$$

$$d\xi \, d\eta = \lambda \, d\lambda \, d\phi \tag{7-667}$$

$$\gamma = \sqrt{\lambda^2 - k^2} \tag{7-668}$$

with the result that

$$\bar{G} = \frac{1}{8\pi^2} \int_0^\infty \int_{-\pi}^\pi \frac{e^{-\sqrt{\lambda^2 - k^2}|z - z'|}}{\sqrt{\lambda^2 - k^2}} e^{i\lambda \cos(\theta - \phi)} \lambda \, d\lambda \, d\theta \tag{7-669}$$

Since

$$J_0(\lambda r) = \frac{1}{2\pi} \int_{-\pi}^\pi e^{i\lambda r \cos \Phi} \, d\Phi \tag{7-670}$$

Eq. (7-669) is the same as the expression

$$\bar{G} = \frac{1}{4\pi} \int_0^\infty \frac{e^{-\sqrt{\lambda^2 - k^2}|z - z'|}}{\sqrt{\lambda^2 - k^2}} J_0(\lambda r) \lambda \, d\lambda \tag{7-671}$$

obtained in Eq. (7-580). Our analysis in Eqs. (7-644) and (7-646) led us to the result that

$$\bar{G}(R) = \begin{cases} \dfrac{e^{ikR}}{4\pi R} & \text{Im } (k) \to 0^+ \\[2mm] \dfrac{e^{-ikR}}{4\pi R} & \text{Im } (k) \to 0^- \end{cases} \tag{7-672}$$

According to Eq. (7-672), when k is regarded as a complex variable, analytic continuation (see Sec. 4-5) demands that

$$\frac{1}{4\pi} \int_0^\infty \frac{e^{-\sqrt{\lambda^2 - k^2}|z - z'|}}{\sqrt{\lambda^2 - k^2}} J_0(\lambda r) \lambda \, d\lambda = \begin{cases} \dfrac{e^{ikR}}{4\pi R} & \text{Im } (k) \geq 0 \\[2mm] \dfrac{e^{-ikR}}{4\pi R} & \text{Im } (k) \leq 0 \end{cases} \tag{7-673}$$

where $R = \sqrt{r^2 + (z - z')^2}$. In Eq. (7-673) r and $z - z'$ are real, and Re $(\sqrt{\lambda^2 - k^2}) > 0$. It must follow that

$$\bar{G} = \frac{1}{8\pi^2} \int_{-\infty}^{+\infty} \int_{-\infty}^{+\infty} \frac{e^{-\gamma|z - z'|}}{\gamma} e^{i[\xi(x - x') + \eta(y - y')]} \, d\xi \, d\eta$$

$$= \begin{cases} \dfrac{e^{ikR}}{4\pi R} & \text{Im } (k) \geq 0 \\[2mm] \dfrac{e^{-ikR}}{4\pi R} & \text{Im } (k) \leq 0 \end{cases} \tag{7-674}$$

where $\gamma = \sqrt{(\xi^2 + \eta^2) - k^2}$ and Re $(\gamma) > 0$.

In spherical coordinates (r,θ,ϕ) the inhomogeneous Helmholtz equation,

$$(\nabla^2 + k^2)\bar{G} = -\delta(\mathbf{r} - \mathbf{r}') \tag{7-675}$$

takes the form

$$\frac{1}{r^2}\frac{\partial}{\partial r}\left(r^2\frac{\partial\bar{G}}{\partial r}\right) + \frac{1}{r^2\sin\theta}\frac{\partial}{\partial\theta}\left(\sin\theta\frac{\partial\bar{G}}{\partial\theta}\right) + \frac{1}{r^2\sin^2\theta}\frac{\partial^2\bar{G}}{\partial\phi^2}$$
$$+ k^2\bar{G} = \frac{-\delta(r - r')\,\delta(\theta - \theta')\,\delta(\phi - \phi')}{r^2\sin\theta} \tag{7-676}$$

It is convenient to separate the r portion of the Laplacian from the θ and ϕ portions, and so we define ∇_r^2 and $\nabla_{\theta,\phi}^2$ by

$$r^2\nabla^2 = \nabla_r^2 + \nabla_{\theta,\phi}^2 \tag{7-677}$$

where

$$\nabla_r^2 = \frac{\partial}{\partial r}\left(r^2\frac{\partial}{\partial r}\right) \tag{7-678}$$

and

$$\nabla_{\theta,\phi}^2 = \frac{1}{\sin\theta}\frac{\partial}{\partial\theta}\left(\sin\theta\frac{\partial}{\partial\theta}\right) + \frac{1}{\sin^2\theta}\frac{\partial^2}{\partial\phi^2} \tag{7-679}$$

The results obtained in Sec. 7-18 suggest that we assume a solution for $\bar{G}$ of the form

$$\bar{G}(r,r';\theta,\theta';\phi-\phi') = \sum_{n=0}^{\infty}\sum_{m=-n}^{+n}\bar{F}_n{}^m(r,r';\theta',\phi')P_n{}^{|m|}(\cos\theta)e^{im\phi} \tag{7-680}$$

Since

$$\nabla_{\theta,\phi}^2[P_n{}^{|m|}(\cos\theta)e^{im\phi}] = -n(n+1)P_n{}^{|m|}(\cos\theta)e^{im\phi} \tag{7-681}$$

it follows that on substituting Eq. (7-680) into

$$(\nabla_r^2 + \nabla_{\theta,\phi}^2 + k^2r^2)\bar{G} = \frac{-\delta(r-r')\,\delta(\theta-\theta')\,\delta(\phi-\phi')}{\sin\theta} \tag{7-682}$$

we obtain

$$\sum_{n=0}^{\infty}\sum_{m=-n}^{n}[\nabla_r^2 + k^2r^2$$
$$- n(n+1)]\bar{F}_n{}^m(r,r';\theta',\phi')P_n{}^{|m|}(\cos\theta)e^{im\phi}$$
$$= \frac{-\delta(r-r')\,\delta(\theta-\theta')\,\delta(\phi-\phi')}{\sin\theta} \tag{7-683}$$

for the determination of $\bar{F}_n{}^m(r,r';\theta',\phi')$. To compute $\bar{F}_n{}^m$, let both sides of Eq. (7-683) be multiplied by $P_\lambda{}^{|\mu|}(\cos\theta)e^{-i\mu\phi}\sin\theta\,d\theta\,d\phi$ and then integrated with respect to θ and ϕ over the surface of a unit sphere. With the aid of the orthogonality relation (7-386) we find

$$[\nabla_r^2 + k^2r^2 - n(n+1)]\bar{F}_n{}^{|m|}\frac{(n+|m|)!}{(n-|m|)!}\frac{4\pi}{2n+1}$$
$$= -\delta(r-r')P_n{}^{|m|}(\cos\theta')e^{-im\phi'} \tag{7-684}$$

For convenience, let us define

$$\bar{F}_n{}^{|m|}(r,r',\theta',\phi') = \frac{2n+1}{4\pi} \frac{(n-|m|)!}{(n+|m|)!} P_n{}^{|m|}(\cos\theta')e^{-im\phi'}K_n(r,r') \tag{7-685}$$

Then Eq. (7-684) becomes

$$[\nabla_r{}^2 + k^2r^2 - n(n+1)]K_n(r,r') = -\delta(r-r') \tag{7-686}$$

or

$$\frac{d}{dr}\left(r^2\frac{dK_n}{dr}\right) + [k^2r^2 - n(n+1)]K_n(r,r') = -\delta(r-r') \tag{7-687}$$

Equation (7-687) can be put into a recognizable form by making the substitution

$$K_n(r,r') = \frac{v_n(r,r')}{\sqrt{kr}} \tag{7-688}$$

Using Eq. (7-688),

$$\frac{d}{dr}\left(r^2\frac{dK_n}{dr}\right) = \frac{1}{\sqrt{kr}}\left(r^2\frac{d^2v_n}{dr^2} + r\frac{dv_n}{dr} - \frac{1}{4}v_n\right) \tag{7-689}$$

so that when $r \neq r'$, Eq. (7-687) becomes

$$r^2\frac{d^2v_n}{dr^2} + r\frac{dv_n}{dr} - \frac{v_n}{4} + [k^2r^2 - n(n+1)]v_n = 0 \tag{7-690}$$

However,

$$-n(n+1) - \tfrac{1}{4} = -(n+\tfrac{1}{2})^2 \tag{7-691}$$

and therefore

$$r^2\frac{d^2v_n}{dr^2} + r\frac{dv_n}{dr} + [k^2r^2 - (n+\tfrac{1}{2})^2]v_n = 0 \tag{7-692}$$

Equation (7-692) was discussed in Sec. 6-16 and has Bessel functions of order $n + \frac{1}{2}$ as solutions. Consequently, when $r \neq r'$, the solutions of Eq. (7-687) are *spherical* Bessel functions. For example,

$$K_n(r,r') = \begin{cases} Aj_n(kr) \\ Bh_n{}^{(1)}(kr) \end{cases} \tag{7-693}$$

is one linearly independent set of solutions of (7-687) when $r \neq r'$. Since the source is neither at the origin $r = 0$ nor at infinity, K_n should remain finite at $r = 0$ and $r = \infty$. The exact behavior of $h_n{}^{(1)}(kr)$ is given by Eq. (6-345) as

$$h_n{}^{(1)}(kr) = (-i)^{n+1}\frac{e^{ikr}}{r} \tag{7-694}$$

We see from Eq. (7-694) that K_n will remain finite as $r \to \infty$, provided that

$$\text{Im}(k) \geq 0 \tag{7-695}$$

Thus the pair of solutions (7-693) is assigned so that

$$K_n = Aj_n(kr) \qquad 0 \leq r < r' \tag{7-696}$$

$$K_n = Bh_n{}^{(1)}(kr) \qquad r' < r < \infty \tag{7-697}$$

Since K_n must be continuous at $r = r'$, we find

$$Aj_n(kr') - Bh_n^{(1)}(kr') = 0 \tag{7-698}$$

and integrating both sides of Eq. (7-687) over an interval 2ϵ centered at $r = r'$ then gives

$$\lim_{\epsilon \to 0} r^2 \frac{dK_n}{dr}\bigg|_{r=r'-\epsilon}^{r=r'+\epsilon} = -1 \tag{7-699}$$

or

$$Akr^2 \frac{dj_n}{d(kr)} - Bkr^2 \frac{dh_n^{(1)}}{d(kr)} = 1 \tag{7-700}$$

Solving Eqs. (7-698) and (7-700) simultaneously, we find

$$A = \frac{h_n^{(1)}(kr')}{\Delta} \tag{7-701}$$

$$B = \frac{j_n(kr')}{\Delta} \tag{7-702}$$

where

$$\Delta = -kr^2 \begin{vmatrix} j_n & h_n^{(1)} \\ j_n' & h_n^{(1)\prime} \end{vmatrix} \tag{7-703}$$

The determinant in Eq. (7-703) is the Wronskian of j_n and $h_n^{(1)}$ and is presumably constant. Therefore, we can evaluate it by using the limiting forms (6-338), (6-340), and (6-341) for j_n and $h_n^{(1)}$ as $kr \to 0$. The result is

$$\Delta = -kr^2 \begin{vmatrix} \dfrac{(kr)^n}{(2n+1)!!} & \left[\dfrac{(kr)^n}{(2n+1)!!} - \dfrac{i(2n-1)!!}{(kr)^{n+1}} \right] \\ \dfrac{n(kr)^{n-1}}{(2n+1)!!} & \left[\dfrac{n(kr)^{n-1}}{(2n+1)!!} + \dfrac{i(n+1)(2n-1)!!}{(kr)^{n+2}} \right] \end{vmatrix} \tag{7-704}$$

which reduces to

$$\begin{aligned}
\Delta &= -kr^2 \left[\frac{i(n+1)(2n-1)!!}{(kr)^2(2n+1)!!} + \frac{i(2n-1)!!}{(2n+1)!!} \frac{n}{(kr)^2} \right] \\
&= -kr^2 \left[\frac{i(2n+1)}{(kr)^2} \frac{(2n-1)!!}{(2n+1)!!} \right] = \frac{1}{ik}
\end{aligned} \tag{7-705}$$

and consequently Eqs. (7-696), (7-697), (7-701), (7-702), and (7-705) combine to give

$$K_n(r,r') = ikj_n(kr_<)h_n^{(1)}(kr_>) \tag{7-706}$$

where

$$\text{Im}\,(k) \geq 0 \tag{7-707}$$

By means of Eq. (7-685), $F_n^{|m|}(r,r',\theta',\phi')$ is recovered and inserted into Eq. (7-680) to yield

$$\bar{G}(r,r';\,\theta,\theta';\,\phi - \phi')$$

$$= \frac{e^{ikR}}{4\pi R} = \frac{ik}{4\pi} \sum_{n=0}^{\infty} (2n+1)j_n(kr_<)h_n^{(1)}(kr_>)$$

$$\sum_{m=-n}^{n} \frac{(n-|m|)!}{(n+|m|)!} P_n^{|m|}(\cos\theta) P_n^{|m|}(\cos\theta') e^{im(\phi-\phi)} \tag{7-708}$$

Equation (7-708) is the desired expansion in spherical coordinates of Green's function defined by Eq. (7-675).

Suppose that the source is placed on the polar axis of the coordinate system. Then $\theta' = 0$, and θ becomes the angle between the source and the observer. Let us distinguish this angle by calling it $\theta = \gamma$. It follows from Eqs. (6-296) and (6-293) that

$$P_n{}^{|m|}(1) = 0 \qquad m > 0 \tag{7-709}$$

and

$$P_n{}^{|m|}(1) = 1 \qquad m = 0 \tag{7-710}$$

Thus for $\theta' = 0$ and $\theta = \gamma$,

$$\sum_{m=-n}^{n} \frac{(n - |m|)!}{(n + |m|)!} P_n{}^{|m|}(\cos \theta) P_n{}^{|m|}(\cos \theta') e^{im(\phi - \phi')} = P_n(\cos \gamma) \tag{7-711}$$

This shows that the complicated sum on the left side of Eq. (7-711) is nothing more than an nth-order Legendre polynomial whose argument is the cosine of the angle between the source and the observer. With this remark Eq. (7-708) reduces to

$$\bar{G} = \frac{e^{ikR}}{4\pi R} = \frac{ik}{4\pi} \sum_{n=0}^{\infty} (2n + 1) j_n(kr_<) h_n{}^{(1)}(kr_>) P_n(\cos \gamma) \tag{7-712}$$

ending our discussion of the expansion of $\bar{G}$ in spherical coordinates.

7-25 INTERPRETATION OF THE INTEGRAL SOLUTION OF HELMHOLTZ'S EQUATION

Let us examine the integral representation of the solution of

$$(\nabla^2 + k^2)\bar{u}(\mathbf{r},\omega) = -\bar{F}(\mathbf{r},\omega) \tag{7-713}$$

a little more closely. It is given by Eq. (7-499) as

$$\bar{u}(\mathbf{r}',\omega) = \int_V \bar{G}(\mathbf{r}|\mathbf{r}') \bar{F}(\mathbf{r},\omega) \, dV + \int_{S(V)} \left\{ \bar{G} \frac{\partial \bar{u}}{\partial n} - \bar{u} \frac{\partial \bar{G}}{\partial n} \right\} dS \tag{7-714}$$

We know from our previous discussions that if

$$\bar{G} = \int_{-\infty}^{+\infty} G e^{-i\omega t} \, dt \tag{7-715}$$

then

$$\bar{G} = \frac{e^{-ikR}}{4\pi R} \tag{7-716}$$

and if

$$\bar{G} = \int_{-\infty}^{+\infty} G e^{i\omega t} \, dt \tag{7-717}$$

then

$$\bar{G} = \frac{e^{ikR}}{4\pi R} \tag{7-718}$$

in order that $G(R,t)$ represent the radiation from a point *source*. Although we normally use Eq. (7-715) as the definition of G, Eq. (7-717) is equally valid and probably occurs more frequently in the literature. If (7-717) is chosen as the definition of $\bar{G}$, then Eq. (7-714) reduces to

$$\bar{u}(\mathbf{r}',\omega) = \frac{1}{4\pi} \int_V \bar{F}(\mathbf{r},\omega) \frac{e^{ikR}}{R} \, dV$$

$$+ \frac{1}{4\pi} \int_{S(V)} \left[\frac{e^{ikR}}{R} \frac{\partial \bar{u}}{\partial n} - \bar{u} \frac{\partial}{\partial n} \left(\frac{e^{ikR}}{R} \right) \right] dS \qquad (7\text{-}719)$$

where $R = |\mathbf{r} - \mathbf{r}'|$.

Equation (7-719) represents the disturbance $\bar{u}$ at $\mathbf{r}'$ in V as the result of superposing contributions from volume sources distributed inside V with a density $\bar{F}(\mathbf{r},\omega)$, and surface sources distributed over the surface $S(V)$ enclosing V. The term

$$\int_{S(V)} \frac{e^{ikR}}{4\pi R} \frac{\partial \bar{u}}{\partial n} \, dS \qquad (7\text{-}720)$$

represents the contribution to $\bar{u}$ at $\mathbf{r}'$ due to surface point sources distributed on $S(V)$ with a surface density $\partial \bar{u}/\partial n$. The remaining term

$$\int_{S(V)} \frac{\partial}{\partial n} \left(\frac{e^{ikR}}{4\pi R} \right) (-\bar{u} \, dS) \qquad (7\text{-}721)$$

represents the contribution to $\bar{u}$ at $\mathbf{r}'$ due to a surface distribution of dipole radiators (double layer) of moment $-\bar{u} \, dS$. This is most easily seen from Fig. 7-11. Suppose that a pair of periodically oscillating charges of opposite sign are located a small distance Δn apart along the normal $\mathbf{n}$ to $S(V)$. The dipole field generated by adding together the Green's function for each charge is

$$u_{\text{dipole}} = \frac{q e^{ikR_1}}{4\pi R_1} - \frac{q e^{ikR}}{4\pi R} \qquad (7\text{-}722)$$

The magnitude of the charge is now allowed to increase without bound as Δn shrinks to zero. It is assumed that this happens in such a way that the product of q and Δn remains fixed: i.e.,

$$q \, \Delta n = m \text{ (const)} \qquad (7\text{-}723)$$

Then

$$\bar{u}_{\text{dipole}} = q \Delta \left(\frac{e^{ikR}}{4\pi R} \right) = m \frac{\Delta(e^{ikR}/4\pi R)}{\Delta n} \qquad (7\text{-}724)$$

and as the two charges approach each other along the normal to S,

$$\lim_{\Delta n \to 0} \bar{u}_{\text{dipole}} = m \frac{\partial}{\partial n} \left(\frac{e^{ikR}}{4\pi R} \right) \qquad (7\text{-}725)$$

The effect of the radiation sources outside of V are accounted for by introducing suitable fictitious monopole and dipole distributions on $S(V)$. As the surface $S(V)$ recedes to infinity, the limiting value of the surface integral in Eq. (7-719) represents the effect of

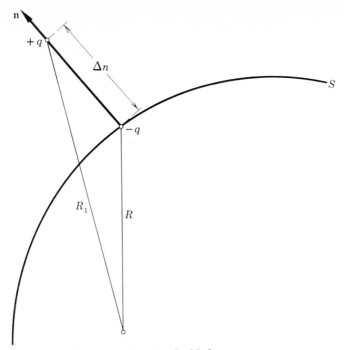

Figure 7-11 Interpretation of a double layer.

sources at infinity. When there are no sources at infinity, the limiting value of the surface integral must be zero, and this places limitations on the behavior of $\bar{u}$. These limitations are summarized in the Sommerfeld radiation condition, a sharp form of which we shall now derive.

7-26 THE SOMMERFELD RADIATION CONDITION†

THEOREM: A sufficient condition for the surface integral

$$\bar{u} = \frac{1}{4\pi} \int_{S(V)} \left[\frac{e^{ikR}}{R} \left(\frac{\partial \bar{u}}{\partial n} \right) - \bar{u} \frac{\partial}{\partial n} \left(\frac{e^{ikR}}{R} \right) \right] dS \tag{7-726}$$

to vanish as $S(V)$ recedes to infinity is that $\bar{u}(r,\theta,\phi)$ should satisfy

$$\lim_{r \to \infty} r \left(\frac{\partial \bar{u}}{\partial r} - ik\bar{u} + \frac{\bar{u}}{r} \right) = 0 \tag{7-727}$$

and

$$\lim_{r \to \infty} \frac{\bar{u}}{r} = 0 \tag{7-728}$$

uniformly in θ and ϕ.

†I. S. Sokolnikoff and R. M. Redheffer, "Mathematics of Physics and Modern Engineering," p. 501, McGraw-Hill, New York, 1958.

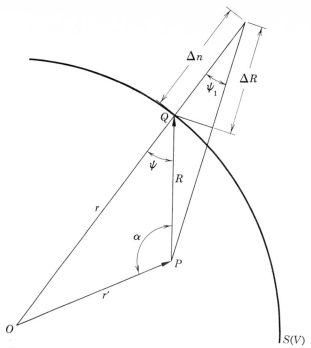

Figure 7-12 Geometry associated with the Sommerfeld radiation condition.

proof: In order to prove this theorem, we shall need several simple geometric results obtainable from Fig. 7-12. It is apparent from the figure that since

$$\frac{\Delta R}{\Delta n} = \cos \psi_1 \tag{7-729}$$

$$\frac{\partial R}{\partial n} = \lim_{\Delta n \to 0} \frac{\Delta R}{\Delta n} = \cos \psi \tag{7-730}$$

we must have

$$\frac{\partial}{\partial n}\left(\frac{e^{ikR}}{R}\right) = \frac{ikRe^{ikR} - e^{ikR}}{R^2} \cos \psi$$

and therefore Eq. (7-726) may be written as

$$\bar{u} = \frac{1}{4\pi} \int_{S(V)} \frac{e^{ikR}}{R} \left[\frac{\partial \bar{u}}{\partial n} - ik\bar{u} \right.$$
$$\left. + ik\bar{u}(1 - \cos \psi) + \frac{\bar{u}}{R} \cos \psi \right] dS \tag{7-731}$$

The further reduction of Eq. (7-731) depends on three geometric results,

$$1 - \cos \psi = O(\epsilon^2) \tag{7-732}$$

$$\frac{\cos \psi}{R} = \frac{1}{r} + O(\epsilon^2) \tag{7-733}$$

$$\frac{r}{R} = 1 + O(\epsilon) \tag{7-734}$$

obtained from Fig. 7-12. The quantity ϵ defined by

$$\epsilon = \frac{r'}{r} \tag{7-735}$$

eventually becomes an arbitrarily small positive number. This happens as r recedes to infinity with r' held fixed. Equations (7-732) and (7-733) are obtained by applying the law of sines to Fig. 7-12, and Eq. (7-734) comes from an application of the triangle inequality. We see that

$$\frac{\sin \psi}{r'} = \frac{\sin \alpha}{r} \tag{7-736}$$

and therefore

$$1 - \cos^2 \psi = \left(\frac{r'}{r}\right)^2 \sin^2 \alpha \tag{7-737}$$

$$\cos \psi = \left[1 - \left(\frac{r'}{r}\right)^2 \sin^2 \alpha\right]^{\frac{1}{2}} \tag{7-738}$$

or

$$\cos \psi = (1 - \epsilon^2 \sin^2 \alpha)^{\frac{1}{2}} \tag{7-739}$$

On expanding Eq. (7-739), we obtain

$$\cos \psi = 1 - \frac{1}{2}\epsilon^2 \sin^2 \alpha - \frac{1}{8}\epsilon^4 \sin^4 \alpha - \cdots \tag{7-740}$$

so that for small ϵ,

$$1 - \cos \psi = O(\epsilon^2) \tag{7-741}$$

Also, from Eq. (7-738),

$$\frac{\cos \psi}{R} = \frac{1}{r}\frac{r}{R}\left[1 - \left(\frac{r'}{r}\right)^2 \sin^2 \alpha\right]^{\frac{1}{2}} \tag{7-742}$$

Applying the triangle inequality to Fig. 7-12 gives

$$r \leq r' + R \tag{7-743}$$

$$1 \leq \frac{r'}{r} + \frac{R}{r} \tag{7-744}$$

$$\frac{R}{r} \geq 1 - \epsilon \tag{7-745}$$

and therefore

$$0 \leq \frac{r}{R} \leq \frac{1}{1 - \epsilon} \tag{7-746}$$

However

$$\frac{1}{1 - \epsilon} = 1 + \epsilon + \cdots \tag{7-747}$$

So we can write

$$\frac{r}{R} = 1 + O(\epsilon) \tag{7-748}$$

for small ϵ.

Let $d\Omega$ be the element of solid angle subtended by dS at 0 in Fig. 7-12. Then, using $dS = r^2\, d\Omega$, Eq. (7-731) becomes

$$\bar{u} = \frac{1}{4\pi} \int_{S(V)} r\, d\Omega \left(\frac{r}{R}\right) e^{ikR} \left[\left(\frac{\partial \bar{u}}{\partial n} - ik\bar{u} + \frac{\bar{u}}{r}\right)\right.$$
$$\left. + (1 + ik)\bar{u}O(\epsilon^2)\right] \qquad (7\text{-}749)$$

or equivalently

$$\bar{u} = \frac{1}{4\pi} \int_{S(V)} d\Omega e^{ikR}[1 + O(\epsilon)]\left[r\left(\frac{\partial \bar{u}}{\partial n} - ik\bar{u} + \frac{\bar{u}}{r}\right)\right.$$
$$\left. + (1 + ik)\frac{\bar{u}}{r}O(1)\right] = \frac{1}{4\pi} \int_{S(V)} d\Omega e^{ikR}\left[r\left(\frac{\partial \bar{u}}{\partial n} - ik\bar{u} + \frac{\bar{u}}{r}\right)\right.$$
$$\left. + (1 + ik)\frac{\bar{u}}{r}O(1)\right] + \frac{1}{4\pi} \int_{S(V)} d\Omega O(\epsilon)e^{ikR}\left[r\left(\frac{\partial \bar{u}}{\partial n}\right.\right.$$
$$\left.\left. - ik\bar{u} + \frac{\bar{u}}{r}\right) + (1 + ik)\frac{\bar{u}}{r}O(1)\right] \qquad (7\text{-}750)$$

We see that $\bar{u}$ is the sum of a pair of integrals,

$$\bar{u} = I_1 + I_2 \qquad (7\text{-}751)$$

and therefore

$$|\bar{u}| \leq |I_1| + |I_2| \qquad (7\text{-}752)$$

However,

$$|I_2| \leq |I_1| \qquad (7\text{-}753)$$

because of the additional factor $O(\epsilon)$ in the integrand of I_2, and consequently

$$|\bar{u}| \leq 2|I_1| \qquad (7\text{-}754)$$

An application of the mean-value theorem to I_1 shows that

$$|I_1| \leq 4\pi \max_{S(V)} \left| r\left(\frac{\partial \bar{u}}{\partial n} - ik\bar{u} + \frac{\bar{u}}{r}\right) + (1 + ik)\frac{\bar{u}}{r}O(1)\right|$$
$$\leq 4\pi \max_{S(V)} \left| r\left(\frac{\partial \bar{u}}{\partial n} - ik\bar{u} + \frac{\bar{u}}{r}\right)\right|$$
$$+ 4\pi \max_{S(V)} O(1)|1 + ik|\frac{|\bar{u}|}{r} \qquad (7\text{-}755)$$

Since $r \to \infty$ as $S(V)$ recedes to infinity, it follows from Eqs. (7-726), (7-754), and (7-755) that

$$\lim_{r \to \infty} \frac{1}{4\pi} \int_{S(V)} \left[\frac{e^{ikR}}{R}\left(\frac{\partial \bar{u}}{\partial n}\right) - \bar{u}\frac{\partial}{\partial n}\left(\frac{e^{ikR}}{R}\right)\right] dS = 0 \qquad (7\text{-}756)$$

provided

$$\lim_{r \to \infty} r\left(\frac{\partial \bar{u}}{\partial n} - ik\bar{u} + \frac{\bar{u}}{r}\right) = 0 \qquad (7\text{-}757)$$

and

$$\lim_{r \to \infty} \frac{\bar{u}}{r} = 0 \qquad (7\text{-}758)$$

uniformly in θ and ϕ.

In Sec. 7-21 it was suggested that one means of solving

$$\left(\nabla^2 - \frac{1}{c^2}\frac{\partial^2}{\partial t^2}\right) u(\mathbf{r},t) = -F(\mathbf{r},t) \tag{7-759}$$

is to Fourier-transform it, solve the resulting Helmholtz equation, and then invert the result back into the time domain. An alternative method is to deal directly with Eq. (7-759) by introducing a time-dependent Green's function.

We wish to solve (7-759) subject to specified *initial conditions*,

$$u(\mathbf{r},0) = f(\mathbf{r}) \tag{7-760}$$

$$\frac{\partial u}{\partial t}(\mathbf{r},0) = g(\mathbf{r}) \tag{7-761}$$

and given *boundary conditions*. These will be of the radiation condition type when the domain is unbounded, and of the Dirichlet or Neumann type when the domain is bounded. The time-dependent Green's function is introduced as the solution of

$$\left(\nabla^2 - \frac{1}{c^2}\frac{\partial}{\partial t^2}\right) G(\mathbf{r},t;\,\mathbf{r}',t') = -\delta(\mathbf{r}-\mathbf{r}')\,\delta(t-t') \tag{7-762}$$

having the following properties:

1. $G(\mathbf{r},t;\mathbf{r}',t') = 0 \quad t < t'$.
2. $G(\mathbf{r},t;\mathbf{r}',t')$ satisfies the homogeneous wave equation except at $t = t'$, $\mathbf{r} = \mathbf{r}'$.
3. $G(\mathbf{r},t;\mathbf{r}',t')$ will satisfy homogeneous boundary conditions on $S(V)$, and
4. homogeneous initial conditions $G = 0,\ \partial G/\partial t = 0$ for $t < t'$.
5. $G(\mathbf{r},t;\mathbf{r}',t')$ satisfies a reciprocity relation $G(\mathbf{r},t;\mathbf{r}',t') = G(\mathbf{r}',-t';\mathbf{r},-t)$ for $t > t'$.

This Green's function can be interpreted as the disturbance at $\mathbf{r}$ occurring at time t due to an earlier disturbance at $\mathbf{r}'$ which happened at time t'. Notice that in the time-dependent reciprocity relation one does not merely interchange the primed and unprimed coordinates. The signs of t and t' must also be reversed. If this step were not taken, then a disturbance at $\mathbf{r}$ and t would be observed at $\mathbf{r}'$ and t' when t' is *less* then t. This would imply that the disturbance was detected before it occurred! By reversing the signs, the disturbance occurring at $\mathbf{r}$ and $-t$ is observed at $\mathbf{r}'$ and $-t'$ where $-t' > -t$ as it should be.

The proof of the reciprocity property 5 follows along the same lines as the proof of Eq. (7-508). Two Green's functions, $G_{+}(\mathbf{r},t;\mathbf{r}',t')$ and $G_{-}(\mathbf{r},-t;\mathbf{r}'',-t'')$, are introduced. Both satisfy identical homogeneous boundary conditions on $S(V)$ as well as homogeneous initial conditions, together with the wave equations,

$$\left(\nabla^2 - \frac{1}{c^2}\frac{\partial^2}{\partial t^2}\right) G_+(\mathbf{r},t;\mathbf{r}',t') = -\delta(\mathbf{r} - \mathbf{r}')\,\delta(t - t') \qquad (7\text{-}763)$$

$$\left(\nabla^2 - \frac{1}{c^2}\frac{\partial^2}{\partial t^2}\right) G_-(\mathbf{r},-t;\mathbf{r}'',-t'') = -\delta(\mathbf{r} - \mathbf{r}'')\,\delta(t - t'') \qquad (7\text{-}764)$$

Applying Green's theorem,

$$\int_V \{G_+ \nabla^2 G_- - G_- \nabla^2 G_+\}\,dV$$
$$= \int_{S(V)} \left\{G_+ \frac{\partial G_-}{\partial n} - G_- \frac{\partial G_+}{\partial n}\right\} dS \qquad (7\text{-}765)$$

to Eqs. (7-763) and (7-764) yields

$$\int_V \{G_+ \nabla^2 G_- - G_- \nabla^2 G_+\}\,dV = -G_+(\mathbf{r}'',t;\mathbf{r}',t')\,\delta(t - t'')$$
$$+ G_-(\mathbf{r}',-t;\mathbf{r}'',-t'')\,\delta(t - t') + \frac{1}{c^2}\int_V \left\{G_+ \frac{\partial^2 G_-}{\partial t^2}\right.$$
$$\left. - G_- \frac{\partial^2 G_+}{\partial t^2}\right\} dV = 0 \qquad (7\text{-}766)$$

The surface-integral contribution from Eq. (7-765) vanishes because we have assumed that G_+ and G_- satisfy identical *homogeneous* boundary conditions on $S(V)$. The last term in Eq. (7-766) can be rewritten by using

$$\int_V \left\{G_+ \frac{\partial^2 G_-}{\partial t^2} - G_- \frac{\partial^2 G_+}{\partial t^2}\right\} dV$$
$$= \frac{\partial}{\partial t}\int_V \left\{G_+ \frac{\partial G_-}{\partial t} - G_- \frac{\partial G_+}{\partial t}\right\} dV \qquad (7\text{-}767)$$

Both sides of Eq. (7-766) are now integrated with respect to time from $t = -\infty$ to $t = t$ where $t > t'$ and $t > t''$. The result is

$$G_+(\mathbf{r}'',t'';\mathbf{r}',t') - G_-(\mathbf{r}',-t';\mathbf{r}'',-t'')$$
$$= \frac{1}{c^2}\int_V \left\{G_+ \frac{\partial G_-}{\partial t} - G_- \frac{\partial G_+}{\partial t}\right\} dV \bigg|_{t=-\infty}^{t=t} \qquad (7\text{-}768)$$

At the lower limit $t = -\infty$, the last term vanishes because of property 4 of the Green's function. Also, the Green's function $G_-(\mathbf{r},-t;\mathbf{r}'',-t'')$ is nonzero only when $-t > -t''$, and this is true of $\partial G_-/\partial t$ as well. However, $-t > -t''$ implies that $t < t''$, and in Eq. (7-768) it was assumed that $t > t'$ and $t > t''$. Therefore G_- and $\partial G_-/\partial t$ vanish at the upper limit $t = t$ in (7-768), and the reciprocity relation

$$G_+(\mathbf{r}'',t'';\mathbf{r}',t') = G_-(\mathbf{r}',-t';\mathbf{r}'',-t'') \qquad (7\text{-}769)$$

is established.

Let us return to the problem of obtaining a formal integral solution of Eqs. (7-759) to (7-761). For this purpose it is convenient to rewrite (7-759) to (7-762) in primed coordinates; thus

$$\left(\nabla'^2 - \frac{1}{c^2}\frac{\partial^2}{\partial t'^2}\right) u(\mathbf{r}',t') = -F(\mathbf{r}',t') \qquad (7\text{-}770)$$

and

$$\left(\nabla'^2 - \frac{1}{c^2}\frac{\partial^2}{\partial t'^2}\right)G(\mathbf{r},t;\mathbf{r}',t') = -\delta(\mathbf{r} - \mathbf{r}')\,\delta(t - t') \tag{7-771}$$

where

$$\nabla'^2 = \frac{\partial^2}{\partial x'^2} + \frac{\partial^2}{\partial y'^2} + \frac{\partial^2}{\partial z'^2} \tag{7-772}$$

By integrating Green's theorem over dt', one finds

$$\int_0^{t+\epsilon} dt' \int_{V'} \{G\,\nabla'^2 u - u\,\nabla'^2 G\}\,dV'$$
$$= \int_0^{t+\epsilon} dt' \int_{S(V')} \left\{G\frac{\partial u}{\partial n'} - u\frac{\partial G}{\partial n'}\right\} dS' \tag{7-773}$$

where ϵ is an arbitrarily small positive number, and u and G satisfy Eqs. (7-770) and (7-771). It follows from (7-770), (7-771), and (7-773) that

$$-\int_0^{t+\epsilon} dt' \int_{V'} G(\mathbf{r},t;\mathbf{r}',t')F(\mathbf{r}',t')\,dV' + u(\mathbf{r},t)$$
$$+ \frac{1}{c^2}\int_{V'}\left\{G\frac{\partial u}{\partial t'} - u\frac{\partial G}{\partial t'}\Big|_{t'=0}^{t'=t+\epsilon}\right\}dV'$$
$$= \int_0^{t+\epsilon} dt' \int_{S(V')}\left\{G\frac{\partial u}{\partial n'} - u\frac{\partial G}{\partial n'}\right\}dS' \tag{7-774}$$

Both $G(\mathbf{r},t;\mathbf{r}',t')$ and $\partial G/\partial t'\ (\mathbf{r},t,\mathbf{r}',t')$ must vanish when $t' > t$ according to property 4 of G. Hence the third term on the left side of Eq. (7-774) must vanish at the upper limit $t = t' + \epsilon$. As $\epsilon \to 0$, we obtain

$$u(\mathbf{r},t) = \int_0^{t+\epsilon} dt' \int_{V'} G(\mathbf{r},t;\mathbf{r}',t')\mathbf{F}(\mathbf{r}',t')\,dV'$$
$$+ \int_0^{t+\epsilon} dt' \int_{S(V')}\left\{G\frac{\partial u}{\partial n'} - u\frac{\partial G}{\partial n'}\right\}dS'$$
$$+ \frac{1}{c^2}\int_{V'}\left\{G\frac{\partial u}{\partial t'} - u\frac{\partial G}{\partial t'}\right\}\Big|_{t'=0}dV' \tag{7-775}$$

Equation (7-775) provides a formal solution to the mixed initial- and boundary-value problem associated with Eq. (7-759). It is clear from (7-775) that $u(\mathbf{r},t)$ is made up of contributions from volume sources distributed throughout V' with a density $F(\mathbf{r}',t')$, single- and double-layer surface sources distributed over $S(V')$, and a term involving the initial conditions at $t' = 0$.

The surface $S(V')$ may now be permitted to recede to infinity. If there are no sources at infinity and the medium is initially at rest so that at $t' = 0$, $u = 0$ and $\partial u/\partial t' = 0$ everywhere, then Eq. (7-775) reduces to

$$u(\mathbf{r},t) = \int_0^{t+\epsilon} dt' \int_{\text{All space}} G(\mathbf{r},t;\mathbf{r}',t')F(\mathbf{r}',t')\,dV' \tag{7-776}$$

We showed in Eq. (7-650) that when no sources are present at infinity, then

$$G(\mathbf{r},t;\mathbf{r}',t') = \frac{\delta[(t - t') - R/c]}{4\pi R} \tag{7-777}$$

where $t - t'$ represents the time that has elapsed since the source was triggered, and $R = [(x - x')^2 + (y - y')^2 + (z - z')^2]^{1/2}$. Thus

$$u(\mathbf{r},t) = \int_0^{t+\epsilon} dt' \int_{\text{All space}} \frac{\delta[(t - t') - R/c]}{4\pi R} F(\mathbf{r}',t') \, dV' \tag{7-778}$$

or

$$u(\mathbf{r},t) = \frac{1}{4\pi} \int_{\text{All space}} \frac{F(\mathbf{r}',t - R/c)}{R} \, dV' \tag{7-779}$$

Notice that the time t in the integrand of Eq. (7-779) has been retarded by a factor of R/c. It is customary to designate retarded functions by enclosing them in square brackets so that

$$[F(\mathbf{r}',t)] = F\left(\mathbf{r}', t - \frac{R}{c}\right) \tag{7-780}$$

With this notation

$$u(\mathbf{r},t) = \frac{1}{4\pi} \int_{\text{All space}} \frac{[F(\mathbf{r}',t)]}{R} \, dV' \tag{7-781}$$

The appearance of retarded quantities in the solution of the time-dependent wave equation is a consequence of the finite speed of propagation. In other words, a signal which is here now must have left somewhere else at an earlier time. The time difference or retardation is how long it took the signal to travel here from its source.

For two space dimensions one expects solutions like Eqs. (7-775) and (7-776), except that the volume V' is replaced by an open surface S', and the boundary $S(V')$ is replaced by the closed curve $C(S')$ forming the complete boundary of S'. The time Laplace transform of the two-dimensional Green's function $G(R,t)$ is given by Eq. (7-524) as

$$\bar{G}\left(\frac{sR}{c}\right) = \frac{1}{2\pi} K_0\left(\frac{sR}{c}\right) \tag{7-782}$$

From a table of Laplace transforms,

$$K_0\left(\frac{sR}{c}\right) = \int_0^\infty \frac{H[t - R/c]}{\sqrt{t^2 - R^2/c^2}} e^{-st} \, dt \tag{7-783}$$

where $H[t - R/c]$ is Heaviside's unit step function defined by

$$H(x) = \begin{cases} 1 & x > 0 \\ 0 & x < 0 \end{cases} \tag{7-784}$$

Therefore the inverse Laplace transform of $\bar{G}(sR/c)$ is

$$G(R,t) = \frac{H[t - R/c]}{2\pi \sqrt{t^2 - R^2/c^2}} \tag{7-785}$$

and the two-dimensional time-dependent Green's function becomes

$$G(\mathbf{r},t;\mathbf{r}',t') = \frac{H[(t - t') - R/c]}{2\pi \sqrt{(t - t')^2 - R^2/c^2}} \tag{7-786}$$

where $t - t'$ is the elapsed time measured from the instant of source triggering, and $R = [(x - x')^2 + (y - y')^2]^{1/2}$.

Suppose we wish to solve

$$\left(\nabla^2 - \frac{1}{c^2}\frac{\partial^2}{\partial t^2}\right) u(\mathbf{r},t) = 0 \tag{7-787}$$

subject to prescribed initial conditions,

$$u = f(\mathbf{r}) \qquad t = 0 \tag{7-788}$$

$$\frac{\partial u}{\partial t} = g(\mathbf{r}) \qquad t = 0 \tag{7-789}$$

According to Eq. (7-775), the solution is

$$u(\mathbf{r},t) = \int_0^{t+\epsilon} dt' \int_{S(V')} \left\{ G\frac{\partial u}{\partial n'} - u\frac{\partial G}{\partial n'} \right\} dS' \tag{7-790}$$

and since

$$G = \frac{\delta[(t - t') - R/c]}{4\pi R} \tag{7-791}$$

Eq. (7-790) is equivalent to

$$u(\mathbf{r},t) = \frac{1}{4\pi} \int_{S(V')} dS' \int_0^{t+\epsilon} dt' \left(\frac{\delta[(t - t') - R/c]}{R} \frac{\partial u}{\partial n'} \right.$$
$$\left. - u\frac{\partial}{\partial n'} \left\{ \frac{\delta[(t - t') - R/c]}{R} \right\} \right) \tag{7-792}$$

The integral of the first term in Eq. (7-792) is relatively easy to evaluate; it is simply

$$\int_0^{t+\epsilon} dt' \frac{\delta[(t - t') - R/c]}{R} \frac{\partial u(\mathbf{r}',t')}{\partial n'}$$
$$= \frac{1}{R}\frac{\partial u}{\partial n'} (\mathbf{r}',t') \Big|_{t'=t-R/c} = \frac{1}{R}\left[\frac{\partial u}{\partial n'}\right] \tag{7-793}$$

The second term in (7-792) involves a little added difficulty because it is necessary to "differentiate" the Dirac delta function. Proceeding formally, we have

$$-\int_0^{t+\epsilon} dt' u(\mathbf{r}',t') \frac{\partial}{\partial n'}\left\{ \frac{\delta[(t - t') - R/c]}{R} \right\}$$
$$= \int_0^{t+\epsilon} dt' u(\mathbf{r}',t')$$
$$\frac{-(R/c)\,\delta'[(t - t') - R/c] + \delta[(t - t') - R/c]}{R^2} \frac{\partial R}{\partial n'} \tag{7-794}$$

where from Fig. 7-12,

$$\frac{\partial R}{\partial n'} = \cos(n',R) \tag{7-795}$$

The second term in Eq. (7-794) integrates to

$$[u]\frac{\cos(n',R)}{R^2} \tag{7-796}$$

leaving

$$-\int_0^{t+\epsilon} dt' u(\mathbf{r}',t') \frac{\cos (n',R)}{Rc} \delta' \left[(t - t') - \frac{R}{c} \right] \tag{7-797}$$

to be evaluated. This can be accomplished by employing integration by parts, and the result

$$\int_{-\epsilon}^{+\epsilon} f(x) \delta'(x) dx = - \int_{-\epsilon}^{+\epsilon} \delta(x) f'(x) dx \tag{7-798}$$

to give

$$-\int_0^{t+\epsilon} dt' u(\mathbf{r}',t') \frac{\cos (n',R)}{Rc} \delta' \left[(t - t') - \frac{R}{c} \right]$$
$$= \left[\frac{\partial u}{\partial t'} \right] \frac{\cos (n',R)}{Rc} \tag{7-799}$$

Thus

$$-\int_0^{t+\epsilon} dt' u(\mathbf{r}',t') \frac{\partial}{\partial n'} \left[\frac{\delta\{(t - t') - R/c\}}{R} \right]$$
$$= [u] \frac{\cos (n',R)}{R^2} + \left[\frac{\partial u}{\partial t} \right] \frac{\cos (n',R)}{Rc} \tag{7-800}$$

and we have shown that Eq. (7-792) becomes

$$u(\mathbf{r},t) = \frac{1}{4\pi} \int_{S(V')} \left\{ \frac{1}{R} \left[\frac{\partial u}{\partial n'} \right] + [u] \frac{\cos (n',R)}{R^2} \right.$$
$$\left. + \left[\frac{\partial u}{\partial t'} \right] \frac{\cos (n',R)}{Rc} \right\} dS' \tag{7-801}$$

or equivalently

$$u(\mathbf{r},t) = \frac{1}{4\pi} \int_{S(V')} dS' \left[\frac{1}{R} \frac{\partial u(\mathbf{r}',t')}{\partial n'} + u(\mathbf{r}',t') \frac{\cos (n',R)}{R^2} \right.$$
$$\left. + \frac{\partial u(\mathbf{r}',t')}{\partial t'} \frac{\cos (n',R)}{Rc} \right]_{t'=t-R/c} \tag{7-802}$$

The vector form of Eq. (7-802) is

$$u(\mathbf{r},t) = \frac{1}{4\pi} \int_{S(V')} d\mathbf{S} \cdot \left[\frac{1}{R} \mathbf{\nabla}'u(\mathbf{r}',t') + \frac{\mathbf{R}}{R^3} u(\mathbf{r}',t') \right.$$
$$\left. + \frac{\partial u(\mathbf{r}',t')}{\partial t'} \frac{\mathbf{R}}{cR^2} \right]_{t'=t-R/c} \tag{7-803}$$

where

$$d\mathbf{S} = \mathbf{n}' \, dS' \tag{7-804}$$

and

$$\cos (n',R) = \frac{\mathbf{n}' \cdot \mathbf{R}}{R} \tag{7-805}$$

Poisson's solution of the wave equation is derivable from Eq. (7-802) or (7-803) as follows. Choose $S(V')$ to be the surface of a sphere of radius ct. Let $\mathbf{r}$ be the position vector of the origin of the sphere, and let $\mathbf{r}'$ be the position vector of any arbitrary point on the surface of the sphere. Then

$$R = |\mathbf{r} - \mathbf{r}'| = ct \tag{7-806}$$

and therefore

$$t' = t - \frac{R}{c} = 0 \tag{7-807}$$

We also notice that

$$\frac{\partial}{\partial n'} = \frac{\partial}{\partial R} \tag{7-808}$$

since

$$\cos (n',R) = 1 \tag{7-809}$$

on $S(V')$.

Using these expressions reduces Eq. (7-802) to

$$u(\mathbf{r},t) = \frac{1}{4\pi} \int_{R=ct} dS' \left\{ \frac{1}{R} \frac{\partial u(\mathbf{r}',0)}{\partial R} + \frac{u(\mathbf{r}',0)}{R^2} \right. \\ \left. + \frac{1}{Rc} \left[\frac{\partial u(\mathbf{r}',t')}{\partial t'} \right]_{t'=0} \right\} \tag{7-810}$$

The element of surface area dS' on $R = ct$ can be expressed in terms of solid angle $d\Omega'$ by the usual formula,

$$dS' = R^2 \, d\Omega' \tag{7-811}$$

thus reducing Eq. (7-810) to

$$u(\mathbf{r},t) = \frac{1}{4\pi} \int_{R=ct} \left\{ \frac{\partial}{\partial R} (Ru(\mathbf{r}',0)) + \frac{R}{c} \left[\frac{\partial u(\mathbf{r}',t')}{\partial t'} \right]_{t'=0} \right\} d\Omega' \tag{7-812}$$

One now observes that

$$\mathbf{r}' = \mathbf{R} + \mathbf{r} \tag{7-813}$$

so that for any arbitrary function f,

$$f(\mathbf{r}') = f(\mathbf{R} + \mathbf{r}) \tag{7-814}$$

Thus

$$\frac{1}{4\pi} \int_{R=ct} f(\mathbf{r}') \, d\Omega' = \frac{1}{4\pi} \int_{R=ct} f(\mathbf{R} + \mathbf{r}) \, d\Omega' \tag{7-815}$$

However, $\mathbf{r}$ is the position vector of the origin of the sphere $R = ct$ and thus remains constant in Eq. (7-815). Consequently, only $\mathbf{R}$ varies over the surface of the sphere. Hence (7-815) gives the mean value of f over a sphere of radius $R = ct$ centered at $\mathbf{r}$. We indicate this by writing

$$M_{ct}[f(\mathbf{r}')] = \frac{1}{4\pi} \int_{R=ct} f(\mathbf{r}') \, d\Omega' \tag{7-816}$$

and we use Eq. (7-816) to simplify (7-812). Since $R = ct$,

$$\frac{\partial}{\partial R} [Ru(\mathbf{r}',0)] = \frac{\partial}{\partial t} [tu(\mathbf{r}',0)] \tag{7-817}$$

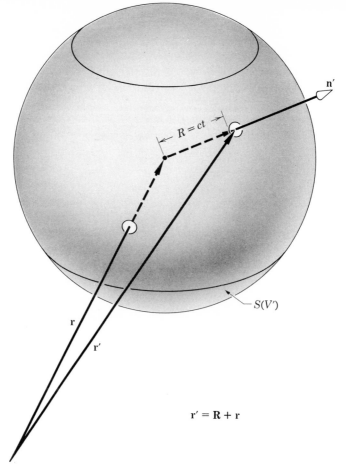

Figure 7-13 Sphere of radius $R = ct$.

$$\mathbf{r}' = \mathbf{R} + \mathbf{r}$$

and

$$\frac{R}{c}\left[\frac{\partial u(\mathbf{r},t')}{\partial t'}\right]_{t'=0} = t\,\frac{\partial u(\mathbf{r}',0)}{\partial t'} \tag{7-818}$$

Eqs. (7-812) and (7-816) give

$$u(\mathbf{r},t) = \frac{\partial}{\partial t}\,M_{ct}[tu(\mathbf{r}',0)] + tM_{ct}\left[\frac{\partial u(\mathbf{r}',0)}{\partial t'}\right] \tag{7-819}$$

or, on using Eqs. (7-788) and (7-789),

$$u(\mathbf{r},t) = \frac{\partial}{\partial t}\,M_{ct}[tf(\mathbf{r}')] + tM_{ct}[g(\mathbf{r}')] \tag{7-820}$$

Equation (7-820) is Poisson's solution of Cauchy's initial-value problem (7-787) to (7-789) for the wave equation.

A solution, similar to Eq. (7-820), can be derived for the Cauchy problem in two space dimensions. For this purpose, it is necessary

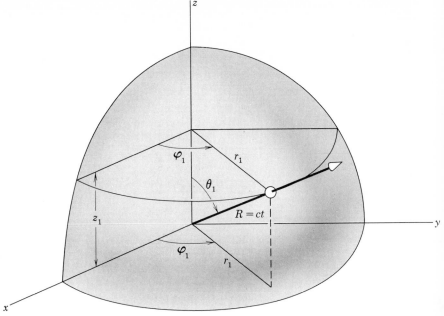

Figure 7-14 The intersection of the sphere $R = ct$ with the plane $z = z_1$.

to reexpress Eq. (7-816) in terms of an integral over a plane. Let the sphere centered at $\mathbf{r}$ be intersected by a plane at a distance z_1 above the equatorial plane, and let θ_1 be the colatitude relative to the z_1 axis defined by the normal to the plane. Spherical coordinates (R,θ_1,ϕ_1), centered in the sphere, are now introduced. These are related to polar coordinates in the plane of intersection by

$$r_1 = R \sin \theta_1 = ct \sin \theta_1 \tag{7-821}$$

$$z_1 = \sqrt{R^2 - r_1^2} = \sqrt{c^2t^2 - r_1^2} \tag{7-822}$$

$$\theta_1 = \cot^{-1}\frac{z_1}{r_1} = \cot^{-1}\frac{\sqrt{c^2t^2 - r_1^2}}{r_1} \tag{7-823}$$

The element of solid angle $d\Omega'$ relative to the center of the sphere is given by

$$d\Omega' = \sin \theta_1 \, d\theta_1 \, d\phi_1 \tag{7-824}$$

However,

$$dr_1 = ct \cos \theta_1 \, d\theta_1 \tag{7-825}$$

and so we can write

$$d\Omega' = \frac{dr_1 \, d\phi_1 \sin \theta_1}{dt \cos \theta_1} = \frac{dr_1 \, d\phi_1}{ct \cot \phi_1} \tag{7-826}$$

or

$$d\Omega' = \frac{dr_1 \, d\phi_1}{ct \sqrt{c^2t^2 - r_1^2}} \tag{7-827}$$

The range $0 \le \theta_1 \le \pi/2, 0 \le \phi_1 \le 2\pi$ corresponds to a hemisphere; hence Eq. (7-816) may be written as

$$M_{ct}[f(\mathbf{r}')] = \frac{2}{4\pi} \int_0^{\pi/2} \int_0^{2\pi} f(\mathbf{r} + \mathbf{R}) \sin \theta_1 \, d\theta_1 \, d\phi_1 \tag{7-828}$$

As θ_1 runs from 0 to $\pi/2$, r_1 runs from 0 to ct because z_1 is fixed. Thus, using (7-824) to (7-827), Eq. (7-828) becomes

$$M_{ct}[f(\mathbf{r}')] = \frac{1}{2\pi} \int_0^{2\pi} \int_0^{ct} \frac{f(\mathbf{r} + \mathbf{R})}{ct \sqrt{c^2 t^2 - r_1^2}} r_1 \, dr_1 \, d\phi_1 \tag{7-829}$$

Let the element area $r_1 \, dr_1 \, d\phi_1$ in the plane of intersection with the sphere be designated by

$$dS_1 = r_1 \, dr_1 \, d\phi_1 \tag{7-830}$$

Then Eq. (7-829) becomes

$$M_{ct}[f(\mathbf{r}')] = \frac{1}{2\pi c} \int_{r_1 \le ct} \frac{f(\mathbf{r} + \mathbf{R})}{t \sqrt{c^2 t^2 - r_1^2}} dS_1 \tag{7-831}$$

and Eq. (7-820) is explicitly given as

$$u(\mathbf{r},t) = \frac{1}{2\pi c} \frac{\partial}{\partial t} \int_{r_1 \le ct} \frac{f(\mathbf{r} + \mathbf{R})}{\sqrt{c^2 t^2 - r_1^2}} dS_1$$
$$+ \frac{1}{2\pi c} \int_{r_1 \le ct} \frac{g(\mathbf{r} + \mathbf{R})}{\sqrt{c^2 t^2 - r_1^2}} dS_1 \tag{7-832}$$

The vector $\mathbf{r}' = \mathbf{r} + \mathbf{R}$ has components

$$\mathbf{r}' = \mathbf{r} + \mathbf{R} = [x + ct \sin \theta_1 \cos \phi_1), (y + ct \sin \theta_1 \sin \phi_1),$$
$$(z + ct \cos \theta_1)] \tag{7-833}$$

or equivalently

$$r' = (x',y',z')$$
$$= \mathbf{r} + \mathbf{R} = [(x + r_1 \cos \phi_1), (y + r_1 \sin \phi_1), (z + z_1)] \tag{7-834}$$

The wave equation in two space dimensions can always be chosen so that the solution and its initial conditions are independent of the z' coordinate in some (x',y',z') coordinate system. For example, let

$$[u(\mathbf{r}',t')]_{t'=0} = u(x',y',0) = f(x',y') \tag{7-835}$$

$$\left[\frac{\partial u(\mathbf{r}',t')}{\partial t'} \right]_{t'=0} = \frac{\partial u(x',y',0)}{\partial t'} = g(x',y') \tag{7-836}$$

Since the initial conditions (7-835) and (7-836) are independent of z', it follows from Eq. (7-834) that (7-832) is explicit given by

$$u(x,y,t) = \frac{1}{2\pi c} \frac{\partial}{\partial t} \iint_{r_1 \le ct} \frac{f[(x + r_1 \cos \phi_1), (y + r_1 \sin \phi_1)]}{\sqrt{c^2 t^2 - r_1^2}} r_1 \, dr_1 \, d\phi_1$$
$$+ \frac{1}{2\pi c} \iint_{r_1 \le ct} \frac{g[(x + r_1 \cos \phi_1), (y + r_1 \sin \phi_1)]}{\sqrt{c^2 t^2 - r_1^2}} r_1 \, dr_1 \, d\phi_1 \tag{7-837}$$

This solves the initial-value problem for

$$\nabla^2 u = \frac{1}{c^2} \frac{\partial^2 u}{\partial t^2} \tag{7-838}$$

in two space dimensions, given the initial conditions,

$$u(x,y,0) = f(x,y) \tag{7-839}$$

$$\frac{\partial u}{\partial t}(x,y,0) = g(x,y) \tag{7-840}$$

We can read some interesting results from Eqs. (7-820) and (7-837). For this purpose we shall introduce the notion of the support of a function. By definition, the support of a function f is the closure of the set of points on which $f \neq 0$. To say that a function f has a compact support means that there is some *closed* and *bounded* domain on which f does not vanish. This domain is called the support of f. For example, if $f = f(x,y,z)$ does not vanish anywhere in or on the solid sphere $x^2 + y^2 + z^2 \leq 1$, but vanishes everywhere outside of it, then f is of compact support, and its compact support is the closed sphere $x^2 + y^2 + z^2 \leq 1$.

It follows from Eq. (7-820) that if the initial conditions $u(x',y',z',0) = f$ and $\partial u/\partial t'(x',y',z',0) = g$ are functions of compact support, then at any fixed point (x,y,z) there exists a *finite* time interval $t_1 \leq t \leq t_2$, outside of which $u(x,y,z,t) \equiv 0$. To see this, one observes that (7-820) represents u in terms of averages over an expanding surface of radius $R = ct$. Since the surface $R = ct$ expands with time, its intersections with the supports of f and g can each be nonzero only for finite time intervals. Thus there must be a finite time interval outside of which u vanishes identically.

The situation for the two-dimensional initial-value problem is different. Even if the initial conditions $u(x',y',0) = f$ and $\partial u/\partial t'(x',y',0) = g$ are of compact support in the x', y' plane, the disturbance $u(x,y,t)$, once it begins, never vanishes at any finite time. That this must be the case can be seen by noticing that Eq. (7-837) represents $u(x,y,t)$ in terms of integrals over the *interior* of an expanding circle of radius $r_1 = ct$. Once the circle passes and encloses the support of f or g, this support will always be in the interior of the circle and will always contribute to an integral in (7-837). The two-dimensional initial-value problem is said to lead to a solution having a wake. We can calculate this wake explicity for the simple case of a line source.

Suppose we let $x = 0$, $y = 0$ in (7-837). This places the point at which u is calculated at the center of the circle $r_1 = ct$ in the r_1, ϕ_1 plane. An infinitely long line source, normal to the r_1, ϕ_1 plane, is assumed to pass through the point $r_1 = r$, $\phi_1 = \phi$ relative to the center of the circle $r_1 = ct$. The corresponding initial conditions on u are

$$(u)_{t=0} = \delta(\mathbf{r}_1 - \mathbf{r}) = \frac{\delta(r_1 - r)}{r_1}\,\delta(\phi_1 - \phi) \tag{7-841}$$

$$\left(\frac{\partial u}{\partial t}\right)_{t=0} = 0 \tag{7-842}$$

and when inserted into Eq. (7-837), these yield

$$u(0,t) = \frac{1}{2\pi c} \frac{\partial}{\partial t} \int_0^{2\pi} \int_0^{ct} \frac{\delta(r_1 - r)\, \delta(\phi_1 - \phi)}{\sqrt{c^2 t^2 - r_1^2}} \, dr_1 \, d\phi_1 \tag{7-843}$$

As a result,

$$u(0,t) = \begin{cases} \dfrac{1}{2\pi c} \dfrac{\partial}{\partial t} \left(\dfrac{1}{\sqrt{c^2 t^2 - r^2}} \right) & r < ct \\ 0 & r > ct \end{cases} \tag{7-844}$$

and therefore

$$u(0,t) = \frac{1}{2\pi c} \frac{\partial}{\partial t} \left[\frac{H(ct - r)}{\sqrt{c^2 t^2 - r^2}} \right] = \frac{1}{2\pi} \left[-\frac{ct H(ct - r)}{(c^2 t^2 - r^2)^{3/2}} + \frac{\delta(ct - r)}{\sqrt{c^2 t^2 - r^2}} \right] \tag{7-845}$$

where $H(x)$ is Heaviside's unit step function,

$$H(x) = \begin{cases} 1 & x > 0 \\ 0 & x < 0 \end{cases} \tag{7-846}$$

and is related to the Dirac delta function by

$$\delta(x) = \frac{dH(x)}{dx} \tag{7-847}$$

We see from Eq. (7-845) that the signal at the origin is zero until $t = r/c$, which is the time it takes the signal to propagate from the source at $r_1 = r$ to the origin at $r_1 = 0$. At $t = r/c$, the delta-function pulse arrives at the origin, followed by a wake which decays as described by the step-function term in (7-845). When $t \gg r/c$, the amplitude of the wake decays as $1/c^2 t^2$. The presence of a wake is characteristic of wave propagation in homogeneous two-dimensional media. Wave propagation in one or three space dimensions does not involve a wake. Since the line source extends to infinity in both directions, perpendicular to the plane in which the solution is computed, it is possible to think of the wake as being associated with the successive arrivals of signals from more and more remote portions of the source.

7-29 THE DIFFUSION EQUATION

The temperature distribution $T(\mathbf{r},t)$ in a homogeneous medium in which heat H is being produced or lost at a rate $\partial H/\partial t$ per unit volume is governed by the inhomogeneous diffusion equation,

$$\left(\nabla^2 - \frac{1}{\alpha} \frac{\partial}{\partial t} \right) T(\mathbf{r},t) = -\frac{1}{k} \frac{\partial H}{\partial t} = -h(\mathbf{r},t) \tag{7-848}$$

where α is the diffusivity, and k is the thermal conductivity of the medium (see Sec. 7-5). All the techniques which we have developed for solving the wave equation and the potential equation are applicable to Eq. (7-848). Thus we can use integral transforms, separation of variables, or a Green's-function method to construct solutions of (7-848).

In harmony with our treatment of wave and potential problems, we shall derive a general solution of (7-848) in terms of a Green's function, thus relegating the real difficulties associated with solving (7-848) to the problem of constructing an appropriate Green's function.

The Green's function for (7-848) is defined as the solution of

$$\left(\nabla^2 - \frac{1}{\alpha}\frac{\partial}{\partial t}\right) G(\mathbf{r},t\,;\mathbf{r}',t') = -\delta(\mathbf{r} - \mathbf{r}')\,\delta(t - t') \tag{7-849}$$

having the following properties:

1. $G(\mathbf{r},t\,;\mathbf{r}',t') = 0$ for $t < t'$. $\hspace{3cm}$ (7-850)
2. $G(\mathbf{r},t\,;\mathbf{r}',t')$ satisfies the homogeneous diffusion equation except at $t = t'$, $\mathbf{r} = \mathbf{r}'$.
3. $G(\mathbf{r},t\,;\mathbf{r}',t')$ will satisfy homogeneous boundary conditions on $S(V)$.
4. Homogeneous initial condition $G = 0$ at $t = t'$. $\hspace{2cm}$ (7-851)
5. $G(\mathbf{r},t\,;\mathbf{r}',t')$ satisfies the reciprocity relation

$$G(\mathbf{r},t\,;\mathbf{r}',t') = G(\mathbf{r}', -t'\,;\mathbf{r}, -t) \tag{7-852}$$

The Green's function $G(\mathbf{r},t\,;\mathbf{r}',t')$ can be interpreted as the temperature at $\mathbf{r}$ observed at time t due to the injection of a unit of heat at time $t' < t$ by an impulsive heat source located at $\mathbf{r}'$. Since $G = 0$ for $t < t'$, the Green's function gives the temperature only for future times $t > t'$ and thus describes how heat diffuses *away* from its initial position.

The sign reversal in the reciprocity relation (7-852) is required by causality, just as in the case of the wave equation. By reversing signs, the heat injected at $\mathbf{r}$ and $-t$ is observed at $\mathbf{r}'$ and $-t'$ where $-t' > -t$ as causality demands. The proof of the reciprocity relation for the diffusion equation differs somewhat from the corresponding proof for the wave equation. The reason is that the wave equation involves a second derivative with respect to time. Therefore, if $u(\mathbf{r},t)$ satisfies the wave equation, then so does $u(\mathbf{r}, -t)$. On the other hand, the diffusion equation involves a first time derivative and thus does not enjoy the same symmetry in time. In fact, if

$$\nabla^2 T(\mathbf{r},t) = \frac{1}{\alpha}\frac{\partial T(\mathbf{r},t)}{\partial t} \tag{7-853}$$

then

$$\nabla^2 T(\mathbf{r}, -t) = \frac{-1}{\alpha}\frac{\partial T(\mathbf{r}, -t)}{\partial t} \tag{7-854}$$

Because of the temporal asymmetry in the diffusion equation, the two Green's functions $G_+(\mathbf{r},t\,;\mathbf{r}',t')$ and $G_-(\mathbf{r}, -t\,;\mathbf{r}'', -t'')$ must satisfy different equations:

$$\left(\nabla^2 - \frac{1}{\alpha}\frac{\partial}{\partial t}\right) G_+(\mathbf{r},t\,;\mathbf{r}',t') = -\delta(\mathbf{r} - \mathbf{r}')\,\delta(t - t') \tag{7-855}$$

$$\left(\nabla^2 + \frac{1}{\alpha}\frac{\partial}{\partial t}\right) G_-(\mathbf{r}, -t\,;\mathbf{r}'', -t'') = -\delta(\mathbf{r} - \mathbf{r}'')\,\delta(t - t'') \tag{7-856}$$

The remainder of the proof of reciprocity is similar to Eqs. (7-765) to (7-768). An application of Green's theorem,

$$\int_V \{G_+ \nabla^2 G_- - G_- \nabla^2 G_+\} \, dV$$

$$= \int_{S(V)} \left\{ G_+ \frac{\partial G_-}{\partial n} - G_- \frac{\partial G_+}{\partial n} \right\} dS \qquad (7\text{-}857)$$

to Eqs. (7-855) and (7-856) yields

$$\int_V \{G_+ \nabla^2 G_- - G_- \nabla^2 G_+\} \, dV = -G_+(\mathbf{r}'',t;\mathbf{r}',t') \, \delta(t - t'')$$

$$+ G_-(\mathbf{r}',-t;\mathbf{r}'',-t'') \, \delta(t - t')$$

$$+ \left(\frac{-1}{\alpha} \right) \int_V \left\{ G_+ \frac{\partial G_-}{\partial t} + G_- \frac{\partial G_+}{\partial t} \right\} dV = 0 \qquad (7\text{-}858)$$

The surface-integral contribution vanishes because G_+ and G_- both satisfy the same homogeneous boundary conditions on $S(V)$. Both sides of Eq. (7-858) are now integrated with respect to time from $t = -\infty$ to $t = t$ where $t > t'$ and $t > t''$. The result is

$$G_+(\mathbf{r}'',t'';\mathbf{r}',t') - G_-(\mathbf{r}',-t';\mathbf{r}'',-t'')$$

$$= \frac{1}{\alpha} \int_{-\infty}^{t} dt \int_V \frac{\partial}{\partial t} (G_+ G_-) \, dV$$

$$= \frac{1}{\alpha} [G_+(\mathbf{r},t;\mathbf{r}',t')G_-(\mathbf{r},-t;\mathbf{r}'',-t'')] \Big|_{t=-\infty}^{t=t} = 0 \qquad (7\text{-}859)$$

since G_+ vanishes at $t = -\infty$ and G_- vanishes at $t = t$ (because $t > t''$ implies that $-t < -t''$). Thus the reciprocity relation (7-852) is established.

7-30 GENERAL SOLUTION OF THE DIFFUSION EQUATION

The formal integral solution of the inhomogeneous diffusion equation is obtained, as usual, in terms of an appropriate Green's function. Thus consider

$$\left(\nabla'^2 - \frac{1}{\alpha} \frac{\partial}{\partial t'} \right) T(\mathbf{r}',t') = -h(\mathbf{r}',t') \qquad (7\text{-}860)$$

together with the corresponding Green's-function equation,

$$\left(\nabla'^2 + \frac{1}{\alpha} \frac{\partial}{\partial t'} \right) G_-(\mathbf{r}',-t';\mathbf{r},-t) = -\delta(\mathbf{r} - \mathbf{r}') \, \delta(t - t') \qquad (7\text{-}861)$$

where

$$\nabla'^2 = \frac{\partial^2}{\partial x'^2} + \frac{\partial^2}{\partial y'^2} + \frac{\partial^2}{\partial z'^2} \qquad (7\text{-}862)$$

Green's theorem is now applied to Eqs. (7-860) and (7-861), and the result is integrated over dt' to give

$$\int_0^{t+\epsilon} dt' \int_{V'} \{G_- \nabla'^2 T - T \nabla'^2 G_-\} \, dV'$$

$$= \int_0^{t+\epsilon} dt' \int_{S(V')} \left\{ G_- \frac{\partial T}{\partial n'} - T \frac{\partial G_-}{\partial n'} \right\} dS' \qquad (7\text{-}863)$$

From this, we obtain

$$- \int_0^{t+\epsilon} dt' \int_{V'} G(\mathbf{r},t;\mathbf{r}',t') h(\mathbf{r}',t')\, dV' + T(\mathbf{r},t)$$

$$+ \frac{1}{\alpha} \int_{V'} [G(\mathbf{r},t;\mathbf{r}',t')\, T(\mathbf{r}',t')] \Big|_{t'=0}^{t'=t+\epsilon} dV'$$

$$= \int_0^{t+\epsilon} dt' \int_{S(V')} \left\{ G \frac{\partial T}{\partial n'} - T \frac{\partial G}{\partial n'} \right\} dS' \qquad (7\text{-}864)$$

where ϵ is an arbitrarily small positive number, and where the reciprocity relation,

$$G_-(\mathbf{r}',-t';\mathbf{r},-t) = G_-(\mathbf{r},t;\mathbf{r}',t') = G(\mathbf{r},t;\mathbf{r}',t') \qquad (7\text{-}865)$$

has been employed.

By virtue of the causality requirement (7-850),

$$[G(\mathbf{r},t;\mathbf{r}',t')\, T(\mathbf{r}',t')]_{t'=t+\epsilon} = 0 \qquad (7\text{-}866)$$

and this leaves us with

$$T(\mathbf{r},t) = \int_0^{t+\epsilon} dt' \int_{V'} G(\mathbf{r},t;\mathbf{r}',t') h(\mathbf{r}',t')\, dV'$$

$$+ \int_0^{t+\epsilon} dt' \int_{S(V')} \left\{ G \frac{\partial T}{\partial n'} - T \frac{\partial G}{\partial n'} \right\} dS'$$

$$+ \frac{1}{\alpha} \int_{V'} G(\mathbf{r},t;\mathbf{r}',0)\, T(\mathbf{r}',0)\, dV' \qquad (7\text{-}867)$$

Equation (7-867) is the formal solution of the mixed initial- and boundary-value problem for the diffusion equation. Clearly, $T(\mathbf{r},t)$ is determined by contributions from volume heat sources distributed throughout V' with a density $h(\mathbf{r}',t')$, surface heat sources distributed over $S(V')$, and the initial temperature distribution $T(\mathbf{r}',0)$.

7-31 CONSTRUCTION OF THE INFINITE-MEDIUM GREEN'S FUNCTION FOR THE DIFFUSION EQUATION

Suppose we wish to solve

$$\left(\nabla^2 - \frac{1}{\alpha} \frac{\partial}{\partial t} \right) G(\mathbf{r},t;\mathbf{r}',t') = -\delta(\mathbf{r} - \mathbf{r}')\, \delta(t - t') \qquad (7\text{-}868)$$

in an unbounded medium of arbitrary dimension $n < \infty$. We can do so quite generally with the aid of the n-dimensional Fourier transform introduced in Sec. 5-18. Some simplification in the calculations will arise if we first observe that for a homogeneous isotropic medium of infinite extent, the Green's function should depend only on the distance R between the source and the observer and on the time $\tau = t - t'$ which has elapsed since the source began to act. With these remarks,

$$G(\mathbf{r},t;\mathbf{r}',t') = G(R,\tau) \qquad (7\text{-}869)$$

where $R = |\mathbf{r} - \mathbf{r}'|$ and $\tau = t - t'$, and the corresponding equation for $G(R,\tau)$ is

$$\left(\nabla^2 - \frac{1}{\alpha}\frac{\partial}{\partial\tau}\right)G(R,\tau) = -\delta(R)\,\delta(\tau) \tag{7-870}$$

Equation (7-870) is now multiplied on both sides by $e^{-i\mathbf{K}\cdot\mathbf{R}}\,dV_\mathbf{R}$ and then integrated over all coordinate space, noting that

$$dV_\mathbf{R} = dx_1\,dx_2\,\cdots\,dx_n \tag{7-871}$$

$$\mathbf{K}\cdot\mathbf{R} = K_1(x_1 - x_1') + K_2(x_2 - x_2') + \cdots + K_n(x_n - x_n') \tag{7-872}$$

$$R = [(x_1 - x_1')^2 + \cdots + (x_n - x_n')^2]^{1/2} \tag{7-873}$$

Since the x_i's range over all possible values, the value $R = 0$ is included in the range of integration, and consequently

$$\frac{\partial\bar{G}}{\partial\tau} + \alpha K^2\bar{G}(\mathbf{K},\tau) = \alpha\,\delta(\tau) \tag{7-874}$$

provided

$$\lim_{R\to\infty}\,[\nabla G(R,\tau) + i\mathbf{K}G(R,\tau)] = 0 \tag{7-875}$$

In Eq. (7-874) $\bar{G}(\mathbf{K},\tau)$ is the n-dimensional Fourier transform of $G(R,\tau)$ and is defined by

$$\bar{G}(\mathbf{K},\tau) = \int_{\text{All } \mathbf{R} \text{ space}} G(R,\tau)e^{-i\mathbf{K}\cdot\mathbf{R}}dV_R \tag{7-876}$$

The corresponding inversion theorem for $G(R,\tau)$ is

$$G(R,\tau) = \frac{1}{(2\pi)^n}\int_{\text{All } \mathbf{K} \text{ space}} \bar{G}(\mathbf{K},\tau)e^{i\mathbf{K}\cdot\mathbf{R}}dV_K \tag{7-877}$$

Equation (7-874) is a simple ordinary differential equation which we can solve by reduction to quadrature as in Eq. (6-55). One finds

$$\frac{\partial}{\partial\tau}\left(e^{\alpha K^2\tau}\bar{G}\right) = e^{\alpha K^2\tau}\left(\frac{\partial\bar{G}}{\partial\tau} + \alpha K^2\bar{G}\right) = \alpha e^{\alpha K^2\tau}\,\delta(\tau) \tag{7-878}$$

and therefore by integration,

$$e^{\alpha K^2\tau}\bar{G}(K,\tau) - \bar{G}(K,0) = \alpha H(\tau) \tag{7-879}$$

or

$$\bar{G}(K,\tau) = \bar{G}(K,0)e^{-\alpha K^2\tau} + \alpha H(\tau)e^{-\alpha K^2\tau} \tag{7-880}$$

Causality requires that

$$G(R,\tau) = 0 \qquad \tau \le 0 \tag{7-881}$$

and by taking the Fourier transform of Eq. (7-881), we see that

$$\bar{G}(K,\tau) = 0 \qquad \tau \le 0 \tag{7-882}$$

Hence

$$\bar{G}(K,\tau) = \alpha H(\tau)e^{-\alpha K^2\tau} \tag{7-883}$$

is the required solution of Eq. (7-874).

The Fourier inversion theorem (7-877) now yields

$$G(R,\tau) = \frac{\alpha H(\tau)}{(2\pi)^n} \int_{\text{All } \mathbf{K} \text{ space}} e^{i(\mathbf{K}\cdot\mathbf{R})-\alpha K^2\tau} \, dV_K \tag{7-884}$$

where

$$dV_K = dK_1 \, dK_2 \cdots dK_n \tag{7-885}$$

Our remaining efforts are directed toward evaluating Eq. (7-884) in closed form. To do this we notice that

$$G(R,\tau) = \frac{\alpha H(\tau)}{(2\pi)^n} \prod_{i=1}^{n} \int_{-\infty}^{+\infty} e^{i(K_iR_i)-\alpha K_i^2\tau} \, dK_i \tag{7-886}$$

where

$$R_i = x_i - x_i' \tag{7-887}$$

and

$$K^2 = \sum_{i=1}^{n} K_i^2 \tag{7-888}$$

If we can evaluate

$$\int_{-\infty}^{+\infty} e^{(iK_iR_i)-\alpha\tau K_i^2} \, dK_i = 2 \int_0^{\infty} e^{-\alpha\tau K_i^2} \cos(K_iR_i) \, dK_i \tag{7-889}$$

then our problem is essentially solved. We notice that

$$\int_0^{\infty} e^{-\alpha\tau K_i^2} \cos(K_iR_i) \, dK_i = \int_0^{\infty} dK_i \sum_{n=0}^{\infty} \frac{(-K_i^2R_i^2)^n}{(2n)!} e^{-\alpha\tau K_i^2} \tag{7-890}$$

and provided that Eq. (7-890) converges uniformly,

$$\int_0^{\infty} e^{-\alpha\tau K_i^2} \cos(K_iR_i) \, dK_i = \sum_{n=0}^{\infty} \frac{(-R_i^2)^n}{(2n)!} \int_0^{\infty} e^{-\alpha\tau K_i^2} K_i^{2n} \, dK_i \tag{7-891}$$

Therefore we must calculate

$$\int_0^{\infty} e^{-\alpha\tau K_i^2} K_i^{2n} \, dK_i \tag{7-892}$$

For this purpose it is convenient to recall the result of Eqs. (6-398) to (6-402):

$$\int_0^{\infty} e^{-x^2} dx = \frac{\sqrt{\pi}}{2} \tag{7-893}$$

Let $x = \sqrt{\alpha\tau} \, K_i$ in Eq. (7-893) to obtain

$$I = \int_0^{\infty} e^{-\alpha\tau K_i^2} \, dK_i = \frac{1}{2}\sqrt{\frac{\pi}{\alpha\tau}} \tag{7-894}$$

and then differentiate Eq. (7-894) n times with respect to $\alpha\tau$. The result is

$$\frac{d^n I}{d(\alpha\tau)^n} = (-1)^n \int_0^\infty e^{-\alpha\tau K_i^2} K_i^{2n}\, dK_i$$

$$= \tfrac{1}{2}\sqrt{\pi}\left[\left(-\frac{1}{2}\right)\left(-\frac{3}{2}\right)\cdots\left(-\frac{2n-1}{2}\right)(\alpha\tau)^{-\frac{1}{2}-n}\right] \qquad (7\text{-}895)$$

Each time the right side of (Eq. 7-894) is differentiated with respect to $\alpha\tau$, a factor of -1 is obtained; thus

$$\frac{d^n I}{d(\alpha\tau)^n} = (-1)^n \int_0^\infty e^{-\alpha\tau K_i^2} K_i^{2n}\, dK_i$$

$$= \frac{1}{2}\sqrt{\frac{\pi}{\alpha\tau}}(-1)^n \frac{1\cdot 3\cdot 5\,\cdots\,(2n-1)}{2^n(\alpha\tau)^n} \qquad (7\text{-}896)$$

It follows from Eq. (7-896) that

$$\int_0^\infty e^{-\alpha\tau K_i^2} K_i^{2n}\, dK_i = \frac{1}{2}\sqrt{\frac{\pi}{\alpha\tau}}\frac{1\cdot 3\cdot 5\,\cdots\,(2n-1)}{2^n(\alpha\tau)^n} \qquad (7\text{-}897)$$

However,

$$1\cdot 3\cdot 5\,\cdots\,(2n-1) = \frac{1\cdot 2\cdot 3\,\cdots\,n\cdot(n+1)\,\cdots\,2n}{2\cdot 4\cdot 6\,\cdots\,2n} \qquad (7\text{-}898)$$

and

$$2\cdot 4\cdot 6\,\cdots\,2n = 2^n(1\cdot 2\cdot 3\,\cdots\,n) = n!\,2^n \qquad (7\text{-}899)$$

Consequently

$$1\cdot 3\cdot 5\,\cdots\,(2n-1) = \frac{(2n)!}{2^n n!} \qquad (7\text{-}900)$$

and therefore

$$\int_0^\infty e^{-\alpha\tau K_i^2} K_i^{2n}\, dK_i = \frac{1}{2}\sqrt{\frac{\pi}{\alpha\tau}}\frac{(2n)!}{n!(4\alpha\tau)^n} \qquad (7\text{-}901)$$

With this result, Eq. (7-891) gives us

$$\int_0^\infty e^{-\alpha\tau K_i^2}\cos{(K_i R_i)}\, dK_i = \sum_{n=0}^\infty \frac{(-R_i^2)^n}{(2n)!}\left[\frac{1}{2}\sqrt{\frac{\pi}{\alpha\tau}}\frac{(2n)!}{n!(4\alpha\tau)^n}\right] \qquad (7\text{-}902)$$

or

$$\int_0^\infty e^{-\alpha\tau_i K^2}\cos{(K_i R_i)}\, dK_i = \frac{1}{2}\sqrt{\frac{\pi}{\alpha\tau}}\sum_{n=0}^\infty \frac{1}{n!}\left(\frac{-R_i^2}{4\alpha\tau}\right)^n$$

$$= \frac{1}{2}\sqrt{\frac{\pi}{\alpha\tau}}\,e^{-R_i^2/4\alpha\tau} \qquad (7\text{-}903)$$

Thus Eq. (7-889) leads to

$$\int_{-\infty}^{+\infty} e^{i(K_i R_i) - \alpha\tau K_i^2}\, dK_i = \sqrt{\frac{\pi}{\alpha\tau}}\,e^{-R_i^2/4\alpha\tau} \qquad (7\text{-}904)$$

and using this result, the n-dimensional infinite-medium Green's function (7-886) can be computed directly,

$$G(R,\tau) = \frac{\alpha H(\tau)}{(2\pi)^n} \prod_{i=1}^{n} \sqrt{\frac{\pi}{\alpha\tau}} \, e^{-R_i^2/4\alpha\tau}$$

$$= \frac{\alpha H(\tau)}{(2\pi)^n} \left(\frac{\pi}{\alpha\tau}\right)^{n/2} \exp\left(\frac{1}{4}\alpha\tau \sum_{i=1}^{n} R_i^2\right)$$

$$= \alpha H(\tau) \left(\frac{1}{4\pi\alpha\tau}\right)^{n/2} e^{-R^2/4\alpha\tau}$$

$$= \alpha H(\tau) \left(\frac{1}{2\sqrt{\pi\alpha\tau}}\right)^n e^{-R^2/4\alpha\tau} \tag{7-905}$$

where

$$R^2 = \sum_{i=1}^{n} R_i^2 = \sum_{i=1}^{n} (x_i - x_i')^2 \tag{7-906}$$

To summarize, the n-dimensional infinite-medium Green's function for the diffusion equation is simply

$$G(R,\tau) = \alpha H(\tau) \left(\frac{1}{2\sqrt{\pi\alpha\tau}}\right)^n e^{-R^2/4\alpha\tau} \tag{7-907}$$

where $R = |\mathbf{r} - \mathbf{r}'|$ is the distance between the source and the point of observation, and $\tau = t - t'$ measures the time which has elapsed since the source was "turned on."

As an example of the application of Eq. (7-907), consider the problem of determining the temperature distribution in an infinitely long rod when the initial temperature distribution $T(x',0)$ is specified. Suppose that no heat sources are present and that G and its derivatives vanish at the infinitely remote end points of the rod. Then Eqs. (7-867) and (7-907) yield

$$T(x,t) = \frac{H(t)}{2\sqrt{\pi\alpha\tau}} \int_{-\infty}^{+\infty} e^{-(x-x')^2/4\alpha t} T(x',0) \, dx' \tag{7-908}$$

for the solution of our initial-value problem.

7-32 PROBLEMS AND APPLICATIONS

1. Compute the solution of

$$\frac{\partial^2 \phi}{\partial x^2} + \frac{\partial^2 \phi}{\partial y^2} = 0$$

subject to the boundary conditions

$$\begin{aligned}
\phi(x,0) &= \phi(x,b) = 0 & 0 \le x \le a \\
\phi(0,y) &= \phi_0 \text{ (const)} & 0 \le y \le b \\
\phi(a,y) &= 0 & 0 \le y \le b
\end{aligned}$$

and find the limit of this solution as $a \to \infty$.

2. Find the solution of

$$\frac{1}{r}\frac{\partial}{\partial r}\left(r\frac{\partial\phi}{\partial r}\right) + \frac{1}{r^2}\frac{\partial^2\phi}{\partial\theta^2} = 0$$

that satisfies the following boundary conditions on the faces of a wedge:

$$\phi(r,\alpha) = f(r) \qquad 0 \le r < \infty$$
$$\phi(r,-\alpha) = g(r) \qquad 0 \le r < \infty$$
$$\lim_{r\to\infty} \phi(r,\theta) = 0 \qquad -\alpha \le \theta \ge +\alpha$$

Specialize this solution to the case in which the boundary conditions are the same on each wedge face: i.e.,

$$f(r) \equiv g(r) = \begin{cases} \phi_0 & 0 \le r \le a \\ 0 & r > a \end{cases}$$

and then let the wedge angle $\alpha = \pi/2$. Compare your result with Eq. (7-181).

3. Consider an infinitely long grounded rectangular cylinder whose generators lie along the z axis. Let its rectangular faces have co-ordinates $x = 0$, $x = a$, $y = 0$, and $y = b$. A point charge is placed at $x = x'$, $y = y'$, $z = z'$ inside the cylinder. Compute the resulting potential inside the cylinder.

4. Repeat the calculation in Prob. 3 for the case of an infinitely long grounded *circular* cylinder.

5. A conducting sphere of radius $r = a$ centered at $r = 0$ is embedded in a homogeneous, isotropic dielectric of inductive capacity ϵ_2. A point charge q is placed at $z = z' > a$ on the z axis. Compute the electric potential everywhere outside the sphere, and calculate the surface charge density induced on the sphere.

6. Suppose we make the sphere in Prob. 5 a dielectric sphere with inductive capacity ϵ_1. Compute the electric potential inside and outside this dielectric sphere.

7. Suppose the point source q in Prob. 6 is allowed to recede to infinity. As a result, the dielectric sphere of inductive capacity ϵ_1 finds itself embedded in a medium of inductive capacity ϵ_2 pervaded by a uniform constant electric field $\mathbf{E}_0$ directed, say, along the z axis. Calculate the potentials and the electric fields inside and outside the sphere.

8. Compute the magnetic fields inside and outside an infinitely long straight wire of radius a and inductive capacity μ_1, given that it carries a current I, and that it is embedded in an external medium of inductive capacity μ_2 containing a magnetic field $\mathbf{B}_0$ directed transverse to the axis of the wire.

9. Calculate the time-dependent Green's function for the one-dimensional wave equation,

$$\left(\frac{\partial^2}{\partial x^2} - \frac{1}{c^2}\frac{\partial^2}{\partial t^2}\right) G(x,t,x',t') = -\delta(x - x')\,\delta(t - t')$$

assuming that G and $\partial G/\partial t$ satisfy the causality condition,

$$G = 0 \qquad t \leq t'$$

$$\frac{\partial G}{\partial t} = 0 \qquad t \leq t'$$

10. Prove the reciprocity relation

$$G(x,t;x',t') = G(x',-t';x,-t)$$

for the Green's function obtained in Prob. 9.

11. Obtain the formal integral solution of the mixed initial- and boundary-value problem for

$$\frac{\partial^2 u}{\partial x^2} - \frac{1}{c^2}\frac{\partial^2 u}{\partial t^2} = -\frac{1}{\rho c^2} f(x,t)$$

by using the Green's function found in Prob. 9 with an appropriate Green's theorem.

12. Solve the Cauchy initial-value problem for the wave equation,

$$\frac{\partial^2 u}{\partial x^2} - \frac{1}{c^2}\frac{\partial^2 u}{\partial t^2} = 0$$

$$u(x,0) = F(x)$$

$$\frac{\partial u}{\partial t}(x,0) = G(x)$$

in a one-dimensional medium of infinite extent. Use the results of Probs. 9 and 11 to obtain your answer, and then compare that answer with Eq. (7-460).

13. Consider the equation

$$(\nabla^2 + k^2)u(\mathbf{r}) = -F(\mathbf{r})u(\mathbf{r}) \qquad\qquad (A)$$

in a volume V, and suppose that its solutions satisfy specified boundary conditions on the surface $S(V)$ enclosing V. The values of k^2 for which this equation can be solved, subject to the specified boundary conditions on u, are called the "eigenvalues" of the equation. These are denoted by $k_n{}^2$, and for each such k_n there is a corresponding eigenfunction $u_n(\mathbf{r})$. The spectrum of eigenvalues k_n may be a discrete set, or a continuum, or both, and the eigenfunctions must satisfy

$$(\nabla^2 + k_n{}^2)u_n(\mathbf{r}) = -F(\mathbf{r})u_n(\mathbf{r})$$

Assume that the eigenfunctions $u_n(\mathbf{r})$ are normalized to unity so that

$$\int_V u_n^*(\mathbf{r})u_n(\mathbf{r})\,dV = 1$$

where $u_n^*(\mathbf{r})$ is the complex conjugate of $u_n(\mathbf{r})$.
Prove that

$$\int_V u_n^*(\mathbf{r})u_m(\mathbf{r})\,dV = \delta_{nm}$$

when n and m are discrete parameters, and prove that

$$\int_V u_n^*(\mathbf{r})u_m(\mathbf{r})\,dV = \delta(n - m)$$

when n and m vary continuously.

14. Let us assume that the eigenfunctions $u_n(\mathbf{r})$, defined in Prob. 13, form a complete set. The Green's function for

$$(\nabla^2 + k^2)u(\mathbf{r}) = -F(\mathbf{r})u(\mathbf{r})$$

is defined as the solution of

$$(\nabla^2 + k^2)G(\mathbf{r},\mathbf{r}') = -F(\mathbf{r})G(\mathbf{r},\mathbf{r}') - \delta(\mathbf{r} - \mathbf{r}') \qquad (B)$$

subject to the conditions that:

(a) $k^2 \neq k_n^2$ for any value of n; i.e., k must not be any one of the eigenvalues k_n.

(b) $G(\mathbf{r},\mathbf{r}')$ must satisfy the same boundary conditions on $S(V)$ as the eigenfunctions $u_n(\mathbf{r})$.

Show that the Green's function $G(\mathbf{r},\mathbf{r}')$ can be expanded in terms of the eigenfunctions $u_n(\mathbf{r})$ as

$$G(\mathbf{r},\mathbf{r}') = \sum_{n=1}^{\infty} \frac{u_n^*(\mathbf{r}')u_n(\mathbf{r})}{k_n^2 - k^2} \qquad (C)$$

provided that the spectrum of eigenvalues $\{k_n\}$ forms a countably infinite set. When the spectrum is continuous, show that

$$G(\mathbf{r},\mathbf{r}') = \int_{V_K} \frac{u^*(\mathbf{r}',\mathbf{K})u(\mathbf{r},\mathbf{K})}{K^2 - k^2}\,dV_K \qquad (D)$$

The volume of integrations V_K in Eq. (D) is the three-dimensional region composed of all the points $K = |\mathbf{K}|$ which satisfy

$$(\nabla^2 + K^2)u(\mathbf{r},\mathbf{K}) = -F(\mathbf{r})u(\mathbf{r},\mathbf{K}) \qquad (E)$$

and which therefore must be eigenvalues of Eq. (A). The point k^2 is specifically excluded from V_K.

15. Consider the three-dimensional Helmholtz equation in an unbounded domain, using the eigenvalue-eigenfunction point of view. For this purpose, let $F(\mathbf{r}) \equiv 0$ in Eq. (A). Show that the normalized eigenfunctions are

$$u(\mathbf{r},\mathbf{K}) = \frac{1}{(2\pi)^{3/2}} e^{i\mathbf{K}\cdot\mathbf{r}}$$

$$u^*(\mathbf{r}',\mathbf{K}) = \frac{1}{(2\pi)^{3/2}} e^{-i\mathbf{K}\cdot\mathbf{r}}$$

and verify that the solution of Eq. (B) as given by Eq. (D) is the same as the result obtained in Eq. (7-630).

16. Use Eq. (C) to solve

$$\nabla^2 G(\mathbf{r},\mathbf{r}') = -\delta(\mathbf{r} - \mathbf{r}')$$

subject to the boundary condition that G must vanish on the six faces of a rectangular box whose sides are at $x = y = z = 0$, and $x = a, y = b, z = c$.

17. Solve

$$(\nabla^2 - k^2)G(\mathbf{r}|\mathbf{r}') = -\delta(\mathbf{r} - \mathbf{r}')$$

in plane polar coordinates, and use your results to derive the addition theorem for hyperbolic Bessel functions,

$$K_0(kR) = I_0(kr_<)K_0(kr_>) + 2 \sum_{n=1}^{\infty} I_n(kr_<)K_n(kr_>) \cos n(\theta - \theta')$$

where

$$R^2 = r_>{}^2 + r_<{}^2 - 2r_>r_< \cos(\theta - \theta')$$

18. Prove that

$$K_0\left(\frac{sR}{c}\right) = \int_0^\infty \frac{H(t - R/c)}{\sqrt{t^2 - R^2/c^2}} e^{-st} \, dt$$

and use this result to solve

$$\left(\nabla^2 - \frac{1}{c^2}\frac{\partial^2}{\partial t^2}\right) G(\mathbf{r},t\,;\mathbf{r}',t') = -\delta(\mathbf{r} - \mathbf{r}')\,\delta(t - t')$$

in an unbounded plane region, assuming that

$$G = 0 \qquad t \le t'$$

$$\frac{\partial G}{\partial t} = 0 \qquad t \le t'$$

19. Show that the infinite-medium Green's function g which satisfies

$$\left(c_1{}^2 \frac{\partial^2}{\partial x^2} + c_2{}^2 \frac{\partial^2}{\partial y^2} - \frac{\partial^2}{\partial t^2}\right) g(x,y,t) = -\delta(t)\,\delta(x)\,\delta(y)$$

$$g(x,y,0) = 0$$

$$\frac{\partial g}{\partial t}(x,y,0) = 0$$

is given by

$$g(x,y,t) = \frac{1}{2\pi c_2{}^2} \frac{H[t - (R/c_1)(1 - \epsilon^2 \cos^2 \theta)]}{\sqrt{t^2 - (R^2/c_1{}^2)(1 - \epsilon^2 \cos^2 \theta)}}$$

where

$$R^2 = x^2 + y^2$$

$$x = y \tan \theta$$

and where c_1 and c_2 are constants such that

$$\epsilon = \left(1 - \frac{c_1{}^2}{c_2{}^2}\right)^{1/2}$$

Interpret this problem physically.

20. Solve the following boundary-value problem in the half space $-\infty < x < +\infty$; $y \ge 0$:

$$\frac{\partial^2 u}{\partial x^2} + \frac{\partial^2 u}{\partial y^2} + k^2 u = 0$$

$$u(x,0) = f(x) \qquad -\infty < x < +\infty$$

21. Repeat the calculation in Prob. 20, this time using the boundary condition

$$\frac{\partial u(x,0)}{\partial y} = g(x) \qquad -\infty < x < +\infty$$

22. Consider a time-harmonic plane wave $u_i = e^{-ikr \cos \theta}$ incident on a circular cylinder $r = a$, where r and θ are two-dimensional polar coordinates such that $0 \le \theta < 2\pi$. The scattered wave u_s must satisfy

$$(\nabla^2 + k^2)u_s = 0 \qquad r \ge a$$

and the boundary condition

$$u_s(a,\theta) = -u_i(a,\theta) = -e^{-ika \cos \theta} \text{ on } r = a$$

Show that

$$u_s(r,\theta) = -\sum_{n=-\infty}^{+\infty} \frac{(-i)^n J_n(ka)}{H_n^{(2)}(ka)} H_n^{(2)}(kr)e^{in\theta}$$

23. Repeat the calculation in Prob. 22, assuming that the appropriate boundary condition on $r = a$ is

$$\left(\frac{\partial u_s}{\partial r}\right)_{r=a} = -\left(\frac{\partial u_i}{\partial r}\right)_{r=a}$$

24. Consider a time-harmonic plane wave $u_i = e^{ikr \cos \theta}$ incident on a sphere of radius $r = a$, where (r,θ,ϕ) are spherical polar coordinates. The scattered wave u_s must satisfy

$$(\nabla^2 + k^2)u_s = 0 \qquad r \ge a$$

and the boundary condition

$$u_s(a,\theta,\phi) = -u_i(a,\theta,\phi) = e^{ika \cos \theta}$$

on the surface of the sphere $r = a$. Show that

$$u_s(r,\theta,\phi) = -\sum_{n=0}^{\infty} (2n+1)i^n P_n(\cos \theta) \frac{j_n(ka)}{h_n^{(1)}(ka)} h_n^{(1)}(kr)$$

25. Repeat the calculation in Prob. 24 for the boundary condition

$$\left(\frac{\partial u_s}{\partial r}\right)_{r=a} = -\left(\frac{\partial u_i}{\partial r}\right)_{r=a}$$

26. Consider the two-dimensional Helmholtz equation in plane polar coordinates (r,θ):

$$(\nabla^2 - k^2)G(r,\theta;r_1,\theta_1) = \frac{-\delta(r-r_1)}{r} \delta(\theta - \theta_1)$$

Show that the solution of this equation in a two-dimensional wedge-shaped region $\{0 \le r < \infty, \ 0 \le \theta \le \alpha\}$ is

$$G = \frac{1}{\alpha} \sum_{n=0}^{\infty} K_{\frac{n\pi}{\alpha}}(kr_>)I_{\frac{n\pi}{\alpha}}(kr_<) \left\{ \cos \frac{n\pi}{\alpha}(\theta - \theta_1) - \cos \frac{n\pi}{\alpha}(\theta + \theta_1) \right\}$$

provided that

$$G(r,0;r_1,\theta_1) = G(r,\alpha;r_1,\theta_1) = 0 \qquad 0 \le r < \infty$$

27. Repeat the calculations in Prob. 26, using the boundary conditions

$$\left(\frac{\partial G}{\partial \theta}\right)_{\theta=0} = \left(\frac{\partial G}{\partial \theta}\right)_{\theta=\alpha} = 0 \qquad 0 \le r < \infty$$

28. Consider the equation

$$(\nabla^2 + k^2)u(x,y,z) = 0$$

and assume that as $k \to \infty$,

$$u \sim e^{ik\psi(x,y,z)} \sum_{n=0}^{\infty} \frac{V_n(x,y,z)}{(ik)^n}$$

where $(\nabla\psi)^2 = 1$. Let $x = x(s)$, $y = y(s)$, $z = z(s)$ be the parametric equation of a spatial curve or ray which intersects $\psi(x,y,z) = $ constant in the normal direction, i.e., along $\nabla\psi$. Show that in terms of the arc length s measured along a ray,

$$V_n(s) = V_n(s_0)e^{-\frac{1}{2}\int_{s_0}^{s}\nabla^2\psi\,ds'} - \frac{1}{2}\int_{s_0}^{s} e^{-\frac{1}{2}\int_{\tau}^{s}\nabla^2\psi\,ds'}\nabla^2 V_{n-1}(\tau)\,d\tau$$

29. Consider two fluid half spaces, 1 and 2, in contact with each other along the plane $z = 0$. The generation of an acoustic pulse by a point source at $r = 0$, $z = h$ in fluid 1 leads to the following boundary-value problem:

Solve

$$(\nabla^2 - k_1^2)u_1 = \frac{-\delta(r)\,\delta(z - h)}{2\pi r}$$

$$(\nabla^2 - k_2^2)u_2 = 0$$

subject to the boundary conditions

$$\rho_1 u_1 = \rho_2 u_2 \qquad z = 0$$

$$\left(\frac{\partial u_1}{\partial z}\right)_{z=0} = \left(\frac{\partial u_2}{\partial z}\right)_{z=0}$$

$$\lim_{|z|\to\infty} \binom{u_1}{u_2} = 0 \qquad 0 < r < \infty$$

Show that the solution to this problem is given by

$$u_1 = \frac{1}{2\pi}\int_0^\infty \left\{\frac{\nu_1\delta_1 \cosh \nu_1 z + \nu_2 \sinh \nu_1 z}{\nu_1(\nu_2 + \nu_1\delta_1)}\right\} e^{-\nu_1 h} J_0(kr)k\,dk \qquad 0 \le z \le h$$

$$u_1 = \frac{1}{2\pi}\int_0^\infty \left\{\frac{\nu_1\delta_1 \cosh \nu_1 h + \nu_2 \sinh \nu_1 h}{\nu_1(\nu_2 + \nu_1\delta_1)}\right\} e^{-\nu_1 z} J_0(kr)k\,dk \qquad z \ge h$$

$$u_2 = \frac{1}{2\pi}\int_0^\infty \frac{e^{\nu_2 z - \nu_1 h}}{\nu_1\delta_1 + \nu_2} J_0(kr)k\,dk \qquad z \le 0$$

where

$$\delta_1 = \rho_2/\rho_1$$

$$\nu_1 = \sqrt{k^2 - k_1^2}$$

$$\nu_2 = \sqrt{k^2 - k_2^2}$$

$$\text{Re}\,(\nu_1) \ge 0$$

$$\text{Re}\,(\nu_2) \ge 0$$

30. Consider the temperature $T(x,t)$ in a semi-infinite bar $0 < x < \infty$, one end of which is subjected to a sinusoidal temperature variation $T(0,t) = T_0 \cos \omega t$. Show that the temperature distribution in this bar is given by

$$T(x,t) = T_0 e^{-x\sqrt{\omega/2\alpha}} \cos\left(\omega t - x\sqrt{\frac{\omega}{2\alpha}}\right)$$

The solution seems to be a damped temperature wave whose speed of propagation becomes infinite as ω increases indefinitely. Can you explain this?

31. Solve

$$\frac{\partial^2 T}{\partial x^2} = \frac{1}{\alpha}\frac{\partial T}{\partial t}$$

subject to the boundary conditions

$$T(0,t) = 0 \qquad \text{for all } t$$

$$\left(\frac{\partial T}{\partial x}\right)_{x=a} = 0 \qquad \text{for all } t$$

given the initial condition

$$T(x,0) = T_0\left(\frac{x}{a}\right) \qquad 0 \le x \le a$$

32. Solve the diffusion equation,

$$\nabla^2 T = \frac{1}{\alpha}\frac{\partial T}{\partial t}$$

in plane polar coordinates (r,θ) subject to the wedge boundary conditions

$$T(r,0,t) = 0 \qquad r > 0,\, t > 0$$

$$T(r,\alpha,t) = T_0 \qquad r > 0,\, t > 0$$

and the initial condition

$$T(r,\theta,0) = 0 \qquad 0 < \theta < \alpha,\, r > 0$$

33. Solve

$$\frac{\partial^2 T}{\partial x^2} = \frac{1}{\alpha}\frac{\partial T}{\partial t}$$

in the half space $x > 0$, given the boundary condition

$$T = T_0 \text{ at } x = 0 \qquad t > 0$$

and the initial condition

$$T = 0 \text{ at } t = 0 \qquad x > 0$$

34. Solve

$$(\nabla^2 - k)G(\mathbf{r},\mathbf{r}') = -\delta(\mathbf{r} - \mathbf{r}')$$

in cylindrical coordinates (r,θ,z) for an unbounded medium.

35. Solve

$$(\nabla^2 - k)G(\mathbf{r},\mathbf{r}') = -\delta(\mathbf{r} - \mathbf{r}')$$

in spherical coordinates (r,θ,ϕ) for an unbounded medium.

<h1 style="text-align:right">references</h1>

chapters 1 and 3—**vector algebra and vector calculus**

BRAND, L., "Vector Analysis," 3d printing, Wiley, New York, 1961.

CHISHOLM, J., and R. MORRIS, "Mathematical Methods in Physics," Chap. 9, Saunders, Philadelphia, 1965.

HAY, G. E., "Vector and Tensor Analysis," Dover, New York, 1953.

KREYSZIG, E., "Advanced Engineering Mathematics," Chap. 5, Wiley, New York, 1962.

LASS, H., "Vector and Tensor Analysis," McGraw-Hill, New York, 1950.

MCQUISTAN, R. B., "Scalar and Vector Fields," Wiley, New York, 1965.

PROTTER, M., and C. MORREY, "Modern Mathematical Analysis," Chap. 7, Addison-Wesley, Reading, Mass., 1964.

SOKOLNIKOFF, I. S., and R. M. REDHEFFER, "Mathematics of Physics and Modern Engineering," Chaps. 4 and 5, McGraw-Hill, New York, 1958.

chapter 2—**matrix and tensor algebra**

BODEWIG, E., "Matrix Calculus," 2d ed., North Holland, Amsterdam, 1959.

FRAZER, R. A., W. J. DUNCAN, and A. R. COLLAR, "Elementary Matrices," Cambridge University Press, London, 1938.

GANTMACHER, F. R., "The Theory of Matrices," 2 vols., Chelsea, New York, 1959.

MARGENAU, H., and G. MURPHY, "The Mathematics of Physics and Chemistry," Chaps. 4, 5, and 10, 2d ed., Vol. I, Van Nostrand, Princeton, N. J. 1956.

PERLIS, S., "Theory of Matrices," Addison-Wesley, Reading, Mass., 1952.

SOKOLNIKOFF, I. S., "Tensor Analysis," Wiley, New York, 1951.

chapter 4—**functions of a complex variable**

AHLFORS, L. V., "Complex Analysis," 2d ed., McGraw-Hill, New York, 1966.

CHURCHILL, R. V., "Complex Variables and Applications," 2d ed., McGraw-Hill, New York, 1960.

COPSON, E. T., "Theory of Functions of a Complex Variable," Oxford University Press, London, 1935.

HILLE, E., "Analytic Function Theory," 2 vols., Ginn, Boston, 1959, 1962.

KNOPP, K., "Theory of Functions," 2 vols., Dover, New York, 1945.

NEHARI, Z., "Conformal Mapping," McGraw-Hill, New York, 1952.

SPRINGER, G., "Introduction to Riemann Surfaces," Addison-Wesley, Reading, Mass., 1957.

TITCHMARSH, E. C., "The Theory of Functions," 2d ed., Oxford University Press, London, 1939.

WHITTAKER, E. T., and G. N. WATSON, "A Course in Modern Analysis," Chaps. 1–9, Cambridge University Press, London, 1940.

chapter 5—integral transforms

CARSLAW, H. S., "Introduction to the Theory of Fourier's Series and Integrals," 3d ed., Macmillan, London, 1930.

CHURCHILL, R. V., "Fourier Series and Boundary Value Problems," 2d ed., McGraw-Hill, New York, 1963.

IRVING, J., and N. MULLINEUX, "Mathematics in Physics and Engineering," Chap. X, Academic Press, New York, 1959.

MATHEWS, J., and R. WALKER, "Mathematical Methods of Physics," Chap. 4, Benjamin, New York, 1964.

SNEDDON, I. N., "Fourier Transforms," McGraw-Hill, New York, 1951.

TITCHMARSH, E. C., "Introduction to the Fourier Integral," Oxford University Press, London, 1948.

TRANTER, C. J., "Integral Transforms in Mathematical Physics," 2d ed., Methuen, London, 1956.

chapter 6—linear differential equations

AGNEW, R. P., "Differential Equations," 2d ed., McGraw-Hill, New York, 1960.

CODDINGTON, E. A., and N. LEVINSON, "Theory of Ordinary Differential Equations," McGraw-Hill, New York, 1955.

GRAY, A., G. B. MATHEWS, and T. M. MACROBERT, "Treatise on Bessel Functions," Macmillan, London, 1922.

HOBSON, E. W., "Theory of Spherical and Ellipsoidal Harmonics," Cambridge University Press, London, 1931.

JOHNSON, D., and J. R. JOHNSON, "Mathematical Methods in Engineering and Physics," Ronald, New York, 1965.

MACROBERT, T. M., "Spherical Harmonics," Methuen, London, 1927; Dover, New York, 1948.

MORRIS, M., and O. E. BROWN, "Differential Equations," 3d ed., Prentice-Hall, Englewood Cliffs, N. J., 1952.

ROSS, S., "Differential Equations," Blaisdell, New York, 1964.

WATSON, G. N., "Treatise on the Theory of Bessel Functions," Cambridge University Press, London, 1944.

chapter 7—**partial differential equations**

COURANT, R., and D. HILBERT, "Methods of Mathematical Physics," Vol. II, Interscience, New York, 1962.

DUFF, G. F. D., "Partial Differential Equations," Toronto University Press, Toronto, 1956.

GARABEDIAN, P. R., "Partial Differential Equations," Wiley, New York, 1964.

JEFFREYS, H., and B. JEFFREYS, "Methods of Mathematical Physics," 3d ed. Cambridge University Press, New York, 1956.

LANCZOS, C., "Linear Differential Operators," Van Nostrand, Princeton, N. J., 1961.

MORSE, P. M., and H. FESHBACK, "Methods of Theoretical Physics," Parts I and II, McGraw-Hill, New York, 1953.

PAGE, C. H., "Physical Mathematics," Van Nostrand, Princeton, N. J., 1955.

SAGAN, H., "Boundary and Eigenvalue Problems in Mathematical Physics," Wiley, New York, 1961.

SNEDDON, I. N., "Elements of Partial Differential Equations," McGraw-Hill, New York, 1957.

SOMMERFELD, A., "Partial Differential Equations in Physics," Academic Press, New York, 1949.

infinite series

There are two general types of infinite series which are frequently encountered in applications: an infinite sum of terms, each of which is a real or complex number, and an infinite sum of terms, each of which is a function of a real or complex variable.

There are two distinct problems connected with such infinite series. The first problem is to determine whether or not a given infinite series converges. When the infinite series is known to converge, then the second problem is to determine the sum to which it converges. This sum can be either a number or a function, depending on whether we are adding up numbers or functions.

Consider an infinite series of real numbers:

$$a_1 + a_2 + \cdots + a_n + \cdots = \sum_{n=1}^{\infty} a_n \tag{A-1}$$

There are many different tests for convergence of series such as Eq. (A-1). Some of these tests provide sufficient conditions for convergence, and some provide only necessary conditions for convergence. The student is reminded that a sufficient condition guarantees convergence while a necessary condition does not. On the other hand, failure of a necessary condition to hold *does* guarantee that the series diverges.

For reference purposes we shall give without proofs a number of different convergence tests. The proofs may be found in most advanced calculus textbooks.

Comparison test for series of positive terms

If, for $n > m$, we have $0 < a_n < b_n$, the convergence of Σa_n follows from that of Σb_n. The divergence of Σb_n follows from that of Σa_n.

The nth-term test

A necessary condition for the convergence of Σa_n is that

$$\lim_{n \to \infty} a_n = 0$$

Convergence of alternating series

If $a_n > 0$ constantly decreases as n increases with $\lim_{n \to \infty} a_n = 0$, then the series

$$a_0 - a_1 + a_2 - \cdots = \Sigma (-1)^n a_n$$

converges. Furthermore the sum S of the alternating series satisfies the inequalities

$$0 < S < a_0$$

Absolute convergence of series

The series Σa_n is convergent if the series $\Sigma |a_n|$ is convergent. However, the convergence of Σa_n does not necessarily imply the convergence of $\Sigma |a_n|$, except when each a_n is non-negative.

If Σa_n converges when $\Sigma |a_n|$ diverges, then we call Σa_n a "conditionally convergent" series. If $\Sigma |a_n|$ converges, then we say that Σa_n is "absolutely convergent."

Cauchy's nth-root test

Let

$$\lim_{n \to \infty} |\sqrt[n]{a_n}| = k$$

If $k < 1$, Σa_n converges absolutely; if $k > 1$, Σa_n diverges; if $k = 1$, the test gives no information.

D'Alembert ratio test

If for sufficiently large n,

$$\left| \frac{a_{n+1}}{a_n} \right| < k < 1$$

then Σa_n converges absolutely; if for sufficiently large n,

$$\left| \frac{a_{n+1}}{a_n} \right| > h > 1$$

then Σa_n diverges; if for sufficiently large n,

$$\left| \frac{a_{n+1}}{a_n} \right| = 1$$

then the test gives no information.

Maclaurin's integral test for positive real series

If the real-valued function $f(x)$ is positive for $x \geq a$ and decreases steadily to zero as x becomes infinite, then

$$\sum_{k=0}^{\infty} f(a + k)$$

is convergent if

$$\lim_{x \to \infty} \int_a^x f(s)\, ds$$

approaches a finite limit given by

$$\int_a^\infty f(s)\, ds$$

and is divergent if

$$\int_a^\infty f(s)\, ds = \infty$$

Riemann's theorem on conditionally convergent series

A conditionally convergent series may be made to converge to any given real number by suitably rearranging the order of the terms.

REMARK: This property depends entirely on the conditional convergence of the series. It can be shown that the sum of an absolutely convergent series is independent of the order of its terms.

Uniform convergence

Let the series of functions

$$\sum_{n=1}^\infty U_n(x) \tag{A-2}$$

converge for each value of x in the interval

$$a \le x \le b$$

The sum of (A-2) defines a function of x,

$$S(x) = \sum_{n=1}^\infty U_n(x) \tag{A-3}$$

The nth partial sum of $\Sigma U_n(x)$ is given by

$$S_n(x) = \sum_{k=1}^n U_k(x) \tag{A-4}$$

The remainder after n terms is given by

$$r_n(x) = S(x) - S_n(x) = \sum_{k=n+1}^\infty U_n(x) \tag{A-5}$$

and r_n is also an infinite series. Since the series converges to $S(x)$,

$$\lim_{n \to \infty} r_n(x) = 0 \tag{A-6}$$

In other words, given any $\epsilon > 0$, there exists an N such that for all $n > N$,

$$|r_n(x)| < \epsilon \tag{A-7}$$

In general, N depends on both ϵ and x, so that

$$N = N(\epsilon, x) \tag{A-8}$$

When N is independent of x for all $a \leq x \leq b$, then the infinite series $\sum\limits_{n=1}^{\infty} U_n(x)$ is said to be uniformly convergent in the interval $a \leq x \leq b$.

In particular:

The convergent series $\sum\limits_{n=1}^{\infty} U_n(x)$ is uniformly convergent in the interval $a \leq x \leq b$, if for each $\epsilon > 0$ there is a number N, *independent of* x, such that the remainder $r_n(x)$ satisfies

$$|r_n(x)| < \epsilon$$

for all $n > N$.

Tests for uniform convergence

The previous tests for convergence become tests for uniform convergence provided their conditions are satisfied uniformly, that is, independently of x. For example, the root test takes the form: If there is a number k *independent of* x such that

$$\lim_{n \to \infty} |\sqrt[n]{U_n(x)}| \leq k < 1$$

then $\Sigma U_n(x)$ converges uniformly.

Similarly, the comparison test for uniform convergence becomes: If $\Sigma w_n(x)$ is a uniformly convergent series such that

$$|U_n(x)| \leq w_n(x)$$

then $\Sigma U_n(x)$ converges uniformly (and absolutely). The simplest example of a uniformly convergent series $\Sigma w_n(x)$ is a convergent series of constants. If we use such a series in the comparison test, the resulting test is known as the:

Weierstrass M test

If there is a convergent series of constants ΣM_n such that

$$|U_n(x)| \leq M_n$$

for all $a \leq x \leq b$, then the series $\Sigma U_n(x)$ is uniformly (and absolutely) convergent on $a \leq x \leq b$. The student should note that a series may converge uniformly but not absolutely or vice versa.

Uniform convergence is very important in practical applications because of the following three properties of uniformly convergent series.

1. Let $\Sigma U_k(x)$ be an infinite series, each term of which is a continuous function of x for $a \leq x \leq b$. If the series is uniformly convergent in $a \leq x \leq b$, then the sum of the series is also a continuous function of x for $a \leq x \leq b$.
2. A uniformly convergent infinite series of continuous functions may be integrated term by term within the interval of uniform convergence. The sum of the integrals then converges uniformly to the integral of the sum function of the original series.

3. If $\Sigma U_n(x)$ is an infinite series of differentiable functions which converge to $S(x)$ for $a \leq x \leq b$, then when the series $\Sigma U_n'(x)$ converges uniformly for $a \leq x \leq b$, it converges to $S'(x)$.

PROBLEMS

1. For what range of α does the series

$$\sum_{k=1}^{\infty} \frac{1}{k^\alpha}$$

    (a) Converge?
    (b) Diverge?

2. For what range of α does the series

$$\sum_{k=1}^{\infty} \frac{1}{k \log^\alpha k}$$

    (a) Converge?
    (b) Diverge?

3. Let the infinite decimal $a \cdot a_1 a_2 \cdots a_n \cdots$ be written in the form of an infinite series,

$$a + \frac{a_1}{10} + \frac{a_2}{10^2} + \cdots + \frac{a_n}{10^n} + \cdots$$

Prove that this series converges.

4. Consider the power series:

$$\sum_{n=1}^{\infty} a_n z^n$$

Suppose that

$$\lim_{n \to \infty} |\sqrt[n]{a_n}| = \frac{1}{R}$$

Find the domain of absolute convergence of this power series and the domain of divergence as well.

5. For what domain of z values does the infinite series

$$\sum_{n=1}^{\infty} \frac{z^n}{n!}$$

converge?

6. Let x be a real variable. For what range of x do the series

$$\sum_{n=1}^{\infty} \frac{\sin nx}{n} \quad \text{and} \quad \sum_{n=1}^{\infty} \frac{\cos nx}{n}$$

converge?

7. Discuss the conditions for uniform convergence of the following series:

(a) $\displaystyle\sum_{n=1}^{\infty} x^n$

(b) $\displaystyle\sum_{n=1}^{\infty} \frac{x^n}{n^3}$

(c) $\displaystyle\sum_{n=1}^{\infty} nx^n$

(d) $\displaystyle\sum_{n=1}^{\infty} \frac{\sin nx}{1 + n^2}$

power-series solution of differential equations

In Chap. 6 we saw that many differential equations of interest in physics take the form

$$\frac{d^2y}{dx^2} + p(x)\frac{dy}{dx} + q(x)y = 0 \tag{B-1}$$

and we learned that, given only one solution of Eq. (B-1), we can obtain the general solution of the inhomogeneous form of (B-1) with the aid of Abel's formula for the Wronskian. The problem is really to obtain the first solution of (B-1). This can usually be done by representing a solution of (B-1) as a Taylor series in x. Instead of considering the general theory of such series solutions of (B-1), we shall confine ourselves to the discussion of special cases.

Legendre's equation

We recall that Legendre's equation is

$$(1 - x^2)y'' - 2xy' + n(n + 1)y = 0 \tag{B-2}$$

and we seek a power-series solution of Eq. (B-2) which is of the form

$$y = \sum_{k=0}^{\infty} a_k x^{k+m} \tag{B-3}$$

We must determine all the coefficients a_k as well as the number m, which is the lowest power of x appearing in the series (B-3). To do these things, we *assume* that Eq. (B-3) is uniformly convergent for some range of x. We then substitute (B-3) into Eq. (B-2) and differentiate term by term, assuming that x is in the convergent range. Needless to say, when we have found all our a_k's, we shall still find it necessary to verify that (B-3) really does converge uniformly for some range of x.

Substituting Eq. (B-3) into (B-2),

$$(1 - x^2) \sum_{k}^{\infty} a_k(k + m)(k + m - 1)x^{k+m-2}$$

$$- 2x \sum_{k}^{\infty} a_k(k + m)x^{k+m-1} + n(n + 1) \sum_{k}^{\infty} a_k x^{k+m} = 0 \tag{B-4}$$

and collecting like powers of x, this becomes

$$\sum_{k}^{\infty} a_k(k + m)(k + m - 1)x^{k+m-2}$$

$$- \sum_{k}^{\infty} a_k[(k + m)(k + m - 1) + 2(k + m)$$

$$- n(n + 1)]x^{k+m} = 0 \qquad \text{(B-5)}$$

Notice that we have not yet indicated the beginning value of the summation index k for the sums in Eqs. (B-4) and (B-5). If we agree that this range is to run from $k = 0$ to $k = \infty$, then we can determine the possible values of the parameter m by means of the following argument. If k can assume only non-negative integer values, then the lowest power of x appearing in Eq. (B-5) is x^{m-2}. The term involving x^{m-2} occurs in the first sum in (B-5), and this term is

$$a_0 m(m - 1)x^{m-2} \qquad \text{(B-6)}$$

In order for Eq. (B-5) to hold for all values of x in some interval, the coefficient of each and every power of x in (B-5) must vanish. Consequently, the coefficient of x^{m-2} vanishes, and this requires

$$a_0 m(m - 1) = 0 \qquad \text{(B-7)}$$

which is called the indicial equation. We can assume that $a_0 \neq 0$ for the following reason. If Eq. (B-3) is not identically zero, then it must have a first term which is not zero for $x \neq 0$. We shall always call this first term $a_0 x^m$. Equation (B-7) now determines m, and we find $m = 0$ or $m = 1$.

The a_k's are now determined by the condition that the coefficients of like powers of x in (B-5) must add up to zero. Equation (B-5) can be put into the form

$$\sum_{k}^{\infty} [a_{k+2}(k + m + 2)(k + m + 1)]x^{k+m}$$

$$- \sum_{k}^{\infty} a_k[(k + m)(k + m + 1) - n(n + 1)]x^{k+m} = 0 \qquad \text{(B-8)}$$

by replacing k by $k + 2$ in the first sum in (B-5). From Eq. (B-8) we obtain the condition

$$a_{k+2} = a_k \frac{(k + m)(k + m + 1) - n(n + 1)}{(k + m + 2)(k + m + 1)} \qquad \text{(B-9)}$$

for Eq. (B-3) to be a solution of (B-2). Because formula (B-9) permits one to calculate a_{k+2}, given a_k, it is called a "recursion relation." To determine all the a_k's, using (B-9), one must choose the first two coefficients, namely a_0 and a_1, arbitrarily; the recursion relation then gives all the remaining ones. The appearance of the two arbitrary constants a_0 and a_1 in the solution of Eq. (B-2) should be expected since (B-2) is a second-order linear differential equation.

Choosing $m = 0$, the recursion relation gives

$$a_{k+2} = a_k \frac{k(k+1) - n(n+1)}{(k+1)(k+2)} \tag{B-10}$$

$$a_2 = -\frac{n(n+1)}{2} a_0$$

$$a_3 = \frac{2 - n(n+1)}{6} a_1$$

$$a_4 = \frac{6 - n(n+1)}{12} a_2 = -\frac{6 - n(n+1)}{12} \frac{n(n+1)}{2} a_0$$

$$a_5 = \frac{12 - n(n+1)}{20} a_3 = \frac{12 - n(n+1)}{20} \frac{2 - n(n+1)}{6} a_1$$

Notice that the numerator of a_4, $[6 - n(n+1)]n(n+1)$, is a polynomial of degree 4 in n and vanishes for $n = -3, 0, -1, 2$. Hence it may be written in the form $n(n-2)(n+1)(n+3)$, and since $24 = 4!$, a_4 becomes

$$a_4 = \frac{+n(n-2)(n+1)(n+3)}{4!} a_0$$

Similar reasoning applied to the other a's gives a set

$$a_2 = -\frac{n(n+1)}{2!} a_0$$

$$a_3 = -\frac{(n-1)(n+2)}{3!} a_1$$

$$a_4 = \frac{n(n-2)(n+1)(n+3)}{4!} a_0$$

$$a_5 = \frac{(n-1)(n-3)(n+2)(n+4)}{5!} a_1$$

By investigating a few more terms and carefully examining the emerging pattern, we can conclude that the coefficient of x^{2r}, namely a_{2r}, must be

$$a_{2r} = (-1)^r \frac{n(n-2) \cdots (n-2r+2)(n+1) \cdots (n+2r-1)}{(2r)!} a_0 \tag{B-11}$$

Similarly, the coefficient a_{2r+1} of x^{2r+1} must be

$$a_{2r+1} = (-1)^r \frac{(n-1)(n-3) \cdots (n-2r+1)(n+2) \cdots (n+2r)}{(2r+1)!} a_1 \tag{B-12}$$

Thus one solution of Eq. (B-2) is given by

$$y_1 = a_0 \left[1 - \frac{n(n+1)}{2!} x^2 + \frac{n(n-2)(n+1)(n+3)}{4!} x^4 \right.$$
$$\left. + \cdots + \frac{a_{2r} x^{2r}}{a_0} + \cdots \right] + a_1 \left[x - \frac{(n-1)(n+2)}{3!} x^3 \right.$$
$$+ \frac{(n-1)(n-3)(n+2)(n+4)}{5!} x^5 + \cdots + \frac{a_{2r+1} x^{2r+1}}{a_1} + \cdots \left. \right] \tag{B-13}$$

We can obtain a second solution of (B-2) associated with the second solution ($m = 1$) of the indicial equation. For $m = 1$, the recursion relation becomes

$$b_{k+2} = b_k \frac{(k + 1)(k + 2) - n(n + 1)}{(k + 3)(k + 2)} \tag{B-14}$$

where now

$$y = x \sum_{k=0}^{\infty} b_k x^k \tag{B-15}$$

If we replace k by $k - 1$ in Eq. (B-14), the result is

$$b_{k+1} = b_{k-1} \frac{k(k + 1) - n(n + 1)}{(k + 2)(k + 1)} \tag{B-16}$$

From a comparison of Eqs. (B-16) and (B-10) we can immediately write

$$\frac{b_{k+1}}{b_{k-1}} = \frac{a_{k+2}}{a_k} \qquad k \geq 1 \tag{B-17}$$

and thus

$$b_2 = -\frac{(n - 1)(n + 2)}{3!} b_0$$

$$b_3 = -\frac{(n - 2)(n + 3)}{12} b_1$$

$$b_4 = \frac{(n - 1)(n - 3)(n + 2)(n + 4)}{5!} b_0$$

$$b_5 = \frac{(n - 2)(n - 4)(n + 3)(n + 5)}{360} b_1$$

The general terms are seen to be

$$b_{2r} = (-1)^r$$
$$\frac{(n - 1)(n - 3) \cdots (n - 2r + 1)(n + 2)(n + 4) \cdots (n + 2r)}{(2r + 1)!} b_0 \tag{B-18}$$

$$b_{2r+1} = (-1)^r$$
$$\frac{(n - 2)(n - 4) \cdots (n - 2r)(n + 3)(n + 5) \cdots (n + 2r + 1)}{(r + 1)[(2r + 1)!]} b_1 \tag{B-19}$$

Thus the solution of Eq. (B-2) corresponding to the case $m = 1$ is given by

$$y_2 = b_0 \left[x - \frac{(n - 1)(n + 2)}{3!} x^3 \right.$$
$$+ \frac{(n - 1)(n - 3)(n + 2)(n + 4)}{5!} x^5 - \cdots$$
$$\left. + \frac{b_{2r} x^{2r+1}}{b_0} + \cdots \right] + b_1 \left[x^2 - \frac{(n - 2)(n + 3)}{12} x^4 \right.$$
$$\left. + \frac{(n - 2)(n - 4)(n + 3)(n + 5)}{360} x^6 - \cdots + \frac{b_{2r+1} x^{2r}}{b_1} + \cdots \right] \tag{B-20}$$

The coefficients in Eqs. (B-13) and (B-20) satisfy the appropriate recursion relations obtained from Legendre's equation. However, the student should carefully observe that this does not necessarily mean that both (B-13) and (B-20) satisfy Legendre's equation itself! Direct substitution of (B-13) into Eq. (B-2) shows that it does indeed satisfy Legendre's equation. Since Legendre's equation is linear, and a_0 and a_1 are arbitrary constants, we conclude that both the series appearing in (B-13) are separately solutions of Legendre's equation. Furthermore, since one series contains only even powers of x while the other has only odd powers of x, their ratio cannot be a constant. Thus the two series appearing in (B-13) must be *linearly independent.* Consequently, (B-13) is already the general solution of (B-2)! What about (B-20)? If Eq. (B-20) is also a solution of Legendre's equation, then the second series in (B-20) must satisfy Eq. (B-2) because the first series does. However, for $n = 2$, the second series in Eq. (B-20) becomes just $b_1 x^2$, which does not satisfy (B-2) for $n = 2$. We have therefore proved that $y_2(x)$, as given by (B-20) is not a solution of Legendre's equation at all! In the case at hand, the single indicial root $m = 0$ determines the general solution of (B-2). The root $m = 1$ is superfluous.

One would like to have some general rules for deciding which roots of the indicial to retain and which to discard. Here are two useful ones:

RULE 1: If the roots of an indicial equation are unequal and do not differ by an integer, then each root of the indicial equation gives rise to a solution of the differential equation. These solutions are linearly independent, and a linear combination of them is a general solution of the differential equation.

RULE 2: If a pair of roots of an indicial equation are unequal and differ by an integer, and the smaller of the two roots makes a coefficient of the series solution indeterminate, then that root determines the general solution of the differential equation.

Legendre's equation is an example of Rule 2. Consider Eq. (B-5) with its first two terms written out explicitly:

$$a_0 m(m - 1)x^{m-2} + a_1(m + 1)mx^{m-1}$$
$$+ \sum_{k=2}^{\infty} a_k(k + m)(k + m - 1)x^{k+m-2}$$
$$- \sum_{k=0}^{\infty} a_k[(k + m)(k + m - 1) + 2(k + m)$$
$$- n(n + 1)]x^{k+m} = 0 \qquad (B\text{-}21)$$

The coefficient of each power of x in Eq. (B-21) must vanish. For the lowest power of x, this condition gives the indicial equation $a_0 m(m - 1) = 0$. the roots of which are $m = 0$ and $m = 1$.

The smaller of these two roots has the property that it makes the coefficient of x^{m-1} vanish, no matter what the value of a_1 is. Hence a_1 is indeterminate for the root $m = 0$ and by Rule 2 $m = 0$ determines the general solution of Legendre's equation.

Convergence

The convergence of the series solution (B-13) must now be examined. According to the ratio test (Appendix A), a series is absolutely convergent provided

$$\lim_{k \to \infty} \left| \frac{u_{k+2}}{u_k} \right| < 1 \tag{B-22}$$

Applying this test to Eq. (B-13) written as

$$y_1 = \sum_{k=0}^{\infty} u_k = \sum_{k=0}^{\infty} a_k x^k \tag{B-23}$$

when

$$\frac{a_{k+2}}{a_k} = \frac{k(k+1) - n(n+1)}{(k+1)(k+2)} \tag{B-24}$$

we find

$$\left| \frac{u_{k+2}}{u_k} \right| = \frac{k(k+1) - n(n+1)}{(k+1)(k+2)} x^2 \tag{B-25}$$

and

$$\lim_{k \to \infty} \left| \frac{u_{k+2}}{u_k} \right| = x^2 \tag{B-26}$$

Hence (B-13) converges absolutely for $-1 < x < +1$.

Suppose that we choose a value of x, say x_0, such that $|x_0| < 1$. Consider the sequence of positive constants $M_k = |a_k x_0{}^k|$. Since Eq. (B-23) converges absolutely for $|x| < 1$, we see that ΣM_k is a convergent series of positive constants such that

$$|u_k(x)| = |a_k x^k| \leq M_k \tag{B-27}$$

for $|x| \leq |x_0| < 1$. It now follows from the Weierstrass M test discussed in Appendix A that (B-23), and thus Eq. (B-13), is *uniformly* and absolutely convergent for $|x| \leq |x_0| < 1$. Consequently, (B-13) may be differentiated term by term for $|x| \leq |x_0| < 1$. This verifies our original assumption about the differentiability of the trial series.

Solution for $|x| > 1$

Suppose we want a solution of Eq. (B-2) which can be used for $|x| > 1$. How do we find one? The answer is that we proceed exactly as before, while observing that if $x > 1$, then $1/x < 1$. In other words, we should seek a power-series solution not in powers of x, but in powers of the reciprocal of x instead.

For this purpose let

$$y = \sum_{k=0}^{\infty} a_k x^{m-k} \tag{B-28}$$

be the solution of Eq. (B-2) for $|x| > 1$. Substituting Eq. (B-28) in (B-2) and collecting like powers of x gives

$$\sum_{k=0}^{\infty} a_k(m-k)(m-k-1)x^{m-k-2}$$

$$-\sum_{k=0}^{\infty} a_k[(m-k)(m-k+1)-n(n+1)]x^{m-k} = 0 \qquad \text{(B-29)}$$

Writing out the two highest powers of x in Eq. (B-29), we find

$$a_0[m(m+1)-n(n+1)]x^m + a_1[(m-1)m-n(n+1)]x^{m-1}$$

$$+\sum_{k=2}^{\infty} a_k[(m-k)(m-k+1)-n(n+1)]x^{m-k}$$

$$-\sum_{k=0}^{\infty} a_k(m-k)(m-k-1)x^{m-k-2} = 0 \qquad \text{(B-30)}$$

As before, if Eq. (B-30) is to hold for all x, then the coefficient of each power of x must vanish. The indicial equation for a series in ascending powers of x is obtained by equating the coefficient of the lowest-power term to zero. In the present case, we have a power series in descending powers of x, and to obtain the corresponding indicial equation, we must equate the coefficient of the *highest*-power term to zero. The result for (B-30) is

$$a_0[m(m+1)-n(n+1)] = 0 \qquad \text{(B-31)}$$

with roots

$$m = n \qquad \text{(B-32)}$$

or

$$m = -n-1 \qquad \text{(B-33)}$$

Equating the coefficients of x^{m-k} to zero in Eq. (B-29) gives

$$a_{k-2}(m-k+2)(m-k+1)$$
$$= a_k[(m-k)(m-k+1)-n(n+1)] \qquad \text{(B-34)}$$

and replacing k by $k+2$ in Eq. (B-34) yields the recursion relation,

$$a_{k+2} = a_k \frac{(m-k)(m-k-1)}{(m-k-2)(m-k-1)-n(n+1)} \qquad \text{(B-35)}$$

Notice that the difference between the two indicial roots (B-32) and (B-33) depends on the parameter n entering into Legendre's equation and will not be an integer unless n is. Consequently, we must examine the series generated by both roots of the indicial equation. Putting $m = n$ in Eq. (B-35) gives

$$a_{k+2} = a_k \frac{(n-k)(n-k-1)}{(n-k-2)(n-k-1)-n(n+1)} \qquad \text{(B-36)}$$

and on expanding the denominator of Eq. (B-36), it reduces to

$$a_{k+2} = a_k \frac{(n-k)(n-k-1)}{(k+2)(k-2n+1)} \qquad \text{(B-37)}$$

from which we obtain

$$a_2 = -a_0 \frac{n(n-1)}{2(2n-1)}$$

$$a_4 = a_0 \frac{n(n-1)(n-2)(n-3)}{8(2n-1)(2n-3)}$$

$$a_6 = -a_0 \frac{n(n-1)(n-2)(n-3)(n-4)(n-5)}{48(2n-1)(2n-3)(2n-5)}$$

$$a_{2r} = (-1)^r a_0$$
$$\frac{n(n-1) \cdots (n-2r+2)(n-2r+1)}{(2 \cdot 4 \cdots 2r)[2n-(2r-1)][2n-(2r-3)] \cdots (2n-1)}$$

and

$$a_3 = -a_1 \frac{n-2}{6}$$

$$a_5 = \frac{a_1}{60}(n-3)(n-4)$$

$$a_7 = \frac{-a_1}{840}(n-4)(n-5)(n-6)$$

Thus for $m = n$ we have

$$y_1(x) = x^n \sum_{k=0}^{\infty} a_k x^{-k} = a_0 x^n \left[1 - \frac{n(n-1)}{2(2n-1)} x^{-2} \right.$$
$$+ \frac{n(n-1)(n-2)(n-3)}{8(2n-1)(2n-3)} x^{-4} - \cdots \left. \right]$$
$$+ a_1 x^n \left[x^{-1} - \frac{(n-2)}{6} x^{-3} + \frac{(n-3)(n-4)}{60} x^{-5} - \cdots \right] \tag{B-38}$$

The highest power in the second series in Eq. (B-38) is x^{n-1}. Thus with $a_0 = 0$ and $a_1 \neq 0$, $y_1(x)$ is not a power series whose highest-power term is x^n. This situation violates the original assumption made in deriving Eq. (B-31); therefore we choose $a_1 \equiv 0$.

We now have

$$y_1(x) = x^n \sum_{k=0}^{\infty} a_{2k} x^{-2k} \tag{B-39}$$

where $a_0 \neq 0$ and

$$a_{2r} = (-1)^r a_0$$
$$\frac{n(n-1) \cdots (n-2r+2)(n-2r+1)}{(2 \cdot 4 \cdots 2r)[2n-(2r-1)][2n-(2r-3)] \cdots (2n-1)} \tag{B-40}$$

as one solution of Legendre's equation for $|x| > 1$.

To obtain a second solution we proceed as before, this time using the second indicial root $m = -(n+1)$ in the recursion relation (B-35), which then becomes

$$b_{k+2} = b_0 \frac{(k+n+1)(k+n+2)}{(k+2)(2n+k+3)} \tag{B-41}$$

Once again we obtain a solution which is the sum of two power series, one of which fails to have $x^{-(n+1)}$ as its highest-power term. For the same reason as before, this series is eliminated by equating the coefficient multiplying it to zero. This leaves

$$y_2(x) = x^{-(n+1)} \sum_{k=0}^{\infty} b_{2k} x^{-2k} \tag{B-42}$$

where $b_0 \neq 0$ and

$$b_{2r} = b_0 \frac{(n+1)(n+2) \cdots (n+2r)}{(2 \cdot 4 \cdot 6 \cdots 2r)(2n+3)(2n+5) \cdots (2n+2r+1)} \tag{B-43}$$

as the second solution of Eq. (B-2) for $|x| > 1$. A comparison of Eqs. (B-42) and (B-39) shows that when one is even, the other is odd, and vice versa; hence $y_2(x)/y_1(x)$ cannot be a constant, and therefore $y_1(x)$ and $y_2(x)$ must be linearly independent solutions of Legendre's equation for $|x| > 1$. The general solution for $|x| > 1$ will be a linear combination of $y_1(x)$ and $y_2(x)$.

Convergence

The series

$$y(x) = x^m \sum_{k=0}^{\infty} a_k x^{-k}$$

will converge absolutely, provided

$$\lim_{k \to \infty} \left| \frac{a_k x^k}{a_{k+2} x^{k+2}} \right| = \lim_{k \to \infty} \left| \frac{a_k}{a_{k+2}} \right| |x|^{-2} < 1$$

Using Eq. (B-36), we find that both (B-39) and (B-42) are absolutely convergent for $|x| > 1$ and absolutely and uniformly convergent for $|x| \geq |x_0| > 1$, provided that n is so chosen that

$$|(n-k-2)(n-k-1) - n(n+1)| > 0$$

in (B-36) for any non-negative integer k.

Legendre polynomials

The general solution (B-13) for $|x| < 1$ is the sum of two series. The first of these series terminates and reduces to a polynomial in x when n is an even positive or an odd negative integer or zero. For example, for $n = 2r$ the first series in (B-13) reduces to the polynomial

$$y(x) = a_0 \left[1 - \frac{n(n+1)}{2!} x^2 + \cdots \right.$$
$$\left. + (-1)^{n/2} \frac{n(n-2) \cdots 2(n+1) \cdots (2n-1)}{n!} x^n \right] \tag{B-44}$$

Similarly, for $|x| > 1$ and $n = 2r$, Eq. (B-39) becomes

$$y_1(x) = a_0 x^n \left[1 - \frac{n(n-1)}{2(2n-1)} x^{-2} + \cdots \right.$$
$$\left. + (-1)^{n/2} \frac{n!}{n(n-2) \cdots 2(n+1) \cdots (2n-1)} x^{-n} \right] \tag{B-45}$$

which reduces to (B-44) when we multiply Eq. (B-45) by

$$(-1)^{n/2} \frac{n(n-2) \cdots 2(n+1) \cdots (2n-1)}{n!}$$

If $n = -(2r+1)$, then the first series in Eq. (B-13) becomes identical to Eq. (B-42). The second series in (B-13) reduces to a polynomial when $n = 2r+1$ or $n = -2r$ for $r \geq 1$. For $n = 2r+1$, $r \geq 1$, the odd series in (B-13) reduces to

$$y(x) = a_1 \left[x - \frac{(n-1)(n+2)}{3!} x^3 + \cdots \right.$$
$$\left. + (-1)^{(n-1)/2} \frac{(n-1)(n-3) \cdots 2(n+2) \cdots (2n-1)}{n!} x^n \right] \tag{B-46}$$

while Eq. (B-39) becomes

$$y(x) = a_0 x^n \left[1 - \frac{n(n-1)}{2(2n-1)} x^{-2} + \cdots \right.$$
$$\left. + (-1)^{(n-2)/2} \frac{n!}{2 \cdot 4 \cdots (n-1)(n+2) \cdots (2n-1)} x^{1-n} \right] \tag{B-47}$$

If we multiply Eq. (B-47) by the constant factor

$$(-1)^{(n-1)/2} \frac{2 \cdot 4 \cdots (n-1)(n+2) \cdots (2n-1)}{n!} \frac{a_1}{a_0}$$

then Eq. (B-47) reduces to (B-46). Finally, when $n = -2r$, $r \geq 1$, the odd series in (B-13) becomes equal to (B-42).

The Legendre polynomials are then defined by setting

$$a_0 = \frac{(2n)!}{2^n (n!)^2} = \frac{(2n-1)(2n-3) \cdots 1}{n!} \tag{B-48}$$

in Eq. (B-39) with the result that a Legendre polynomial $P_n(x)$ of order n is given by the expression

$$P_n(x) = \frac{1 \cdot 3 \cdot 5 \cdot 7 \cdots (2n-1)}{n!} \left[x^n - \frac{n(n-1)}{2(2n-1)} x^{n-2} \right.$$
$$\left. + \frac{n(n-1)(n-2)(n-3)}{2 \cdot 4 (2n-1)(2n-3)} x^{n-4} - \cdots \right] \tag{B-49}$$

Bessel's equation

We seek a solution of Bessel's equation,

$$x^2 y'' + x y' + (x^2 - n^2) y = 0 \tag{B-50}$$

in a series of ascending powers of x:

$$y(x) = \sum_{k=0}^{\infty} a_k x^{k+m} \tag{B-51}$$

Inserting Eq. (B-51) into (B-50), we obtain

$$\sum_{k=0}^{\infty} (k + m)(k + m - 1)a_k x^{k+m} + \sum_{k=0}^{\infty} (k + m)a_k x^{k+m}$$

$$+ \sum_{k=0}^{\infty} a_k x^{k+m+2} - \sum_{k=0}^{\infty} n^2 a_k x^{k+m} = 0 \qquad \text{(B-52)}$$

or

$$\sum_{k=0}^{\infty} a_k[(k + m)^2 - n^2]x^{k+m} + \sum_{k=0}^{\infty} a_k x^{k+m+2} = 0 \qquad \text{(B-53)}$$

Writing out the first two lowest-order terms in Eq. (B-53) then gives

$$a_0(m^2 - n^2)x^m + a_1[(m + 1)^2 - n^2]x^{m+1}$$

$$+ \sum_{k=2}^{\infty} a_k[(k + m)^2 - n^2]x^{k+m} + \sum_{k=0}^{\infty} a_k x^{k+m+2} = 0 \qquad \text{(B-54)}$$

Indicial equation

The indicial equation is obtained as before by equating the coefficient of the lowest power of x to zero. This gives

$$a_0(m^2 - n^2) = 0 \qquad \text{(B-55)}$$

with roots $m = \pm n$.

Equating the coefficient of x^{k+m} to zero in Eq. (B-53) yields the recursion relation

$$a_k[(k + m)^2 - n^2] + a_{k-2} = 0 \qquad \text{(B-56)}$$

Thus

$$a_k = \frac{-a_{k-2}}{(m - n + k)(m + n + k)} \qquad \text{(B-57)}$$

determines a_k in terms of a_{k-2} for $k \geq 2$, provided neither $m - n$ nor $m + n$ is a negative integer. Using the indicial roots $m = \pm n$, this condition is seen to be equivalent to the requirement that $2n$ is not a negative integer when $m = n$, and that $-2n$ is not a negative integer when $m = -n$. These conditions guarantee that the denominator of Eq. (B-57) is never zero. Since the second term in Eq. (B-54) does not become indeterminate for either of the indicial roots $m = n$ or $m = -n$, we must equate a_1 to zero. However, $a_1 = 0$ together with (B-57) shows that all the odd coefficients $a_1, a_3, a_5, \ldots$, etc., must vanish.

It follows from the recursion relation (B-57) that

$$a_{2k} =$$

$$\frac{(-1)^k a_0}{\substack{(m - n + 2)(m - n + 4) \cdots (m - n + 2k) \\ (m + n + 2)(m + n + 4) \cdots (m + n + 2k)}} \qquad \text{(B-58)}$$

Consider the denominator in Eq. (B-58). If we choose $m = n$, then it reduces to

$$(2 \cdot 4 \cdots 2k) \cdot 2(n + 1) \cdot 2(n + 2) \cdots 2(n + k) \qquad \text{(B-59)}$$

and since

$$2 \cdot 4 \cdots 2k = 2 \cdot 1 \cdot 2 \cdot 2 \cdot 2 \cdot 3 \cdot 2 \cdot 4 \cdots 2 \cdot k = 2^k k! \qquad \text{(B-60)}$$

while

$$2(n+1) \cdot 2(n+2) \cdots 2(n+k)$$
$$= 2^k (n+1)(n+2) \cdots (n+k) \qquad \text{(B-61)}$$

we may write Eq. (B-58) as

$$a_{2k} = \frac{(-1)^k a_0}{2^{2k} k! (n+1)(n+2) \cdots (n+k)} \qquad \text{(B-62)}$$

Then for the case $m = n$, Eq. (B-51) becomes

$$y(x) = a_0 x^n \left[1 + \sum_{k=1}^{\infty} \frac{(-1)^k x^{2k}}{2^{2k} k! (n+1)(n+2) \cdots (n+k)} \right] \qquad \text{(B-63)}$$

while for the case $m = -n$, one finds

$$y(x) = b_0 x^{-n} \left[1 + \sum_{k=1}^{\infty} \frac{(-1)^k x^{2k}}{2^{2k} k! (-n+1)(-n+2) \cdots (-n+k)} \right.$$
$$\qquad \text{(B-64)}$$

It is customary to define

$$a_0 = \frac{1}{2^n \Gamma(n+1)} \qquad \text{(B-65)}$$

and

$$b_0 = \frac{1}{2^{-n} \Gamma(-n+1)} \qquad \text{(B-66)}$$

so that the series (B-63) and (B-64) may be rewritten in the form

$$y(x) = J_n(x) = \sum_{k=0}^{\infty} \frac{(-1)^k (x/2)^{n+2k}}{k! \Gamma(n+k+1)} \qquad \text{(B-67)}$$

$$y(x) = J_{-n}(x) = \sum_{k=0}^{\infty} \frac{(-1)^k (x/2)^{-n+2k}}{k! \Gamma(-n+k+1)} \qquad \text{(B-68)}$$

Assuming that $2n$ is not an integer, an application of the ratio test analogous to Eq. (6-187) shows that Eqs. (B-67) and (B-68) are uniformly convergent for all $0 < x < \infty$, thus justifying the term-by-term differentiation used to obtain these series.

The power series (B-67) defines a Bessel function $J_n(x)$ of order n. This definition applies, regardless of whether $2n$ is an integer or not. However, when $2n$ is not an integer, then the ratio of the two series (B-67) and (B-68) cannot be a constant, and under these conditions $J_n(x)$ and $J_{-n}(x)$ must be linearly independent solutions of Bessel's equation.

Problems and Applications

1. The following differential equation,

$$x(1-x)y'' + [\gamma - (\alpha + \beta + 1)x]y' - \alpha\beta y = 0$$

is known as "Gauss' hypergeometric differential equation." Prove that the hypergeometric function,

$$y = F(\alpha,\beta,\gamma;x) = 1 + \frac{\alpha\beta x}{1!\gamma} + \frac{\alpha(\alpha+1)\beta(\beta+1)}{2!\gamma(\gamma+1)} x^2$$
$$+ \frac{\alpha(\alpha+1)(\alpha+2)\beta(\beta+1)(\beta+2)}{3!\gamma(\gamma+1)(\gamma+2)} x^3 + \cdots$$

is a particular solution of Gauss' equation satisfying the initial condition $y(0) = 1$. Calculate the radius of convergence of this series.

Show that in general

$$F(\alpha,\beta,\gamma;x) = \frac{\Gamma(\gamma)}{\Gamma(\alpha)\Gamma(\beta)} \sum_{n=0}^{\infty} \frac{\Gamma(\alpha+n)\Gamma(\beta+n)}{\Gamma(\gamma+n)} \frac{x^n}{n!}$$

Show that

$$y = x^{1-\gamma}F(\alpha - \gamma + 1, \beta - \gamma + 1, 2 - \gamma; x)$$

is a second solution of the hypergeometric equation, valid about $x = 0$.

2. The confluent hypergeometric differential equation is

$$xy'' + (\gamma - x)y' - \alpha y = 0$$

Obtain the following series representation for a confluent hypergeometric function,

$$y = {}_1F_1(\alpha,\gamma;x) = 1 + \frac{\alpha}{\gamma} x + \frac{\alpha(\alpha+1)}{2!\gamma(\gamma+1)} x^2 + \cdots$$

about $x = 0$. When γ is not an integer, show that

$$y = x^{1-\gamma}{}_1F_1(1 + \alpha - \gamma, 2 - \gamma; x)$$
$$= x^{1-\gamma} + \sum_{k=1}^{\infty} \frac{(1 + \alpha - \gamma) \cdots (k + \alpha - \gamma)}{k!(2 - \gamma) \cdots (k + 1 - \gamma)} x^{k+1-\gamma}$$

is a second linearly independent confluent hypergeometric function. Compute the radius of convergence in each case.

3. Consider the following differential equation known as "Weber's equation":

$$y'' + (n + \tfrac{1}{2} - \tfrac{1}{4}x^2)y = 0$$

Obtain two power-series solutions of Weber's equation valid about $x = 0$ and of the form

$$y_1 = e^{-\frac{1}{4}x^2}\left[1 - \frac{n}{2!}x^2 + \frac{n(n-2)}{4!}x^4 \right.$$
$$\left. - \frac{n(n-2)(n-4)}{6!}x^6 + \cdots \right]$$

$$y_2 = e^{-\frac{1}{4}x^2}\left[x - \frac{(n-1)}{3!}x^3 + \frac{(n-1)(n-3)}{5!}x^5 \right.$$
$$\left. - \frac{(n-1)(n-3)(n-5)}{7!}x^7 + \cdots \right]$$

HINT: First make the transformation $y = e^{-\frac{1}{4}x^2}v$, and then consider the resulting differential equation in v.

Calculate the radius of convergence of each series.

4. Show that a Legendre polynomial of order n may be expressed in terms of the hypergeometric function as

$$P_n(\cos \theta) = F\left(n + 1, -n, 1; \frac{1 - \cos \theta}{2}\right)$$

Under what conditions does the hypergeometric equation reduce to Legendre's equation?

5. The differential equation

$$xy'' + (1 - x)y' + \alpha y = 0$$

is known as "Laguerre's differential equation." It is important in the theory of the hydrogen atom. Obtain the power-series solution

$$y = a_0\left[1 - \alpha x + \frac{\alpha(\alpha - 1)}{(2!)^2} x^2 - \cdots \right.$$
$$\left. + (-1)^r \frac{\alpha(\alpha - 1) \cdots (\alpha - r + 1)}{(r!)^2} x^r + \cdots \right]$$

of Laguerre's equation, valid about $x = 0$. Compute its radius of convergence, and show that when α is a positive integer, the Laguerre function reduces to a polynomial of degree α in x.

6. Consider the differential equation

$$xy'' + (k + 1 - x)y' + (\alpha - k)y = 0$$

where k is a non-negative integer. Prove that this equation has a solution of the form

$$y = \frac{d^k}{dx^k} L_n(x) = L_n^k(x)$$

where $L_n(x)$ is a Laguerre polynomial of degree n in x.

7. Consider the differential equation

$$xy'' + 2y' + \left(n - \frac{k - 1}{2} - \frac{x}{4} - \frac{k^2 - 1}{4x}\right)y = 0$$

Show that this equation has a particular solution of the form

$$y = e^{-x/2}x^{(k-1)/2}L_n^k(x)$$

index

Reversal rule, 26, 28, 29
Riemann, 127
Riemann-Lesbesgue lemma, 210
Riemann mapping theorem, 141
Riemann surface, 147, 157
Rodrigue's formula, 274

Saddle point, 145
Saltus, 341
Scalar, 3
Scalar product, 5
Scalar transformation law, 52
Scattering of time-harmonic waves, from a
    cylinder, 432
  from a half plane, 431
  from a half space, 433
  from a sphere, 432
  from a wedge, 432
Schmidt orthogonalization process, 13, 179
Seismograph, 246
  critically damped, 249
  logarithmic decrement of, 248
  overdamped, 249
  underdamped, 249
Separation of variables, 333
Singularities, of an analytic function, 154
    158
  essential, 155
  isolated, 154
Solid angle, 100
Solution, of Laplace's equation in a half
    space, 338
  of Laplace's equation in polar coordi-
    nates, 343
  nontrivial, 31
  parametric, 32
  of potential problems in two dimensions,
    323
  trivial, 31
Solution of differential equations in power
    series, 445
  Bessel's equation, 454
  confluent hypergeometric equation, 457
  hypergeometric equation, 456
  Laguerre's equation, 458
  Legendre's equation, 445
  Weber's equation, 457
Solution of ordinary differential equations
    with variable coefficients by transform
    methods, 303
Sommerfeld radiation condition, 405
Sommerfeld's integral, 388
Special functions, 255
  associated Legendre functions, 272, 275
  Bessel functions, 261
  beta function, 259

Special functions, factorial function, 257
  gamma function, 256
  Hankel functions, 269
  Hermite polynomials, 281
  hyperbolic Bessel functions, 270
  Legendre polynomials, 272
  Neumann functions, 264
  spherical Bessel functions, 279, 401
  spherical harmonics, 276
Spectrum, 38, 39
Sphere with handles, 146
Stationary point, 145
Step function, 420
Streamlines, 144
Sturm-Liouville problem, 299
Support of a function, 419
Support compact, 419
Surface, connectivity of, 104
Surface circulation, 110
  open, 103
  Riemann, 147, 157
  total boundary of, 103
Surface curl, 110
Surface discontinuities, 107
Surface divergence, 109
Surface gradient, 110
Surface sources of vorticity, 110
Systems, of linear equations, 30
  of ordinary differential equations, 307
  overdetermined, 30
  underdetermined, 30
  well determined, 30

Taylor's series, 139
Temperature distribution, in an infinite
    rod, 427, 434
  in a semi-infinite rod, 434
Temperature wave, 434
Tensor, antisymmetric, 53
  associated metric, 54
  Cartesian, 119
  contravariant, 48, 51
  covariant, 48, 51
  divergence of, 119
  inner product of, 49
  metric, 54
  mixed, 48
  outer product of, 49
  skew symmetric, 53
  stress, 119
  summation convention for, 49
  symmetric, 53
  transformation properties of, 50
Tensor addition, 48
Tensor algebra, 47
Tensor contraction, 49